Second Edition

A Human Voyage
Exploring Biological Anthropology

Anne Keenleyside
TRENT UNIVERSITY

Richard Lazenby
UNIVERSITY OF NORTHERN BRITISH COLUMBIA

D1504859

NELSON
EDUCATION
CELEBRATE LIFELONG LEARNING

1914–2014: Nelson Education celebrates 100 years of Canadian publishing

NELSON / EDUCATION

A Human Voyage:
Exploring Biological Anthropology,
Second Edition
by Anne Keenleyside and Richard Lazenby

**Vice President, Editorial
Higher Education:**
Anne Williams

Executive Editor:
Maya B. Castle

Executive Marketing Manager:
Amanda Henry

Developmental Editor:
Katherine Goodes

**Photo Researcher and
Permissions Coordinator:**
Carrie McGregor

**Senior Production
Project Manager:**
Natalia Denesiuk Harris

Production Service:
MPS Limited

Copy Editor:
June Trusty

Proofreader:
MPS Limited

Indexer:
Shan Young

Design Director:
Ken Phipps

Managing Designer:
Franca Amore

Interior Design:
Cathy Mayer

Cover Design:
Cathy Mayer

Cover Image:
Adrian Neal/Getty Images (human
fetus); Karl Ammann/Getty Royalty
Free (young chimpanzee); PASCAL
GOETGHELUCK/SCIENCE PHOTO
LIBRARY (skulls)

Compositor:
MPS Limited

**Library and Archives Canada
Cataloguing in Publication Data**

Keenleyside, Anne, 1962–, author

    A human voyage : exploring
biological anthropology / Anne
Keenleyside, Trent University,
Richard Lazenby, University of
Northern British Columbia.
— Second edition.

Includes bibliographical references
and index.

ISBN 978-0-17-653191-1 (pbk.)

    1. Physical anthropology
—Textbooks. I. Lazenby, Richard
A., 1952–, author II. Title.

GN60.K44 2014   599.9
C2014-904324-4

ISBN-13: 978-0-17-653191-1
ISBN-10: 0-17-653191-2

This book is dedicated to our mentors, colleagues, and friends Shelley Saunders (A.K. and R.L.) and Mark Skinner (R.L.), who started us on this voyage.

—*Anne Keenleyside and Richard Lazenby*

Brief Contents

Table of Contents

Preface

The important thing is not to stop questioning. Curiosity has its own reason for existing.
—Albert Einstein (1879–1955)

WHY THIS BOOK NOW?

There seems to be no shortage of textbooks in the field of biological (also called physical) anthropology; many have been released in new editions. As university teachers, we have field-tested several of these over the past 20 years or more. So you might reasonably ask: Why yet another? The simple answer is that the time has arrived for this particular book; indeed, it is possibly well overdue. When Nelson proposed the somewhat brash idea of writing the first biological anthropology book written by Canadian biological anthropologists for Canadian postsecondary students, we welcomed the opportunity (perhaps with more than a little naïveté). And thus *A Human Voyage* was launched!

The growth of the field in Canada is such that it is clearly time for such a text. The professional association for the discipline, known as CAPA/ACAP (a rather long acronym for the much lengthier title Canadian Association for Physical Anthropology/l'Association Canadienne d'Anthropologie Physique), has grown considerably since its inception in the early 1970s and boasted well over 160 members in 2012, representing several generations of teachers and their students. As well, university and college courses in the field (and in related subjects such as human ecology, human adaptability, medical anthropology, and forensic anthropology) have seen enrolment increase steadily over the past several decades; also growing is the number of graduate programs leading to advanced degrees (M.A. or Ph.D.). This growth is reflected in a broad range of nationally and internationally recognized academic scholarship, carried out not just in Canada but around the world, which covers virtually all facets of the discipline from the latest developments in evolutionary theory to interpretations of the fossil record, insights into nonhuman primate ecology and behaviour, modern population biology, and applied biocultural anthropology.

As teachers, one lesson we have taken from our own students over the years is that their conceptual and theoretical learning is greatly enhanced when practical examples and references resonate geographically, socially, and culturally. As we suspect many of our colleagues across Canada have done in the past, we often bring material into class highlighting Canadian scholarship to supplement that provided by the text, even in the recently evolved Canadian editions of existing (non-Canadian) texts. The intent of *A Human Voyage* is to put that knowledge and experience "between the covers." This book, then, is unabashedly Canadian in its focus and content, but not to the point of being parochial. An important point we make throughout this second edition of *A Human Voyage* is that human biocultural diversity crosses national boundaries: research done in Canada has significance around the world. At the same time we acknowledge that these boundaries and the political and economic entities that create and maintain them can have profound impacts on human biology—the history of colonization and the health of Aboriginal populations in Canada and elsewhere stands as one of many such examples, as does the unique geographic distribution of rare traits such as Tay-Sachs disease (see Chapter 13), which has followed population migration over the ages.

CONNECTING THE DOTS ...

Textbooks in biological anthropology typically adhere to a particular structure, beginning with an overview of the discipline's history, a bit of evolutionary theory, and some dabbling (at times outright wading) into the genetic mechanisms underlying population variation. This is then followed by a number of chapters discussing the evolutionary history and biobehavioural diversity of our closest living relatives, the nonhuman primates. This overview sets the stage for introducing the story of our own evolving lineage of the past several million years, beginning in Africa and tracing the global expansion of human migration. Eventually we end up in the here and now, and conclude with several chapters discussing modern population biology, its historical antecedents and geographic patterning. This is a logical, tried-and-true model, and in writing this text we have chosen to follow a similar structure. The benefit in doing so is that it provides a text that will have a familiar feel for the instructor, which in turn will make for an easy transition when adapting its content for the student.

In keeping with this model, *A Human Voyage* is presented in 16 chapters divided into four parts: **Deep Currents** introduces the history of biological anthropology as a field of study and its development in Canada, as well as the theoretical foundation and structure of human variation; **Tropical Currents** traces the evolution of our nearest primate relatives and the fascinating adaptations and behaviours expressed by those species still among us; **Ancient Currents** delves into the 7-million-year-old story of how our particular ancestors came to be human, some of it speculative and controversial; and **Modern Currents** focuses on the complex variations that exist among living human populations, how they came about, and their importance for humanity as we look forward into the 21st century and beyond.

A FEW COMMENTS FOR THE STUDENT

This is *your* book—it was written for students with little or no background in the field and in such a way as to make the story of human evolution not only accessible but also enjoyable. However, in reading this second edition of *A Human Voyage*, you will see that the path to our past is not always clearly defined, and you may well wonder how we know anything at all! Do not be deterred—this is simply science at work. The possibility that we could have several plausible explanations for how we came to be as we are today is a cornerstone of modern science (a classic example being the adoption of upright walking, known as bipedalism, discussed in Chapter 8). However, it is also true that while a number of credible scenarios *may* be proposed based on available evidence, there was in fact *only one* pathway taken by those many generations of your ancestors and their descendants—step by step by step. The journey along that pathway culminated in the diverse, complex global species—modern *Homo sapiens*—of which you are a member. It is quite possible, if not actually probable, that none of our current interpretations is an entirely accurate account of that voyage, although the weight of evidence may favour one over other reasonable explanations. This is why we have entitled this book *A Human Voyage* rather than *The Human Voyage*, which would presume that somehow we possessed a complete and precise understanding of the past. This is a claim no one can justifiably make.

Our hope is that this second edition and the course you are taking will encourage a critical perspective and sense of wonder in each of you. Each chapter begins with specified learning outcomes—these are not meant to be exhaustive but to illustrate some of the objectives we hope you will achieve in working through the text. Each chapter ends with a concise summary (Learning Keys) that recounts the key ideas we have covered in the chapter, the significant key terms associated with these essential points, and a few questions you might want to ask yourself about what you have learned. We also pose critical thinking questions to have you challenge what you have just read in the previous pages. The Learning Keys and questions are your best bet to understanding the substance of each chapter's content, and perhaps doing very well in the course you are taking. In that regard, *A Human Voyage* is as much about the art of questioning as it is about our current understanding of our species—its diversity, its history, and its possible future. As the authors of *A Human Voyage*, we will gauge its success by the degree to which it leaves you, the student, feeling somewhat dissatisfied with the descriptions, interpretations, and arguments provided, considerably more aware that there is a very robust—although still imperfect—body of evidence detailing humankind's evolutionary story, and much less complacent and accepting of the current state of our species and its impact on this planet.

WHAT'S NEW IN THE SECOND EDITION?

This second edition of *A Human Voyage* has been revised cover to cover in light of several reviewers' excellent suggestions to improve clarity and student accessibility. Each chapter has been updated to reflect the current state of the literature, with over 200 new references added to an already extensive bibliography. We have also made significant improvements to both chapter-opening material (specifying Learning Objectives according to *Bloom's Revised Taxonomy*) as well as ending material in the form of informative and visually accessible Learning Keys (ideas, key terms, and questions). The Learning Keys presented in each chapter are a metaphor—as keys, they "unlock" the essential learning points covered; they link to the Key Concepts and the Key Terms, thus tying together all of the major elements covered in the chapter. The following provides a brief chapter-by-chapter synopsis:

Chapter 1 ("Introduction to Biological Anthropology") sees the addition of two new features: an expanded description of the significant role of molecular anthropology in the discipline, and a new Profile box highlighting the research of Dr. Tracy Prowse (McMaster University) in the use of archaeological isotopes to explore patterns of diet and migration in prehistory. We have also rewritten the historical accounts of the discipline of biological anthropology, making it more accessible to students.

Chapter 2 ("Science and the Development of Evolutionary Theory") provides a review of the practice of science as a way of knowing and the foundations for understanding evolutionary theory, from Plato to Darwin. In this second edition, we have revised and shortened a number of sections, improving clarity and understanding of important concepts including uniformitarianism, Linnaean classification, Lamarckian inheritance, and Darwinian evolution.

Chapter 3 ("The Biological Basis of Human Variation") features expanded sections on the functions of DNA and on ancient DNA.

Chapter 4 ("From Variant to Species") presents a new section covering the principles of the Hardy-Weinberg Equilibrium (explored further in Appendix B, a new addition to this edition). In a new table, we clearly outline the assumptions under which evolution (changes in gene frequency) would not occur as specified by the tenets of the Hardy-Weinberg Equilibrium. Also new to Chapter 4 is a revised treatment of epigenetic inheritance, making this important although complex topic much more accessible to students. New material describing the ideas of homology and homoplasy has been added, preparing students for subsequent discussion of primate and human evolution.

Chapter 5 ("What It Means to Be a Primate") includes new content featuring research by a number of well-known Canadian primatologists. The sections on mapping nonhuman primate genomes and primate cloning have been amalgamated and updated. The section on primate feeding and foraging has been expanded to include a discussion of the relationship between body size, molar cusp morphology, foraging group size and diet, sex differences in diet, and methods used to study primate diets. The discussion of primate conservation has been shifted from Chapter 15 in the first edition to the end of this chapter.

Chapter 6 ("Primate Behavioural Ecology") is characterized by the addition of two new sections, one focusing on hunting and meat eating, and the other on the use of nonhuman primates as models for early hominin behaviour. The discussion of social living has been shifted from Chapter 5 in the first edition to this chapter and has been expanded. The sections on culture among nonhuman primates and language and communication studies have both been expanded to include more examples, and in the case of the latter, to highlight some of the controversies surrounding ape language studies. A new box contributed by Dr. Linda Fedigan (University of Calgary) profiles the history of primatology in Canada.

Chapter 7 ("Primate Evolution") features a revised section on primate classification that includes a discussion of the difference between crown and stem primates. The section on dietary reconstruction has been expanded to include a discussion of the techniques used to explore primate diets. Updated sections on Paleocene, Eocene, Oligocene, and Miocene primates include new fossil primate discoveries, and a new Profile box highlights research by Dr. Mary Silcox (University of Toronto) on plesiadapiforms.

Chapter 8 ("What It Means to Be a Hominin") outlines the major developments in hominin evolution, focusing on bipedalism, dental reduction, and encephalization. New findings regarding variation in the bony labyrinth, the midtarsal break in the foot, and the debate regarding the endurance running hypothesis have been added. More informative illustrations of the major anatomical changes accompanying bipedal locomotion have been developed to enhance student understanding of these often complex changes. The discussion of the obstetric dilemma is now contrasted with Dunsworth's recently advanced concept of the Energetics of Gestation and Growth. Our revised discussion of bipedalism emphasizes the emerging consensus that there may have been many different styles of bipedal locomotion explored by our hominin ancestors over the past 5 million years.

Chapter 9 ("Hominin Origins: From Ape to Australopithecine") begins the story of hominin evolution, from *Sahelanthropus* to *Australopithecus*. Each section has been updated to include the most recent analyses (such as the recently described hominin molar from Ishango), and we have completely revised our discussion of *Ardipithecus*, emphasizing its unique bipedal morphology. An important new addition centres on the incredible finds from Malapa, South Africa, attributed to the new species *Australopithecus sediba*. A new Profile box is included, contributed by Dr. Tracy Kivell (University of Kent), one of the principal researchers of the *Au. sediba* fossil sample, focusing on the hand bones and noting that *Au. sediba* would have been quite capable of the fine precision grips needed for stone tool manufacture.

Chapter 10 ("The Emergence of the Genus *Homo*") includes an expanded discussion of the Dmanisi fossils.

Chapter 11 ("The Advent of Humanity") features a new Profile box highlighting research by Dr. Mirjana Roksandic (University of Winnipeg) on Middle Pleistocene hominins in Eastern Europe. The section on the Neandertal genome has been significantly expanded to include a box highlighting the most recent genetic studies of these hominins. Similarly, the discussion of the Denisovan fossils has been lengthened to include recent advances in the study of their DNA.

Chapter 12 ("The Emergence of Anatomically Modern Humans") presents new genetic findings from Siberia that cast light on the ancestry of the first inhabitants of North and South America.

Chapter 13 ("Contemplating Modern Human Diversity") explores the basis of modern human diversity by first examining the historic and contentious concept of race. New weblinks are provided, along with updates to our model of the "Six Fallacies Concerning Race." We have also revised the Race and Biomedicine section to consider the practice of "direct-to-consumer" genetic engineering, an idea that is becoming increasingly of interest in the realm of so-called personalized medicine.

Chapter 14 ("Biology of Contemporary and Past Populations") features two new Profile boxes, one contributed by Dr. Stacie Burke (University of Manitoba) highlighting her research on tuberculosis in Canada, and the other written by Dr. Helen Kurki (University of Victoria) profiling her studies of body shape variation among small-bodied populations. Expanded discussions of nutrition in contemporary populations and activity patterns of past populations are also included.

Chapter 15 ("Biological Anthropology as Applied Science") examines several biological anthropology fields that fall under the rubric of applied science. Collaborators Tina Moffat (McMaster University), Dan Sellen (University of Toronto), and Warren Wilson (University of Calgary) describe their work, looking at breastfeeding practices of immigrant mothers in a new Focus On box. A new section, written by Sylvia Abonyi from the University of Saskatoon, explores the practice of community-based research with Canada's Indigenous peoples. Finally a new Profile box contributed by Tanya Peckmann (St. Mary's University) examines one of the most frequently asked of student questions: "Can I have a career doing forensic anthropology?"

Chapter 16 ("Human Legacies, Human Prospects") includes new information in the sections on demography, population growth, and political economy. As in the first edition, we return to another very common student question "Are humans still evolving,?" with updated research on the proposed role of the *CCR5Δ32* gene and immune response.

Appendix A is new to this edition and provides a comparative depiction of the human and nonhuman primate skeleton, labelling the major bones and illustrating the significant differences related to the evolution of unique human features such as bipedal locomotion, craniodental reduction, and encephalization.

Appendix B is also a new addition to this text. It outlines the major tenets of the Hardy-Weinberg Equilibrium theorem introduced in Chapter 4. This appendix models the effect of selection on changing allele frequencies in a population using the standard binomial formula $p^2 + 2pq + q^2 = 1$. The Hardy-Weinberg Equilibrium theorem is illustrated with a real-world example, modelling allelic variation in the *CYP2C8* gene that moderates drug effectiveness in treating malarial infection in Africa.

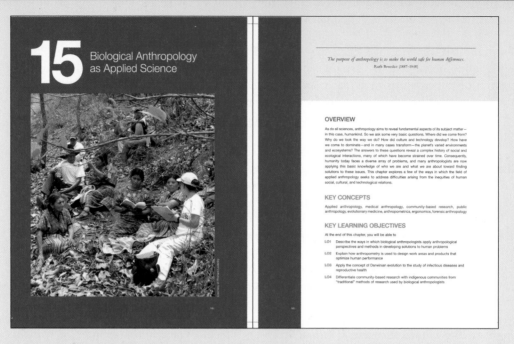

Chapter Openers

Each chapter begins with an Overview section that summarizes the content that will be covered in that chapter. A Key Concepts section introduces students to central ideas that will be discussed in the chapter. These key concepts are followed by a series of Key Learning Objectives based on Revised Bloom's taxonomy to guide the student learner through the chapter content.

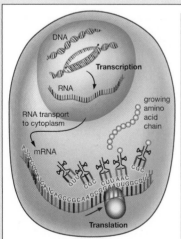

FIGURE 3.7 Transcription occurs in the nucleus of the cell and involves the partial separation of the strands of a DNA molecule and the synthesis of a complementary single-stranded RNA molecule known as messenger RNA. Translation occurs in the cytoplasm of the cell. Here the information carried by the messenger RNA is translated into a protein molecule at the ribosome.

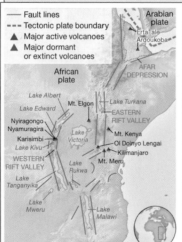

FIGURE 9.2 The African continent was transformed during the Miocene by several significant geologic events, including uplifting along a major fault recognized today as the Great Rift Valley, which extends from Ethiopia in the north to Malawi in the south. Numerous hominin fossil localities are associated with the Rift Valley.

Maps, Photographs, and Illustrations

Colourful visuals, many of which are unique to this text, are used to illustrate key concepts and information and to help students master the material.

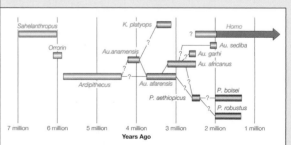

FIGURE 9.16 Depiction of one possible reconstruction of Pliocene hominin evolutionary relationships. The complexity of hominin morphological and behavioural diversity is such that one could contrive a number of different models, none of which may be correct. Note that in almost every instance, the line connecting two forms is presented with a question mark, reflecting the uncertainty inherent in deriving phylogenetic reconstructions. In this depiction, *K. platyops* is retained as a separate genus, although at this time most paleoanthropologists would suggest placement of this form within *Au. afarensis*.

© Dr. Dennis O'Neil. Used with permission.

Pedagogical Boxes

Each chapter includes one or more boxed features that delve more deeply into the subject matter and history of biological anthropology. These boxes take three forms:

Retrospection boxes emphasize key ideas or seminal developments in the field's literature and provide insight into how the discipline has taken shape over the years.

BOX 1.3 RETROSPECTION: Sherwood L. Washburn and "The New Physical Anthropology" (1951)

"In the past, physical anthropology has been considered primarily as a technique. Training consisted in learning to take carefully defined measurements and in computing indices and statistics. The methods of observation, measurement, and comparison were essentially the same, whether the object of the study was the description of evolution, races, growth, criminals, constitutional types, or army personnel. Measurements were adjusted for various purposes, but measurement of the outside of the body, classification, and correlation remained the anthropologist's primary tools [...] If a new physical anthropology is to differ effectively from the old, it must be more than the adoption of a little genetic terminology. It must change its ways of doing things to conform with the implications of modern evolutionary theory [...] The new physical anthropology has much to offer to anyone interested in the structure or evolution of man, but this is only the beginning. To build it, we must collaborate with social scientists, geneticists, anatomists, and paleontologists. We need new ideas, new methods, new workers. There is nothing we do today which will not be done better tomorrow."

Sherwood Washburn (1911–2000) was one of the more influential figures in modern biological anthropology. His work in primate anatomy and behaviour—continued and developed by many of his students, whose interests ranged widely—transformed the discipline from a descriptive field mired in Platonic **typology** to one that embraced a population-based perspective in which variation among members of a group was key to understanding the process of biological adaptation and evolution. According to Washburn, a **processual** approach required a consideration of process (how things happen), function (how things work), comparison (how things

Transactions of the New York Academy of Sciences, Ser. II, 13 (1951): 258–304.

BOX 3.1 FOCUS ON ... Stem Cell Research in Canada

Stem cells are found in all tissues and play a crucial role in growth, development, and maintenance of the body. Humans and other mammals possess two different types of stem cells: embryonic and adult. Embryonic stem cells, created four to five days after conception, are able to develop into any type of specialized cell in the body, ranging from blood cells to those found in connective tissues and vital organs. Sources of these **pluripotent** cells include embryonic and fetal tissue, as well as blood from the placenta and umbilical cord. In contrast, adult stem cells, derived from a variety of adult tissues, repair and regenerate these tissues by constantly reproducing themselves.

Stem cells were discovered in the 1960s by two Canadians, biophysicist James Till and physician Ernest McCulloch, while they were conducting research on radiation. Over the past decade, Canadian scientists have played a leading role in stem cell research, and in 2001 the Stem Cell Network was established by 80 scientists from universities and hospitals across Canada to promote this research, with the ultimate goal of developing therapies to treat a variety of diseases and conditions. Potential applications of stem cell therapy include creating tissues for transplantation; treating degenerative diseases such as Alzheimer's, Parkinson's, diabetes, heart disease, and muscular dystrophy; and developing and testing new medications. Current research projects in Canada include investigating the potential of using stem cells to repair brain injury resulting from stroke; damaged heart muscle resulting from cardiac arrest; and spinal cord injuries.

Despite its potential to improve the lives of millions of people in Canada and around the world, no other area of medical research has generated as much controversy as stem cell research. Heated debate has arisen regarding the ethical, legal, and social implications of that research. At issue is the creation and use of embryos as a source of stem cells, and the fear that this might lead to human cloning. In 2002, the Canadian Institutes of Health Research (CIHR) established strict guidelines for human stem cell research (see www.cihr-irsc.gc.ca/e/42071.html), and scientists are increasingly focusing on adult stem cells in order to avoid the ethical issues associated with us

Focus On boxes provide in-depth analysis of particular topics covered in the chapter.

Profile boxes—written by some of our colleagues—illustrate the exceptional scholarship typifying biological anthropology in Canada. We could have included many more of these, but for some reason, our editors felt that a 1,000-page textbook might not be appropriate!

BOX 1.2 PROFILE ... Chemical Traces of Past Human Behaviour

Courtesy of Tracy Prowse

Stable isotope analysis is a method that analyzes the chemical composition of body tissues that are preserved in the archaeological record, such as bones, teeth, and hair. This method is now commonly used in bioarchaeological research to investigate questions relating to past diet and geographic origins. This is based on the fact that what we eat and drink is incorporated into our body's tissues during life and this chemical signal is preserved in these tissues after death, most commonly measured in isotope variation in carbon, nitrogen, and oxygen (see Chapter 10). More recently, stable isotope analysis has been used in modern forensic cases to identify the geographic origins of unidentified human remains.

A number of biological anthropologists in Canada have made significant contributions to isotopic investigations of human diet, geographic origins, and migration. Early bioarchaeological research using stable isotopes investigated the adoption of maize in southern Ontario through the analysis of carbon and nitrogen isotopes. Anne Katzenberg and colleagues published groundbreaking papers on the pattern and timing of weaning

All of these researchers investigate aspects of past life through isotopic analysis of preserved human tissues.

My own bioarchaeological research explores diet and geographic origins in Roman Italy using stable isotope analysis and palaeopathological evidence. I am interested in understanding what life was like under the control of the Roman Empire, and how this control played out differently in the lives of the people who lived at that time. My research explores a number of different questions about the past. One question concerns the investigation of diet and dental health, and understanding how an individual's changing role in the household and society may have impacted dietary choices. My investigation of carbon and nitrogen isotopes in a Roman-period skeletal sample from Isola Sacra (near Rome) showed that consumption of marine foods varied with age, suggesting that access to certain foods changed throughout the life course.

Another area of research is the investigation of geographic origins and migration in the Roman world. I have explored geographic origins of the people buried at Isola Sacra and patterns of migration in the Mediterranean region using oxygen isotopes in teeth. This research showed that the majority of people at Isola Sacra came from Rome and its environs, and those who immigrated from outside the area did so as children, in contrast to the commonly held view that migration was only an adult male activity. My current field and research

population genetics
a science concerned with variation in gene frequencies within populations and the forces that modify them over time

Key Terms and Glossary

Each chapter features key terms and their definitions in the margin, beside where they appear in the text. A cumulative glossary is provided at the back of the book.

End-of-Chapter Learning Keys

Connecting to the key concepts and learning objectives listed in the chapter-opening pages, each chapter ends with the learning keys shown below and on the next page:

KEY IDEAS

- A hominin is a member of the clade (lineage) comprising all taxa leading toward humans after diverging from the chimpanzee clade.
- Bipedalism in considered the essential behavioural shift defining all hominins but may have evolved in different ways at different times in hominin evolution.
- Bipedalism likely originated in a semi-forested habitat but over time became established as a terrestrial adaptation associated with open-country foraging.
- Anatomical changes linked to bipedalism occur throughout the skeleton, literally from head to toe (position of the foramen magnum, reshaped pelvis and loss of a grasping big toe).

Key Ideas A bulleted summary of the chapter content highlights the major themes, issues, and concepts covered.

KEY TERMS

encephalized (p. 169)

obligate bipeds (p. 169)

facultative bipedalism (p. 170)

obstetric dilemma (OD) (p. 176)

energetics of gestation and growth (EGG) (p. 177)

endurance running (p. 183)

canine honing (p. 184)

endocasts (p. 187)

expensive tissue hypothesis (ETH) (p. 190)

Key Terms A listing of the most important key terms in the chapter helps student remember important concepts.

Key Questions to Ask Myself Student-centred questions are written from the learner's perspective, inviting the student to engage in a novel way with the chapter content.

Key Critical Thinking Questions Provocative questions are designed to critically engage students with the chapter content and to promote individual learning as well as seminar-style discussion.

Key Things to Do Next This is a student reminder of, and an invitation to, the **Biological Anthropology CourseMate** website, where a wealth of support content is available. This website brings course concepts to life with interactive learning and exam preparation tools that integrate with the printed textbook. Students activate their knowledge through quizzes, games, and flashcards, among many other tools. Visit NELSONbrain.com to start using **CourseMate.** Enter the Online Access Code from the card included with your text. If a code card is *not* provided, you can purchase instant access at NELSONbrain.com.

Bibliography

In-text citations throughout the book provide the sources from which the materials are drawn. Sources from 2004 to date, along with a few of the most important "classic" works, are listed in the Selected Bibliography at the back of the book, while earlier sources are available on the CourseMate site for students (accessible through NELSONbrain.com; an additional charge may apply), with the Instructor Resources at www.nelson.com/humanvoyage2e, and on the Instructor's Resource CD (ISBN 978-0-17-656068-3).

ANCILLARIES

About the Nelson Education Teaching Advantage (NETA)

The **Nelson Education Teaching Advantage (NETA)** program delivers research-based instructor resources that promote student engagement and higher-order thinking to enable the success of Canadian students and educators. To ensure the high quality of these materials, all Nelson ancillaries have been professionally copyedited.

Be sure to visit Nelson Education's **Inspired Instruction** website at www.nelson.com/inspired to find out more about NETA. Don't miss the testimonials of instructors who have used NETA supplements and have seen student engagement increase!

Planning Your Course: *NETA Engagement* presents materials that help instructors deliver engaging content and activities to their classes. **NETA Instructor's Manuals** not only identify the topics that cause students the most difficulty, but also describe techniques and resources to help students master these concepts. Dr. Roger Fisher's *Instructor's Guide to Classroom Engagement* accompanies every Instructor's Manual.

Assessing Your Students: *NETA Assessment* relates to testing materials. **NETA Test Bank** authors create multiple-choice questions that reflect research-based best practices for constructing effective questions and testing not just recall but also higher-order thinking. Our guidelines were developed by David DiBattista, psychology professor at Brock University and 3M National Teaching Fellow, whose research has focused on multiple-choice testing. A copy of *Multiple Choice Tests: Getting Beyond Remembering,* Prof. DiBattista's guide to writing effective tests, is included with every Nelson Test Bank.

Teaching Your Students: *NETA Presentation* has been developed to help instructors make the best use of Microsoft® PowerPoint® in their classrooms. With a clean and uncluttered design developed by Maureen Stone of StoneSoup Consulting, **NETA PowerPoints** feature slides with improved readability, more multimedia and graphic materials, activities to use in class, and tips for instructors on the Notes page. A copy of *NETA Guidelines for Classroom Presentations* by Maureen Stone is included with each set of PowerPoint slides.

Technology in Teaching: *NETA Digital* is a framework based on Arthur Chickering and Zelda Gamson's seminal work "Seven Principles of Good Practice in Undergraduate Education" (*AAHE Bulletin*, 1987) and the follow-up work by Chickering and Stephen C. Ehrmann, "Implementing the Seven Principles: Technology as Lever" (*AAHE Bulletin*, 1996). This aspect of the NETA program guides the writing and development of our digital products to ensure that they appropriately reflect the core goals of contact, collaboration, multimodal learning, time on task, prompt feedback, active learning, and high expectations. The resulting focus on pedagogical utility, rather than technological wizardry, ensures that all of our technology supports better outcomes for students.

Instructor Resources

All NETA and other key instructor ancillaries are provided on the *Instructor's Resource CD* (ISBN 978-0-17-656068-3), with the Instructor Resources at www.nelson.com/humanvoyage2e, and at the Instructor Resource Center at www.nelson.com/login and http://login.cengage.com.

NETA Test Bank: This resource was written by Alexis Dolphin, Western University. It includes over 640 multiple-choice questions written according to NETA guidelines for effective construction and development of higher-order questions. The Test Bank was copyedited by a NETA-trained editor for adherence to NETA best practices. Also included are 50 essay-type and over 50 short-answer-type questions.

The NETA Test Bank is available in a new, cloud-based platform. **Testing Powered by Cognero®** is a secure online testing system that allows you to author, edit, and manage test bank content from any place you have Internet access. No special installations or downloads are needed, and the desktop-inspired interface, with its drop-down menus and familiar, intuitive tools, allows you to create and manage tests with ease. You can create multiple test versions in an instant, and import or export content to other systems. Tests can be delivered from your learning management system, your classroom, or wherever you want.

NETA Instructor's Manual: This resource was written by Alexis Dolphin, Western University. It is organized according to the textbook chapters and addresses key educational concerns, such as why should anthropology matter to students and typical stumbling blocks that student face and how to address them.

NETA PowerPoint: Microsoft® PowerPoint® lecture slides for every chapter have been created by Julie Cormack, Mount Royal University. An average of 25 slides are provided per chapter, many featuring key figures, tables, and photographs from *A Human Voyage*, Second Edition. NETA principles of clear design and engaging content have been incorporated throughout, making it simple for instructors to customize the deck for their courses.

Image Library: This resource consists of digital copies of figures, short tables, and photographs used in the book. Instructors may use these JPEGS to customize the NETA PowerPoint or create their own PowerPoint presentations.

Day One: *Day One—Prof InClass* is a PowerPoint presentation that instructors can customize to orient students to the class and their text at the beginning of the course.

CourseMate provides immediate feedback that enables students to connect results to the work they have just produced, increasing their learning efficiency. It encourages contact between students and faculty: you can choose to monitor your students' level of engagement with CourseMate, correlating their efforts to their outcomes. You can even use CourseMate's quizzes to practise "just in time" teaching by tracking results in the Engagement Tracker and customizing your lesson plans to address their learning needs. In the password-protected area, CourseMate also contains all instructor supplements for downloading at your convenience.

Student Ancillaries

Biological Anthropology CourseMate: The more you study, the better the results. Make the most of your study time by accessing everything you need to succeed in one place.
Biological Anthropology CourseMate includes

- An interactive ebook that includes note-taking and highlighting functionality
- Interactive teaching and learning tools, including
  - Premium quizzes (Check Your Comprehension quizzes, matching quizzes)
  - Demonstrate Your Critical Thinking questions
  - Explore Core Concepts discussion questions
  - Focus On Core Issues questions
  - Flashcards
  - Identify the Skeleton tool
  - Resource, Readings, and Websites list, and much more

Visit NELSONbrain.com to start using CourseMate. Enter the Online Access Code from the card included with your text. If a code card is *not* provided, you can purchase instant access at NELSONbrain.com.

ACKNOWLEDGMENTS

This labour of love would not have been possible without the help and support of numerous friends and colleagues. At Nelson, we wish to thank former sales representative Erin Carlson for planting in our heads the idea to do this project, and Executive Editor Maya Castle for her tireless effort in promoting the text and guiding us from the first through the second edition. Special thanks go to our developmental editor, Katherine Goodes, for her patience and persistence in keeping us on schedule and on budget! Thanks also go to Nelson's permissions editor, Carrie McGregor; production project manager, Natalia Denesiuk Harris; copy editor, June Trusty; and project manager, Naman Mahisauria.

We also acknowledge the support of our colleagues across Canada and beyond who shared many of their stories, insights, and images to make this a better book. We are especially grateful to the following colleagues who contributed written material and photographs for the book or the associated CourseMate website: David Begun (University of Toronto), Stacie Burke (University of Manitoba), Julie Cormack (Mount Royal University), Alan Cross (Simon Fraser University), Jerry Cybulski (formerly with the Canadian Museum of History), Michelle Drapeau (Université de Montréal), Linda Fedigan (University of Calgary), Tracey Galloway (University of Manitoba), Todd Garlie (U.S. Army Research, Development and Engineering Command, Natick, Massachusetts), Tracy Kivell (University of Kent), Helen Kurki (University of Victoria), Carol MacLeod (Langara College), Tina Moffat (McMaster University), Mary Pavelka (University of Calgary), Tanya Peckmann (St. Mary's University), Tracy Prowse (McMaster University), Dan Sellen (University of Toronto), Mirjana Roksandic (University of Winnipeg), Mary Silcox (University of Toronto), Mark Skinner (Simon Fraser University), Matt Skinner (University College London), Matt Tocheri (National Museum of Natural History, Smithsonian Institution), and Warren Wilson (University of Calgary).

We also thank Henry Schwarcz (McMaster University) and Jane Evans (NERC Isotope Geosciences Laboratory, United Kingdom) for their helpful comments, and the following individuals for contributing many of the wonderful photographs in the book: Ian Colquhoun (University of Western Ontario), Tosha Dupras (University of Central Florida), Lisa Gould (University of Victoria), Kayla Hartwell (Wildlife Care Center of Belize, Belmopan, Belize), Bonnie Kahlon (McMaster University), Shannon McPherron (Max Plank Institute for Evolutionary Anthropology), Mary Pavelka (University of Calgary), Tracy Prowse (McMaster University), Amy Scott (University of Manitoba), Pascale Sicotte (University of Calgary), Travis Steffens (researcher/photographer, Ankarafantsika, Madagascar), and Andrzej Weber (University of Alberta). Thank you to Leah Andrews (Adam Scott Collegiate, Peterborough) for doing some of the background research for the book, and to our students for their encouragement. Special thanks go to those who participated in the reviewing process for this second edition and whose comments helped bring this text to fruition:

Julie Cormack, Mount Royal University

Paul Erickson, Saint Mary's University

Samanti Kulatilake, Mount Royal University

Carol MacLeod, Langara College

Bob Muckle, Capilano University

Katherine Patton, St. Francis Xavier University

Dennis Sandgathe, Simon Fraser University

Mary Silcox, University of Toronto Scarborough

Finally, we are eternally grateful for the support given and the sacrifices made by family and friends, who never let us forget that biological anthropologists are human, too!

ABOUT THE COVER

Humans share two biological voyages, recounted in this text and reflected on the cover. The first is a developmental voyage, from conception to death, during which our unique biology is expressed, challenged, and modified by the diverse circumstances and environments in which we grow and age. The second is the continuing evolutionary voyage, written in our primate heritage from ancestor to descendent, upon which we can look back with fascination and only wonder at the future.

ABOUT THE AUTHORS

Anne Keenleyside

Anne Keenleyside is an Associate Professor and Chair of the Department of Anthropology at Trent University in Peterborough, Ontario, where she has been based since 2002. She received her Ph.D. in anthropology from McMaster University and also holds a Bachelor of Education degree from the Ontario Institute for Studies in Education. Trained as a bioarchaeologist, she has conducted fieldwork in Nunavut, Siberia, Russia, Romania, and Tunisia, and for the past decade has been investigating the health and diet of an ancient Greek colonial population on the Black Sea coast of Bulgaria. Most recently, she has embarked on the analysis of newly recovered skeletal remains from the last expedition of Sir John Franklin (1845–1848) to the Canadian Arctic.

Richard Lazenby

Richard Lazenby is Professor and founding member of the Anthropology Department at the University of Northern British Columbia, Prince George, British Columbia. Richard arrived at UNBC in 1994 after receiving his Ph.D. at McMaster University (1992) and a brief sojourn as a Post-Doctoral Fellow at the University of Guelph. His overarching research interest is to understand how life history (growth, aging, diet, activity) shapes both external and internal skeletal morphology. Most recently he has been working with colleagues at the University of Calgary and at the Max Planck Institute for Evolutionary Anthropology in Leipzig, Germany, exploring the application of 3D microcomputed tomographic imaging to investigate patterns of asymmetry related to hand use in humans, nonhuman primates, and fossil hominins.

1 Introduction to Biological Anthropology

> *Civilization is a movement and not a condition, a voyage and not a harbour.*
>
> Arnold J. Toynbee (1889–1975)

OVERVIEW

As practised in North America, biological anthropology is one of four major fields of anthropology and encompasses a multitude of subspecialties. Although the history of biological anthropology dates to the late 18th century, only in the past 60 years has the discipline emerged as a modern field of scientific inquiry—one that emphasizes process, adaptation, and variation. Today, biological anthropology embraces a biocultural perspective, especially in the study of modern human diversity. Through basic research, the discipline has made it clear that humans are uniquely evolved organisms in a complex system of ecological, physical, and cultural environments, past and present. An applied research focus addresses contemporary social questions, including those arising from forensic science, medical anthropology, and nutritional anthropology.

KEY CONCEPTS

Variation, multidisciplinary research, holism, biocultural perspective, basic and applied research, evolutionary and developmental processes, basic and applied research

KEY LEARNING OBJECTIVES

At the end of this chapter, you will be able to

LO1   Describe biological anthropology as a subdiscipline of anthropology that studies past and present human and nonhuman primate variation

LO2   Compare several major subfields within the domain of biological anthropology

LO3   Apply a biocultural perspective to understanding modern human variation

LO4   Distinguish between typological and processual ways of thinking about human diversity

LO5   Assess the merits of both laboratory and field research in biological anthropology

LO6   Describe a situation in which you might apply biocultural knowledge to solving a contemporary social problem

A young male hominin[1] stands quietly at the edge of a marsh, some 1.5 million years in the past, at a place we now know as East Africa. He is watching a small herd of impala that have gathered on the far side. It is the end of the dry season and water is everywhere, deep and swift in channels braiding through the wetland, which was much more easily crossed before the rains came. The hominin walks on two legs, as did his ancestors, although much more at ease than did they. This form of locomotion is an uncommon sight on the sun-drenched African savannah, but it allows for efficient travel over long distances, carrying pear-shaped chopping tools roughly fashioned from flint, or long, sharpened sticks. His upright posture affords him a view of the open plain not available to the four-footed predators—the forebears of leopard and lion—with whom he must compete for his dinner and be wary of lest he become theirs. He is more than one-and-a-half metres tall and not yet an adult—still, much taller than his ancestors. His frame is lean, his legs long—features that suit his species well, for they must follow herds of wildebeest and antelope across open country where shade is scarce. As he stands at the marsh edge, gentle breezes wash over his long torso and limbs. Even though warm, the breezes whisk away beads of sweat from his skin, cooling his body. The grasses weave to and fro, brushing against his hairless, darkly pigmented legs. He sees that there is no easy crossing at this point; the impala should be safe for now. But it has been several days since his family made their last kill, and scavenging has been poor; the hominin suffers the impatience of youth and chooses to pursue the prey on his own. In doing so he learns a harsh lesson—biology and cultural adeptness cannot in every instance protect one from rash choices. The water in the bog is deeper than he imagined, the bottom softer. He struggles to move forward, then to turn back, but is caught in the mire. Soon he cannot move at all, and the more he struggles to loosen his feet, the more deeply his long legs sink into the mud. He falls helplessly forward into the water, among the rushes and grasses; his arms find nothing solid beneath him to keep his head above the murky surface ...

PROLOGUE: IN THE BEGINNING ...

Although lost to his family and the community of early humans, our young hominin was only temporarily lost to history. His misfortune became amazingly good fortune for a small band of his large-brained descendants, baking under the hot African sun. The year was 1984. With finely crafted tools of steel and synthetic fibre, they painstakingly excavated his almost complete fossilized skeleton from the dry sediments of his once watery grave. The bones and associated evidence preserved in the deposits that captured him, carefully recovered, analyzed, and interpreted, would reveal his history, which was, in fact, part of your own ...

So ...

Welcome to the story of yourself, of your parents and grandparents, of your children, and of your children's children. Welcome to the story of human generations, of relatives you have never met and will never meet. It is a remarkable story, deep in dust, in bone and blood and stone. It is a story distinguished by some degree of certainty but also by much ambiguity, a story filled with mystery and imbued with wonder. It is a story written and rewritten and waiting to be written yet again, perhaps by you. Welcome to your evolution!

BIOLOGICAL ANTHROPOLOGY: A DIVERSITY OF INTERESTS AND AN INTEREST IN DIVERSITY

biological anthropology

the study of the biological origins, evolution, and contemporary diversity of humans and their primate relatives

Biological anthropology is the scientific study of humankind as one variety of animal among many, as living beings whose intention on conception is to be born, become sexually mature, find a mate (or two, or three ...), reproduce, grow old, and die. Along the way, we must find ways to nurture our bodies as well as our minds. To these ends, we eat food, eliminate waste, heal wounds, and avoid or survive disease. We satisfy curiosity, play joyfully, and encounter anger, love, jealousy, and grief. Many of these experiences are shared with other organisms, closely related and otherwise (Figure 1.1). Some are arguably unique to the domain of human experience; each, however, conjures up questions of keen interest to

---

1. "Hominin" is a term we use to refer to members of our ancestral lineage. This fictionalized account portrays the last moments of the "Turkana Boy," also known by his Kenya National Museum designation WT 15000, an almost complete skeleton of *Homo ergaster* discovered in 1984–85.

FIGURE 1.1 Biology ties together all living things. Both the common lab mouse and the common chimpanzee have figured prominently in developing a better understanding of ourselves, even though one is a much closer relative.

(L to R) Ljupco Smokovski/Shutterstock.com; Ronald van der Beek/Shutterstock.com; Courtesy of Richard Lazenby

biological anthropologists (see, for example, Meredith Small [1995] for an interesting take on love and sex, and Muller and Wrangham [2009] on male violence toward women as an evolved characteristic). The human expression of life events is the product of our particular evolutionary history, and to fully appreciate what we are all about from birth to death, generation to generation, we need to appreciate how these features appeared and were shaped over several million years of ancestral births, reproductions, and deaths.

Not all of us, of course, succeed in life's undertakings; failure in whole or in part is common. Many conceptions do not reach full gestation, let alone maturity, or they do so but become children whose growth is compromised by circumstances such as poverty, ill health, and ecological, social, or political instability. Some of us do not find mates or reproduce, while our siblings have several mates and scads of children. Some have lives filled more with grief than with love. This is the fullness and richness of the human condition, and it underscores what is most real about the living world—the **variation** within it. Joseph Weiner (1979, 5), a noted environmental physiologist and biological anthropologist, once observed that "it is not so much the fact of variation, but the significance of variation which demarcates the new bio-anthropology." The significance of that variation, for those humans now living and for their ancestors' ancestors, is what biological anthropology as a field of inquiry aims to discover, explore, and understand.

variation
observable differences within a class of objects, the source of which may be genetic or environmental or both in interaction

ANTHROPOLOGY'S SCOPE: WHO WE ARE, WHAT WE ARE, WHY WE ARE

There is a good chance that you have already determined what your major will be during your undergraduate career. It may even be anthropology. But there are a number of other possibilities: biology, chemistry, psychology, mathematics, political science, geography, economics, First Nations studies, history, gender studies, or sociology ... the list goes on. (We know this because we have had such students in our own classes.) The fact that a course in biological anthropology attracts students from diverse backgrounds illustrates two important points. First, there is something inherently compelling about the story of "us," of humankind. In this age of an "electronically shrinking planet" (a concept that the Canadian literary critic and communications theorist Marshall McLuhan [1911–1980] popularized as the "global village"), it is understandable that we wonder about where we came from, our similarities and differences, and our relationships. "Difference" surrounds us, especially in countries such as Canada, where Aboriginal peoples (the original migrants) have been living for many thousands of years and where in recent centuries immigration has done so much to shape our society (Figure 1.2). It is no surprise, then,

NEL **CHAPTER 1** Introduction to Biological Anthropology 5

forensic anthropology

the application of anthropological knowledge to solving offences committed against people, including homicide and war crimes

multidisciplinary

an investigative approach that brings the expertise of a number of disciplines to bear on a particular question within an existing field of study

interdisciplinary

an investigative approach that brings diverse fields together to create a new arena of study

anthropology

the global and comparative study of humankind, past and present

holism

the integrated study of all aspects of human life, biological, cultural, historical, psychological, etc., in order to develop a comprehensive view of the whole of the human condition

FIGURE 1.2 Canada's population is a rich mosaic of peoples and cultures from around the globe.

Toronto Star/GetStock.com

that reflections of our origins and diversity confront us every day. The subject matter of biological anthropology is often the focus of cover stories in literary fiction, in Hollywood movies, in popular magazines, and on television. The subspecialty of **forensic anthropology** alone has become extremely visible in popular culture. The second point, equally important, is that anthropology is becoming increasingly **multidisciplinary** *and* **interdisciplinary** and is drawing from and contributing to many other fields that study humankind and our primate relatives past and present (see Box 1.1).

In North America, biological anthropology is one of several subfields in the larger domain of **anthropology** (from the Greek *anthropos*, meaning "human" + *logy*, meaning "to speak of") (Figure 1.3). Anthropology is a broad discipline that crosses the social, life, and physical sciences; embracing **holism** as a central

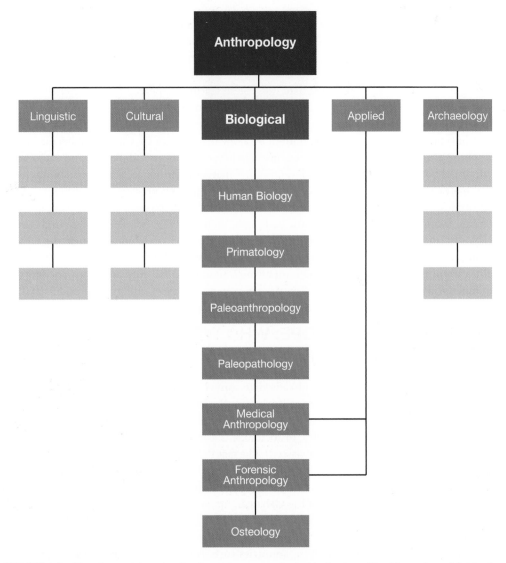

FIGURE 1.3 The diverse interests of anthropology are reflected in the breadth of its major subfields, the specializations within them, and the application of anthropological knowledge.

BOX 1.1   FOCUS ON ... Collaboration

Collaboration, or the sharing of ideas, information, and research effort across fields, characterizes many disciplines. This reflects two interdependent phenomena. The first is that the questions we pose often do not have clearly defined boundaries: they are "fuzzy" questions that touch on a number of subject areas, each of which can bring something to the table in search of a fuller comprehension. The second is that our particular subject of study—humankind—is not reducible to the bits and pieces that researchers of an earlier generation studied as distinct entities. We have since learned that the whole is vastly greater—and a lot more interesting—than the sum of its parts! A multidisciplinary approach describes the situation where researchers from different fields of study combine their efforts to address a particular question or research theme using the methods and bodies of theory from within their own discipline. Interdisciplinarity, on the other hand, develops when new insights emerge from the integration of concepts from other fields into a novel perspective or understanding, often creating new fields of inquiry (e.g., feminist studies). Let us look at a couple of examples to illustrate what we mean.

In the opening section of this chapter, we presented a vignette covering a moment in the life—and death—of what eventually became an extremely important fossil discovery, the so-called Turkana Boy from West Turkana, East Africa, dated to c. 1.5 million years (see Chapter 10). This fictionalized account described not only what this individual looked like, but aspects of his environment (plants, animals, climate, geography) and behaviour (diet, mobility, culture). In the true spirit of *multidisciplinary* research, this diverse information was compiled from the work of specialists in numerous fields—paleoanthropology, paleontology, geology, paleoecology, chemistry, and physics, to name a few—all working together on one great story: the discovery of who this individual was, and where, when, and how he lived (Walker and Leakey 1993).

Our second example illustrates *interdisciplinary* research. One of the great challenges facing public health today—in Canada and around the world—is the **pandemic** described by the World Health Organization (WHO) as "globesity." A significant proportion of humanity now tip the scales in the categories of overweight and obese (OW–OB). As a debilitating condition, OW–OB shows no respect for age, gender, class, or nationality; it crosses all boundaries. The costs to the health care system and to the economy more generally run into billions of dollars. Also, when viewed at the community level, we often find inequities in the **prevalence** of OW–OB. Recently, one of us (Lazenby) took part in a study to document childhood OW–OB in Prince George, British Columbia. An important finding was that, though the prevalence of OW–OB was high in the sample as a whole, children of First Nations ancestry were more at risk for being OW–OB than non–First Nations children—a pattern well established for Canada as a whole (Figure 1.4).

This difference was not rooted in ancestral biology (and we did not expect it to be), but in history and political economy. We could fully understand the pattern of OW–OB among Prince George schoolchildren only by integrating information describing the social and economic determinants of health—education, income, housing, family structure, access to health care. These in turn had to be contextualized within a colonial and post-colonial historical framework. What emerged from this interdisciplinary analysis was a broader, more nuanced understanding of the variation in human biological outcomes produced by nonbiological forces.

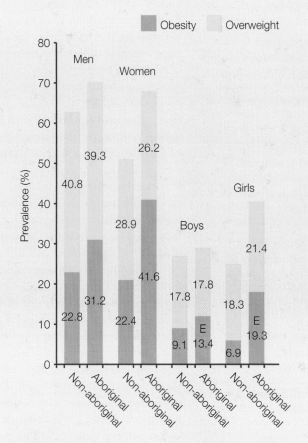

FIGURE 1.4 Children from self-identified First Nations families are at higher risk for being overweight or obese than non–First Nations children.

P.T. Katzmarzyk. (2008). "Obesity and physical activity among Aboriginal Canadians," *Obesity* 16: 184–190. Reprinted by permission from John Wiley and Sons.

defining feature, it is dedicated to the historical and comparative study of human diversity. What do we mean by this? Simply that among all the various fields that study "humans" (including psychology, sociology, political science, economics, and history), anthropology is concerned not with a particular aspect of what makes us what we are, but with *all* aspects. Moreover, anthropology aims to discover the threads that weave together all the characteristics that make each of us not only unique as an individual, but also a part of a larger collective enterprise—that of humanity. Historically, the subfields of anthropology complementing biological anthropology are cultural anthropology, archaeology, and anthropological linguistics. **Cultural anthropology** focuses on comprehending the meaning and origins of social and cultural complexity through **ethnography**, while **archaeology** investigates the material record of human history (written and otherwise), as well as the landscape on which it was played out, extending some two and a half million years into the past. **Anthropological linguistics** examines the origin, evolution, and structure of language(s), the relationships among them, and the social use of language in managing human affairs.

An important consideration is that, while each of these subfields is very much its own distinct discipline with particular bodies of theory and method, all are part of anthropology.[2] Archaeologists, for example, also study social and cultural complexity, its origins and development, and thus use many of the models of cultural anthropology; anthropological linguists have produced language maps charting the prehistoric migrations of human populations that closely approximate similar maps produced through genetic analyses (Henn et al. 2012). Cultural anthropology, archaeology, and linguistics often contribute to the field of biological anthropology as it searches for a fuller understanding of humans as biological organisms. A good example of this integrative approach is Kurki and colleagues' (2008) comparative study of body-size proportionality in small-bodied foragers from past and present South African and Andaman Island populations.

Kurki and her co-workers examined the correspondence of body size and shape to climate, **thermoregulation**, and energetic efficiency using subsistence adaptation, archaeological history, and linguistic affinity to define samples and to explain the observed patterns of variation. Such studies exemplify what we refer to as a **biocultural** perspective, which recognizes that throughout human history, culture has in many ways influenced biological variation by acting as a mediator between individuals and their environment. Similarly, cultural differences may be significantly affected by biological differences within and between human populations (as we explore in Part IV, Modern Currents). An essential message here is that while we often isolate and study a particular aspect of what we are as humans, that aspect is part of a larger whole and can be fully appreciated only by situating it within that whole.

The comparatively new subfield of **applied anthropology**—which has roots in all of the other fields of the discipline—applies anthropological knowledge to challenges arising from the intricacies and inequities of human relationships, as well as to more practical questions such as the ergonomic design of clothing, vehicles, and furnishings. Applied anthropologists often find themselves working with government agencies and/or nongovernmental organizations (NGOs) seeking solutions to problems that may be local (e.g., forensic anthropologists assist police forces at crime scenes) or global (e.g., nutritional anthropologists contribute to the development of international food aid programs). Applied work is a full-time vocation for some anthropologists; more often, though, people who would otherwise consider themselves biological, cultural, linguistic, or archaeological anthropologists don the cloak of the applied anthropologist when called on to bring their expertise to a specific issue at hand.

Fields within Fields: The Scope of Biological Anthropology

In the past in Canada, you would find biological anthropologists working in universities, typically in anthropology departments, although in some instances, in archaeology departments (e.g., at Simon Fraser University and the University of Calgary). Today, biological

---

2. Specialization is typical of almost all fields of study, including the other branches of anthropology, reflecting the rapid growth and diversification of "science" from the late 19th through the 20th centuries.

anthropologists can be found outside the traditional venue of anthropology departments. For example, a number of our colleagues now teach and carry out research in anatomy and cell biology departments associated with medical schools, and others have pursued independent careers as consultants. Some work for nongovernmental agencies such as HealthBridge, as well as in museums—for example, the Canadian Museum of History in Gatineau, Quebec. These changes reflect how the discipline has broadened its areas of inquiry and application, now that innovative theory and analytical methods have expanded the scope of the field. To take one example, it might surprise you to learn that by studying genetically distinct strains of mice, biological anthropologists have developed a better appreciation of how genes regulate growth and development to create novel **cranial morphology** (Hallgrímsson et al. 2007; Figure 1.5); this in turn has helped us better understand problems such as cleft palate in humans. You might think it a stretch to jump from mice to people, but it is not as great a leap as it would seem, given that the genetic program regulating many aspects of development has been highly conserved[3] over tens of millions of years of evolution and is shared widely among mammals (see Chapter 4).

In much the same way that anthropology comprises several major subfields, biological anthropology includes a number of specializations, all bound by a common interest in understanding more about who we are, where we came from, how we live, and how we behave. There is considerable communication and cross-fertilization of information and ideas among

cranial morphology
the relative size and shape configuration of the various bones of the skull

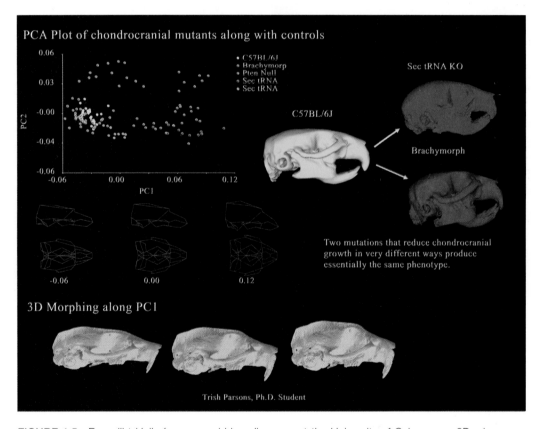

FIGURE 1.5 Benedikt Hallgrímsson and his colleagues at the University of Calgary use 3D microcomputed tomographic imaging of different mouse strains to understand the regulation of facial growth and development. This work is relevant to mammalian evolutionary history as well as to understanding defects of human development, such as cleft palate.

Courtesy of Benedikt Hallgrímsson

3. To speak of something as "conserved" in the context of evolutionary biology is to suggest that there has been very little genetic change over millions of years. Interestingly, however, the regulation of that highly conserved genetic program may well have changed over time, leading to new evolutionary outcomes.

these specializations, and now and then some very intense disagreements as to "how things work" as well! This is something we hope you will come to appreciate as you progress through your course and this text.

Biological anthropologists approach human diversity and variation from two basic directions: that of the living and that of the dead. Regarding the latter, their studies focus on the hard tissues—bones and teeth—that survive decomposition for considerable lengths of time. However, in extraordinary circumstances, such as might be encountered with forensic work or in archaeology (e.g., mummification), we are fortunate to be able to study the soft tissue remains of deceased individuals. For example, in 1999, the partial remains of a young man, no older than many of you, were discovered emerging from melting glacial ice in northwestern British Columbia, near the Yukon border (Figure 1.6). Named Kwäday Dän Ts'ínchi (Long Ago Person Found) by the Champagne and Aishihik First Nations in whose traditional territory the discovery occurred, this individual was found associated with a number of artifacts, including clothing and hunting implements. The biological and cultural remains offered a unique window into the life of one of our First Nations ancestors (Beattie et al. 2000). Only with the exceptional cooperation and goodwill of all involved—the scientific community and the Champagne and Aishihik First Nations elders, band leaders, and community members—have we come to know an individual who lived 550 years ago. This project exemplifies the success of **community-based research** within a biocultural framework (Schell et al. 2007).

FIGURE 1.6 In 1999, the rare discovery of partial remains of a mummified individual in northwestern British Columbia provided unique insight into the lives of First Nations people.

Courtesy of Al Mackie

community-based research

an approach in which investigators work directly with a community to develop, organize, and implement a research program

Discoveries such as Kwäday Dän Ts'ínchi are as rare as they are significant. More often, biological anthropologists studying the past glean information from the varied surfaces and internal structures, and from the chemical and molecular composition of bones and teeth. And it is not simply a matter of those who work with the dead talking with "like-minded" colleagues: an exciting synergy results when our knowledge of lives once lived merges with knowledge of lives being lived now. Our understanding of the disease experience among First Nations peoples today has been illuminated by the study of the physical signs of ill health seen in skeletal remains of past populations (Waldram, Herring, and Young 2006). We know, for example, that the increased prevalence of dental disease among indigenous peoples is a product of the transition to "Western" diets with their excess of refined carbohydrates, as pre-contact populations show little evidence of tooth decay.

Skeletal Biology

An undergraduate curriculum in biological anthropology typically includes a course in human **osteology** (see Appendix A for a comparative overview of skeletal anatomy). The study of bones and teeth has long been a mainstay of the discipline. There are many reasons why. The skeleton is the last biological tissue to decompose and is often preserved for hundreds or even thousands of years (and once fossilized, millions of years). It is the only permanent record of the human biology of peoples who are no longer among us. And it is rich in information, whether one is studying an individual skeleton, a collection of skeletons sampled from past populations, or even fragments of skeletons (Katzenberg and Saunders 2008). Besides indicating fundamental features such as age and sex, bones and teeth bear a history of population affinity, environmental adaptation, growth and development, health and disease, diet, and activity (either as general aspects such as sexual division of labour, or regarding specific activities such as occupation), as well as signals of cultural practices, including migration, mobility, and marriage patterns (Gosman et al. 2011).

osteology

the descriptive and comparative study of bones and teeth

Developments in the analysis of bone chemistry, including **isotopes** of carbon, nitrogen, and oxygen, have expanded our horizons by pinpointing specific population relationships, cultural practices, human–disease interactions, and diet (see Box 1.2). One interesting example is the application of isotope data to establish the time frame for the cultural practice of infant weaning. Our bodies incorporate into our tissues various chemical isotopes from the foods we eat, making it possible to identify the makeup of an individual's diet over the course of his or her lifetime from preserved remains (such as bones, teeth, and hair). Using this approach, Tracy Prowse and colleagues (2008) compared isotopes of carbon (δ^{13}C) and nitrogen (δ^{15}N) from juvenile and adult skeletons excavated from the Imperial Roman (100–300 CE) site of Isola Sacra and were able to show that weaning began with the introduction of transitional foods by the end of the first year and was completed by two to two-and-a-half years of age in that population. Similarly, Waters-Rist et al. (2011) found that weaning in both Early and Late Neolithic peoples from the *Cis*-Baikal region of Siberia occurred between the ages of two and three years, although the former introduced complementary foods to infants at a later age and completed weaning over a shorter time period.

isotopes

an isotope is a measurable form of a chemical element varying in the number of neutrons within its nucleus (e.g., ^{12}C and ^{14}C are different isotopes of carbon; an atom of the former has 6 protons and 6 neutrons and the latter has 2 extra neutrons)

BOX 1.2   **PROFILE ... Chemical Traces of Past Human Behaviour**

Courtesy of Tracy Prowse

Stable isotope analysis is a method that analyzes the chemical composition of body tissues that are preserved in the archaeological record, such as bones, teeth, and hair. This method is now commonly used in bioarchaeological research to investigate questions relating to past diet and geographic origins. This is based on the fact that what we eat and drink is incorporated into our body's tissues during life and this chemical signal is preserved in these tissues after death, most commonly measured in isotope variation in carbon, nitrogen, and oxygen (see Chapter 10). More recently, stable isotope analysis has been used in modern forensic cases to identify the geographic origins of unidentified human remains.

A number of biological anthropologists in Canada have made significant contributions to isotopic investigations of human diet, geographic origins, and migration. Early bioarchaeological research using stable isotopes investigated the adoption of maize in southern Ontario through the analysis of carbon and nitrogen isotopes. Anne Katzenberg and colleagues published groundbreaking papers on the pattern and timing of weaning in past populations, and more recently her work has examined prehistoric diet in the Lake Baikal region, Siberia. Christine White has explored diet, migration, and geographic identity of ancient Mayan populations using a range of stable isotopes. Other Canadian biological anthropologists and archaeologists specializing in stable isotope research include Jocelyn Williams, Sandra Garvie-Lok, Michael Richards, Vaughn Grimes, and one of the authors of this book, Anne Keenleyside, among others.

All of these researchers investigate aspects of past life through isotopic analysis of preserved human tissues.

My own bioarchaeological research explores diet and geographic origins in Roman Italy using stable isotope analysis and palaeopathological evidence. I am interested in understanding what life was like under the control of the Roman Empire, and how this control played out differently in the lives of the people who lived at that time. My research explores a number of different questions about the past. One question concerns the investigation of diet and dental health, and understanding how an individual's changing role in the household and society may have impacted dietary choices. My investigation of carbon and nitrogen isotopes in a Roman-period skeletal sample from Isola Sacra (near Rome) showed that consumption of marine foods varied with age, suggesting that access to certain foods changed throughout the life course.

Another area of research is the investigation of geographic origins and migration in the Roman world. I have explored geographic origins of the people buried at Isola Sacra and patterns of migration in the Mediterranean region using oxygen isotopes in teeth. This research showed that the majority of people at Isola Sacra came from Rome and its environs, and those who immigrated from outside the area did so as children, in contrast to the commonly held view that migration was only an adult male activity. My current field and research project is the bioarchaeological analysis of geographic origins and migration using a sample from a rural Roman cemetery at Vagnari, southern Italy.

The most important aspect about all of this research is that you have to start with an interesting and compelling anthropological question. Stable isotope analysis, like any other analytical technique, is only as good as the research questions you ask.

Source: Courtesy of Dr. Tracy Prowse, Department of Anthropology, McMaster University

paleopathology

literally, the study of ancient disease and trauma

As a branch of osteology, **paleopathology** focuses on characterizing patterns of disease and trauma in archaeological human remains. Many illnesses and injuries leave tell-tale marks on or within bones and teeth, and paleopathologists study these marks in order to understand how human populations in the past suffered from, and coped with, life's many challenges. Some skeletal changes clearly show a specific cause (e.g., syphilis or a broken bone). Many paleopathological studies, however, report on the presence of generalized, nonspecific disease stress or overall patterns of wounds reflecting the kinds of weapons used in ancient times. In these cases, skeletal changes may suggest disease processes, chronic exposure to infectious agents (e.g., bacteria or parasites), environmental challenges such as food shortages resulting in malnutrition, or activities associated with occupation or interpersonal violence. For example, Keenleyside and Panayotova (2006) relate cranial lesions in 3rd- to 5th-century BCE Greek colonists on the Black Sea to diet and infectious or parasitic diseases (Figure 1.7). In a different vein, Faccia and Williams (2007) have shown that the pattern of vertebral lesions known as "Schmorl's nodes" seen in modern people experiencing chronic back pain can be informative regarding the degree to which humans in the past may have suffered from this debilitating condition. Clearly, we have as much to learn about the past from the present as we have about the present from the past.

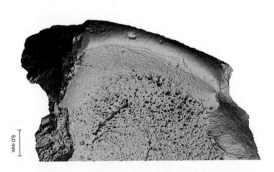

FIGURE 1.7 A porous lesion within the orbit of the eye, known as *cribra orbitalia*, is an example of a nonspecific marker of metabolic disease or parasitic infection, seen here in a young adult male from the Kalfata necropolis from the ancient Greek colonial site of Apollonia Pontica.

Courtesy of Richard Lazenby

Paleoanthropology

paleoanthropology

the study of human evolution through fossils and the circumstances in which they are found

hominin

a term inclusive of modern humans and their bipedal ancestors

Few specializations within biological anthropology receive as much media attention as **paleoanthropology**, the study of human evolution as represented in the fossil remains of our **hominin** ancestors and those of our primate relatives (Figure 1.8). This attention is not owing to the spectacular nature of such discoveries, because most cannot be described that way. Rather, interest in paleoanthropology is due more to the fact that fragments of bone and tooth eked out of parched desert terrain, or excavated from deep in caves, may have huge implications for understanding—possibly even rewriting—human evolutionary history. In 2007, Matt Tocheri and his colleagues found themselves under an intense media spotlight when their 3D analysis of wrist bones from the controversial *Homo floresiensis* skeleton from Indonesia indicated that this discovery, dating between c. 95 to 17 thousand years ago (Morwood et al. 2009), was anatomically quite primitive, more similar to our million-plus-year-old relatives in Africa (Tocheri et al. 2007, and see Chapter 10, Box 10.2). Such stories hold a deep fascination for many of us, inside and outside the field of paleoanthropology.

FIGURE 1.8 Paleoanthropologist Matthew Skinner examines the fossilized facial skeleton of a prehistoric monkey recovered from the site of Asbole, Afar, Ethiopia.

Courtesy of Matthew Skinner

The study of the fossil record of human evolution can be laborious, with fieldwork often carried out in inhospitable landscapes and in areas of the world having long histories of political instability (such as the Horn of Africa, where a number of momentous discoveries—including that of the famous "Lucy" partial skeleton[4]—have been made). And once found, the analysis—cleaning, reconstruction, description, and comparison—may require months or years of additional painstaking effort, although typically in the more welcoming and benign surroundings of a museum or university laboratory. However, the rewards of this research can be as immense as the task itself. In the past 50 years, our view of human evolutionary history has been transformed several times, from one of a rather simplistic more-or-less linear evolutionary "tree" perhaps only 2 million years in the making, to one viewed today as a complex (and complicated) "bush" occupied by numerous ancestors and descendants and extending into the past as much as 6.5 million years.

Interpretation of this rich record has brought forth keen and at times raucous debate, during which very different and even opposing views have been advanced. These disputes may revolve around whether a particular fossil find should be considered a hominin at all. If it is generally agreed to be one, debate may then centre on which **taxon** it belongs to. Indeed, questions have been raised as to how many hominin taxa should be recognized at all, and of these, which gave rise to later forms. That such disagreements occur should not lead you to conclude that paleoanthropology is in acrimonious disarray. Quite the contrary, these debates are healthy and reflect serious attempts to make sense of natural biological variation from fragmentary "windows" widely dispersed in space and time. In spite of these limitations, there is a broad consensus regarding how we define ourselves and view the major developments that characterize the evolution of humankind (see Part III, Ancient Currents).

taxon
a formal designation of biological classification; plural taxa (e.g., we are all members of the taxon *Homo sapiens*)

Human Biology

Human biology is the branch of biological anthropology that aims to understand modern population diversity, its historical antecedents, and its relationship to the lived environment. In other words, it aims to discover *what* and *who* we are in the context of *where* and *when* we are. A human biologist may just as easily be found in a North American urban neighbourhood

human biology
a branch of biological anthropology that examines modern population diversity

studying the relationship between socioeconomic status and childhood obesity (Moffat et al. 2005) as in a rural village in Nepal studying breastfeeding and wage labour (Moffat 2002; Figure 1.9) or investigating the differences in health outcomes between younger and older First Nations people in Canada and the use of traditional versus Western health care practices (Wilson et al. 2011). The underlying theme in each of these studies is the relationships among biology, culture, and environment, with the understanding that "environment" is defined quite broadly to include not just a person's physical surroundings but also the social and political circumstances within which that person grows, lives, works, raises a family, and dies.

Historically, human biologists have documented population variation in growth and development through measures such as body size, shape, and proportion—a method known as **anthropometry**. Comparative studies of height, weight, and muscle and fat

FIGURE 1.9 As a human biologist, Tina Moffat—shown here with her Nepalese research assistant, Lakhpa Lama (middle) and a village elder in 1998—studies how modern populations adapt to diverse physical and social environments.

Courtesy of Tina Moffat

anthropometry
the measurement of body form

4. "Lucy," discovered in 1974 in the Afar region of Ethiopia, has the more formal scientific name of *Australopithecus afarensis* (see Chapter 9).

CHAPTER 1 Introduction to Biological Anthropology

hypoxia

low oxygen availability, characteristically associated with high altitude

adaptability

the tendency for an organism to achieve increased functional capacity through a modification of body form and/or physiological pathway when faced with an environmental stressor

molecular anthropology

the study of population diversity at the level of the gene and its products (both structural and regulatory proteins)

DNA

deoxyribonucleic acid, the fundamental genetic material of life

genomics

the comparative and evolutionary study of the genomes of different species

functional genomics

the study of the dynamic actions and interactions of genes and proteins

mitochondrial DNA (mtDNA)

DNA found within the mitochondria in a cell

whole-genome variation

the presence of many common genetic variants throughout the genome, the study of which permits a more detailed reconstruction of evolutionary events and population history

mass can be very informative about population health and nutrition. Similarly, understanding how different human populations adapt morphologically and physiologically to environmental extremes (e.g., Arctic cold, desert heat, tropical humidity, and high-altitude **hypoxia**) has been a keen subject of study for human biologists interested in human **adaptability** (see Chapter 14). High-altitude populations in the Andes, Tibet, and Ethiopia, for example, are known to have evolved different metabolic pathways (e.g., red blood cell concentration) in coping with the stress of low oxygen availability above 4,000 metres (Beall 2006).

Many human biologists are interested in the impact of "modernization," during which significant transformations occur in the political economy of local populations. An excellent example of this approach is the long-term study of changes in Inuit growth, development, and health during the transition from traditional to modern ("Western") lifeways in the latter half of the 20th century, including the shift from subsistence hunting to wage labour, from "country" to processed foods, and from levels of relatively high activity to increasingly more sedentary lifestyles (Shephard and Rode 1996). This transition has been linked to changes in fertility patterns, increases in morbidity and mortality (illness and death), near-epidemic levels of adolescent suicide, rising challenges from accumulating environmental toxins such as PCBs and dioxins (Van Oostdam et al. 2005), and trends toward greater levels of childhood obesity (Galloway et al. 2012). Similar approaches have been used to study pastoral peoples in varying habitats, such as Africa, the Andes, and Siberia (e.g., Leonard and Crawford 2003).

Molecular Anthropology

Although the term "**molecular anthropology**" was first coined in 1962 (Chiu and Wildman 2011), it is fair to say that it is only since the mid-1980s that the study of human and nonhuman primate genomes has become transformative, a fact that has much to do with the rapid development of technologies able to sequence the genetic code of recent and fossil **DNA** (also known as "ancient DNA"; see Chapter 3). Indeed, the rate at which researchers are able to identify DNA sequences (termed "throughput") increased 40,000-fold between 2004 and 2011 (Ståhl and Lundeberg 2012). A process that a decade ago took several weeks at a cost of tens of thousands of dollars can now be accomplished in less than a day for a fraction of that cost. The impact of these developments in **genomics** extends far beyond anthropology, with applications in plant and animal biology, forensic science, and perhaps most significantly in medicine. We live in an era in which we are not only able to ascertain gene sequences but identify what they do, a branch of molecular biology known as **functional genomics**. Much of this effort has been directed toward ascertaining the genetic basis of diseases such as diabetes, various cancers, and cardiovascular diseases (Solyom and Kazazlan 2012).

Within biological anthropology and related fields, molecular analyses have opened up many new areas of inquiry, challenging existing interpretations and posing many new questions. Early developments include analyzing hemoglobin structure to construct a "molecular clock" to date the evolutionary separation of humans and apes (Wilson and Sarich 1969; see Chapter 7), and the analysis of **mitochondrial DNA** (**mtDNA**; see Chapter 3) variation in living humans to ascertain the timing of divergence and migration of our early modern human ancestors out of Africa (Cann et al. 1987); later analyses extended this approach to the male sex-determining Y-chromosome (Jobling and Tyler-Smith 1993). Our understanding of these particular events has evolved in the intervening years, through many technological refinements in molecular approaches to the past. Today, the study of **whole-genome variation** in gene sequences is allowing researchers to study the origin and migration of different human populations, as well as the degree of admixture and fluctuations in population sizes (Stoneking and Krause 2011; Figure 1.10)—genomics has become a window into human history, which we explore in greater detail in Part III, Ancient Currents.

Primatology

One of the more memorable lines ever delivered in a classic Hollywood film was uttered by Robert Armstrong in the role of film director Carl Denham during the closing scene of the original 1933 epic *King Kong* (© 1933 RKO Pictures): "It wasn't planes that did the job. T'was

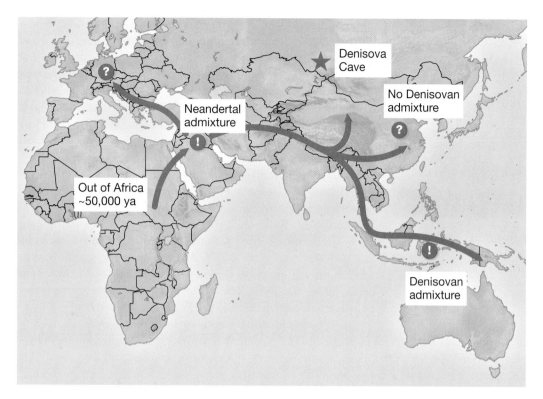

FIGURE 1.10 Molecular anthropology is shedding new light on the African origin of modern humans and subsequent migrations, as well as possible admixture with older human populations such as Neandertals. The routes identified in such maps are indicators of direction, not exact pathways of migration.

Adapted from Stoneking, M. and Krause, J. 2011. *Learning about human population history from ancient and modern genomes. Nature Reviews*: Genetics 12: 603–614.

Beauty that killed the Beast." Beauty in this instance was Canadian actress Fay Wray and the "Beast" was a larger-than-life gorilla, discovered on remote "Skull Island" as the object of worship and reverence by the local population. We suspect that Edgar Wallace and Merian C. Cooper, who wrote and produced the film, would have benefited from a course or two in **primatology**, the scientific study of the biology and behaviour of nonhuman primates (prosimians, monkeys, and apes). While it is true that human societies have developed symbolic relationships with our nearest relatives throughout recorded history, it is also true that the *anthropological* study of primates is younger than the original version of *King Kong*.

Primatologists[5] study nonhuman primates for two fundamental reasons. First, primates are inherently interesting—as much as any other creature, from bacteria to blue whales. They live fascinating lives beyond the realm of human experience, about which we are naturally curious. In this sense, we study primates to understand primates. At the same time, we study primates to understand ourselves. We are closely related, and to some nonhuman primates, *very* closely related. In this respect, primates are models—they serve as windows into our evolutionary past as well as into our present, into how our ancestors may have lived many millions of years ago and how we behave today (Stanford 2012). The fundamental point here is that the individual reading this sentence at this moment (that would be you) is a primate, but one very particular kind of primate. And as you will find out in this course, you can learn much about yourself by knowing more about your nearest relatives.

Public awareness of primates and their relationship to ourselves owes less to cinematic blockbusters than it does to the work of specific individuals working in the field, famously studying the larger-bodied and seemingly more socially complex great apes, such as the

primatology
the study of the morphology, behaviour, and evolution of nonhuman primates

---

5. Humans are one among many different kinds of primates, and for comparison it is often convenient to make the distinction between humans and nonhuman primates. A "primatologist" may come from different disciplines, such as anatomy and psychology, as well as anthropology.

FIGURE 1.11 Primatologist Ian Colquhoun studies social behaviour in black lemurs of Madagascar.

Courtesy of Sylvie Colquhoun

chimpanzee (Jane Goodall), the gorilla (Dian Fossey, whose life and tragic death also captured Hollywood's gaze), and the orangutan (Biruté Galdikas). Of course, we now appreciate that behavioural complexity is a characteristic feature of nonhuman primates generally, and not just apes. Why, for example, should Madagascar prosimians choose to be active at dawn and dusk rather than during the day (Colquhoun 2006; Figure 1.11)? How do social behaviours such as infanticide interact with ecological factors such as food distribution to determine group size in New and Old World monkeys (Chapman and Pavelka 2005)? Why should human children and chimpanzees share a fondness for beginning a painting with the colour yellow and drawing in diagonal lines (Zeller 2007)? Should it surprise us that humans are not the only primate with an archaeological record of stone tool use (Mercader et al. 2007)? As even these few questions suggest, nonhuman primates present us with diverse opportunities to better know ourselves. These and many other interesting questions are pursued further in Part II, Tropical Currents.

In the domain of primatology, conservation is an area of increasing importance (Agoramoorthy 2012). Nonhuman primates have evolved highly complex relationships with their habitats, often serving as **keystone species**, and thus are highly susceptible to dramatic changes imposed by human activity (e.g., deforestation, poaching). As a consequence, they have come to occupy a prominent and unenviable status on the list of endangered and threatened species (see the International Union for the Conservation of Nature's *Red Book*). Vietnam, for example, is home to 25 primate species and subspecies, only two of which (the rhesus and the long-tailed macaque) are ranked as "Least Concern." Primatologists alone cannot resolve such dire situations, but they can provide the knowledge that will better enable responsible governments and agencies to seek solutions.

Applied Biological Anthropology

As noted earlier, an "applied" discipline is one in which the methods and models developed within an academic field are brought to bear ("applied") on present-day problems or needs of human societies. Biological anthropologists undertake applied projects in a number of areas, including forensic science, health and wellness, primate conservation, and ergonomics (see Chapter 15).

Forensic anthropologists are often called on to assist local police forces, coroner services, or medical examiners[6] to identify human remains that—as a result of natural causes or human intention—cannot be identified through more common methods (Figure 1.12). Many of these "case files" are suspicious deaths and subject to criminal investigation; others may represent the outcome of accident or misfortune. In each case, the forensic examination aims to provide biological information pertinent to identity (age, sex, body size, ancestry) and to the circumstances of death (e.g., evidence of trauma, elapsed time since death). It is not uncommon that the remains submitted for examination turn out to be nonhuman (e.g., mammals such as bear or deer), or bones from unmarked archaeological burials.

In the past two decades, a number of forensic anthropologists have worked on large multidisciplinary teams under the auspices of prominent organizations such as the United Nations or Physicians for Human Rights to investigate mass graves resulting from armed conflict (Figure 1.13). These can be particularly difficult exercises. Often, many bodies are involved, there is evidence of brutal violence, and partly decomposed soft tissue is present; all of this is compounded by the trying nature of political realities (local, national, and international) and by the presence of family members seeking answers (Skinner and Sterenberg 2005).

---

6. Different provinces in Canada have different administrative structures providing public oversight to death investigation. British Columbia, for example, has the Coroners Service and Alberta has the Office of the Chief Medical Examiner.

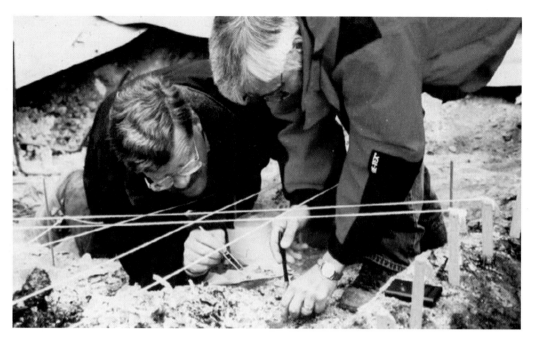

FIGURE 1.12 Richard Lazenby (right) and forensic odontologist Dr. David Hodges recover remains from a cremated homicide victim in northern British Columbia.

Courtesy of Richard Lazenby

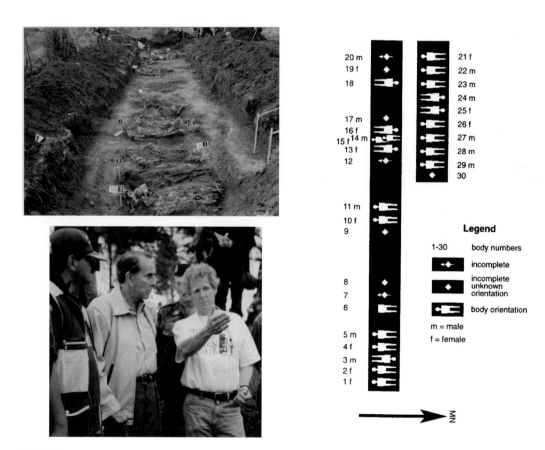

FIGURE 1.13 Forensic anthropologists often assist in the excavation of human remains to gather evidence for crimes against humanity and to provide closure to survivors. Here, Dr. Mark Skinner (gesturing in lower image) discusses excavation strategy for a mass grave in the former Yugoslavia.

Courtesy of Mark Skinner

CHAPTER 1 Introduction to Biological Anthropology

medical anthropology

a branch of applied anthropology examining the interplay of culture, biology, health/wellness, disease/illness, and the art of medicine, both traditional and Western

In the area of population health, biological anthropologists are contributing to the subspecialty of **medical anthropology**. Health forms one of the major intersections of biology and culture, influencing not only the experience of disease but also perceptions of wellness (Young and Rees 2011). Within this domain, community-based approaches are shown to provide benefits beyond an understanding of this intersection. Under this model, local communities work in partnership with researchers to design, implement, and publicize research. Sylvia Abonyi, a Canada Research Chair in Aboriginal Health in the Department of Community Health and Epidemiology, University of Saskatchewan, has been working with Aboriginal communities in northern Saskatchewan to document local understanding and experience with HIV/AIDS and Hepatitis C (Research Project Steering Committee 2006; see Chapter 15). Tracey Galloway of the University of Manitoba has been studying growth, nutrition and obesity among Inuit children (Galloway et al. 2012). Ethnopharmacologist Lidia Nistor Baldea and colleagues (2010) have documented a number of local plants traditionally used by the James Bay Cree of northern Quebec that are effective in regulating dietary glucose levels, which may provide more culturally relevant pharmacologic benefit in treating type II diabetes.

A SCIENCE OLD AND NEW

typology

a static perspective of the world ascribed to the 4th-century BCE Greek philosopher Plato, in which "ideals" or "types" were perceived to be real, and variation as observed in the world was considered a deviation from ideal reality

Earlier in this chapter, we quoted Joseph Weiner on the significance of variation, which he saw as central to defining a "new" biological anthropology. Change occurs in all fields of study as new ideas and ways of thinking emerge, new discoveries are made, and revolutionary technologies are developed. Think of the incredible transformation of communication studies over the past two decades—the term "URL," now defined in the *Oxford English Dictionary*, did not exist prior to 1992! Biological anthropology has also witnessed significant changes in perspective (albeit less dramatic) (see Box 1.3) and is marked by a shift from studying varieties "*of* mankind" toward variation "*within* humankind."

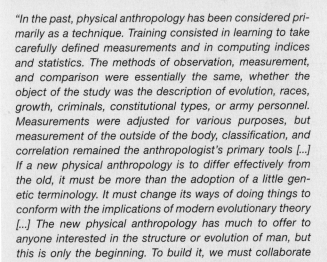

BOX 1.3 RETROSPECTION: Sherwood L. Washburn and "The New Physical Anthropology" (1951)

"In the past, physical anthropology has been considered primarily as a technique. Training consisted in learning to take carefully defined measurements and in computing indices and statistics. The methods of observation, measurement, and comparison were essentially the same, whether the object of the study was the description of evolution, races, growth, criminals, constitutional types, or army personnel. Measurements were adjusted for various purposes, but measurement of the outside of the body, classification, and correlation remained the anthropologist's primary tools [...] If a new physical anthropology is to differ effectively from the old, it must be more than the adoption of a little genetic terminology. It must change its ways of doing things to conform with the implications of modern evolutionary theory [...] The new physical anthropology has much to offer to anyone interested in the structure or evolution of man, but this is only the beginning. To build it, we must collaborate with social scientists, geneticists, anatomists, and paleontologists. We need new ideas, new methods, new workers. There is nothing we do today which will not be done better tomorrow."

Sherwood Washburn (1911–2000) was one of the more influential figures in modern biological anthropology. His work in primate anatomy and behaviour—continued and developed by many of his students, whose interests ranged widely—transformed the discipline from a descriptive field mired in Platonic **typology** to one that embraced a population-based perspective in which variation among members of a group was key to understanding the process of biological adaptation and evolution. According to Washburn, a **processual** approach required a consideration of process (how things happen), function (how things work), comparison (how things

Source: "The New Physical Anthropology," *Transactions of the New York Academy of Sciences*, Ser. II, 13 (1951): 258–304.

differ within and among living and extinct forms), and evolution (where and when things appear). He was among the first in our discipline to champion the use of experimental approaches; he introduced the notion (borrowed from paleontology) of **mosaic evolution**; and he argued that it was necessary to incorporate ideas, methods, and results from other disciplines in order to produce a more comprehensive understanding of primate and human origins, evolution, and adaptation. Washburn was critical of perspectives that ignored biological realities ("race") or that embraced them at the expense of anthropological realities ("sociobiology").

Washburn's 1951 article was published at a time of significant change in the biological sciences, known as the "New Synthesis" (see Chapter 2), which merged the then distinct fields of population (laboratory) genetics and naturalistic (field) biology. This was a transformational shift in those disciplines, which up until then had studied evolution more or less independently. It was Washburn's paper that brought that revolution into the arena of human and primate anatomy and biology. In time, it led to a renaming of the field from "physical" to "biological" anthropology, to reflect the change from (physical) description to (biological) process.

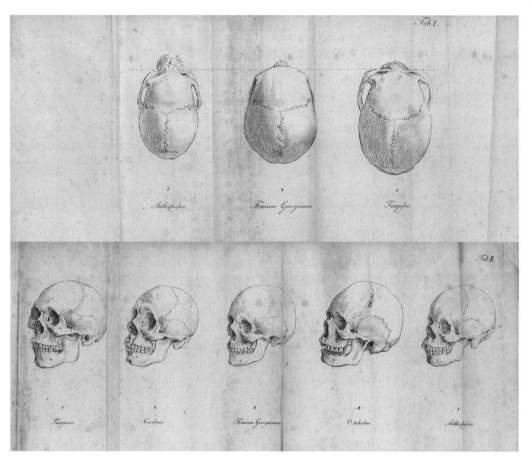

processual

a view of organismic diversity and evolution emphasizing the current and historical dynamic interactions of organisms with their environment and ecology

mosaic evolution

the concept that functional complexes in organisms have independent evolutionary histories and have changed at different times and rates in the fossil record

FIGURE 1.14 Blumenbach noted distinctive differences in cranial size and shape among his "five varieties of man."

Edinburgh University Library, Special Collections Department. K.32.43/2 BLUMENBACH, J. F. "De Genesis Humani Varietate Nativa," Plates I and II.

The roots of the "old physical anthropology"[7] can be traced to Johann Friedrich Blumenbach (1752–1840), a comparative anatomist trained at the University of Göttingen, Germany, who developed an early classification of humankind based on a comparative study of records of encounters with distant peoples by European traders and explorers and on a collection of skulls brought back from these journeys (Figure 1.14).

7. At the beginning of the 20th century, "physical anthropology" was the name given to the field we now refer to as "biological anthropology." The original label reflected the discipline's emphasis at the time on observable and measurable physical features of human populations.

craniometry

literally, the metrical assessment of the size and shape of the human skull

While Blumenbach's classification may have been "racial" and consistent with the use of the term in 18th-century natural history, it was not "racist" as we understand that term today. Blumenbach believed that varieties of "man" graded from one into another over geographic distance and that the differences in cultural and technological "accomplishment" among varieties could be ascribed to disparities in "opportunity" rather than innate character (Bhopal 2007; see Chapter 13). We should emphasize two points regarding Blumenbach's interest in skulls. First, it was common in the 18th and 19th centuries for comparative anatomy to focus on the head, especially cranial size and shape. The practice of **craniometry** was a clear reflection of the significance attached to the brain—the mind in particular—which was seen as the locus of intellect and reason. Second, while Blumenbach did not rank his varieties from first to last, many who followed him did (see Gould 1996) and for much of the 19th and early 20th centuries, the discipline of physical anthropology was vexed with questions of race and notions of in-born qualitative differences.

Before World War II, research in biological anthropology was very much typological and descriptive, concerned less with variation within populations and the processes responsible for producing and maintaining variation (see Box 1.3) than with documenting physical distinctions between them. Most practitioners were not anthropologists at all, having been trained mainly in anatomy or psychology. Nonetheless, in fields such as osteology, primatology, and paleoanthropology, important discoveries were made. For example, in 1925, Raymond Dart (1893–1988), a South African professor of anatomy, reported on the original discovery of *Australopithecus africanus*, a putative early human ancestor (see Chapter 9). Similarly, in the 1930s, the Canadian anatomist Davidson Black (1884–1934), at the time working at the Peking University Medical College, brought to light remains of another hominin fossil form, which he named "Sinanthropus pekinensis" (now known as *Homo erectus*). These paleoanthropological discoveries added fuel to the debate regarding where humankind originated: Africa, Asia, or Europe? The enigmatic (and as it turned out, fraudulent) Piltdown Man, "discovered" in England in 1911, was a preferred progenitor for our species in many eyes, a view having more to do with class and race than with scientific rigour.[8]

In North America, anthropologists and anatomists were hard at work establishing the discipline through descriptive and comparative studies of human and nonhuman primate skeletons. This research was carried out for the most part on excavated remains from Native American archaeological sites or on anatomical preparations of anatomy school cadavers and unclaimed bodies.[9] Early in the 20th century, Aleš Hrdlička (1869–1943) became the first curator of physical anthropology at the Smithsonian Institution's National Museum of Natural History. His comparative study of crania from Alaska, Siberia, and Asia led him to propose that Aboriginal peoples colonized the Americas by migrating across the Bering Strait some 15,000 years ago.

A prominent voice in the field's development was Franz Boas (1858–1942). Initially trained in physics and geography, Boas later studied physical anthropology in Berlin in the 1880s. He also undertook ethnographic studies of Aboriginal peoples of the Pacific Northwest (primarily British Columbia). Boas is largely responsible for establishing the discipline of anthropology as an independent academic field of study in North America. His contributions

---

8. The Piltdown forgery was a concoction of fragments of modern human cranium with a modified orangutan jaw. While the actual perpetrator(s) have never been conclusively identified, it is generally held that the purpose of the fraud was to reinforce and justify prevailing views that the progenitors of humankind could be linked directly with the dominant European (particularly British) ruling classes (Spencer 1990).

9. Two major sources of such osteological remains are the Hamann-Todd Collection at the Cleveland Museum of Natural History (with more than 3,000 individuals) and the Smithsonian Institution's Terry Collection (with 1,700-plus skeletons). In Canada, the J.C.B. Grant Collection at the University of Toronto is a more modest (202 known individuals) but nonetheless significant resource for comparative osteological research.

to the early development of biological anthropology are numerous. One of Boas's most significant contributions was his research on stature and head size in adult immigrants from Southern and Eastern Europe and their American-born children. Boas demonstrated that biological "potential" is not a fixed entity, but is influenced by the environment in which growth occurs. While not without controversy (Gravlee, Russell, and Leonard 2003; Sparks and Jantz 2003), Boas's research on immigrants and their children remains a seminal work in the study of human adaptability. It was also one of the first scientific rebuttals of the growing spectre of the American **eugenics** movement.

In Canada, biological anthropology as a formally organized academic discipline is much younger than its American counterpart. Indeed, for the most part, it developed following the post-Washburn transition of the field from the "old" to the "new" (see Box 1.3), although some important research did take place in the pre-World War II era. One example is the 1929 study by University of Toronto anatomist J.C.B. Grant, *Anthropometry of the Cree and Saulteaux Indians in Northeastern Manitoba*, published by the Archaeological Survey of Canada.

The roots of modern Canadian biological anthropology can be traced to the (then) National Museum of Man in Ottawa,[10] where Larry Oschinsky was Curator of Physical Anthropology between 1958 and 1963 (Ossenberg 2001), and to the University of Toronto, where, following his appointment in 1958, James Anderson taught anatomy and human osteology in the Department of Anthropology (Jerkic 2001). Research at this time was heavily weighted toward the comparative skeletal biology and osteology of Aboriginal archaeological populations, with Oschinsky focusing on Arctic-adapted peoples and Anderson emphasizing southern Ontario groups as represented by **ossuary** samples. At the same time, both of these pioneers also took part in major studies of childhood growth in Canada and the United States. It would be reasonable to state that most biological anthropologists in the postsecondary education and museum systems in Canada (and many abroad) can trace their academic pedigree to the doctoral program at the University of Toronto, beginning in the late 1950s and early 1960s (Jerkic 2001).

Although the early years emphasized research on the skeletal biology of past populations, the specializations of human biology and primatology were also becoming established toward the end of the 1960s and early 1970s. Prominent human biologists included Frank Auger at the Université de Montréal, Jamshed Mavalwala and Emöke Szathmáry at the University of Toronto, and Joseph So and Hermann Helmuth at Trent University. Similarly, primatology was developing a strong presence, with (among others) Frances Burton (Toronto), Anne Zeller (Waterloo), and in western Canada, James Paterson (Calgary), and Linda Fedigan (Alberta, now at the University of Calgary).

Growth of the discipline in Canada has been quite exceptional over the past four decades; many institutions have a number of biological anthropologists on staff, often in different academic departments. By now, several generations of students have gone on to become professors mentoring students of their own. Moreover, all of the various specializations have strong, internationally recognized participation, and exceptional graduate training opportunities exist in each.

---

10. The name was changed to the Canadian Museum of Civilization in 1986 following a competition among staff, and subsequently to the Canadian Museum of History in 2014.

KEY IDEAS

- Human *variation* is both biological and cultural; consequently, understanding human variation requires a *biocultural* perspective.

- The scope of biological anthropology is broad, from human biology to molecular anthropology to primatology, among many other fields.

- Research to understand human differences often uses a *multidisciplinary* approach across a number of fields of research.

- Anthropology provides a *holistic* view of the diversity of human differences.

- *Applied anthropology* uses knowledge created through basic research to suggest solutions to many real-world problems.

- Modern biological anthropology studies the functional, developmental, and evolutionary *processes* underlying human and nonhuman primate variation.

KEY TERMS

variation (p. 5)

interdisciplinary (p. 6)

holism (p. 6)

biocultural (p. 8)

community-based research (p. 10)

adaptability (p. 14)

genomics (p. 14)

typology (p. 18)

processual (p. 19)

KEY QUESTIONS TO ASK MYSELF

1. Why is variation important? What would my world, my life, be like if people and cultures did not differ?

2. Can my understanding of my world be described as holistic? If not, what am I missing?

3. Biological anthropology studies a lot of different things. If I were to pick one subfield that most interests me, what would it be? Why would I pick that one?

4. Every day, news stories describe problems people face, from my home town to countries far away. What can I learn in this course that could help me understand what answers to these problems might look like?

KEY CRITICAL THINKING QUESTIONS

1. A biocultural perspective acknowledges the interplay of biology and culture. Do you think this concept is relevant and applicable to all of the various subspecialties of biological anthropology?

2. In North America, much of the early research in biological anthropology was conducted on skeletal remains recovered from archaeological sites, representing the remains of Aboriginal peoples' ancestors. This work is still carried out today, although within a community-based research or consultative framework in which local First Nations bands are active participants and contributors to the research program. What do you think are the benefits of such an approach? What limitations to research, if any, might follow from it?

KEY THINGS TO DO NEXT

CourseMate Visit **CourseMate** at www.nelson.com/humanvoyage2e to build your comprehension, practise your critical thinking skills, review core concepts, and explore other resources at your disposal.

> *A new scientific truth does not triumph by convincing its opponents and making them see the light, but rather because its opponents eventually die, and a new generation grows up that is familiar with it.*
>
> Max Planck (1858–1947)

OVERVIEW

The scientific method, in which hypotheses formulated from existing theory are tested by observation and experiment, has become a powerful tool for the study of nature. Since the 15th century, the development of modern science through the application of reason has inspired a new interpretation of the world. It was once thought that our world was static, hierarchical, and recently created. Scientific reasoning has shown us that, in fact, it is geologically ancient and rich in biological variation, geographic diversity, and species succession through time. Among many other advances in scientific knowledge, Darwin's theory of evolution and its mechanism of natural selection has become the foundation of modern biology. Although modified and extended since its appearance in 1859, evolution remains the only comprehensive framework for understanding contemporary population variation within and between species as well as the origins of that variation.

KEY CONCEPTS

World view, scientific method, contingency, theory, paradigm, hypothesis, essentialism, scientific revolution, uniformitarianism, diversity, evolution, Darwinism, adaptation, natural selection

KEY LEARNING OBJECTIVES

At the end of this chapter, you will be able to

LO1   Describe the essential features of the scientific method

LO2   Summarize the four essential elements of the theory of evolution by natural selection

LO3   Demonstrate the theory of uniformitarianism using contemporary examples

LO4   Contrast the evolutionary theories of Lamarck with those of Darwin and Wallace

LO5   Defend Darwinian evolutionary theory as an explanation for biological variation from the arguments of Intelligent Design

LO6   Devise an example of microevolutionary change in the occurrence of an infectious disease in a human population, applying the concepts of natural selection and reproductive fitness

> *"I keep six honest serving-men*
> *(They taught me all I knew);*
> *Their names are What and Why and When*
> *And How and Where and Who."*

> Rudyard Kipling (1902)

PROLOGUE: WORLD VIEWS AND THE ELEPHANT'S CHILD

adaptation

a state of existence or a process by which an organism is or becomes better suited to its circumstances of life

niches

the conditions of environments in which organisms live, including climate, space, predator–prey relationships, and mate availability

morphology

study of the size, shape, and configuration of an organism and its various parts

analogous

a similarity in structure or function resulting from independent adaptation to comparable circumstances in life, rather than evolutionary descent

pheromone

a chemical signal capable of causing a specific response in members of the same or closely related species

epistemology

the study or theory of knowledge, including its production, validation, and application

secular

separate and apart from religious tradition or edict; worldly

The above lines introduce Kipling's "The Elephant's Child," one of his *Just So Stories*. The story of the Elephant's Child recounts how all living elephants came to have "long noses." In other *Just So Stories,* we learn how the camel acquired its hump, the leopard its spots, and the rhinoceros its skin (and even why people in Africa are darkly pigmented!). Two ideas are common to these accounts: change and **adaptation**. In Kipling's stories, the long-nosed elephant, the spotted leopard, and the humped camel are more suited to their particular ecological **niches** than their pre-existing bulbous-nosed, unspotted, and humpless forebears. Each has become—in a manner *just so*—somehow more fit to its circumstances of life.

To contrive a "just so" story to explain all that exists in nature is one way for us to appreciate the "what and why and when" of things. But it is not an especially satisfying one, if only because it provides very simplistic (albeit humorous) explanations for what are extremely complex and variable **morphologies**. The Elephant's Child's curious encounter with a conniving crocodile (Figure 2.1) does not really help us understand how an elephant's trunk develops during gestation as a fusion of the embryonic nose and upper lip, or why the African elephant has two lobes at the tip of its trunk (**analogous** to "fingers") and the Asian elephant only one, or how a bull elephant uses its trunk to detect **pheromones** produced by a sexually receptive female. Each of these developmental, anatomical, and physiological adaptations requires more thoughtful consideration of its separate yet interdependent "what and why and when."

All human cultures have world views that they apply to make sense of the physical, biological, and historical domains of nature, their relationships and interdependencies, and in particular how people, as creatures both similar to and different from other animals, fit into that magnificent complexity. Some world views develop as magico-religious **epistemologies**. Two well-known examples are the Judaeo–Christian Old Testament Book of Genesis (1st millennium BCE) and the Five Classics of K'ung Fu-tzu (Confucius). Others develop from more **secular**, material traditions. The most widely accepted of these latter world views arose during the European Enlightenment of the 17th to 19th centuries, an era in the development of Western civilization characterized by the application of reason and the scientific method in pursuit of more intellectually satisfying answers to "what, why, and when." Originating in the late 15th and early 16th centuries with discoveries by Nicolaus Copernicus, Leonardo da Vinci, Johannes Kepler, and Isaac Newton, among many others (and deeply rooted in Grecian, Arabic, and Asian philosophies and sciences—see Box 2.1), the Scientific Revolution transformed not just *what* we understood of the world, but *how* we understood it.

FIGURE 2.1 Sketch of the Elephant's Child and the crocodile from Kipling's *Just So Stories*.

The Elephant's Child having his nose pulled by the Crocodile, illustration from '*Just So Stories for Little Children*' by Rudyard Kipling, pub. London, 1951 (litho), Kipling, Joseph Rudyard (1865–1936) (after)/ Private Collection/The Stapleton Collection/The Bridgeman Art Library.

RETROSPECTION: Arun Bala and "Dialogical Science"

"There is a shared Eurocentric presumption ... that the historical roots of modern science must lie exclusively in Europe simply because modern science developed in Europe. This is wrong. The roots of modern science are "dialogical"—that is, the result of a long-running dialogue between ideas that came to Europe from a wide diversity of cultures through complex historical and geographical routes ... But modern science was not simply the result of a passive accumulation of ideas and practices from non-Western traditions of thought. Rather, it was the outcome of a process of integrating seminal discoveries from many cultures and combining them within Europe into a new synthesis not achieved elsewhere ... There is a ... broader cultural advantage in nurturing a deeper appreciation of the dialogical roots of modern science. An understanding of the way scientific knowledge advanced through the interaction of ideas drawn from different cultures would subvert attempts to use history either to promote the hegemony of one single culture or to make the existence of diverse cultures an excuse for confrontation and conflict."

When we use the term "science" to describe what we do, it is generally taken to mean "Western (modern) science." However, Arun Bala contends that this perspective is ethnocentric as well as historically inaccurate. It fails to acknowledge the important scientific accomplishments of Asian, Arabic, and Indian cultures (others could be noted), whose ideas flowed into medieval Europe and into the minds of thinkers such as Copernicus, Galileo, Kepler, and Newton. Bala's argument is in keeping with the holistic spirit of anthropology as well as to a central theme of this text: **contingency**. Knowledge and understanding are contingent on past knowledge, on "cooperation and competition" among existing ideas and perceptions (Boyd 2006). As Bala suggests, recognizing the contingent "dialogical" nature of knowledge has two major implications. First, it undermines any singular claim to authority or ownership with respect to scientific knowledge and discovery: knowledge builds upon knowledge. Second, the fact that many of the major ideas attributed to Western science developed from diverse and heterogeneous sources topples the accusation that Western science is inherently imperialistic and disdainful of such knowledge—a claim often made within contemporary critiques of science. While this may be true of individual scientists, it is not true of science as a method or way of knowing. It is important that we acknowledge that Western science has a deep history, one that extends far beyond its geographic horizon. It is also important to appreciate that an individual practising within any knowledge tradition (Western, Chinese, Cree, Maori, or any other) will be influenced by that cultural environment. Within any particular culture, individual experiences will vary and will shape our view of the world, adding nuance to our understanding and interpretation of the mysteries around us (Cassell 2002).

Source: *The Dialogue of Civilizations in the Birth of Modern Science.* 1–5. New York: Palgrave MacMillian.

In this chapter we introduce science as a way of knowing and we explore its **methodology**. In particular, we examine the development of **Darwinism,** which is to this day the unifying conceptual framework for contemporary biology, including biological anthropology. Because all evolution, both organic and intellectual, derives from predecessors, this chapter also presents a brief overview of the people, events, and circumstances that were central to the development of evolutionary thought and theory from its pre-Enlightenment origins to the publication of Darwin's *The Origin of Species* in 1859.

WHAT IS SCIENCE?

In reading this chapter, you should realize that "science" is not something foreign, something "out there" done only by supposedly highly intelligent people (i.e., scientists). In fact, science is a way of knowing. Every one of us applies it to almost every decision we make, usually without realizing that we are "doing science." We could be comparing brands of dish soap at the market, playing Ultimate Frisbee, or planning which route is most efficient in getting us from point A to point B. Consider the following statement: "Students who do not read the text will have the same grade, on average, as those who do read it." This proposition can be examined as a scientific problem. Information could be collected from a number of students describing the degree to which they are either "readers" or "non-readers,"

contingency

being dependent on the occurrence or existence of a prior event or thing

methodology

the study of the methods applied to research generally or within a particular discipline

Darwinism

evolution resulting from natural selection acting on random variation in populations, through which more fit individuals are favoured in "the struggle for existence"; as conceived by Charles Darwin

and their resulting course grades compared. Science begins with a problem or a question, the solution to which requires gathering suitable observations or evidence from appropriate subjects, followed by a careful analysis and interpretation of results (which may or may not support our expectations). So we might wonder whether there is a relationship between the cost of dish soap and its cleaning effectiveness, or spin rate and the flight path of a Frisbee.

For some problems in science we may have an *a priori* feeling for the outcome. (What do *you* think we would find for our "textbook reader/non-reader" question?) But for most questions we ask about the world, the answers are not at all clear before we make our observations or conduct experiments. Indeed, other researchers studying the same question using alternative samples or methods may arrive at different conclusions. This does not mean that the previous research was faulty; rather, it tells us that the problem under investigation is more complex than we thought and requires additional study, new hypotheses, and further samples and data. This aspect is one of the most important cornerstones of modern science—it has the quality that we refer to as "self-correcting." This is typical for many of the subdisciplines of anthropology that we introduced in Chapter 1. As we will see, this dynamic self-regulating property of the scientific method is what makes it such a powerful tool for investigating a universe of complex physical and natural phenomena.

What Is Theory?

In contemporary science, **theory** is paramount; it provides a coherent framework, supported by a body of evidence, for understanding patterns of relationships among "things" in the world (indeed, in the universe). Two examples: Einstein's general theory of relativity explains gravitation (the attraction exerted by objects of differing masses, underlying our everyday experience of "weight"), and Darwin's theory of evolution accounts for **phylogenetic** relationships among living and extinct organisms and how new species may emerge from existing forms. Of course, not all bodies of theory are as grand as general relativity or evolution. Most deal with more specific relationships on a much smaller scale. Life history theory, for example, concerns itself with variation among organisms in developmental and behavioural events that take place from conception to death, such as rate of maturation, gestation length, fertility and longevity, or body and brain size **allometry** (Schwartz 2012). Theory not only derives from research but also directs future research and allows us to make reasoned predictions about how the world works. These predictions are called hypotheses, and the more that our hypotheses are substantiated through repeated observation and testing, the more a theory assumes the character of a scientific law.

From Hypothesis to Law

Humans are curious creatures, as are many organisms (including the Elephant's child!). We wonder at things we do not understand, and we generally feel more comfortable having an explanation—a theory—of some sort to account for the mysteries that surround us. When we use the scientific method to understand a particular mystery, we are seeking an explanation using observation and evaluation. It is just that: a method. The road to theory begins with curiosity, stimulating a question (called a **null hypothesis**), which can then be tested and either confirmed or falsified.

Testing a hypothesis requires the careful collection of observations, facts, or evidence—**data**—from an appropriate experiment or a **sample** of subjects. Statements such as "In Toronto, most people with Facebook profiles are Euro-Canadian women between 20 and 40 years of age" or "There is no difference in the prevalence of HIV/AIDS in sub-Saharan Africa and Vancouver's Downtown Eastside" (Figure 2.2) are examples of testable hypotheses. How we state the hypothesis is critical, for it identifies not only the character of the sample to be studied (Canadian Facebook users, people in sub-Saharan Africa or Vancouver's Downtown Eastside) but also the nature of the evidence required (Who uses Facebook? Who has HIV/AIDS?),

---

a priori

arguing from cause to effect; deduced from prior knowledge or presumption

theory

explanatory statements or arguments related to particular sets of phenomena supported by observation or experiment

phylogenetic

relating to evolutionary histories of ancestry and descent; also *phylogeny*

allometry

refers to patterns of size and shape change among parts of organisms at different sizes, or among related organisms either living or extinct

null hypothesis

in statistics, a proposition that there is no difference among samples, conditions, outcomes, etc., that can be disproved through experiment or observation

data

observations, measurements, facts (known or assumed) that form the basis for a conclusion; singular *datum*

sample

a subset of a whole that represents its qualities with regard to the characteristics under study; for example, if three-quarters of a population of university students have a piercing, approximately the same proportion in a sample selected from that population should have a piercing as well as any **assumptions** that need to be taken into account (i.e., we assume that women of all cultural backgrounds living in Toronto have equal access to Facebook accounts). This evidence—these data—are the variables we measure, observe, or describe; they may be explanatory factors (age, sex, ethnicity, residence) or outcomes (disease status, Facebook registration).

From the perspective of scientific discovery, it does not matter so much whether our hypothesis is confirmed or refuted.[1] Both outcomes are informative and lead us to develop new questions, devise new tests, and collect new data,

FIGURE 2.2 A view of Hastings Street on Vancouver's Downtown Eastside, notoriously known as "Canada's poorest postal code."

© The Canadian Press/Jonathan Hayward

assumption

a condition or feature unverified or uncontrolled but taken to be as stated for the purpose of argument

thereby continuing the cycle of discovery (Figure 2.3). This is the nature of science, and it leads to more robust theories, and sometimes even new ones. Note also that the status of a theory does not depend on the "correctness" of any given prediction—hypotheses come and go all the time. What matters is the balance of evidence over a number of studies that either supports or challenges the current theory. Some theories may be so weakened (found to be more wrong than right) by new findings that they are effectively replaced by new perspectives consistent with these findings. In the 19th century, for example, Darwin's theory of evolution supplanted the one proposed by the French natural historian Lamarck, as we discuss later in this chapter.

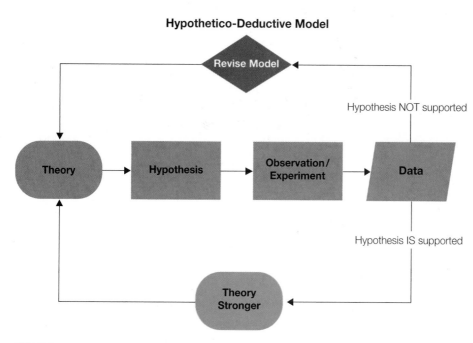

FIGURE 2.3 The scientific method is a self-correcting and self-reinforcing process of discovery.

---

1. We talk about falsification/confirmation as either positive/negative results. Because most scientists like to be optimistic about their research, hypotheses are typically worded in such a way that "falsification" is the desired (positive) outcome. Generally speaking, although it may seem counterintuitive, confirmation of a hypothesis amounts to a negative finding!

So, theory leads to the formulation of hypotheses that, when tested, either strengthen or weaken the theory at hand and prompt the formation of still more hypotheses. This cycle is the foundation of the scientific method. Our understanding of natural phenomena is always in a state of flux, and vigorous (and healthy) scientific debate often emerges when hypotheses and data support alternative points of view. An excellent example is the recent controversy over the evolutionary status of significant fossil discoveries in Indonesia, popularly known as the "Hobbits." Arguments have developed in scientific literature over whether these finds represent pathologically deformed members of a recent modern human population or are relics of an isolated premodern human species (Brown 2012).[2]

Over time, a theory's strength builds as the volume of supporting evidence grows, until contradictory arguments are no longer generated. At that point a scientific consensus has been reached and a theory assumes the character of a "law." No doubt you have heard of the Law of Gravity[3] and if you have taken a course in geology, you will also be familiar with the **Law of Superposition**. As a rule, scientific laws are rare, since declaring a theory to be a "law" has a very particular meaning within science. Essentially, a law states that a relationship or outcome will *always* hold true in a given set of specific circumstances. Apples that break loose from trees will always fall to earth, and sediments in oceans and lakes are always laid down in succession, with the oldest layer at the very bottom.

It is also true that some well-documented theories have yet to be formally rebranded as laws even though they have accumulated such a weight of evidence that their fundamental tenets are seen to be "law-like." The theory of biological evolution is a case in point. Its central premises of variation, selection, and adaptation (discussed later) have been observed and verified time and time again. There are two reasons for a general reluctance to view evolutionary theory as a law. First, we are able to document the formation of new species[4] only retrospectively, by looking to the fossil record (see Chapter 4), which makes speciation a theoretical prediction of Darwinian evolution, not a fact of it. The second reason lies outside science and involves opposing world views. Especially (but not exclusively) in the United States, there is significant political and social resistance from certain religious quarters to viewing evolution as a bona fide theory, let alone a law (see Box 2.2).

Normal Science and Paradigm Shifts

Volumes have been written on the nature and history of science, what it is and what it means, and how and why we do it (e.g., Kwa 2011). In 1962, Thomas Kuhn, a physicist, historian, and philosopher of science, published a **seminal** work entitled *The Structure of Scientific Revolutions*. This book is widely acknowledged as an important critique of the practice of what we call "normal" science. For Kuhn, normal science is what scientists do day in and day out: they study nature from within a particular tradition of "conceptual boxes supplied by professional education" (Kuhn 1962, 5). These boxes constitute a **paradigm**—a term you may have heard before and we guarantee you will hear it many more times throughout your university career. Paradigms are vital to the practice of science, for without them we would not be able to develop theory and form hypotheses.

The essential message of Kuhn's work concerns how paradigms "shift"—that is, how the aforementioned conceptual boxes (scientific traditions) change. In simple terms, a paradigm is transformed when scientists are faced with facts that cannot be ignored or explained by the paradigm in present use. The idea of Darwinian evolution was a paradigm shift, in that it replaced the widely held concept of special creation with the natural origin

Law of Superposition

layers ("strata"; singular "stratum") within a sedimentary geological deposit are laid down from oldest to most recent, permitting assignment of relative dates to items contained in the deposit

seminal

relating to "seed"; in this context, a seminal work is one that becomes a foundation for generations of subsequent ideas and developments

paradigm

a conceptual framework within which bodies of theory are developed, directing the course of future investigation

---

2. We discuss this particular controversy in Chapter 10.

3. The Law of Gravity was originally derived from Sir Isaac Newton's Second Law of Motion describing the acceleration of objects.

4. Speciation is a fascinating issue that we explore in more detail in Chapter 4; much depends on which concept of species one applies to the question.

In the 18th century, the "accepted wisdom" of essence, order, and purpose lent itself to a view of creation known as Natural Theology. Its most articulate proponent was the Reverend William Paley (1743–1805) as expressed in his book *Natural Theology* (1802). Paley's argument is most famously exemplified through his "watchmaker analogy." Highly integrated and complex objects such as pocket watches and people clearly require a designer—that is, a Divine Creator. Such "arguments from design" were not uncommon in the latter days of the Enlightenment (Mayr 1982).

© iStock/Thinkstock

Arguments from design remain with us in the 21st century, despite having been discredited in courts of law (Raff 2007). Rising from the ashes of an ideology known as "scientific creationism," the current version, known as Intelligent Design (ID), critiques Darwinian evolution via the concept of "irreducible complexity" (Manson 2003). This argument, simply put, is that anything with multiple interrelated components can exist and function only if all of its various elements were present from the beginning. ID also argues that such complexity could not have developed through slow, gradual evolutionary change. However, this central premise of ID has failed to stand the test of scientific scrutiny. For example, complex structures such as the mammalian eye are not only manifestly imperfect but also have diverse and numerous intermediate forms. As well, some organisms (e.g., bacteria) lack components present in their closely related "irreducibly complex" relatives (Pellan and Matzke 2006).

But it is not so much that ID is conceptually flawed and fails to account for process, history, and relationships among living things; rather, it is the political and social agenda of ID that is the real story here. Its considerable weight as socially conservative religious ideology is exemplified by two recent newsworthy events. The first was an attempt by members of the Dover, Pennsylvania, school board to insinuate ID into its science curriculum. This action culminated in an acrimonious trial in 2005[5] after a coalition of local parents sued the board. Having heard testimony regarding the scientific merits of both sides (ID and evolutionary biology), Judge John E. Jones ruled for the parents, noting that ID is not science—a position that garnered him "death threats for Christmas" (Raff 2007, 403).

Our second example is in some ways more disconcerting, for it poses disturbing questions as to how the merits of scientific inquiry are judged. In the spring of 2006, Dr. Brian Alters, an education professor at McGill University, learned that his funding application to the Social Sciences and Humanities Research Council of Canada (SSHRC) to study the growing influence of ID in Canada had been refused. In the view of the SSHRC review panel, Alters had not given "adequate justification for the assumption in the proposal that the theory of evolution, and not intelligent design theory, was correct" (Boswell 2006). The implication of this statement is profound, for it sets evolutionary theory and ID on an equal footing when in fact no such parallel exists. The former is based on the rigorous methods of science, the latter on faith; one is an apple, the other an orange! Recall that scientific theory is derived from testable (and tested) hypotheses, predictions, and observations and is subject to constant verification and falsification. Evolutionary theory has the benefit of 150 post-Darwinian years (and counting) of accumulated scientific evidence supporting its fundamental premises.

Often lost in the creation–evolution "debate" is the important point that evolutionary theory does not negate religious belief, the practice of faith, or human spirituality, all of which are extremely important aspects of who we are as social and cultural beings. Evolution speaks only to the material, natural world of organic diversity and its history, and it does so fairly, eloquently, and rigorously. Yet ID has a significant number of adherents among Canadians, as a Canadian Press–Decima Research poll released in the summer of 2007 revealed. For example, 26% of respondents agreed that "God created human beings pretty much in their present form at one time in the last 10,000 years or so," while 34% agreed with the statement that "human beings have developed over millions of years from less advanced forms of life, but God guided this process." However, Canadians are comparatively more secular than our neighbours to the south. In a similar poll, 46% of Americans agreed with the first of these statements.

of species and the understanding of variation. Other examples include the germ theory of disease for understanding infection (see Chapter 14) and plate tectonics as a model for theorizing about the configuration of continents. The rest of this chapter will examine how paradigm shifts during the European Enlightenment changed our understanding of the world generally, and our understanding of biology and human biocultural evolution specifically.

---

5. There have been several such trials in the United States, the most famous of which was the Scopes Monkey Trial, which took place in Tennessee in 1925. A full account of this trial can be found at www.law.umkc.edu/faculty/projects/ftrials/scopes/scopes.htm.

EVOLUTIONARY THOUGHT FROM PLATO TO DARWIN

stasis

a state of equilibrium characterized by the absence of change

Today when we think of *evolution*, it is quite natural to think of *change*, of something new originating from something that existed in the past. We think of ancestors and descendants, each in some way different from the other and becoming more so with the passage of time. However, "change" is a recent idea in Western science. Before the 17th century, the perception of nature had been one of **stasis**. From geographic landscapes to the organisms on them and ultimately to the relationships among them, the idea that everything exists as it has always been easily fits with our direct experience of the world. A human life span is short with respect to evolutionary modification, which occurs over many generations. And when local geographies were seen to change, it was usually in very dramatic fashion (e.g., earthquakes, volcanic eruptions, floods)—a fact that featured prominently in 18th-century attempts to explain extinction and the appearance of new forms in the emerging science of **paleontology**. As far as organisms were concerned, no one had witnessed the appearance of a new species; the dominant view was that animals were **immutable**, or permanent in form. Moreover, it was believed—especially in the West—that humankind was not simply different from other animals, but *designed* to be so, a product of supernatural creation (Box 2.2). In the following pages, we introduce some of the prominent thinkers whose work, intentionally or not, contributed to the development of evolutionary theory as we understand it today. As we will see, the paradigm of stasis failed to hold up under an accumulating weight of evidence for diversity and change among both living and extinct organisms; ancestors and their descendants.

paleontology

the study of fossilized life forms

immutable

unchanging over time, or unchangeable; an idea traceable to the Greek philosopher Aristotle, stating that forms exist today as they were when created, have not changed in the past, and cannot change in the future

One thing more—the "revolution" in natural history (biology) that we associate with the development of Darwinian evolutionary theory is really a story that occurred within the Western intellectual tradition. There is good reason for this. In the centuries prior to the European Enlightenment, non-Western scholars had already developed ideas about organic evolution of species and had situated humankind within nature rather than apart from it. Taoist philosophy and modern biological science—including evolutionary thought—have many elements in common (Barnett 1986). The Roman poet Lucretius (c. 99–55 BCE) argued against supernatural intervention in nature and described how new organisms arose and then diverged over time. Islamic scholars, notably Al-Jahiz (c. 776–869 CE), not only had developed a theory of evolution, but also had conceived the principle of natural selection—anticipating Darwin by almost a millennium (Haleem 1995)! It would seem then, that the "revolution" in biology occurred in Europe because it was in the West that there was something to revolt against—an established although erroneous doctrine of stasis and immutability. The question we must first address is this: How and when did such a perspective arise and take hold?

Essence, Order, and Purpose: Plato, Aristotle, and the "Ladder of Creation"

geocentrism

the concept that the earth is the centre of the known universe, around which all other heavenly bodies revolve; attributed to the Greek astronomer Ptolemy but known before his time

Every morning the sun rises in the east, and every evening it sets in the west. Clearly it appears to circle the earth once every day, and what could be plainer than that? So it seemed to most of humanity for most of history. This idea, **geocentrism** (Figure 2.4) can be traced to the early Greek philosophers, including Plato (c. 427–347 BCE) and Aristotle (384–322 BCE). A geocentric view of the world also agreed well with emerging Judaeo–Christian world views, in particular, accounts of Creation that embraced an earth- and human-centred perspective.

The philosophies of Plato and Aristotle held particular sway through the ages. Their impact on our understanding of the world was long-standing. Plato proposed a theory, known as **essentialism**, that separated human perceptions of nature into two aspects. First were the material objects apparent to the senses, which were variable and subject to change. Second were the corresponding "forms" for each of these objects. These forms could be perceived only by the mind and were perfect in every regard as well as unchangeable. For Plato, "reality" existed as the form or *essence* of a thing, which we experience imperfectly through our senses: smell, sight, sound, taste, and touch.

essentialism

Plato's idea that what exists in the world and is experienced by the human senses is an imperfect representation of an underlying, perfect, and immutable ideal, or essence, knowable only by the mind

Consider this simple example: In your mind you can conjure up an image of a "chair" because you understand the essential qualities of what we might call *chair-ness*. But if you were to go shopping for a chair, you would likely find a wide variety of items called "chairs," none of which perfectly matched the image, the essence, of "chair" that you had constructed in your mind. Of course, today we understand that Plato's imperfect material objects are in fact the very real natural variations present in the world. Unlike Plato, we see the variety of different chairs we have to choose from as real, and the essence of "chair-ness" as imaginary. At this moment you may be thinking, "So why is this important to evolutionary theory?" If so, ask yourself a simple question: If Plato's perspective on what is real (the immutable essence) and what is not (actual variation) were accurate, how could anything evolve? Indeed, evolution could not occur, because in the Platonic world view the essence remains intact, despite any change in the expression of its imperfections (variation) through time.

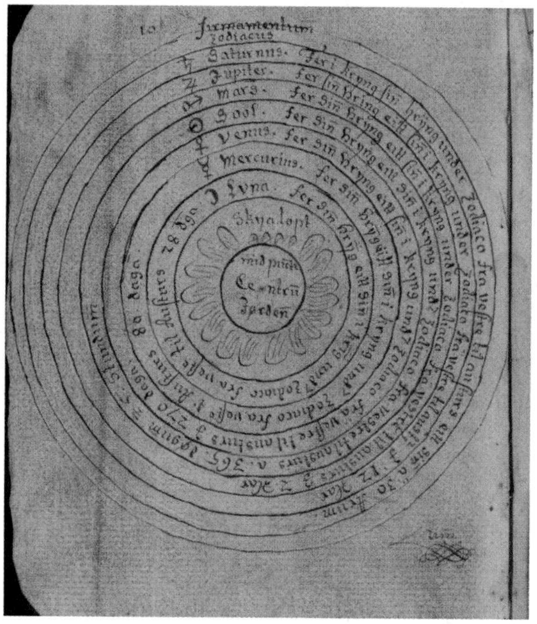

FIGURE 2.4 Ptolemy's geocentric model of the universe situated earth at the centre, with all else revolving around it.

Courtesy of the National and University Library of Iceland.

Plato also advanced the idea that everything that exists can be ordered hierarchically, as if on a ladder, rung upon rung, from the lowest mineral entity to, ultimately, the supernatural. In the Judaeo—Christian world view, God rests on the highest rung of all. This idea of a scale in nature (known as the **Great Chain of Being**) was more explicitly developed by Aristotle in 350 BCE. As with Plato's essentialism, the Great Chain of Being requires that nature be static and immutable. It insists that all things exist as they are and where they are, in a fixed position relative to all other things and for all time. Implicit in this hierarchy is the idea of a final purpose or direction to Creation. The Aristotelian idea that there exists a purposeful order from simple to complex, from least perfect to perfect, is termed **teleology** (from the Greek, *telos*, meaning "end" or "purpose"). However, under such schemes it is not possible to "progress" up the ladder, from simple to complex—stasis rules!

Classical Greek perceptions of nature were rediscovered during the European Renaissance of the 12th and later the 14th through 16th centuries. Incorporated as they were into the doctrine of the Christian Church, and consequently into the learning of all formally educated people, it is not surprising that the dominant view of the world was one of immutable essence, order, and purpose.

Great Chain of Being
Aristotle's ordered, hierarchical, and static view of the world

teleology
a perspective proposing that there are end points, or "final causes," toward which natural phenomena are oriented and suggestive of a design, goal, or purpose in the world

From Renaissance to Revolution

In Europe, the Renaissance gave way to the Enlightenment, an era notable for revolutions, ranging from the social and political (the French Revolution) to the economic (the Industrial Revolution). However, both of these upheavals were preceded by the Scientific Revolution, a transformation touched off by considerations of a very different kind of revolution—that of the earth around the sun. The **heliocentric**[6] view of the universe, proposed by Nicolaus Copernicus in 1543, was a truly profound idea. In effect, it demoted our planet from its hallowed position as "centre of the universe" to that of one among many objects circling one among many stars in the sky (Figure 2.5). Although published the year he died, Copernicus's

heliocentrism
the now well-established view that the planets in our solar system revolve about the sun; the Copernican model also incorporates the essential ideas of the daily rotation of the earth on a tilted axis

---

6. The heliocentric model is yet another example of the West following the East; the major elements of Copernican theory can be found in early Vedic Sanskrit texts dating to the 7th century BCE.

CHAPTER 2 Science and the Development of Evolutionary Theory

FIGURE 2.5 *Astronomer Copernicus: Conversation with God* by Jan Matejko (1872).

© Paul Almasy/CORBIS

ideas had become widely known throughout Europe before then. Along with Galileo's writings on experimental methods and Vesalius's study of human anatomy, heliocentrism opened the door to a comparative, rational, and secular study of the natural world, including the place and role of "Man" within it. The scientific revolution made it possible to challenge accepted notions of time, geological process, natural history, and organic diversity and complexity—all central to later development of evolutionary theory.

Contributing to the new ideas emerging during the Enlightenment was the European exercise in exploration, empire building, and colonization. The so-called "voyages of discovery" by Captains James Cook and Louis-Antoine de Bougainville, among many others, filled European "cabinets of curiosity" (Figure 2.6) with thousands of previously unknown plants and animals. Everything from ants to apes, along with "trophies" collected from encounters with newly "discovered" human populations, found their way into European collections (Holmes 2006). The naturalists on board these explorations broadened (indeed, shattered) European perceptions of biological diversity.

Despite the changed attitudes toward discovery and knowledge brought about by the Scientific Revolution, the European view of the natural world remained mired in notions of stasis dominated by the paradigms of essentialism and the Great Chain of Being. How is it, then, that in the relatively short span of 200 years, nearly 20 centuries of established and Church-sanctioned doctrine accounting for the Origins of Everything came to be unravelled? We can identify three major paradigm shifts that laid the foundations for a new evolutionary approach to biology (a term not even coined until early in the 19th century). The first was a new perspective on time, in particular regarding the age of the earth and the processes that constantly shape it (giving rise to the disciplines of geology and paleontology). The second, noted above, was the increasing awareness of the rich diversity of life, not just in the European countryside, but in distant and very different lands. Out of this awareness came the methods and sciences of **taxonomy**, "ecology," and biogeography. Finally, there was a gradual acceptance of the possibility of biological change—that species were indeed mutable. This central idea laid the groundwork for theories of biological evolution.

Time

That the earth is not just thousands of years old, but many hundreds of thousands (indeed, many millions) of years old, is a comparatively recent finding, dating only to the mid-18th century. Before then, chronologies based on biblical events were assumed to be true. The best-known of these was developed by James Ussher (1581–1656), Anglican Archbishop of Armagh, Ireland. Calculating from the life spans and lineages of named male persons from the Old Testament and the length of the reigns of kings, Ussher arrived at a date for Creation as the eve of October 23, 4004 BCE (Barr 1984–85).[7] The first serious challenge to such chronologies is attributed to the Scottish naturalist and geologist James Hutton (1726–1797), who developed the concept of **uniformitarianism**. Hutton's study of volcanic and sedimentary deposits in the Scottish Highlands led him to believe that these features formed gradually

taxonomy

the method by which organisms are classified and assigned to a group (a taxon; plural, taxa) based on shared biological, ecological, and behavioural relationships

uniformitarianism

a philosophy in geology that argues that the natural processes affecting the earth and observable today have remained constant (uniform) through geologic time

7. It is often erroneously stated that Ussher calculated his age for the earth using all of the "begats" in the Old Testament.

FIGURE 2.6 *The Cabinet of Curiosity of Ole Worm*, 17th-century Danish physician.

Smithsonian Institution Libraries

over long periods of time (Figure 2.7), as a result of forces that continued to be active and observable—in other words, forces uniform in time and space (Jackson 2006). Landscapes are eroded by wind and water, and recreated through sedimentary and volcanic activity.

Wider recognition of the concept of uniformitarianism is generally credited to the eminent 19th-century English geologist Sir Charles Lyell (1797–1875). Lyell authored the highly influential three-volume treatise *Principles of Geology*. He firmly established Hutton's uniformitarian thesis, which demanded a considerable antiquity for the world. Yet at the same time, Lyell expressed disdain for notions of organic evolution, and in the second volume of his *Principles*

FIGURE 2.7 Differences in the orientation of sedimentary layers, depicted here in the Richardson Mountains in the Northwest Territories, are among a variety of geologic features Hutton was able to observe in Scotland. To Hutton, such features could only occur slowly over vast quantities of time.

© Jim Talbot

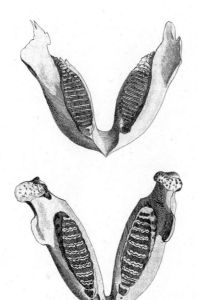

FIGURE 2.8 Cuvier's comparison of mammoth and living Indian elephant mandibles provided support for the concept of extinction.

Georges Cuvier (1799). "Mémoire sur les espèces d'éléphans vivantes et fossiles, lu le premier pluvose an 4 (21 January 1796)." Mémoires de l'Institut National des Sciences et des Arts, sciences mathématiques et physiques (mémoires) 2: 1–22, pls. 2–6.

comparative method

understanding relationships among organisms by examining the similarities and differences present in various aspects of their biology

principle of correlation of parts

the idea that organisms are integrated wholes and that change in one part cannot occur without altering the whole (usually by rendering it dysfunctional)

extinction

the complete disappearance of a particular species owing to factors that may be internal (related to the organism's biology) or external (related to environmental change over which the organism has no influence)

catastrophism

Cuvier's notion that fossil forms are produced through series of cataclysmic events and that changes from one kind to the next in succession result from new forms arriving from areas not affected by the event

he promoted the concept of "centres of creation" to account for the diversity of species. Nonetheless, Lyell's work on the formation and transformation of landscapes had a strong impact on a young English naturalist, Charles Darwin, during his five-year voyage aboard *HMS Beagle*.[8]

Uniformitarianism, which required that the earth be of great age, was an important element in the development of evolutionary theory, as it afforded sufficient time for the gradual transformation of species. By the mid-18th century, it was already well established that geological deposits contained many kinds of life forms no longer present in the same region. The systematic study of fossils is due in great part to the work of the French natural historian and "father of vertebrate paleontology" Georges Cuvier (1769–1832). Cuvier contributed much to the development of the **comparative method** in natural history, although he did not subscribe to evolutionary ideas that were becoming widely discussed in his day. Indeed, his insistence that organisms are functionally integrated wholes (an idea known as the **principle of correlation of parts**) presented a barrier to accepting the possibility of evolutionary development, as Cuvier could not imagine how a single part of an organism can change without rendering the whole animal dysfunctional and thus unable to survive.

Cuvier, however, did establish the fact of **extinction**— a subject of much speculation for at least the previous century—through his careful comparative analyses of fossil and living forms (Figure 2.8). Of course, extinction posed a problem for Cuvier: if species do not evolve but may eventually die out, how can we still have species at all? Cuvier proposed that through geological time, some plants and animals in a given region are lost to creation through intermittent cataclysms—that is, large-scale natural disasters such as earthquakes or floods. Such events were not unknown to recent European experience, as evidenced by the great Lisbon earthquake of 1755 (Figure 2.9), and may well have influenced Cuvier's thinking. The living forms lost through such disasters were replaced by the in-migration of organisms from adjacent regions not affected by these events.[9] In 1832 the English theologian and historian of science William Whewell coined the term **catastrophism** to describe Cuvier's theory of cyclical geologic revolutions. It is important to understand that while catastrophism and uniformitarianism were considered opposing ideas in the 19th century, they are not mutually exclusive. Indeed, a number of mass extinctions in the course of geologic history have been tied to catastrophic events, such as extraterrestrial impacts (Israde-Alcántara et al. 2012) or climate change (Cahill et al. 2012).

Diversity

While the question of the earth's antiquity was slowly being settled, the issue of what to make of the strangeness of never-before-seen plants and animals displayed in public and private museums was taking shape.

---

8. Indeed, in a letter dated August 29, 1844, to Leonard Horner, a geologist (and Lyell's father-in-law), Darwin wrote of the impact of the *Principles* on his own thinking: "I always feel that my books come half out of Lyell's brains & that I can never acknowledge this sufficiently." (Burkhardt 1996, 83).

9. Cuvier did not resort to notions of special creation to explain the repopulation of areas inundated by natural disaster, nor did he ascribe any particular cataclysmic change to specific biblical events, such as the Noahic flood.

FIGURE 2.9 The Lisbon earthquake of 1755 was a powerful reminder of how natural events could alter landscapes, providing for Cuvier's account of local extinctions.

Courtesy of PEER-NISEE, University of California, Berkeley.

A central challenge to describing the world, however, is labelling it. Think how you would tell your friends about all of the different books your professors have assigned for your courses if they had no titles, or the great variety of MP3s you have downloaded on your iPod if they lacked names. Where would Google be without the URL? Now you have a sense of the challenge faced by natural historians confronted with myriad kinds of organisms, both familiar and exotic. Fortunately, humans have a long history of living in close relationship with plants and animals, in the endless quest of both getting food and avoiding becoming food. In this endeavour, identifying the natural world becomes crucial to daily living. As a result all human cultures have developed **classification** systems—called folk taxonomies—that are meaningful to them (Medin and Atran 2004).

The English naturalist John Ray (1627–1705) is credited with publishing, in 1693, the first formal classification of animals based on sound scientific reasoning. Although the Greek philosopher Aristotle had used the terms "genus" and "species" two millennia earlier, Ray was the first to employ these concepts in terms of descent—that is, with regard to reproduction. He also supported the argument that fossils represented once-living forms; he even produced a classification of nonhuman primates as they were known at the time (the *Anthropomorpha*, although he excluded humans). However, Ray was also a devout Christian and a founder of **Natural Theology**, a philosophy that sought to explain the diversity of organisms as exemplars of Divine Creation which greatly influenced Natural Theology's strongest advocate, William Paley (see Box 2.2).

While we credit John Ray for laying the groundwork for reasoned arguments based on comparative morphology as an approach to cataloguing the world, it was the Swedish botanist Carolus Linnaeus (1707–1778) who founded the modern method of taxonomy. While Linnaeus penned numerous volumes and dissertations, he is best known for his monumental work *Systema naturae* (*Systems of Nature*), first published in 1735 and subsequently revised through 13 editions (Figure 2.10). According to Linnaean taxonomy, all plants and animals can be uniquely assigned to a category denoted by class, order, genus, and species. You, for example, are a member of the Class Mammalia, Order Primates, Genus *Homo*, and Species *sapiens*. In the 10th edition of *Systema naturae* (1758), Linnaeus proposed that a method of **binomial nomenclature** serve as the unique identifier of organisms, labelled according to the latter

classification

the act of arranging or sorting objects according to features held in common; assigning such objects to a proper class

Natural Theology

a philosophy of theology founded on principles of observation of the world in a context of Creation, rather than on arguments from divine revelation

binomial nomenclature

a "two-name" system developed by Linnaeus to identify all plants and animals according to genus and species

FIGURE 2.10 Carolus Linnaeus: The frontispiece from *Systema naturae*, 6th ed. 1748.

Courtesy of Michael Philip

two ranks in his system: genus and species. This edition forms the foundation of modern taxonomy[10] (although the categories proposed by Linnaeus have been expanded considerably—see Chapter 4). Linnaeus's system was both practical and logical and brought order to an emerging chaos as natural history expanded its geographic and temporal horizons. We also acknowledge Linnaeus for devising the first "modern" classification of humankind, in the 1735 edition of *Systema naturae*. Initially this was based solely on biological criteria, but in the 1758 edition it was expanded to include cultural, behavioural, and cognitive traits. At that time he also assigned humans the taxonomic label *Homo sapiens*. Linnaeus ranked four varieties[11] of *Homo sapiens*, consistent with his belief in Aristotle's Great Chain of Being (Table 2.1).

Mutability

While new ways of thinking about the age of the earth, about fossil forms and extinction, and about how to classify and study natural diversity were fundamental to the development of evolutionary theory, all of the historical figures we have introduced so far believed that species were immutable. A major step toward a theory of biological evolution was made by the prominent French naturalist, Georges-Louis Leclerc, Comte de Buffon (1707–1788). Buffon was an aristocrat and so was able to pursue a life's work in natural history. His magnum opus, the 44-volume *Histoire naturelle, générale et particulière,* appeared over several decades, with contributions by a number of his contemporaries. The importance of Buffon's work cannot be understated. Within it lie the origins of cell theory as well as a theory of heredity termed **pangenesis**, borrowed from the ancient Greek physician Hippocrates and later adopted by Charles Darwin. Buffon is credited as the founder of **zoogeography**. Recognizing that there must be strong links between biology and geography, he proposed that

pangenesis

a discredited theory of heredity arguing that particles in body cells and organs can be influenced by their environment, and once transferred to the sex cells pass on these influences to the next generation

zoogeography

the study of the geographic distribution of animals and the ecological communities to which they belong

TABLE 2.1 Linnaeus' Classification of *Homo sapiens, Systema naturae*, 10th ed. (1758)

Variety	Skin Colour	Temperament	Character	Vestments	Governed by
Americanus	red	choleric	obstinate	paint	custom
Europæus	white	sanguine	capricious	close-fitting	laws
Asiaticus	lurid	melancholic	haughty & avaricious	loose	opinion
Afer	black	phlegmatic	indolent	grease	caprice

Source: Adapted from e.g., Gunnar Broberg in Spencer, 1997, Vol 1, p. 617.

---

10. Today the Systema naturae has been supplanted by the International Code on Zoological Nomenclature (ICZN).

11. Linnaeus identified a number of other varieties or species within the genus *Homo*, either fanciful (H. sapiens monstrous and H. sapiens ferus, "monstrous man" and "wild man"), or in order to capture reports from travellers of human-like creatures in distant lands (the designation H. troglodytes, "cave-dwelling man," was applied to the Asian ape, orangutan).

organisms are capable of being transformed ("degenerated") as their environmental circumstances alter through time or migration. Taken in combination, these ideas represented a theory of **microevolution**—a concept accounting for much of the diversity we observe within species today. Although shocking by current standards, Buffon even proposed that one could test his theory that environmental circumstances modify species characters by charting how long it would take for Senegalese natives of West Africa to "turn white" if moved to Denmark (Marks 1997)! However, he did not accept the possibility of **macroevolution** leading to the origin of new species. Nonetheless, Buffon was the first to formally articulate a modern **biological species concept** (see Chapter 4) based on reproductive isolation (Mayr 1982).

Somewhat ironically, while Buffon himself did not accept that species were mutable, his patronage and support of Jean-Baptiste-Pierre-Antoine de Monet, Chevalier de Lamarck (1744–1829) (Figure 2.11), eventually gave us the first modern theory of species evolution. With Buffon's support, Lamarck gained a position as professor of invertebrate zoology at the Royal Botanical Garden in Paris. This was fortuitous as it afforded Lamarck the opportunity to organize and catalogue the large collections of "insects and worms" kept by the museum (he even coined the term "invertebrate" to distinguish these forms from the "higher" animals). Lamarck's research on invertebrate diversity contributed to his theory of evolution, most fully described in his two-volume monograph *Philosophie zoologique,* published in 1809. In contrast to both his predecessors and his contemporaries, Lamarck viewed organisms and their environmental circumstances as interacting dynamically to produce ever-increasing complexity and "perfection." This perfection was pursued according to Lamarck's two "laws" (more appropriately seen as rules): the **Law of Use and Disuse**, and the **Law of Inheritance of Acquired Characteristics**.

What do these "laws" mean? Lamarck's first law proposes that organisms do not proceed uniformly toward a state of perfection but must constantly adjust to changes in their circumstances. In Lamarck's scheme, the adjustment of organism to environment is the culmination of a cascade of events: (1) as environments change, the needs of animals change to maintain harmony with these new circumstances; (2) these new needs are satisfied by changes in an organism's behaviour and habits (which Lamarck called "efforts"); (3) these behavioural changes physiologically alter—develop, enlarge, or reduce as necessary—some aspect of the organism's structure. Schematically: environmental changes direct changes in an organism's needs, which in turn direct changes in behaviours and habits, which eventually lead to anatomical modification.

It is in Lamarck's second law that we encounter the truly evolutionary component of his theory, however. The Law of Inheritance of Acquired Characteristics proposes that when both parents possess a particular adjustment acquired during their own lifetimes, they will pass that feature on to their offspring. In this way, features acquired by parents are inherited by offspring. The long neck of the giraffe modified to reach leaves on ever-higher branches is the most often cited example of Lamarckian inheritance, but let us return to our Elephant's Child's long trunk (Figure 2.12). Without recourse to crocodiles, how do we explain such an appendage?

FIGURE 2.11 The French naturalist Jean-Baptiste Lamarck is credited with the first modern operational theory of organic evolution, termed "Lamarckism."

Portrait of Jean-Baptiste de Monet (1744–1829) Chevalier de Lamarck, 1802–03 (oil on canvas), Thevenin, Charles (1764–1838)/Private Collection/The Bridgeman Art Library.

microevolution

small-scale evolutionary events occurring within a population over the span of a few generations, affecting the frequency of specific characters and not involving species formation

macroevolution

large-scale evolutionary events, typically viewed over geological time, leading to speciation and the formation of higher taxonomic categories

biological species concept

species defined on the basis of reproductive inclusion within its membership and reproductive isolation from other species

Law of Use and Disuse

Lamarck's first law, which suggests that the use or disuse of parts, reflecting an organism's needs and circumstances, will cause that part to develop or reduce accordingly

Law of Inheritance of Acquired Characteristics

Lamarck's second law stipulates that those changes resulting from use and disuse will, if occurring in both parents, be transmitted to offspring

FIGURE 2.12 Could Lamarckian inheritance explain the elephant's trunk?

© Henk Bentlage/Shutterstock

Erasmus Darwin (Charles' grandfather) believed that it resulted from an elephant's "need" to eat grasses but it had difficulty bending its knees! As the grasses were shortened by constant browsing, the trunk would "need" to develop further. For his part, the Italian naturalist Giuseppe Gautieri thought it was a matter of the elephant having a "desire" to smell that it was unable to indulge because its head was too distant from the soil (Corsi 2005).

Lamarck did not specify the mechanism or process by which this "acquired" information was passed from one generation to the next. Lamarck viewed evolution as the consequence of imperceptible changes in circumstances, behaviour, and morphology over extended periods of time. Furthermore, he did not believe that environment directly caused structures to alter or to appear anew: the organism's "needs" and "behaviours" were always intermediaries in Lamarck's evolutionary scheme.

Lamarckian ideas of evolutionary change have been largely dismissed.[12] Indeed, they had become so within many (although not all) scientific circles during his lifetime—so much so that Lamarck died in relative obscurity and poverty.

Yet Lamarck's ideas had profound significance for evolutionary thought. He viewed the organic world as subject to change, seriously challenging the notion of immutability, and he provided—for the first time—mechanisms by which species could be transformed from one form into another. The idea of the "evolution" of diversity, complexity, and adaptation, hinted at in scholarly writing of the 17th and 18th centuries, was now becoming more accessible *and* acceptable to a populace whose appreciation of the consequences of "change" had been fuelled by larger events in society—for example, the French and Industrial Revolutions.

DARWIN, WALLACE, AND THE "MEANS OF NATURAL SELECTION"

Having read some of the history of ideas leading toward a theory of organismic evolution, you may have a sense that it was almost inevitable that someone somewhere in the course of the 19th century would "discover" the concepts we now credit to Charles Darwin. Indeed, by the mid-19th century two English naturalists—Darwin and Alfred Russel Wallace—had reached essentially the same conclusions regarding the origin and evolution of species captured by the term Darwinism. While perhaps serendipitous, it is not at all surprising as evolutionary ideas had been taking shape for some time. As Corsi notes (2005, 81): "Books

---

12. Lamarckian ideas persisted in Soviet Russia well into the 20th century under the guise of Lysenkoism, a doctrine named for Trofim Lysenko, the politically powerful director of the Soviet Institute for Agricultural Sciences. Lysenko believed that one could use Lamarck's Law of Inheritance of Acquired Characteristics to enhance plant yields, and applied it in an attempt (which failed) to revive an agricultural system in collapse under the Stalinist regime. In Chapter 4 we discuss an interesting and controversial argument that Lamarckian evolution actually does occur and indeed plays a significant role in the formation of species diversity and adaptation.

and people, ideas and specimens travelled throughout Europe to a far greater extent than we have cared to investigate."

Notions of species transmutation were becoming more acceptable, especially in French, Italian, and German scientific circles. This increasing acceptance owed much to Darwin's grandfather, Erasmus Darwin (1731–1802), author of *Zoonomia* (1796). In this widely read work, the elder Darwin discussed the transformation of species through series of successive changes (although he still attributed their first appearance to an act of Creation and the mechanism responsible was not specified). In England, however, from the 1820s to the 1840s, the scientific establishment was giving evolution a cool reception: the influential Charles Lyell fiercely dismissed Lamarck's theory. Natural Theology was widely accepted with little comment, for its premise that there was an omnipotent designer accorded well with the British class structure, the power of the Church of England, and the relative political stability of Victorian times.

In 1844, however, this contentment was shattered by the anonymous publication of *Vestiges of the Natural History of Creation*, in which the author (now known to be Robert Chambers, a Scottish book publisher, journalist, and amateur geologist) laid out a theory for the progressive evolution of everything from the solar system to humankind. The book was widely denounced as a threat to the status quo, especially among the ruling classes, the scientific elite, and the clergy. But it was also widely read, selling 24,000 copies in the first decade of publication (far more than Lyell's *Principles of Geology*!). While not disavowing Creation, *Vestiges* argued that organisms evolved through geological time in a slow, gradual progression toward increasing complexity.

Given the existence of evolutionary thought propounded by the likes of Erasmus Darwin, Chambers, and Lamarck, it seems fair to ask: How has Charles Darwin's name become synonymous with organic evolution when others before him had been writing about species transformation, and when one of his contemporary countrymen (Wallace) independently arrived at not only the same theory, but the same mechanism, **natural selection**?

natural selection
the nonrandom preservation or elimination of variants through competition within and between species promoting differential reproductive success

VOYAGES TO NATURAL SELECTION

Charles Darwin and Alfred Russel Wallace (Figure 2.13) were both English, both naturalists by vocation, and both of questionable health. Beyond that, they had little in common (Hull 2005). Darwin (1809–1882) was born into prosperity; his father and grandfather had built successful careers in medicine. It was presumed that Darwin would continue the tradition of medicine, but he showed little affinity for it while studying at the University of Edinburgh. Nor did he find himself especially suited for the clergy, for which he trained at Cambridge. At each of these universities, he allowed his studies to lapse while he pursued his real passions, which were natural history and geology. At Cambridge he studied with the mineralogist and botanist John Henslow, who, through botanical research, taught Darwin that the key to understanding variation *between* species was to understand geographic variation *within* species (Kohn et al. 2005).[13] It was Henslow who secured for Darwin the position of naturalist on the second survey voyage of *HMS Beagle* (Figure 2.14). This was, of course, a momentous occurrence in the history of biology, even though when Darwin boarded ship in 1831, he was very much cast in the Creationist mindset and accepted the stability of species. Yet by the time he disembarked five years later, Darwin had embraced an evolutionary perspective and had established the fundamental premise of his theory— namely, that geographic varieties are **incipient species**. Darwin, however, was a careful and thorough naturalist, and he would spend the following two decades amassing evidence to support his theory, during which time he composed—but did not publish—two short outlines of his theory (in 1842 and 1844).

incipient species
related populations that, although capable of successful reproduction, are prevented from doing so by some barrier and that as a result may increasingly diverge to the point of becoming separate species

---

13. Henslow maintained a creationist perspective. Much like Buffon before him, he advocated that geography could produce variation within species but that species themselves were immutable.

FIGURE 2.13 Charles Darwin (left) and Alfred Russel Wallace (right). Both men arrived at a theory of evolution by natural selection in the mid-19th century.

© PoodlesRock/GraphicaArtis/Corbis (left); Alfred Russel Wallace (oil on canvas), Evstafieff (19th century)/Down House, Downe, Kent, UK/© English Heritage Photo Library/The Bridgeman Art Library (right)

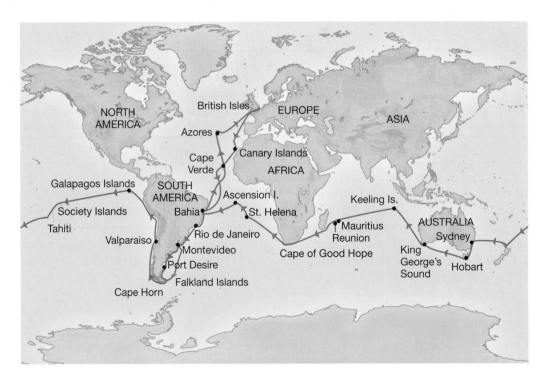

FIGURE 2.14 Voyage of *HMS Beagle* 1831–1836.

Alfred Russel Wallace (1823–1923) was born into far more modest circumstances, the eighth of nine children. Wallace was forced to withdraw from school at an early age to begin a long series of apprenticeships (including surveying and map making), all the while educating himself, especially in natural history. Having read other naturalists' accounts of travels afar, including Darwin's, Wallace was inspired to leave London in 1848 at the age of 25, joining an expedition to South America as naturalist. The four years that Wallace spent charting the waters and collecting specimens in and around the mouth of the Amazon were not entirely successful (his ship burned and sank on its return voyage to England, taking with it the plant and animal collections he had hoped to sell). However, the book he published on his return gained the attention of the Royal Geographical Society, which sponsored Wallace on a series of travels through the Malay Archipelago between 1854 and 1862, reporting on natural history, geography, and local cultures. It was during this time (reportedly through the fog of a malarial "fit") that he arrived at the conclusion that a process such as natural selection could account for the formation of new species.

Despite their different backgrounds, Darwin and Wallace shared much in common. Both men were naturalists; both had travelled to distant lands and encountered new species in new environments; both were familiar with the efforts of breeders who produced new varieties of species by artificially selecting for particular traits at the expense of others (Figure 2.15); both had read widely, including Lyell's *Principles of Geology* and Chambers' *Vestiges*; and both were recognized in British scientific circles—albeit Darwin much more so because of the class to which he was born.

Perhaps most important, both men had read *An Essay on the Principle of Population,* a slim book published in 1798 by a Scottish economist, the Reverend Thomas Robert Malthus (1766–1834).[14] Malthus' essay is as relevant today as it was in 1798—perhaps very much

FIGURE 2.15 Breeders artificially select for particular features, "creating" novel forms as a result.

Charles Darwin (1868). *Variation of Animals and Plants Under Domestication.*

14. There is some question as to the impact that Malthus had on either Darwin or Wallace. Malthus is not accorded prominence in the writings of either man—indeed, he is mentioned only twice in Darwin's *The Origin of Species* (Hull 2005). As Hull observes, both men were living and writing during the rise of competitive, dog-eat-dog laissez-faire economics in Victorian England. In this regard, the Scottish free trade economist Adam Smith may have had as much to do with the development of evolutionary theory as his countryman Malthus!

more so (see Chapter 16). Historians of science contend that it was Malthus who provided the key to unlocking the mechanism of natural selection. Concerned with the plight of Scottish farmers and working people, he observed that a population always grows at a rate in excess of growth in the resources necessary to sustain it. If left unchecked, such populations would, without exception, be subject to misery, pestilence, famine, and warfare. The key that both Darwin and Wallace stumbled upon was as simple as it was elegant: individuals within populations are *not* equally likely to suffer from deprivation or failure to thrive. By virtue of differences in endowment (health, intellect, morphology, prowess, etc.), some would always be more successful in competing for those resources necessary for survival *and reproduction* (food, friends, mates, etc.). Thus they would be *naturally* selected in the "struggle for existence" and would leave more offspring similar to themselves, at the expense of less fortunate and less competitive members of their species. In other words, they would have greater **reproductive fitness.**[15]

In a nutshell, Darwin had come to realize as early as 1838, and Wallace some years later, that evolution by natural selection consisted of four elements:

1. All populations vary, individual by individual; often noticeably in terms of size and shape, but also in smaller and more subtle yet no less important ways, such as in shades of colour or expressions of behaviour.
2. All populations have the potential to reproduce at a rate in excess of the rate at which necessary resources (food, space, mates, and so on) increase.
3. Competition for limited resources occurs not just *between* members of different species, but, more important, *among* individuals *within* species.
4. At any given moment and in any given circumstance, heritable characteristics possessed by individual "X" increase the likelihood of successful reproduction and survival of offspring, relative to those of individual "Y."[16]

To many people today, these four elements seem self-evident—indeed, simplistic. Of course individuals vary. And of course some are more adept than others at acquiring the necessities of life. How could it be otherwise? But in English scientific circles of the mid-19th century, to bring these ideas together as an argument for the evolution of species amounted to an astonishing declaration. Darwin was well aware of the impact his theory would have. He had, after all, witnessed the reaction to the publication of Chambers' *Vestiges*—a reaction that in part underlay Darwin's reticence to publish. This changed dramatically in 1855, with the appearance of a short article in the *Annals and Magazine of Natural History* entitled "On the Law Which Has Regulated the Introduction of New Species" by A.R. Wallace. The story of the impact this paper had on Darwin, and on the efforts made by his confidantes and supporters (most notably Charles Lyell and the botanist Joseph Hooker) to get him to publish, is fascinating and full of intrigue.

Darwin wrote to Wallace on May 1, 1857: "By your letter & even still more by your paper in Annals, a year or more ago, I can plainly see that we have thought much alike & to a certain extent have come to similar conclusions" (Burkhardt 1996, 172). Wallace subsequently produced an unpublished paper (*On the Tendency of Varieties to Depart Indefinitely from the Original Type*) in which he outlined not only his ideas concerning evolution but also the essence of natural selection as the mechanism (although he did not use that term). What else was he to do but mail it to Darwin for comment? Darwin, naturally, was stunned by this further coincidence, and for good reason—the focus of all of his 20 years' work was laid out before

reproductive fitness

a measure of the success of an individual in the production of offspring across generations; your children, and their children, and so on all constitute your reproductive fitness

---

15. It is important to distinguish between fitness as an "expected" outcome versus fitness as a "realized" outcome. We explore this contrast in Chapter 4.

16. Note that "circumstance" matters immensely. Change the situation, and individual "Y" may be "more fit" than individual "X"! How would you compare your fitness in an isolated Arctic landscape with that of an Inuit hunter? Or an Inuit mother compared to her Aborigine counterpart in the Australian outback?

him, described in detail by a self-taught layman of lesser social standing! On June 1, 1858, Darwin wrote to Lyell seeking advice. The solution contrived by Lyell and others—and with Darwin's consent—was to have a joint paper read at the Linnaean Society on July 1, 1858—an arrangement with which Wallace himself was satisfied, deferring to Darwin's eminence as a naturalist.[17] A little more than a year later, Darwin published what he considered an abstract of his theory, some 700 pages in length—*The Origin of Species by Means of Natural Selection, Or the Preservation of Favoured Races in the Struggle for Life*—a book that is arguably the most significant ever published in the history of biology (Figure 2.16).

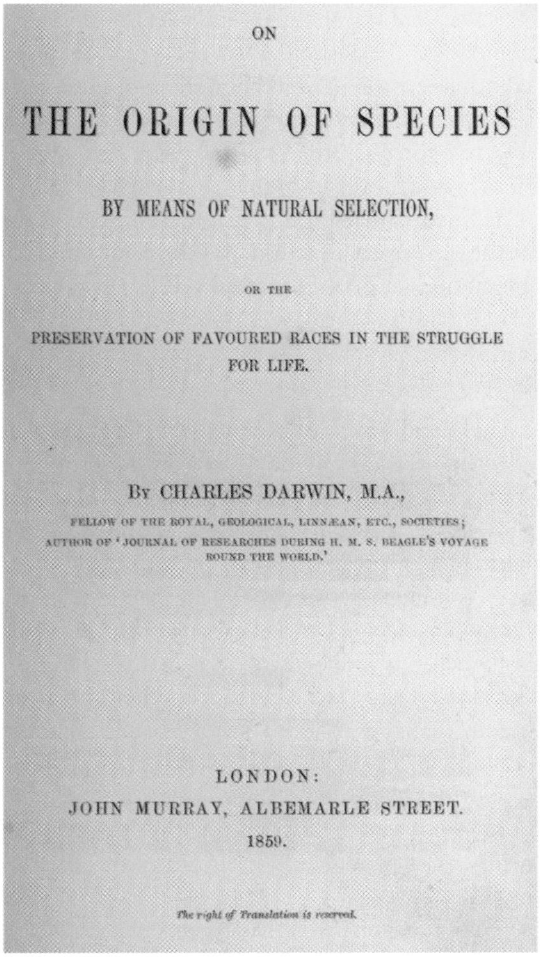
ON

THE ORIGIN OF SPECIES

BY MEANS OF NATURAL SELECTION,

OR THE

PRESERVATION OF FAVOURED RACES IN THE STRUGGLE FOR LIFE.

BY CHARLES DARWIN, M.A.,

FELLOW OF THE ROYAL, GEOLOGICAL, LINNÆAN, ETC., SOCIETIES;
AUTHOR OF 'JOURNAL OF RESEARCHES DURING H. M. S. BEAGLE'S VOYAGE ROUND THE WORLD.'

LONDON:
JOHN MURRAY, ALBEMARLE STREET.
1859.

The right of Translation is reserved.

FIGURE 2.16 Darwin's *Origin* is arguably the most influential book ever published in the field of natural history (biology).

Charles Darwin (1859). *On the Origin of the Species*.

What Is Natural Selection?

Biologists have documented many examples of natural selection through which populations have adapted to their circumstances of life. You can Google landmark examples such as "Industrial melanism" and "Galapagos ground finch beak size and drought." Regarding humans, there are classics such as James Neel's "thrifty genotype" hypothesis for the increased incidence of Type II diabetes among indigenous populations, and Frank Livingstone's work on *Plasmodium falciparum* malaria and sickle cell anemia. The re-emergence of drug-resistant infectious diseases such as tuberculosis reflects adaptation of the pathogen to the selective force of antibiotics—a significant public health concern at the global level today (see Chapter 14).

Developments in molecular biology have opened new avenues for identifying the effects of natural selection at the genetic level (Jin et al. 2012), in terms not only of the presence or absence of particular genetic variants, but also of the manner in which those variants are expressed. For example, many African populations have a higher frequency of a genetic variant known as *A(-6)*, which promotes salt retention—an adaptive feature in hot, humid climates, where sweating removes electrolytes such as sodium (a component of salt) necessary for normal cellular metabolism and neuronal function. Non-African populations with less need to retain salt have recently evolved a different variant, *G(-6)*, to reduce salt retention. This is adaptive in contexts where lifestyle factors (diet, activity) increase the risk of high blood pressure (hypertension), a risk that is raised even further by high levels of sodium in the body.

17. In fact, the "joint paper" consisted of Wallace's manuscript, which he had sent to Darwin, an extract from Darwin's *The Origin of Species* manuscript, and a letter written by Darwin to the American botanist Asa Gray attesting to Darwin's priority.

The core feature of natural selection is that it acts on variation that is normally present in a population. If a particular variant—such as *G(-6)*—provides an advantage to those individuals who have it, then the likelihood is that the variant will increase in frequency in the population over time and that less advantageous variants of a trait will decrease in frequency. The selective forces in the "salt retention" example are (1) heart disease in non-African populations, which leads to higher frequencies of *G(-6)* promoting salt excretion; and (2) the need to maintain normal cellular function in African populations, which increases the occurrence of the *A(-6)* variant aiding in salt retention. Trait frequencies are continually modified across generations at different rates in different populations and, given sufficient time and isolation, may lead to the formation of new species (see Chapter 4).

Missing Links

Darwin and Wallace provided a theory and a mechanism by which species could evolve by adapting to their circumstances of life, grounded in variation and natural selection. Neither, though, was able to supply a mechanism of inheritance by which such adaptations could actually be passed from one generation to the next. It was clear that selected variation was heritable—plant and animal breeders had shown it to be so time and time again. Neither man had much sympathy for the Lamarckian idea of inheritance of acquired characteristics. Darwin conceived of inheritance working through a process (pangenesis), whereby each body cell type created particles called gemmules, which were transported to the germ cells (sperm and egg) and brought together at conception to form a new individual. To Darwin's credit, he knew that any theory of inheritance would have to account for all possible outcomes—for example, why offspring sometimes appeared as a "blend" of both parents, and sometimes expressed a feature that occurred only in one and not the other, and sometimes bore a trait that appeared in neither parent. Unfortunately, pangenesis was not that mechanism, a fact of which Darwin was aware at his death in 1882, but for which he could offer no alternative.

Yet the alternative had been published in a European journal in 1866, in a short paper outlining the results of a series of experiments documenting inheritance in pea plants. These experiments had been carried out by a somewhat reclusive Austrian biologist and Augustinian monk, Gregor Mendel (see Chapter 3), now considered the father of the science of genetics. Some debate exists as to whether Darwin was ever aware of Mendel's work. Most likely he was not, and in any case he might not have given Mendel's ideas much credence, for Darwin viewed variation as the product of natural selection, whereas Mendel saw it as the outcome of hybridization (Sclater 2006). Darwin was not alone in his ignorance of Mendel's paper. Indeed, it received very little attention, and as a consequence, the vital "link" tying variation to natural selection and inheritance would remain "lost" until the end of the 19th century.

The history of evolutionary thought is part of the larger history of Western science, the origin of which many link to the adoption of Copernicus's heliocentric model of the universe. In truth, its roots are much deeper and more widely spread, extending several millennia into Islamic, Indian, and Asian scholarship. But it was the development of the scientific method that opened doors to new ways of thinking about the organic world, with its emphasis on hypothesis and observation, reason and fact. This transformation occurred rapidly throughout the European Renaissance and Enlightenment. In this chapter we have presented only a handful of the ideas and individuals who shaped these developments (Figure 2.17). By the time Darwin's *The Origin of Species* was published in 1859, the themes of "essence, order, and purpose" in which species were seen as created and immutable, had given way to one of variation, diversity, and evolution over long spans of geological time. The rise of evolutionary biology in the 19th century must also be viewed in the larger context of the social, political, and economic transformation of Europe, highlighting notions of competition, class, and change.

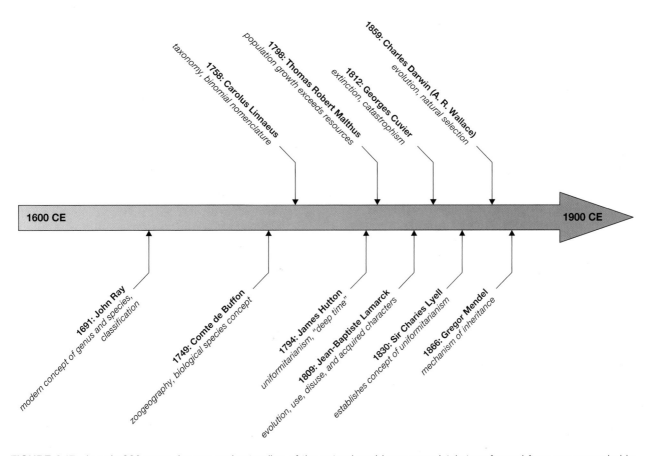

FIGURE 2.17 In only 300 years, human understanding of the natural world was completely transformed from one grounded in early Greek philosophy and church doctrine to one based on a secular, scientific world view.

LEARNING KEYS

KEY IDEAS

- Science is one way in which we understand the world, through a combination of theory, hypothesis, and observation.

- Theories are developed and modified through application of the scientific method, in which a hypothesis is tested against data derived from observation or experiment.

- In biology, evolutionary theory developed over many centuries to explain organismic variation and the appearance of new species.

- Essentialism, attributed to Plato, proposes that it is the idea ("essence") of a thing that is real, while the actual physical representations of that thing (variation) are deviations from reality.

- Aristotle developed the concept of the Great Chain of Being, in which everything in the world could be arranged in a static and unchanging hierarchy or scale, from least significant to most significant.

- The origin of modern Western scientific understanding can be traced to Copernicus's 16th-century notion of the heliocentric (sun-centred) universe.

- Between the 16th and 19th centuries, new understanding of the age of the earth, the geographic diversity of life, and the emergence of paleontology laid the foundation for a scientific theory of biological evolution.

- Catastrophism, an idea attributed to Cuvier, proposed that the change in the fossil record through time occurred through local extinction events (catastrophes) and the migration of new forms to replace them, rather than through evolution.

- The growing awareness of the vast diversity of living forms led to a new system of scientific classification, known as "Linnaean taxonomy," a central feature of which is binomial nomenclature (genus and species).
- The first modern theory of evolution is attributed to Lamarck, invoking two principles: the Law of Use and Disuse, and the Law of Inheritance of Acquired Characteristics.
- Two British naturalists, Charles Darwin and Alfred Russel Wallace, independently arrived at a theory of evolution through natural selection.
- A central concept in natural selection is reproductive fitness: an organism best adapted to current circumstances will most likely survive to leave more offspring.
- A key element missing in the theory of evolution by natural selection as proposed by Darwin and Wallace was an understanding of inheritance, that is, how traits were passed from parent to offspring.

KEY TERMS

epistemology (p. 26)

contingency (p. 27)

Darwinism (p. 27)

theory (p. 28)

null hypothesis (p. 28)

data (p. 28)

assumption (p. 29)

paradigm (p. 30)

stasis (p. 32)

essentialism (p. 32)

Great Chain of Being (p. 33)

heliocentrism (p. 33)

uniformitarianism (p. 34)

catastrophism (p. 36)

binomial nomenclature (p. 37)

pangenesis (p. 38)

microevolution (p. 39)

macroevolution (p. 39)

biological species concept (p. 39)

natural selection (p. 41)

reproductive fitness (p. 44)

KEY QUESTIONS TO ASK MYSELF

1. If evolution doesn't really have a goal, then why am I here?

2. Is Darwin's theory of evolution the only theory explaining the origin of new species?

3. What about the creation myths I learned about in my other anthropology course?

4. How is it that two men half a world apart could come up with the same idea for how species could evolve over time by something called natural selection?

KEY CRITICAL THINKING QUESTIONS

1. In this chapter, we suggested that it was perhaps inevitable that someone, at some time during the 19th century, would propose a theory of evolution that would, even in its earliest form, provide a reasonable argument for the origin of species. Indeed, as you learned, it happened twice at almost the same time (Darwin and Wallace). What do you think these historically contingent developments suggest about the nature of Western science as a way of understanding the world?

2. Michael Ruse, a philosopher of science and Darwinian scholar, once observed that "Darwinism is a term much like Christianity or Marxism, in that everybody 'knows' what it means, and yet on not very close inspection it turns out that everybody's meaning is slightly different" (Ruse 1992, 74). Is Ruse correct? How different from or similar to that of your classmates is your understanding of Darwinism? Discuss how and why such differences and similarities might arise.

KEY THINGS TO DO NEXT

 Visit **CourseMate** at www.nelson.com/humanvoyage2e to build your comprehension, practise your critical thinking skills, review core concepts, and explore other resources at your disposal.

3 The Biological Basis of Human Variation

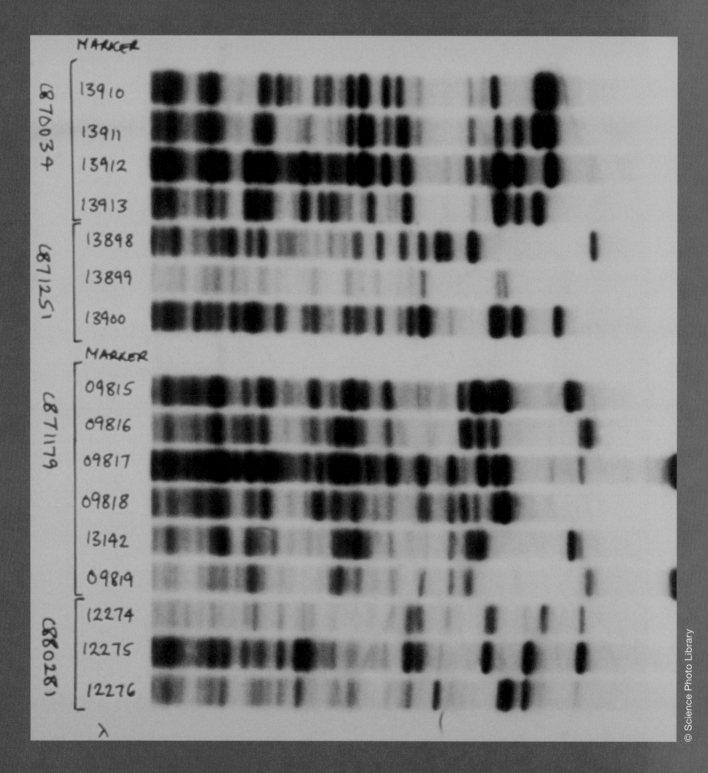

*The capacity to blunder slightly is the real marvel of DNA.
Without this special attribute, we would still be
anaerobic bacteria and there would be no music.*

Lewis Thomas (1913–1993)

OVERVIEW

In order to understand the mechanisms underlying human evolution and variation, we need to have a thorough understanding of genes and how traits are inherited. This chapter introduces you to the basics of genetics, starting with the blueprint of life—DNA (deoxyribonucleic acid). We explore the role of DNA in protein synthesis, the nature of chromosomes, the mechanisms by which cells divide, sources of variation, and how our understanding of genetics came about. We also examine the genetic basis of common human traits and explore some of the controversial applications of genetics research. As you will learn in this chapter, the integration of genetics and biological anthropology has allowed researchers to address a diversity of anthropological questions.

KEY CONCEPTS

Mutation, heredity, mechanisms of inheritance, heritability, genetic determinism

KEY LEARNING OBJECTIVES

At the end of this chapter, you will be able to

LO1   Describe DNA and the functions it serves

LO2   Distinguish between mitosis and meiosis

LO3   Apply your knowledge of DNA to determine how its extraction and analysis might be applied to archaeological samples

LO4   Compare and contrast polygenic and monogenic traits

LO5   Evaluate the challenges that behavioural geneticists face

LO6   Predict the genotype and phenotype of future offspring, using your knowledge of how traits are transmitted from one generation to the next

PROLOGUE: THE GENE SCENE

genetics

the study of genes and how traits are transmitted from one generation to the next

genes

sequences of DNA that code for proteins

stem cells

unspecialized cells that have the ability to differentiate into specialized cells in the body

nucleus

a structure in eukaryotic cells that contains the genetic material

prokaryotes

organisms that lack a cell nucleus

pluripotent

having the ability to differentiate into different tissue types

The past few decades have seen tremendous advances in the field of **genetics**. In the 1980s, British geneticist Sir Alec Jeffreys developed a method of DNA fingerprinting for use in crime scene investigations, producing the first DNA fingerprint in 1984. As any of you who have watched *CSI* or *Bones* know, DNA has become a key tool for identifying perpetrators and victims of crimes. It has also found its way into many other aspects of our society. Genetic testing is now being used to identify paternity, to predict inherited disorders such as Huntington's disease, and to locate the **genes** that may predispose an individual to cancer, among other diseases. Indeed, this sort of testing has become a multimillion-dollar business. Now that the genome of many individuals has been mapped (see opening photo), we have a complete blueprint of our own genetic makeup, and we are currently awaiting completion of genome maps for other primates, including earlier hominins (see Chapters 5 and 11). In the meantime, scientists are eagerly searching for genes that might extend our lives, prevent obesity, and protect us from disease. At the same time, though, ethical and moral concerns about genetic testing and manipulation in the form of cloning remind us of past abuses (see Chapter 13).

THE BUILDING BLOCKS OF LIFE

Cells are the basic building blocks of life. There are a number of different kinds of cells, including those that make up various tissues in the body (e.g., bone, skin, nerve, and muscle cells), sex cells (sperm and ovum), and **stem cells**, which are unspecialized cells that can differentiate into any type of specialized cell (see Box 3.1). Except for the sex cells and mature red blood cells, every cell in the human body contains the same genetic information.

The earliest organisms appeared some 3.7 billion years ago. They had DNA in their cell walls but lacked a **nucleus**. Known as **prokaryotes**, these organisms had limited capabilities and reproduced by splitting in two. Even today, the most diverse and successful

---

BOX 3.1

FOCUS ON ... Stem Cell Research in Canada

Stem cells are found in all tissues and play a crucial role in growth, development, and maintenance of the body. Humans and other mammals possess two different types of stem cells: embryonic and adult. Embryonic stem cells, created four to five days after conception, are able to develop into any type of specialized cell in the body, ranging from blood cells to those found in connective tissues and vital organs. Sources of these **pluripotent** cells include embryonic and fetal tissue, as well as blood from the placenta and umbilical cord. In contrast, adult stem cells, derived from a variety of adult tissues, repair and regenerate these tissues by constantly reproducing themselves.

Stem cells were discovered in the 1960s by two Canadians, biophysicist James Till and physician Ernest McCulloch, while they were conducting research on radiation. Over the past decade, Canadian scientists have played a leading role in stem cell research, and in 2001 the Stem Cell Network was established by 80 scientists from universities and hospitals across Canada to promote this research, with the ultimate goal of developing therapies to treat a variety of diseases and conditions. Potential applications of stem cell therapy include creating tissues for transplantation; treating degenerative diseases such as Alzheimer's, Parkinson's, diabetes, heart disease, and muscular dystrophy; and developing and testing new medications. Current research projects in Canada include investigating the potential of using stem cells to repair brain injury resulting from stroke; damaged heart muscle resulting from cardiac arrest; and spinal cord injuries.

Despite its potential to improve the lives of millions of people in Canada and around the world, no other area of medical research has generated as much controversy as stem cell research. Heated debate has arisen regarding the ethical, legal, and social implications of that research. At issue is the creation and use of embryos as a source of stem cells, and the fear that this might lead to human cloning. In 2002, the Canadian Institutes of Health Research (CIHR) established strict guidelines for human stem cell research (see www.cihr-irsc.gc.ca/e/42071.html), and scientists are increasingly focusing on adult stem cells in order to avoid the ethical issues associated with using embryonic ones.

---

life forms on the planet—such as bacteria— are prokaryotes! Between 1.5 and 1 billion years ago, the first multicellular organisms appeared, known as **eukaryotes**. These possessed a nucleus containing DNA (Figure 3.1) and had the ability to perform a greater number of functions, grow larger, and produce more energy than prokaryotes.

DNA is a macromolecule consisting of smaller molecules called **nucleotides**, which are composed of a sugar, a phosphate, and one of four nucleic acid **bases**: adenine (A), guanine (G), cytosine (C), and thymine (T). DNA is found in the nuclei of cells (**nuclear DNA**, or **nDNA**) on long strands called **chromosomes** (Figure 3.2). Genes are made up of segments of DNA, and their location on the chromosomes is referred to as their **locus**. DNA is also found in **mitochondria** (mitochondrial DNA, or mtDNA), which are structures that generate energy for the cell. Mitochondrial DNA contains fewer genes (only 37), and unlike nuclear DNA, it is inherited only through females.[1] Thus both males and females get their mtDNA from their mother. While much smaller overall, mtDNA is more plentiful than nDNA because each cell contains hundreds or even thousands of mitochondria and hence a similar magnitude of mtDNA.

The double helix structure of the DNA molecule was published in 1953 by James Watson and Francis Crick, who in 1962, along with Maurice Wilkins, received for their work the Nobel Prize for Medicine. However, it was an X-ray image of the molecule, taken in 1952 by a young British scientist named Rosalind Franklin, that provided them with the necessary clues to its structure (Figure 3.3). Tragically, Franklin died of ovarian cancer before the Nobel Prize was awarded.[2]

DNA has the ability to replicate—that is, make copies of itself. This process of **replication** takes place before new cells are produced. The action of **enzymes** causes the strands of the DNA molecule to separate. Free nucleotides join up with the corresponding bases on the separated strands (A with T and C with G) to form new duplicate strands (Figure 3.4). The result is two copies of the DNA molecule, each carrying the same genetic information.

Usually, DNA replicates without any difficulties, but occasionally **mutations** occur, altering the sequence of bases. These mutations are, variously, **point mutations**, in which there is a change in one base of the gene sequence (say, an A–T pair for a G–C pair); **deletions**, resulting in missing segments of DNA; **insertions**, characterized by the addition of extra DNA; or **inversions**, which involve the reversal of a section of DNA. A variety of factors can cause

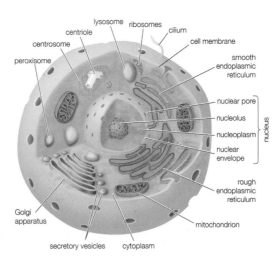

FIGURE 3.1 A typical eukaryotic cell contains a nucleus within which DNA is found.

© Universal Images Group/Getty

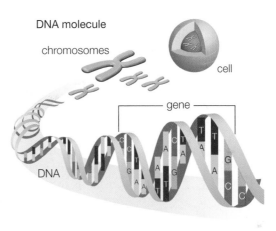

FIGURE 3.2 The DNA molecule has a double helix structure that allows it to replicate, or make copies of itself.

---

1. While mitochondrial DNA is present in the tail of sperm, it is not injected into the ovum at fertilization as the tail falls off when the sperm enter the ovum. So your mitochondrial DNA comes entirely from the ovum.
2. A documentary of her discovery, entitled *Secret of Photo 51*, was produced by Nova in 2003. Several books have also been written about her life and work.

eukaryotes

organisms that have within their cells a nucleus containing DNA

nucleotides

the basic structural units of a DNA or RNA molecule, consisting of a phosphate, sugar, and base

bases

chemical units making up part of DNA and RNA molecules. There are four bases in DNA: adenine, thymine, guanine, and cytosine. In RNA, thymine is replaced with uracil

nuclear DNA (nDNA)

DNA found within the nucleus of a cell

chromosomes

structures composed of DNA and found in the nucleus of cells

locus

the location of a gene on a chromosome

mitochondria

structures within a cell that generate energy for that cell

replication

the process whereby a duplicate copy of a molecule (i.e., DNA) is made

enzymes

proteins that catalyze chemical reactions in the body

mutations

alterations to genes or chromosomes

point mutations

changes in base pairs of gene sequences

deletions

mutations characterized by the loss of DNA

insertions

mutations characterized by the addition of DNA into a length of chromosome

inversions

mutations in which a section of DNA is reversed

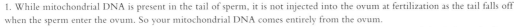

mutations, including exposure to chemicals, sunlight, and radiation. This explains why you put on a lead apron before you have radiographs taken at the dentist's office, and why you slather on sunscreen during the summer months (although usually not nearly enough).

Mutations occur frequently and most of them are neutral—that is, they have no effect on the organism. Some mutations can actually be beneficial. One example relates to the gene that codes for the *CCR5* protein, a chemical receptor used by HIV to gain entry into target cells. One mutated form of this gene, *CCR5-Δ32*, is characterized by a deletion of a segment of 32 base-pairs. This damages the receptor, thus preventing HIV from entering cells. As a consequence, individuals who carry two copies of the mutated allele are generally immune to HIV infection and individuals who carry one copy have some protection from infection, or experience slower progression of the disease if they do become infected (Marmor et al. 2001).[3] Harmful mutations can also occur, such as the one that results in sickle cell anaemia, a common disease in sub-Saharan Africa and parts of Asia (see Chapter 4).

In some cases, the effect of a mutation on an organism depends on the environment in which that organism lives. A classic example involves the English peppered moth, of which two varieties exist: light and dark. The story, as revealed by British ecologist H.B.D. Kettlewell, who conducted the original study, goes like this. Before the Industrial Revolution, the dark-coloured variety of the moth was rare. With the advent of coal-burning factories in the 18th and 19th centuries, the darker variety became more common and the lighter variety less so. Why? A darkening of tree bark by pollution meant that the darker moth became more difficult for predators to spot, and the lighter variety, once well camouflaged, became more visible. Consequently, the lighter variety was targeted and their frequency declined. With improvements in air quality, the situation reversed itself and the lighter variety again became more common. Thus a mutation that gave rise to two different colours of moths was beneficial to dark moths during the Industrial Revolution but deleterious to them at other times. Despite criticisms of Kettlewell's experiments, this phenomenon of **industrial melanism** remains a good illustration of natural selection in operation.[4]

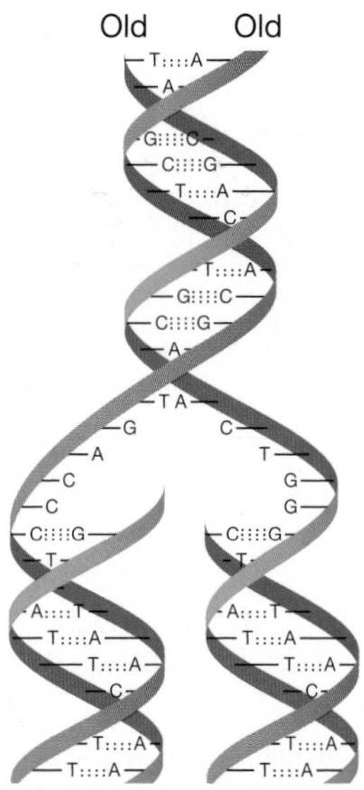

Genetic variations arising from mutation are attracting considerable attention for how they affect our susceptibility to diseases such as Alzheimer's, diabetes, asthma, and schizophrenia. The simplest types are **single nucleotide polymorphisms (SNPs)**, which are genetic variations produced by a point mutation—for example, the substitution of thymine for adenine. Comprising about 90% of all genetic variation, SNPs also appear to play a role in how people respond to medication.

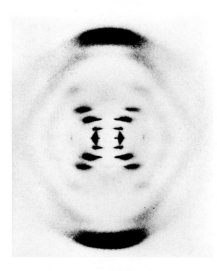

FIGURE 3.3 This X-ray diffraction photograph of DNA provided clues to its double helix structure.

© Science Photo Library

FIGURE 3.4 DNA replicates before a cell divides. This means that each new cell contains the same genetic material.

industrial melanism
increased pigmentation resulting from human modification of the environment, such as occurred during the Industrial Revolution

single nucleotide polymorphisms (SNPs)
genetic variations that are produced by the substitution of a single nucleotide in a sequence. SNPs are point mutations that occur in at least 1% of the population

3. *CCR5-Δ32* has been linked not only to HIV but also to smallpox and bubonic plague.

4. In her book *Of Moths and Men: The Untold Story of Science and the Peppered Moth* (2003), Judith Hooper contends that Kettlewell's experiments were likely fraudulent, noting that he released his moths, which are normally active at night, during the day; that these moths do not normally land on tree trunks; that bats, not birds, are their main predators; and that Kettlewell demonstrated the camouflaging effect of colour by reportedly photographing dead moths that he had pinned or glued to tree trunks himself! Her claims have been vigorously attacked.

The Functions of DNA

The most important function of DNA is **protein synthesis**. Proteins are macromolecules made up of **amino acids**, of which there are 20 in all. Nine of these are classified as essential amino acids as they cannot be manufactured by the body and must be obtained from the diet, while the remaining amino acids are nonessential, meaning that they can be produced by the body and therefore do not need to be obtained from elsewhere (Table 3.1). The differences between proteins lie in the number of amino acids they contain and how they are arranged. For example, some proteins are made up of a single **polypeptide** chain, whereas others consist of multiple chains joined together and arranged into a three-dimensional shape (Figure 3.5). Proteins perform a wide range of vital functions in the body, including providing mechanical support, forming and repairing tissue, regulating metabolic activities, and transporting molecules. For example, proteins such as collagen in bone and keratin in hair and fingernails provide structural support and strength, enzymes facilitate biochemical reactions and play an important role in metabolism, hemoglobin carries oxygen in the blood, insulin maintains blood sugar at a healthy level, and antibodies help protect the body against infection.

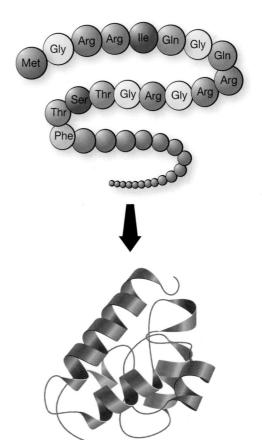

protein synthesis

the process by which amino acids are assembled to form proteins

amino acids

molecules that make up proteins

polypeptide

a chain of amino acids

FIGURE 3.5 Amino acids are chemically linked by peptide bonds to form a polypeptide (top). Proteins are made up of one or more polypeptides that are folded together into a three-dimensional structure (bottom).

TABLE 3.1 Essential and Nonessential Amino Acids

Essential Amino Acids	Nonessential Amino Acids
Histidine	Alanine
Isoleucine	Arginine
Leucine	Asparagine
Lysine	Aspartic Acid
Methionine	Cysteine
Phenylalanine	Glutamine
Threonine	Glutamic Acid
Tryptophan	Glycine
Valine	Proline
	Serine
	Tyrosine

ribosomes

structures found in cells that are involved in the assembly of proteins

RNA

ribonucleic acid

messenger RNA (mRNA)

a form of RNA that carries the genetic instructions of a DNA molecule to the site of protein synthesis

transcription

transfer of genetic information carried by DNA to RNA

cytoplasm

the substance found within the cell membrane and surrounding the nucleus

translation

synthesis of a chain of amino acids based on a message carried in RNA

codons

each codon is a unit of three bases/nucleotides that code for a particular amino acid

genetic code

the sequence of nucleotides in DNA or RNA that determines the specific amino acid sequence in protein synthesis

transfer RNA (tRNA)

RNA molecules that carry amino acids to ribosomes, where they are used in protein synthesis

somatic cells

all cells in the body, with the exception of the sex cells

mitosis

division of the somatic cells resulting in the production of two identical daughter cells

diploid

having a full set of paired chromosomes; in humans, each somatic cell contains 23 pairs of chromosomes

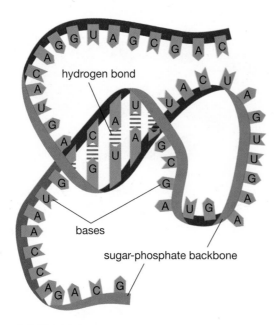

FIGURE 3.6 Unlike DNA molecules, RNA molecules are usually single-stranded.

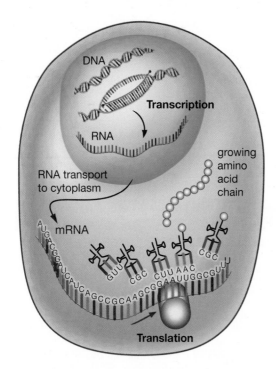

FIGURE 3.7 Transcription occurs in the nucleus of the cell and involves the partial separation of the strands of a DNA molecule and the synthesis of a complementary single-stranded RNA molecule known as messenger RNA. Translation occurs in the cytoplasm of the cell. Here the information carried by the messenger RNA is translated into a protein molecule at the ribosome.

Protein synthesis occurs outside the nucleus in structures called **ribosomes**. Because the DNA molecule cannot travel through the nucleus membrane, its message must be copied into a form that can be carried to the ribosome. This is accomplished through the formation of **RNA**. Unlike DNA, the RNA molecule is single-stranded and has uracil instead of thymine as one of its bases. It also contains a different type of sugar (Figure 3.6).

In the first stage of protein synthesis, the two strands of the DNA molecule partially separate and free nucleotides arrive and join together with the corresponding bases on the separated strands to form **messenger RNA (mRNA)**—a process known as **transcription** (Figure 3.7). The messenger RNA then leaves the nucleus as a single-stranded molecule and travels to the **cytoplasm**, where its message is translated with the assistance of the ribosome, to which the messenger RNA attaches. Facilitating this process of **translation** are **codons** on the messenger RNA that specify particular amino acids. These amino acids, each of which consists of complementary three-base sequences, or anticodons which carry the **genetic code**, are carried by **transfer RNA (tRNA)** molecules to the ribosome, where they are joined together by peptide bonds to form a polypeptide. Once the entire messenger RNA molecular has been read and the complete protein has been assembled, the latter breaks away and begins its task.

CELL DIVISION

Mitosis

As noted above, DNA has the ability to replicate and does so prior to cell division—a process required for growth as well as maintenance of tissues. The division of **somatic cells** is known as **mitosis**. Each cell in the human body contains 46 single-stranded chromosomes. The first step in mitosis is the replication of these chromosomes, resulting in 46 double-stranded chromosomes (Figure 3.8). These duplicate pairs line up at the centre of the cell and then diverge so that the strands are separated. The individual strands move toward opposite ends of the cell, the cell membrane constricts in the middle, and two new cells are formed, each containing 46 single-stranded chromosomes. The end result is two identical **diploid** cells.

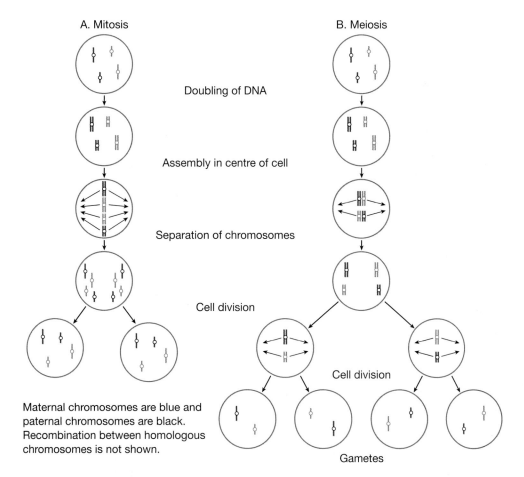

A. Mitosis

Doubling of DNA

Assembly in centre of cell

Separation of chromosomes

Cell division

B. Meiosis

Cell division

Gametes

Maternal chromosomes are blue and paternal chromosomes are black. Recombination between homologous chromosomes is not shown.

FIGURE 3.8 Mitosis involves one cell division and results in two identical daughter cells that are identical to the parent cell. Meiosis, in contrast, involves two cell divisions and results in four daughter cells, each containing half of the genetic material of the parent cell.

Meiosis

The sex cells, sperm and egg, (also known as **gametes**) also divide, in a process known as **meiosis**. Unlike mitosis, however, this process involves *two* cell divisions and the production of *four* **haploid** daughter cells, each containing only 23 chromosomes (Figure 3.8). The reason for this should (we hope) be obvious—male and female gametes pair up at conception to form a **zygote** with the full complement of 46 chromosomes, half from mom and half from dad. These may be visualized and numbered by size in a **karyotype**. As illustrated in Figure 3.9, humans have 22 pairs of **autosomal chromosomes** and 1 pair of sex chromosomes.

In the first stage of meiosis, which occurs within ovarian cells called **oogonia** and testicular cells called **spermatogonia**, 46 single-stranded chromosomes replicate to produce 46 double-stranded chromosomes (Figure 3.8). These paired chromosomes arrange themselves and line up at the centre of the cell. The pairs separate, members of each pair move to opposite ends of the cell, and the cell divides to produce two diploid daughter cells, each containing 23 double-stranded chromosomes. In the second stage, each of these daughter cells divides and the paired chromosomes separate, resulting in four haploid cells.

So far, the process is a match to mitosis; however, there are some important differences on the female side of things. The initial division in the female ovary produces two **primary oocytes**, but (unlike male spermatocytes) they are not created equal. One oocyte sequesters most of the contents of the cytoplasm. If this were mitosis, it would end here. However, the goal is to produce functional eggs and sperm, and to be able to do so, they need to go through one more reduction division, to produce viable haploid gametes. As before, things are a bit

gametes
sex cells; ovum or sperm

meiosis
cell division resulting in the formation of the sex cells

haploid
having a single set of unpaired chromosomes; in humans, each of our sex cells contains 23 single-stranded chromosomes

zygote
fertilized egg

karyotype
arrangement of the full set of chromosomes by numbered pairs

autosomal chromosomes
chromosomes other than the sex chromosomes

oogonia
ovarian cells

spermatogonia
testicular cells

primary oocytes
immature ova

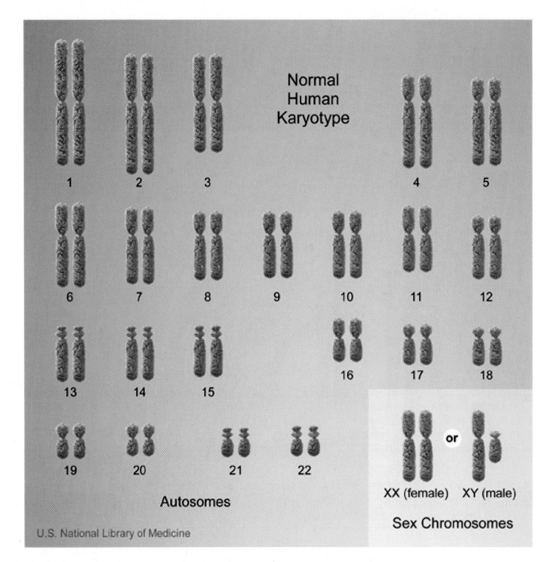

FIGURE 3.9 Humans possess 22 pairs of autosomal chromosomes and 1 pair of sex chromosomes.

U.S. National Library of Medicine

polar bodies

small cells that are the by-product of meiosis in females

recombination (crossing over)

the exchange of genes between homologous chromosomes during meiosis

homologous chromosomes

chromosomes that go together in a pair

nondisjunction

the failure of chromosome pairs to separate properly during meiosis

trisomy

a condition characterized by an extra chromosome

different in females. The primary oocyte does not divide equally: through the process of unequal cytoplasmic cleavage, one of the haploid cells—the ovum—receives the majority of the cytoplasm. Thus, while all four of the resultant sperm cells are viable, only the ovum is in females. The other female daughter cells, termed **polar bodies,** are resorbed.

There is another very significant difference between men and women. While men produce sperm throughout their adult lives, women have a limited supply of eggs, most of which are produced during fetal development. And most of these (perhaps as many as 1 million) are recycled. At puberty, a human female has perhaps four hundred primary oocytes; over her reproductive lifespan of perhaps 35 years, these are released "monthly" in hope of being fertilized.

We mentioned earlier that mutation is an important source of variation. Meiosis increases variation through a process called **recombination** (Figure 3.10). Also referred to as "crossing over," this occurs when genetic material is exchanged between **homologous chromosomes** during cell division. Problems can occur during meiosis in such a way that chromosome strands fail to separate properly during the final division. The end result of this **nondisjunction** is fewer or more chromosomes than normal; the cell receiving the extra chromosome is referred to as trisomic. The best-known example of **trisomy** is Down syndrome (named after the 19th-century British physician John Langdon Down, who first described the condition), which results from nondisjunction of the ovarian 21st chromosome. Thus, at fertilization, Down syndrome children have three rather than the normal two copies of chromosome 21. **Monosomy**, where an individual has fewer than the normal complement of chromosomes, may also occur. Females with Turner syndrome, for example, are missing one X chromosome and consequently have sexual characteristics that are usually underdeveloped.

MECHANISMS OF INHERITANCE

As you learned in Chapter 2, Darwin did not know the source of variation on which natural selection acted or how traits were transmitted from parent to offspring. He was influenced by the theory of pangenesis and believed that offspring were somehow a blend of the traits of the parents. It was not until the early 20th century that scientists became aware of the work of Gregor Mendel (Figure 3.11), who identified the source of variation and the mechanisms of inheritance. An Augustinian monk who lived in what was then Austria, Mendel was trained in physics but developed an interest in botany and spent eight years of his life conducting hybridization experiments on plants. He presented the results of his experiments at the 1865 meeting of the Brünn Natural History Society and published his report the following year (Mendel 1866).[5]

Mendel's scientific training served him well because he chose the garden pea plant (*Pisum sativum*) for his studies, noting that it exhibited traits that were either present or absent (referred to today as **discrete** or **Mendelian traits**). The pea plant also has the ability to self-pollinate, which gave Mendel effective control over which plants could become the parents of the next generation—in particular, self-fertilized versus **cross-fertilized** plants. After carrying out a series of breeding cycles to produce pure-breeding plants (i.e., ones that give rise to plants with the same physical characteristics in each successive generation), Mendel crossed pea plants with different characteristics (e.g., tall vs. short height, yellow vs. green seeds, smooth vs. wrinkled seeds; Figure 3.12) and observed the physical appearance (i.e., the **phenotype**) of the next generation of plants. He found that all exhibited the same characteristics. In the case of height, all of the plants were tall; in the case of seed colour, all were yellow. Thus the tall and yellow factors were visible and the short and green factors were hidden. He concluded from this that every plant carried two factors for each trait, one provided by each parent. We refer to these factors today as **alleles**—alternative forms of a gene that occur at the same location on homologous chromosomes. The allele that is expressed is the **dominant** allele; that which is hidden is **recessive**.

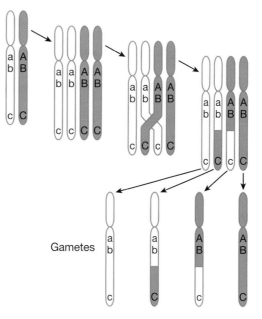

Crossing over and recombination during meiosis

Gametes

FIGURE 3.10 The process of recombination or crossing over involves the shuffling of genetic material from one chromosome to another. It is a source of genetic variation.

FIGURE 3.11 Gregor Mendel

© Hulton Archive/Getty

monosomy

a condition characterized by the absence of one copy of a chromosome pair

discrete (Mendelian) traits

traits that are controlled by genes at a single locus; also referred to as monogenic traits

cross-fertilized

plants (or animals) that are fertilized by fusing the reproductive cells of two different organisms belonging to the same species

phenotype

the observable characteristic of an organism

alleles

alternative forms of a gene

dominant

the allele or trait that is expressed

recessive

the unexpressed allele or trait that is genetically hidden by its dominant counterpart

5. While Mendel is widely recognized today as the founder of genetics, his work has generated controversy, with some contending that he falsified his data (Fisher 1936)—claims that have been vehemently denied (Hartl and Fairbanks 2007).

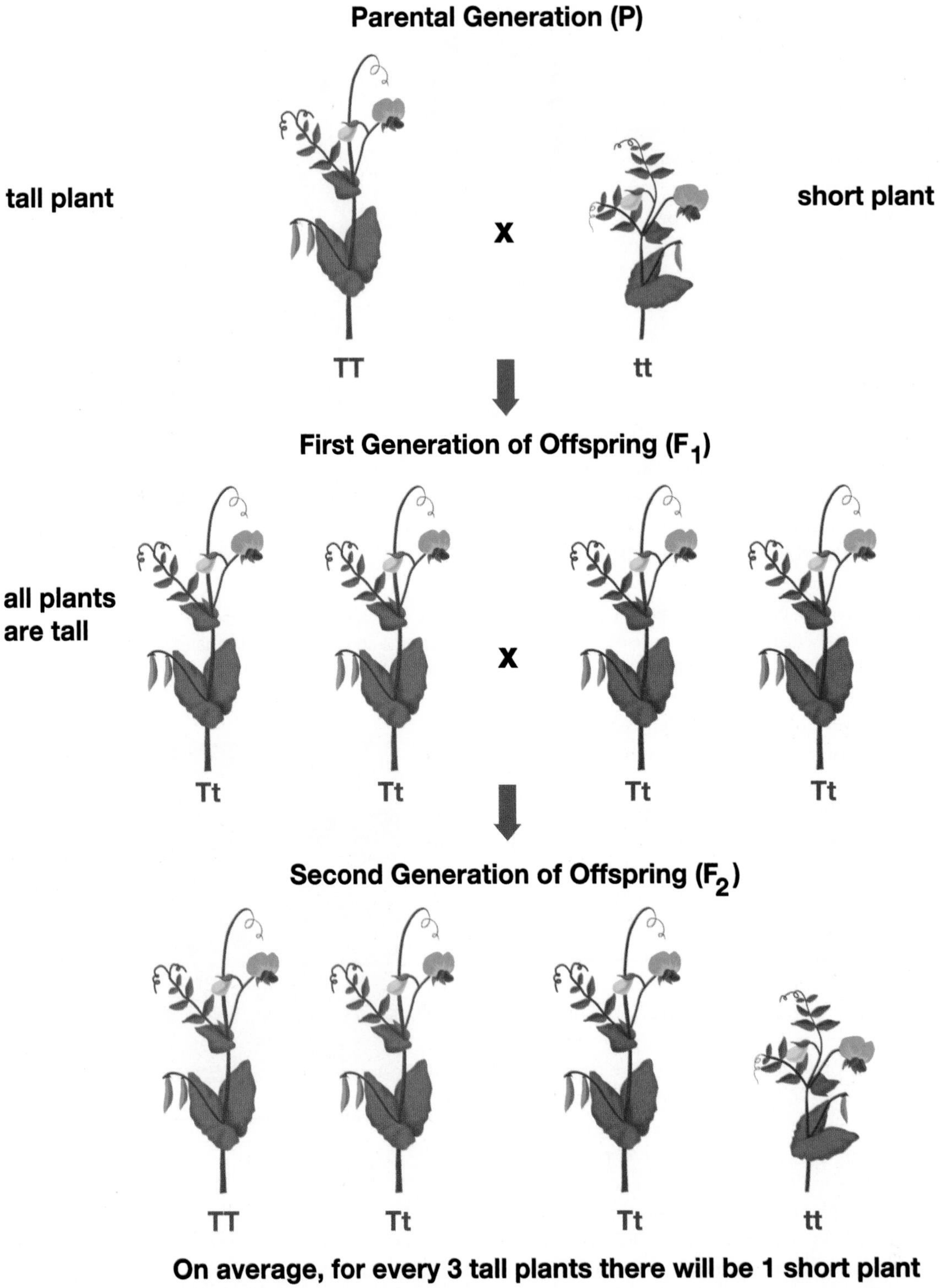

Parental Generation (P)

tall plant   X   short plant

TT   tt

First Generation of Offspring (F₁)

all plants
are tall

Tt   Tt   X   Tt   Tt

Second Generation of Offspring (F₂)

TT   Tt   Tt   tt

On average, for every 3 tall plants there will be 1 short plant

FIGURE 3.12 When Mendel crossed tall pea plants with short ones, all of the offspring were tall. When he then crossed this generation, three-quarters of the offspring were tall and one-quarter was short.

In his second set of experiments, Mendel crossed all of the offspring produced by his initial experiments, referred to as the first, or F₁ generation,[6] and studied the appearance of the second, or F₂ generation. In the case of height, when all first-generation tall plants

---

6. In this terminology, "F" refers to "filial," a term meaning "offspring"; thus, F₁ indicates the first-generation offspring, F₂ the second, and so on.

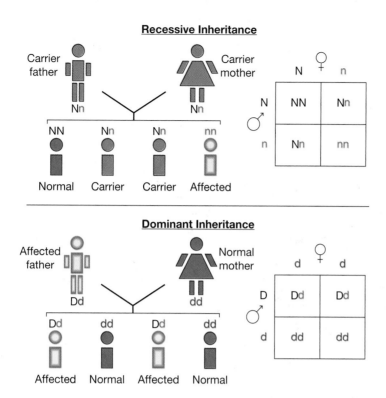

FIGURE 3.13 Mendel's experiments revealed that two factors, or alleles, are responsible for each trait. As indicated in the Punnett squares on the right, the dominant allele is expressed as a capital letter (e.g., N), and the recessive allele is expressed as a lowercase letter (e.g., n). Dominant traits are therefore expressed in individuals who are NN or Nn, and recessive traits are expressed only in individuals who are nn.

were crossed, the result was three tall plants and one short plant. This can be represented schematically in a **Punnett square** (see Figure 3.13). If you remember that all F_1 tall plants carry two different alleles—one for the dominant tall trait, which we will represent as "T," and one for the recessive short trait, which we will represent as "t," the **genotype** of all of these first-generation plants will be Tt. In contrast, one-quarter of the second-generation plants will have the genotype TT, one half will be Tt, and one quarter will be tt. In other words, the recessive trait is expressed only when both recessive alleles are combined in an offspring. When the two alleles are identical (e.g., TT or tt), an organism is said to be **homozygous** for that gene ("homo" = "same"), while those with different alleles (e.g., Tt) are said to be **heterozygous** ("hetero" = "different").

The traits that Mendel observed in his pea plants were **monogenic traits**—that is, controlled by a single gene. An excellent illustration in humans is the ABO blood group system. If you have ever given or received blood, more than likely you know your blood "type." Our blood type is determined by the inheritance of one of three alleles (A, B, or O) from each parent. A and B are dominant alleles; O is recessive. However—and this is an added wrinkle—because the A and B allele are "equally dominant," there are six possible genotypes and four possible phenotypes. In this case, A and B are considered **co-dominant**. Thus individuals with "type A" blood are either AA or AO, those with "type B" blood are BB or BO, those with type O blood can only be OO (since "O" is recessive), and those with type AB blood are AB, thanks to co-dominance.

One of the most-studied Mendelian traits is the ability to taste phenylthiocarbamide (PTC), a bitter synthetic compound that some people can taste and others cannot. The ability to taste PTC is determined by a dominant allele, and about 75% of the world's population can taste this substance. The discovery of this difference in taste sensitivity came about in the early 1930s, when a chemist accidentally released some of the powder into his lab, leading one of his co-workers to complain of a bad taste in his mouth, while he himself could taste nothing (Fox 1932).

Punnett square

a way of graphically representing the genotypic outcomes when crossing organisms with the same or different genotypes

genotype

the genetic makeup of an organism

homozygous

having two identical alleles at a single genetic locus

heterozygous

having two different alleles at a single genetic locus

monogenic traits

traits that are controlled by genes at a single locus

co-dominant

a trait in which both alleles are expressed

Scientists have pondered the significance of the ability to taste PTC, and believe that the trait may have evolved in order to prevent humans from eating toxic plants (Boyd 1950). More recent studies have explored the relationship between taste sensitivity and other phenotypic traits such as cigarette smoking. Several studies, for instance, have demonstrated that among humans, the ability to taste PTC is less prevalent in smokers than in nonsmokers (Cannon et al. 2005; Enoch et al. 2001). Interestingly, chimpanzees also vary in their ability to taste PTC, an observation first reported in 1939 (Fisher, Ford, and Huxley 1939). This ability appears to have developed through a separate mutation that occurred after humans and chimps diverged (Wooding et al. 2006). As with humans, it too may have evolved to enable chimpanzees to avoid eating toxic plants (ibid.); if so, this would be an excellent example of convergent evolution (see Chapter 4).

As a result of his experiments, Mendel formulated two principles of inheritance known as the **principle of segregation** and the **principle of independent assortment**. According to the first of these, which we now know arises during meiosis, traits are transmitted by a large number of independent units (genes). These occur in pairs—that is, every individual has two copies, which may be the same or variant (alleles). These copies are randomly separated during the production of sex cells so that each sex cell contains only one allele from each parent. In other words, each of us inherits one allele from each parent. According to the principle of independent assortment, the segregation of any given pair of genes during meiosis does not influence the segregation of any other pair. In other words, the genes are not linked. Returning to our pea plants, this means that yellow seeds are not always found with tall height. The main reason for this outcome is that these two genes are not located on the same chromosomes. While this is the case for many genes, there are, in fact, some traits that are linked together (i.e., they are found on the same chromosome) and that tend to be inherited together, especially if their coding sequences are close to each other. A special case of linkage occurs with respect to the X chromosome, and most **sex-linked** genes are carried on this chromosome.

One of the best-known examples of an **X-linked** trait is red–green colour blindness. Individuals with this feature have difficulty distinguishing colours in the red–green wavelength range. Around 6 to 8% of humans today express this trait, and most of them are males. Because it is a recessive trait, individuals who carry the normal gene on the X chromosome lack this trait, and females who have one dominant gene and one recessive gene are **carriers** with normal colour vision (Figure 3.14). However, females who inherit the recessive allele from both parents and males who inherit the recessive allele from their mothers are red–green colourblind, as illustrated in this **pedigree** diagram.

Another well-known example of an X-linked trait is hemophilia, a genetic disorder characterized by the inability of blood to clot. As with red–green colour blindness, this recessive trait is far more common in males than females, although about 10% of females who are carriers of the recessive allele will exhibit reduced blood-clotting activity (they are protected from the most severe form of the condition). Because the gene for this disorder is carried as a recessive on the X chromosome, males who inherit the recessive gene from their mother will have the disease, while females who inherit one defective X chromosome will be carriers. Males who have the disease will always pass on the recessive gene to their daughters, but none of their sons can inherit the gene from their dad. The disorder can also result from a spontaneous mutation (about 30% of cases). Hemophilia is known

principle of segregation

the separation of alleles during the production of sex cells so that each sex cell contains only one allele from each parent

principle of independent assortment

the distribution of one pair of alleles into the sex cells does not influence the distribution of another pair of alleles

sex-linked

traits that are controlled by genes located on one of the sex chromosomes

X-linked

traits that are controlled by genes located on the X chromosome

carriers

individuals who are heterozygous for a recessive trait and who do not physically manifest the trait

pedigree

a diagram that illustrates the transmission of a genetic trait from one generation to subsequent generations of a family

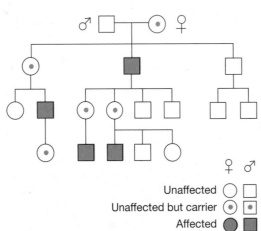

Unaffected ○ □
Unaffected but carrier ⊙ ▣
Affected ● ■

FIGURE 3.14 Red–green colour blindness is an X-linked trait. Males who inherit the recessive allele from their mothers, and females who inherit the recessive allele from both parents, are red–green colourblind. In contrast, females who inherit the recessive allele from only one parent are carriers.

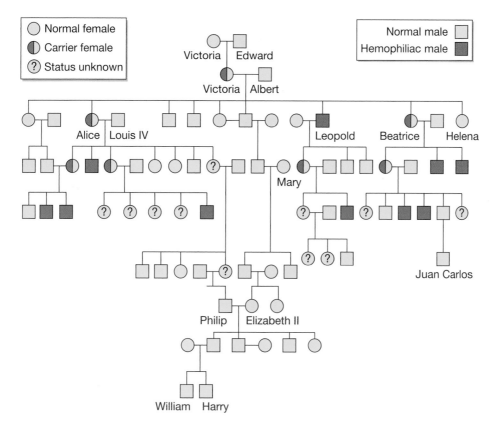

FIGURE 3.15 Hemophilia was once known as the "royal disease" because of its high frequency in European royal families.

to have affected the British monarchy. Queen Victoria transmitted the gene to her son, who in turn passed it on to his descendants (Figure 3.15).

Sex linkage may also occur with regard to the Y chromosome, in which case only males will express the trait and fathers will pass it to all their male offspring. However, because the Y possesses very few genes, the proportion of sex linkage through Y is very small. At one time the "male hairy ear" trait (hypertrichosis pinnae auris) was thought to be transmitted through Y linkage; this has since been shown not to be the case (Lee et al. 2004).

Pleiotropy

A single gene can influence multiple phenotypic traits. These genes are known as **pleiotropies**. One of the best-known examples relates to **phenylketonuria (PKU)**, a genetic disorder characterized by the body's inability to convert the amino acid phenylalanine into another amino acid, tyrosine, due to the lack of an enzyme called phenylalanine hydroxylase. In individuals who lack this enzyme, phenylalanine increases to toxic levels in the blood and other tissues, leading to mental and developmental disabilities, among other symptoms. PKU is inherited as an autosomal recessive gene, which means that an individual must have both recessive alleles to develop the disorder. The pleiotropic effect of this gene lies in the fact that phenylalanine also plays a role in the production of melanin, the pigment that gives skin and hair its colour. Individuals with PKU do not produce sufficient melanin and consequently exhibit lighter hair, skin, and eyes. Today, screening newborns for PKU is routinely done, and elevated levels of phenylalanine can be treated with proper dietary measures (see Chapter 14).

pleiotropies
genes that influence more than one trait

phenylketonuria (PKU)
a genetic disorder characterized by a deficiency in the enzyme phenylalanine hydroxylase, resulting in the accumulation of excessive amounts of phenylalanine

Polygenic Traits

In contrast to monogenic traits such as the ABO blood group system, a multitude of human physical characteristics are controlled by many genes that interact with one another and with the environment. **Polygenic traits** (also known as "continuous traits") include hair and eye colour, stature, and body weight (visit the CourseMate site for a discussion of the question "Do genes make us fat?"). Given our current knowledge of genetics, one might assume that the genes underlying these traits have all been identified, especially now that the human genome has been mapped. However, scientists have yet to identify the genes underlying many basic physical characteristics. Skin colour, for example, is thought to be controlled by perhaps as many as half a dozen genes, but the exact number and the mutations responsible for light and dark pigmentation remain unknown, although a "freckle gene" associated with red hair and fair skin has been identified (Bastiaens et al. 2001). Similarly, three genes that control eye colour have been identified (those for green, blue, and brown eyes), but the genetic basis of other eye colours remains unknown, and we do not yet know the precise mechanisms of inheritance or how exactly eye colour changes over time.

BEHAVIOURAL GENETICS

Researchers have long recognized that a number of human behaviours have a genetic component. We know, for example, that some behaviours run in families and that we share certain behavioural patterns with our closest living relatives, the chimpanzees. However, determining the **heritability** of human behaviours such as homosexuality, aggression, and intelligence has proven to be extremely challenging, and considerable debate has arisen regarding the extent to which genes ("nature") vs. environment ("nurture") underlie such behaviours (visit the CourseMate site for a discussion of the question "Is there a gay gene?"). Indeed, the nature–nurture controversy has shifted back and forth over the past century between viewing genes as the primary determinants of human behaviour and recognizing the crucial role played by cultural and environmental factors in shaping such traits.

A good example of a complex behaviour that appears to have a genetic component is aggression. If you have ever seen the classic 1956 movie *The Bad Seed*, you will know that the main premise is that violent behaviour can be inherited, showing up in seemingly innocent-looking children who unleash a reign of terror on those around them. Research in the field of psychiatric genetics, in particular, has focused on the ways in which genes may be linked to aggressive behaviour, and a large number of biological agents are now known to influence aggression, including hormones, enzymes, and growth factors (Anholt and Mackay 2012).

Researchers in behavioural genetics face a number of challenges, including the fact that behaviours are difficult to define and quantify. As complex traits, they involve multiple genes, and deciphering whether genes are a cause or an influencing factor is difficult. In addition, the field of behavioural genetics has generated considerable controversy with respect to the ethical, moral, legal, and social implications of assigning genetic causes to human traits such as homosexuality and aggression. For example, the identification of "susceptibility genes" for aggressive behaviour could potentially lead to abuses such as the implementation of measures designed to oppress certain segments of the population. In recent years, a new paradigm in behavioural genetics has emerged that emphasizes a balanced view, one that recognizes that while much of our behaviour is rooted in our genes, we have the capacity to modify and change our behaviour (Drew 1997, 48).

TAMPERING WITH MOTHER NATURE: THE ETHICS OF GENETIC MANIPULATION

If you could determine your child's genetic profile, would you? Should you? It is one thing to manipulate genes in an attempt to cure a disease such as cystic fibrosis or sickle cell anaemia, but it is quite another to alter genes to change an individual's physical appearance or personality. Such genetic manipulation might take the form of germ-line gene therapy, in which genetic alterations are made to the sex cells, or somatic-cell gene therapy, in which changes are made to the somatic (or body) cells. Transferring a new gene into a cell is a complicated process involving several steps. The ultimate goal of gene therapy is to replace a damaged or faulty gene by inserting a healthy version into the same location on a particular chromosome. While some degree of error can be tolerated with respect to somatic cells, any error in the sex cells could potentially have devastating consequences, and there is great potential for abuse of this technology. For example, the technique of germ-line gene therapy to cure a genetic disorder could be appropriated by a cosmetics company to change an individual's skin colour. For now, the greatest potential of gene therapy lies in its ability to treat chronic infectious and degenerative diseases.

The development of recombinant DNA technology in the 1970s allowed scientists to insert pieces of DNA from one organism into the DNA of another. This technique has allowed for the manufacture of insulin and other substances that can be used for medical treatments, as well as the production of hardier strains of plant and animal products. While the principle behind this technique is not that different from altering plants and animals through selective breeding—which humans have been doing for thousands of years—it has generated tremendous controversy. Critics have highlighted the dangers of such practices, including the possibility of prompting allergic reactions and more serious medical conditions in individuals who consume genetically modified foods.

Issues have also arisen surrounding genetic screening. Such screening is normally done at fertility clinics in order to avoid implanting embryos with genetic disorders such as Down syndrome. However, a survey of in vitro fertilization clinics in the United States revealed that some prospective parents have requested screening to select for embryos that *have* a particular disease or disability such as deafness in order to ensure that their children will have the same condition as themselves (Baruch et al. 2008).

Cloning, the creation of an exact genetic copy of a molecule, cell, or organism, has also generated considerable controversy.[7] Since Dolly the sheep was cloned in 1997 (Figure 3.16), numerous other animals have been cloned, and serious concerns have been raised about human cloning. We know from animal experiments that clones are often born with birth defects or develop significant health problems leading to early death. You may recall, for instance, that Dolly suffered from the early onset of arthritis. Opponents of cloning also warn that this technology could be used to harvest organs from cloned humans.

FIGURE 3.16 Dolly the sheep with her first offspring.

© AP Photo/John Chadwick

MAPPING THE HUMAN GENOME

In the late 1980s, researchers began work on mapping the human genome, and by 2001 a nearly complete sequence had been mapped by the National Human Genome Research Institute (NHGRI) (IHGSC 2001) and by Celera Genomics (Venter et al. 2001). As a result of this endeavour, we now know that the human genome contains about 3 billion base pairs and 20,000 to 25,000 genes (IHGSC 2004). One of the most significant results of this map has been the discovery that most of our DNA is noncoding. In fact, less than 2% of our DNA codes for proteins. The remaining DNA, once referred to as junk DNA but now more commonly referred to as **noncoding DNA**, was initially thought to have no function at all. We now know, however, that within this DNA are millions of switches that control the

noncoding DNA

multiple copies of a base sequence that may be repeated on the same chromosome or dispersed throughout the genome

---

7. Clones are only genetically identical. Phenotypic variation exists owing to epigenetic and environmental factors.

behaviour of cells and tissues. These groundbreaking findings, uncovered by an international research project called ENCODE (Encyclopedia of DNA Elements), have the potential to lead to cures for many human diseases.

A common misconception is that the human genome mapped by these institutes represents *the* human genome. The reality is that no such thing exists, and what we call "the human genome" is merely a reference and does not account for all of the variability that exists within the human species (Weiss 2012). In fact, the NHGRI derived its map using the DNA of only 24 individuals and Celera Genomics from only five individuals, all of whom were Caucasian. To address this shortcoming, a group of scientists launched the Human Genome Diversity Project (HGDP) in 1991 with the goal of mapping global genetic diversity by collecting DNA from hundreds of different populations worldwide. Such a sample would permit scientists to explore the evolutionary histories of these populations and to identify genes that may play a role in their susceptibility or resistance to particular diseases.

This project has generated vehement opposition, particularly from indigenous peoples who have characterized it as an example of "scientific colonialism," with the underlying objective to patent this genetic data for commercial purposes, such as developing medical cures for wealthy individuals in industrialized countries. Concerns have also been expressed about how informed consent would be obtained, and how such research would impact on these populations psychologically, socially, and economically. At the very (and unlikely) extreme, claims have been made that the genetic data collected will be used to develop biological weapons against indigenous populations. Perhaps the most important issue arising from the HGDP is that of ownership and human rights.

Other large-scale projects involving the collection and analysis of genetic data have also been initiated. These include the Genographic Project, launched in 2005 by the National Geographic Society and IBM to investigate the migratory history of our species using DNA donated by hundreds of thousands of people from around the world, and the 1000 Genomes Project, initiated in 2008 to sequence the genomes of at least 1,000 individuals from different populations worldwide with the goal of producing a comprehensive catalogue of human genetic variation. In addition, in the past few years the genomes of other species, including a number of primate species (see Chapter 5) and Neandertals (see Chapter 11), have been or are being mapped.

ANCIENT DNA

ancient DNA (aDNA)
DNA in ancient (i.e., nonmodern) remains recoverable from hard tissues (bones and teeth) and in exceptional cases of preservation, from hair and soft tissue.

In the 1980s, a new subfield of biological anthropology focusing on the extraction and analysis of **ancient DNA (aDNA)** emerged. Ancient DNA was first derived from human remains in 1985, when scientists retrieved DNA from a 2,400-year-old Egyptian mummy (Pääbo 1985). Since that time, it has been recovered from a variety of tissues, including bones, teeth, mummified remains, and preserved brain tissue (Doran et al. 1986; for an excellent review of aDNA research, see Mulligan 2006). Applications include examining the origins of anatomically modern humans and the position of Neandertals in our evolutionary history (Krings et al. 1997) (see Chapter 11); identifying genetic diseases such as thalassemia (Yang 1997); detecting and diagnosing infectious diseases such as tuberculosis, leprosy, and plague (Bos et al. 2011; Donoghue et al. 2005; Schuenemann et al. 2011; Spigelman et al. 2002); exploring population movements (Raff et al. 2011); determining biological relationships within skeletal samples (Dudar et al. 2003); and determining sex (Faerman et al. 1998; Stone et al. 1996). Most of these studies have utilized mitochondrial DNA because its greater quantity in cells means that it is more likely to survive than is nuclear DNA in very old specimens. Increasingly sophisticated methods of DNA sequencing, most notably high-throughput sequencing technologies, have also allowed for the production of thousands or millions of sequences at once, at lower cost than is possible with older methods. In Canada, facilities devoted to ancient DNA research include the Paleo-DNA Laboratory at Lakehead University, the McMaster Ancient DNA Centre, and the Ancient DNA Lab at Simon Fraser University.

One of the problems with early attempts to extract DNA from archaeological remains was that there was often very little remaining and what did survive was fragmentary and degraded, especially in very old specimens. A major breakthrough came in the mid-1980s with the development of a technique known as **polymerase chain reaction (PCR)**. This technique revolutionized the study of aDNA because it enabled scientists to amplify (i.e., make millions of copies of) DNA from only a single molecule. This development provides more DNA for researchers to analyze. This technique has come at a cost, however, as any modern DNA that may have contaminated ancient specimens is amplified as well. Indeed, contamination has been a major stumbling block in the analysis of ancient DNA. Sources of modern DNA include dead skin cells, sweat, saliva, dandruff, and blood, and contamination can occur at a number of stages, including during the excavation itself and in the laboratory afterward. Because of the high potential for contamination, strict precautions must be taken when preparing archaeological samples for DNA analysis. Contamination controls include working in a laboratory dedicated specifically to the study of aDNA; wearing protective gowns, gloves, and masks; performing multiple extractions; and extracting and sequencing samples in more than one laboratory (Cooper and Poinar 2000; Yang and Watt 2005).

Ancient DNA specimens from temperate environments are much trickier to sequence because they contain high levels of environmental contamination, primarily derived from bacteria and other microbes inhabiting the ancient bone. The average ancient DNA sample taken from, say, a human tooth or bone is often less than 1% short, degraded pieces of human DNA; the rest is bacterial DNA. This contamination often makes it too expensive to sequence the tiny amounts of endogenous DNA (which degrades over the years due to exposure to the elements) remaining in a sample. Now, Carpenter and Bustamante and their colleagues (Carpenter et al. 2013) have hit upon a way to enrich or increase the proportion of ancient human DNA in an environmental sample from about 1.2% to nearly 60%—rendering it vastly easier to sequence and analyze. It is hoped that this new method, known as the "whole-genome capture approach," will enable ancient DNA researchers to more economically sequence a larger number of specimens.

polymerase chain reaction (PCR)

a technique used to amplify or make copies of DNA

LEARNING KEYS

KEY IDEAS

- DNA is the universal code of life and consists of nucleotides made up of a phosphate, base, and sugar.

- Its main function is protein synthesis but it also regulates other important processes such as growth and development.

- DNA has a double helix structure that allows it to make copies of itself.

- RNA differs from DNA in that it is a single-stranded molecule and has uracil instead of thymine as one of its bases.

- Mitosis is the division of somatic, or body cells, into two identical daughter cells, each containing the full complement of DNA.

- Meiosis is the division of the sex cells into four non-identical daughter cells, each containing half the genetic material of the original parent cell.

- Mutation and recombination, or crossing over, are major sources of variation on which natural selection acts.

- Proteins are made up of chains of amino acids, and serve a variety of functions, including providing mechanical support, forming and repairing tissue, regulating metabolic activities, and transporting molecules.

- Gregor Mendel's experiments with pea plants demonstrated that traits are transmitted by genes that occur in pairs (i.e., alleles) which are randomly separated during the production of sex cells so that each sex cell contains only one allele from each parent.

- Monogenic traits are controlled by genes at a single locus.

- Polygenic traits such as stature and obesity are controlled by genes found at more than one locus.

- Behavioural genetics is the study of the genetic basis of human behaviours such as homosexuality and aggression.

- The study of ancient DNA can provide valuable insight into our evolutionary history and allow scientists to identify genetic and infectious diseases in skeletal remains, determine biological relationships within skeletal samples, examine population movements, and determine sex from ancient remains.

KEY TERMS

genes (p. 52)

nuclear DNA (p. 53)

mutations (p. 53)

protein synthesis (p. 55)

RNA (p. 56)

mitosis (p. 56)

meiosis (p. 57)

recombination (crossing over) (p. 58)

alleles (p. 59)

monogenic traits (p. 61)

polygenic traits (p. 64)

ancient DNA (aDNA) (p. 66)

KEY QUESTIONS TO ASK MYSELF

1. If I have brown eyes but both of my parents have blue eyes, should I be worried that one or both of my parents is not biologically related to me?

2. Why is it that some populations have higher rates of birth defects than others? How might this be explained from a biocultural perspective?

3. Why do humans have 46 chromosomes while guinea pigs have 64 and algae have 148?

KEY CRITICAL THINKING QUESTIONS

1. Why are children in the same family often so different from one another? To what extent do you think genes vs. the environment have shaped the personalities of you and your siblings?

2. Why haven't traits such as poor eyesight been selected out of the population by now?

KEY THINGS TO DO NEXT

CourseMate Visit **CourseMate** at www.nelson.com/humanvoyage2e to build your comprehension, practise your critical thinking skills, review core concepts, and explore other resources at your disposal.

4 From Variant to Species

Modification of form is admitted to be a matter of time.

Alfred Russel Wallace (1823–1913)

OVERVIEW

In this chapter, we examine how evolutionary theory has advanced through the 20th century to adopt a more expansive view of variation, selection, and adaptation. We explore ways in which biologists have grappled, with some success and a great deal of frustration, with the fundamental questions of "What is a species?" and "What is speciation?" We wrap up this chapter, and this opening section to *A Human Voyage*, by contrasting two models used to classify biological diversity—*clade* and *grade*—that enable researchers to draw comparisons among different species and understand their evolutionary history. This will set the stage for subsequent chapters as we chart our course through the history of ourselves and our nearest primate relatives.

KEY CONCEPTS

Variation, neo-Darwinism, Hardy-Weinberg Equilibrium, modes of selection, non-Darwinian mechanisms, species and speciation, modes of evolution, classification, cladistics, homology, homoplasy

KEY LEARNING OBJECTIVES

At the end of this chapter, you will be able to

LO1   Describe the relationship among variant, variability, and variation

LO2   Explain the principles of the Hardy-Weinberg Equilibrium, specifying conditions under which evolutionary change does not occur

LO3   Apply the biological species concept to understand why highly variable organisms such as domestic dogs are considered a single species, and the concept of hybridization to understand why dogs can successfully mate with wolves

LO4   Distinguish a gradistic from a cladistic classification in terms of how each categorizes groups of organisms (such as primates) based on similarities and differences

LO5   Assess the importance of processes other than natural selection, such as genetic drift and founder effect, for producing population variation within a species and subsequently in the creation of new species

LO6   Construct models of how a population evolves under conditions of directional, stabilizing, and diversifying selection

PROLOGUE: SWEET ACCIDENTS OF HISTORY

Between 1663 and 1673, the French monarch Louis XIV sent more than 700 *filles du roy* (King's Daughters) to New France. His intent was to provide wives for the men of the recently established colonies and to foster permanent settlement. Prior to 1663 the ratio of men to women had reached 169:100, and the king had taken it upon himself to "adopt" young girls of childbearing age (mostly orphans or women lacking family support), provide for their transport to the New World, and supply each with a dowry. They brought little else with them. However, one of these women arrived with something slightly different, slightly unique. She debarked at Québec carrying a genetic mutation responsible for Leber hereditary optic neuropathy (LHON), a disorder affecting mostly young adult males and resulting in progressive loss of central vision in one or both eyes. Recently, geneticist Anne-Marie Laberge and her colleagues at the Université de Montréal identified this young King's Daughter using pedigree analysis and genealogical records (Laberge et al. 2005a).

Three different mutations within the mitochondrial genome cause LHON, the most common of which is G11778A, responsible for 52% to 92% of cases worldwide. However, though LHON is relatively rare among French Canadians, 86% of those with the condition carry a much less common mutation called T14484C—the one that arrived, complete with a king's dowry, in 1669. In evolutionary biology, this event is known as a **founder effect**. Charles Darwin was unaware of founder effects (although he had unknowingly documented their outcome in describing his famous finches); nor was he aware of the many other processes beyond natural selection that are implicated in shaping biological diversity through the ages.

Interestingly, although our LHON *fille du roy* founder was married in Québec City almost 350 years ago, her descendants migrated to southwestern Québec, near Montréal, where LHON is most common today (Figure 4.1). As it happened, the high degree of cultural, linguistic, and religious isolation characteristic of the 8,500 or so French colonists who established New France between 1608 and 1759 is recognized as a major factor determining the high prevalence of as many as 30 known genetic disorders among modern Québécois families (Laberge et al. 2005b). Through the study of such population differences we have gained new insights into not only the biology of human diversity, but also the historical and cultural factors that have shaped its geography.

founder effect

the potentially biased sampling of the genetic variation in a species due to the isolation of a small number of its members

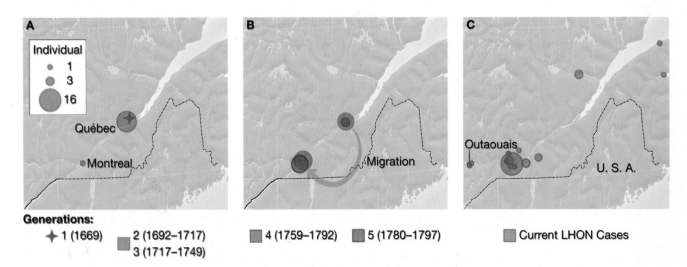

FIGURE 4.1 A single female founder married in Québec City in 1669 is credited with establishing the hereditary disorder LHON in New France; migration of her descendants to the Montréal region is responsible for the current geographic distribution of cases.

Anne-Marie Laberge, Michele Jomphe, Louis Houde, Helene Vezina, Marc Tremblay, Bertrand Desjardins, Damian Labuda, Marc St-Hilaire, Carol Macmillan, Eric A. Shoubridge, and Bernard Brais, "A 'Fille du Roy' Introduced the T14484C Leber hereditary Optic neuropathy Mutation in French Canadians," *The American Journal of Human Genetics*, Vol. 77, no. 2 (August 2005). Copyright © 2005 The American Society of Human Genetics Published by Elsevier Inc. Reprinted with permission.

VARIANT, VARIATION, VARIABILITY

In Chapter 2 we discussed how differences among individuals are central to Darwin's theory of evolution. In fact, it is impossible to imagine how evolutionary change could occur if every member of a sexually reproducing species was alike in all respects, since differential reproductive success presumes that some individuals have an advantage over others in seeking and acquiring necessities such as food, space, and mates. These competitive benefits exist because individuals (**variants**) have a tendency to differ (**variability**), which can be characterized along a continuum of expression (**variation**) (Figure 4.2). As described in Chapter 3, variation may be characterized in terms of the frequency of different phenotypes or genotypes (alleles) present in a population. However, the existence of variation alone is not a guarantee that evolution will occur. For that to happen, one (or more) of a number of evolutionary forces—described later in this chapter—must act on that variation in such a way that these frequencies are modified. Indeed, with the development of a theorem central to the study of **population genetics** known as the **Hardy-Weinberg (H-W) Equilibrium** (see Appendix B and Table 4.1), we are able to specify the conditions under which allele or phenotype frequencies *will not change* from one generation to the next (i.e., they will remain in equilibrium). Showing that these conditions are not in effect suggests that evolutionary forces are in fact acting and altering the relative frequencies of existing alleles/phenotypes. In other words, evolution is indeed occurring. Take a moment to examine Table 4.1; it is easy to see that it would be an extremely rare instance in which all of the Hardy-Weinberg assumptions might hold true, from which we would conclude that evolutionary change is a ubiquitous feature of the organic world in which we live.

variants
individuals within populations having different expressions of a trait

variability
the tendency for members of a population to exhibit different versions of a particular trait

variation
the expression of differences for a characteristic among members of a population

population genetics
a science concerned with variation in gene frequencies within populations and the forces that modify them over time

Hardy-Weinberg (H-W) Equilibrium
a model specifying the conditions under which the frequency of alleles or phenotypes in a natural population remain in equilibrium unless acted on by one or more evolutionary forces

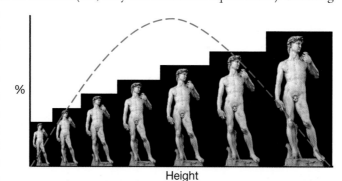

%

Height

FIGURE 4.2 Variability in height reflects the interaction of inheritance and development. Most variants (individuals) are somewhat "average" in height, but some are short and others comparatively tall; collectively, variation in height can be plotted as a normal distribution (bell curve, represented by the dashed line).

© m.bonotto/Shutterstock

TABLE 4.1 A number of assumptions must be met in order for a population to achieve Hardy-Weinberg Equilibrium.

Assumption	Implication
Mutation does not occur	No new alleles are introduced into the population's gene pool
The population is in effect infinitely large	Denies the possibility of random change in allele frequency that might occur when populations are small (genetic drift)
All members of the population have the potential to mate and all mating is random	Denies the possibility of increasing the level of genetic homozygosity through inbreeding
Natural selection is not occurring	All variants are equally favoured; none is more successful (adapted) than another and therefore increasing its representation in the population
Migration does not occur	Individuals neither leave nor enter the population (gene flow), thereby removing or introducing variation

Darwin's "Big Book" (as *The Origin of Species* has come to be known) was filled with examples of variation within and between species, illustrating his principle of natural selection. However, he was unaware of the source of that variation and how it was transmitted from one generation to the next. Our modern understanding of these missing elements took shape in the late 19th century with the "rediscovery" of Gregor Mendel's principles of inheritance by the Dutch botanist Hugo de Vries (1848–1935) and, independently, by the German botanist Carl Correns (1864–1933). While de Vries and Correns explored patterns of inheritance in the tradition of Mendel, credit for situating the "gene"[1] as the locus of variation, and the founding of the science of genetics, belongs to the British biologist William Bateson (1861–1926). Indeed, in the first decades of the 20th century, genetics was a field ripe with innovations and experiments that investigated the mechanisms and products of inheritance, clarifying notions of dominant and recessive traits, heterozygosity, homozygosity, **heterosis**, and mutation. These early geneticists (including Bateson in England, Wilhelm Johannsen in Denmark, and T.H. Morgan in the United States) experimented with organisms that were able to reproduce quickly and that could be managed efficiently in a laboratory environment—plants, algae, and insects.

In the early days of the field of population genetics, there was much disagreement as to whether natural selection acting on population variation was a more important evolutionary force than mutation as the original source of that variation (Mayr 1982). This debate was more or less settled in 1942, when Sir Julian Huxley published his important work *Evolution: The Modern Synthesis*. That book was based on three guiding principles: (1) selection is the paramount force in evolution; (2) evolution entails gradual change over many generations; and (3) evolution occurs within populations. These principles form the core of what many biologists now refer to as neo-Darwinism—the marriage of mutation as the source of variation with natural selection as the mechanism that determines whether a mutation is helpful (i.e., adaptive) or otherwise.

A New Synthesis in the Making?

Darwinism today is a very different theory from that originally proposed in the 19th century. Indeed, Darwinian evolutionary theory as shaped over the past 50 years is considerably different from what Huxley proposed in 1942. For that reason, we find it more appropriate to drop the prefix "neo" and simply refer to modern evolutionary theory as Darwinism. These more recent understandings—regarding, for example, the roles of *non*-Darwinian mechanisms of change (Kimura 1983; discussed later in this chapter), the **epigenetic** origin of novel heritable variation through development (Hall 2012b), and gene function and regulation underlying the emerging field of genomics (Bartel 2009)—have greatly expanded how we view variation within and between species as well as the process of **speciation** itself.

Evolutionary Developmental Biology

In much the same way that Huxley's *Modern Synthesis* combined laboratory genetics with field biology, one of the more significant developments in the past 20 years has been the fusion of evolutionary theory with developmental biology. This merging of evolution with development (known familiarly as evolutionary developmental biology or **evo-devo)** is not a new idea but it has emerged in modern form as a powerful paradigm unifying two fundamental biological realities. On the one hand, we see a fantastic range of variability in living organisms; on the other, we have a highly conserved genome, by which we mean that significant fractions of DNA sequences are shared, more or less unchanged, among these varied life forms. Recall from Chapter 3 that very little DNA (about 1.5%) actually codes for protein production, although recent research suggests as much as 5% of the genome

heterosis

also known as heterozygote advantage; the tendency for offspring of genetically distinct individuals to have increased vigour as they are less likely to express deleterious recessive alleles, which increase in frequency when males and females with similar genetic background mate

epigenetic

mechanisms acting during mitosis (development) to modify gene expression without modifying the actual DNA sequence; may result in heritable variation

speciation

the formation of new species from pre-existing forms

evo-devo

evolutionary developmental biology; a branch of evolutionary theory that invokes a prominent role for embryonic development and epigenetic mechanisms in the ontogeny and phylogeny of phenotypes

---

1. The term "gene" was coined by the Danish geneticist W.L. Johannsen in 1909 as a disambiguation of de Vries' notion of "pangenes."

is "functional" (Lindblad-Toh et al. 2011). Evolutionary developmental biology helps us understand how very small quantities of coding DNA can produce such vast amounts of biological variation.

Considerable amounts of human noncoding DNA are shared by species as diverse as mice, fish, and fruit flies, and are known to be associated with many human diseases. In fact, the same species of fruit fly, *Drosophila melanogaster*, studied by early geneticists such as T.H. Morgan in the effort to shed light on the role of mutation in inheritance, are now being used to comprehend the genetic basis of human illnesses ranging from autism to addiction to sleep disorders (e.g., Yuan et al. 2006). But why is so much of the same DNA found across such a broad range of organisms, and how do we account for the fact that we have such an amazing variety of outcomes? Well, when you think about it, we actually have a lot in common with most flies and fish: we all have a head-end and a tail-end, we all have a bilateral (two-sided) body plan built on the notion of symmetry, we all have light-sensitive organs for perception, and we all have appendages, be they wings, fins, or legs. In short, it makes good evolutionary sense to not continually reinvent a wheel, but rather to tinker with it—turning genes on and off at different intervals during development or increasing or decreasing their activity—to reach different end points (Veraska et al. 2000).

Biologists have long appreciated that phenotypes are "plastic" and are products of the interaction of genes and environment (this kind of **phenotypic plasticity** is a topic explored in depth in Chapter 14). For example, you might be taller than your parents because you enjoyed better nutrition as a child. However your children will not necessarily be taller as a result of your increased stature; they inherit your genes, not your dinner! In evo-devo, a concept called **transgenerational epigenetic inheritance** (Daxinger and Whitelaw 2012) argues that in some circumstances, environmentally mediated development can result in new phenotypes that may be passed on to the next generation.

From Germ Plasm Theory to Epigenetic Inheritance Systems

The notion of transgenerational epigenetic inheritance stands in contradiction to one of the fundamental tenets of Darwinian evolutionary theory—namely, that germ cells (sperm and egg) and somatic (body) cells are independent. Put another way, after fertilization occurs, germ cells produce more germ cells as well as body cells, as the zygote develops into the fetus, the fetus into the infant, and so on. However, body cells only produce more body cells. This principle was set in place over a century ago by the German biologist August Weismann (1834–1914), who in 1893 published his "germ plasm theory." Weismann aimed to debunk Lamarck's notion of the inheritance of acquired characteristics (see Chapter 2) by arguing that only changes (by mutation or recombination) in the sperm and egg were heritable.

We now know that there are a number of ways in which information can be passed from one generation to the next irrespective of changes in DNA base sequences. These have been termed epigenetic inheritance systems (EISs; see Jablonka 2011), of which there are several involving both DNA and RNA. One of the best understood EISs is associated with chromatin markers such as histones and methyl groups—proteins that assist in maintaining chromosome structure and gene expression. Chromatin markers can be established by the cell's environment as well as by external conditions (e.g., nutrition). As such, these markers can vary from one cell to the next, even though the underlying genetic base-pair sequences in all of the cells remain stable and unchanged. In a manner of speaking, differences in chromatin marks form epigenetic phenotypes which, as recent studies in rodents have shown, can be inherited over a number of generations (Whitelaw 2006). The existence of epigenetic inheritance systems can have profound effects, both in the short term (establishing human disease patterns (Rakyan et al. 2011; see Box 4.1) and in an evolutionary context. Again, rodent studies have demonstrated an EIS effect for male fertility (reduced sperm count and motility) following exposure to pesticides—an effect that lasted for several generations (Anway et al. 2005). Similar concerns have been raised regarding recent fertility declines in humans (Perry 2008).

phenotypic plasticity
a potential for individuals to modify their phenotype in response to variation in external conditions in order to maintain homeostasis and function

transgenerational epigenetic inheritance
the transmission of novel phenotypic features from parent to offspring acquired without recourse to modification in DNA base sequences

BOX 4.1   FOCUS ON ... Programming the Fetus

In the 1990s, British researchers noticed a rather unusual geographic distribution of adult male mortality and morbidity for heart disease, hypertension, and diabetes in the United Kingdom (Barker 1998), a pattern that mimicked the pattern for infant mortality. Intrigued, David Barker and his colleagues sought out old medical records to see if they could find a link in the health history of the affected individuals. They were surprised to find that the strongest correlation was with birth weight: full-term babies born with low birth weight were more likely to die in infancy; furthermore, if they survived, they were at increased risk for heart attack, stroke, and impaired glucose metabolism as older adults.

Barker proposed that the fetus was responding to poor maternal nutrition by economizing on the use of nutrients received across the placenta. Development of less important organs (e.g., kidney and pancreas) was in this way compromised to ensure adequate nutrition for essential organs such as the brain. The outcome was, in effect, a program for late-onset chronic diseases, earning Barker's hypothesis the name "fetal programming." Over the years, numerous studies have confirmed and expanded this association in other countries, as well as in women. In a recent review, De Boo and Harding (2006) list seven well-documented diseases related to fetal programming, and almost a dozen others with weaker associations. These include common ailments such as hypertension, coronary heart disease, type II diabetes, and stroke.

Maternal nutrition, and by extension that of the developing fetus, has been identified as the primary impetus to "fetal programming." This was illustrated through a classic "natural experiment" that took place during World War II, known as the Dutch Hunger Winter of 1944–45. The occupying forces of Nazi Germany placed an embargo on food supplies to the western Netherlands, leaving citizens without adequate nutrition. By February 1945 the average energy intake was less than 600 calories per day, and as many as 18,000 people died from malnutrition or related causes by the time the embargo was lifted in May 1945. But the Hunger Winter also left a rich scientific legacy, one that documented the disease epidemiology of starvation over several generations. The resulting *Dutch Famine Birth Cohort Study* documented significant health outcomes in children born to mothers who lived through the Hunger Winter, including greater likelihood of diabetes, adult obesity, and heart disease. Interestingly, an unexpected finding was that children born to these children were also smaller than expected, suggesting a "carry-over" of the effect of starvation from one generation to the next.

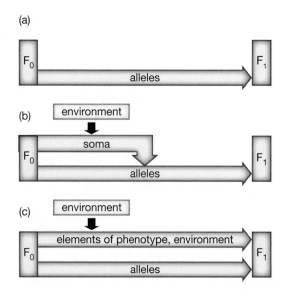

(a)

(b)

(c)

FIGURE 4.3 The modern debate on methods of inheritance incorporates (a) Mendelian notions of DNA transmission from parent (F₀) to offspring (F₁), as well as (b) modification of DNA via environmental effects on the organism (soma; neo-Lamarckian inheritance), and (c) pluralistic models including both genetic (DNA) and epigenetic pathways.

Reprinted from *Trends in Ecology*, Volume 27, Issue 6, Bonduriansky, R., "Rethinking Heredity, Again," 2012 with permission from Elsevier.

Researchers are just now probing the significance of epigenetic inheritance from the perspective of phenotypic plasticity, adaptation, and evolution (Richards et al. 2010). One of the more profound impacts however, is the expansion of the concept of biological inheritance itself, from the narrow (termed "hard") perspective that all inherited characteristics are coded in DNA to a more pluralistic concept embracing both genetic and non-genetic modes of inheritance (Bonduriansky 2012). A major implication of this shift is a re-emergence of Lamarckian (termed "soft") notions of inheritance (Hall 2012a) and the realization that the environment is not just active in shaping phenotypes, but also in creating them (Figure 4.3).

SPECIES NOW AND THEN

Look around your classroom. Whether in a class of 30 or 300, as a human you are a member of a larger collection ("population") of humans exhibiting a richness of genotypic and phenotypic diversity reflecting unique genetic heritages and developmental histories. The same can be said of populations of chimpanzees or honey bees. However, in spite of all of their wonderful variation, humans are humans and chimps are chimps; we are different kinds of creatures. This raises a seemingly simple question: How do we proceed from the smaller events that alter gene frequencies and their developmental expression within populations from one generation to the next (termed microevolution) to achieve the larger-scale changes over many generations that result in the formation of new species (termed macroevolution)?

This is the great challenge of evolutionary biology, and while we understand much more today than did Darwin and his contemporaries, it remains very much an elusive and vexing question for at least three reasons (Searle 1998). First, biologists have had a difficult time agreeing on what is meant by the term "species" (a definitional problem); second, speciation events are notoriously difficult to study (an operational problem); and finally, little is understood about species formation and genetic evolution (a knowledge deficit problem). As a first step in exploring this challenge, we need to address a fundamental question: What is a species, and how do we know one when we see one?

Species and Species Concepts

The idea of "species" as a collection of organisms (**demes** or populations) bound together by a shared morphology, ecology, genome, reproduction, and behaviour is central to fields as diverse as **biogeography**, evolutionary biology, paleontology, classification, and conservation (Hausdorf 2011). Yet which of these shared features takes precedence in the definition of a species has long been debated within biology. Although use of the term has considerable antiquity (see Chapter 2), the most commonly cited definition of "species" in the modern era is attributed to the evolutionary biologist and historian of science Ernst Mayr (1942, 120), who wrote that species are "groups of actually or potentially interbreeding natural populations which are reproductively isolated from other such groups." Known as the biological species concept (BSC), this view hinges on the notion of reproductive isolation, which applies fairly well to wild-living **sympatric** populations but is inappropriately applied to **allopatric** species. For example, it is illogical to invoke the BSC to argue that the common marmoset (*Callithrix jacchus*), a New World monkey native to Brazil, is a species distinct from *Galago moholi*, a form of lesser bushbaby living in southern and eastern Africa. These two allopatric primates are neither "actually or potentially interbreeding" by virtue of nothing less than the Atlantic Ocean! Yet in the case of the sympatric bushbaby species *Galago moholi* and *Galago senegalensis* (Figure 4.4), reproductive isolation becomes a relevant and defining feature, as these species overlap both geographically and ecologically.

The BSC can also be problematic in cases of **parapatric** species, whose ranges abut one another, thus affording the potential for reproduction. The Hamadrayas and Olive baboons are a good example. These distinctive species of Old World monkey are known to interbreed along their shared geographic border. Yet other baboon species, such as the Chacma and Yellow baboon, whose ranges also share a boundary, do not. In fact, interbreeding between closely related species within **hybrid zones** is not uncommon among wild-living primates (Arnold and Meyer 2006) and is known to occur among macaques, gibbons, capuchins, orangutans, and red-tailed and blue monkeys.

Typically, the offspring of interspecific hybrid crosses tend to be sterile or to suffer reduced fertility or survivorship, and thus are effectively reproductively isolated. However, in some situations hybrid individuals may be better adapted to the transitional ecologies that can define hybrid zones, and exhibit higher degrees of reproductive success compared to parental species, as recently shown for male hybrid baboons in Ethiopia (Bergman et al. 2008). Similarly, (Delmore et al. 2010) from the University of Calgary found that hybrid brown lemurs in Madagascar were as fit as parental species.

That such interspecific crosses produce viable offspring suggests a recent evolutionary divergence. Patterson and colleagues (2006) have proposed that our earliest hominin ancestors of c. 6.5 Ma continued to interbreed with members of the emerging chimpanzee lineage for a million years or so *after* the initial divergence of these lineages (see Chapter 9, Box 9.2).

demes
local breeding populations; a deme is a subset of a species within which most members find a mate

biogeography
the study of the geographic distribution of organisms, habitats, and evolutionary history as it relates to landscape and ecology

sympatric
refers to species that coexist in the same geographic region

allopatric
refers to species that "live apart" and do not occupy the same geographic locale; allopatric species are presumed to exist in genetic isolation

parapatric
refers to species whose ranges are contiguous but not overlapping; gene flow is possible

hybrid zones
ecological regions in which closely related species overlap in occurrence, allowing for interbreeding to occur, producing hybrid offspring

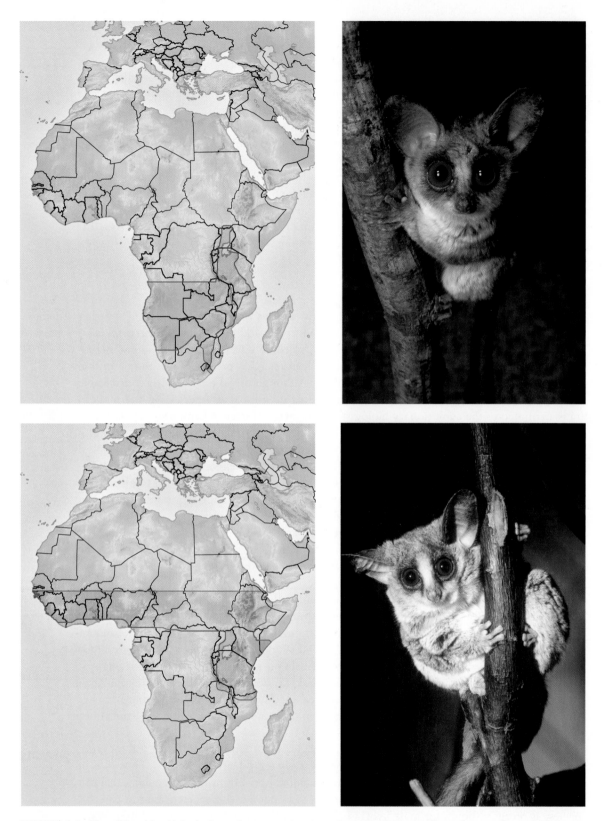

FIGURE 4.4 The utility of the biological species concept rests on the potential for interbreeding to occur, which in turn requires geographic proximity (sympatry). *Galago moholi* (top) and *Galago senegalensis* (bottom) are sympatric species whose ranges overlap in Uganda and Tanzania.

© Oxford Scientific/Getty (top); © Gary Retherford/Photo Researchers, Inc. (bottom)

Indeed, based on genetic evidence from the Y chromosome and mtDNA, Tosi and colleagues (2000) have argued that the stumptail macaque of Southeast Asia is a viable species that arose through a hybridization event involving the toque macaque and the crab-eating macaque during the Pleistocene glaciations.

Are Other Species Concepts More Useful?

If the BSC is problematic in some instances, are there other ways to define "species" that might be more useful? A number of alternatives have been proposed—as many as 24 by some counts (Hey 2001). Groves (2007) characterized the differences among species concepts as either "theoretical" or "operational," depending on whether reproductive isolation or potential for interbreeding is a key feature of the concept.

As you might expect, for reproductive isolation to be maintained between sympatric species, isolating mechanism(s) of some sort must have developed that act either before (pre-) or after (post-) mating (Table 4.2). As noted earlier in the context of hybridization, *post*-mating mechanisms ensure failure of the gamete or developing zygote, the early death of the hybrid if it is indeed born, or infertility if the hybrid manages to survive to adulthood.[2] *Pre*-mating isolating mechanisms are various and tend to prevent individuals of different species from meeting or mating in the first place. These mechanisms may be behavioural (such as different mating rituals, e.g., bird songs) or mechanical (such as differently sized or shaped male and female genitalia), or they may be ecological (such as differences in habitat use, e.g., arboreal versus terrestrial).

Paterson (1985) argued some time ago that "species" are maintained not by post-mating mechanisms but rather by who chooses to mate with whom (pre-mating mechanisms),

TABLE 4.2 Reproductive isolating mechanisms may assume a variety of forms that either prevent current mating or restrict future mating between species.

Type	Acts Through
Pre-Mating: Space	Mating is prohibited by physical barriers such as rivers or by occupation of different zones within habitats (ground vs. tree-dwelling)
Pre-Mating: Time	Mating is prohibited by activity cycles (day vs. night) or seasonality (spring vs. fall mating)
Pre-Mating: Behaviour	Members of different species are unresponsive to mating rituals (e.g., displays) or signals (songs, pheromone)
Pre-Mating: Function	In sexually reproducing species, male and female genitalia are not mechanically suited by virtue of size, shape, or other attributes of form
Post-Mating: Gamete incompatibility	Although mating may occur, the sperm and egg are not biochemically compatible, preventing fertilization
Post-Mating: Inviability	Although mating and fertilization may occur, the organism is not viable and dies during development (as a zygote or fetus) or immediately after birth if carried to term
Post-Mating: Sterility	Hybrid offspring are born but are infertile when mated with like hybrids

2. As noted earlier, hybrids may successfully produce offspring, especially if they mate with one of the parental forms. A liger, for example, results from a cross between a male lion and a female tiger (tigons result from the opposite cross). Female ligers and tigons are fertile when mated with a male lion or tiger, but male ligers and tigons are infertile. Consequently, ligers and tigons remain simply hybrids, not species in their own right.

proposing the **recognition species concept (RSC)**. He suggested that species have evolved in such a way that they know how to identify appropriate potential mates. The RSC posits that members of a species share a Specific Mate Recognition System (SMRS), which may consist of calls, facial or body markings, chemical signals, or movements.[3] An interesting example is the galago, a small nocturnal primate native to Africa (see Figure 4.4). In recent years, a number of new species have been identified by "splitting" previously known forms into separate groups. Galagos are nocturnal animals and in the dark of night rely on vocalizations and odours in order to communicate with **conspecifics** to find appropriate mates. Ambrose (2003) has proposed that three separate species be distinguished within Allen's galago (*Galago alleni*), found in Central Africa, based on a distinctive auditory SMRS used in both contact and alarm situations.

The fact that there are a variety of species concepts points to one very important conclusion: the real world is not as easily sorted out as one would think. As with all classifications, how we group things (i.e., organisms) together depends entirely on those features we define, and emphasize, as important. In some ways the exercise that biologists undertake in describing and identifying species is analogous to how we might organize our kitchen cupboards or clothes closets: features we determine as distinctive about cups and saucers and shirts and dresses factor into how they are grouped together.

What about Species in the Fossil Record?

Of course, concepts such as the BSC and the RSC are not particularly helpful when all we have to examine are patterns of variation rather than the processes that gave rise to and have maintained those patterns (such as reproduction or behaviour; Groves 2007). The fossil record represents the classic situation where we need to distinguish among diverse forms but—save for inventing a time machine—have no recourse to criteria based on concepts such as the BSC or RSC—we can neither observe actual mating nor detect calls or odours. And there are numerous interesting questions that rest on being able to make a reasonable identification of extinct species. We might want to know, for example, how many species of early hominin lived more or less contemporaneously in Africa c. 2 Ma at a time when our own genus, *Homo*, was becoming established. For that matter, how many hominin species were roaming throughout Europe and the Near East only 250,000 years ago? Which in turn summons this broader question: Who—or what—were the Neandertals (Weaver et al. 2007)? And how can we know, when we study the beginning of this human voyage of ours, which dates back some 6 million years, whether we are looking at a human ancestor or an ancestor of the chimpanzees?

Essentially, the task is one of dividing the fossil record into meaningful segments. To that end, we have two dimensions with which to work—morphology and time (Wood and Lonergan 2008). Morphological species (**morphospecies**) are defined on the principle that if fossil forms appear sufficiently different in shape or appearance, they qualify as different species, irrespective of time. Clearly, cows are not horses and chickens are not eagles. While the idea of morphological species might seem self-evident and simplistic, it is likely the oldest of all ways to differentiate one species from another. No doubt our recent ancestors found being able to distinguish cows from horses quite handy!

On a more serious note, were Neandertals different enough from us in appearance to qualify as a species distinct from us? Should we designate them *Homo neanderthalensis* rather than *Homo sapiens* (see Chapter 11)? Basically, we are asking whether fossil phenotypes are clearly distinguishable. Do they have features that set them apart from other fossil forms? Do they produce clusters of supposedly related kinds? The crux of the morphospecies concept is this: What constitutes "sufficiently different" (Figure 4.5)? A wide variety of sophisticated statistical methods have been brought to bear on this issue; generally, these aim to identify the "smallest cluster of individual organisms that is 'diagnosable' on the basis of the preserved morphology" (Wood and Lonergan 2008, 366).

---

3. Some scholars have argued that the RSC is really an operational variant of the BSC (see Holliday 2003) and can be subsumed within that species concept.

The notion of **chronospecies** relies instead on a temporal framework to distinguish one species from another. Thus, if two fossils are separated by a significant passage of time—which may include an apparent gap during which they do not overlap—they are often considered distinct species. This approach may be used in conjunction with the morphospecies concept if one of the fossil forms possesses one or more characteristics not evident in the other.

How Do New Species Evolve?

Although evolutionary biologists might disagree over definitions, they do not dispute that species exist. This implies that one or more processes exist through which one kind of organism gives rise to another over time. We often ponder the **tempo and mode of evolution:** At what rate does it proceed? What pattern of diversity arises from it? These questions can be asked only with regard to the fossil record, because no one can predict the rate or pattern of future evolution.

As we have seen, Darwin and Wallace proposed natural selection as the principal force driving organismic evolution with a tempo of slow, gradual change—a mode of evolution termed **anagenesis** (also known as Darwinian gradualism, or **phyletic evolution**). New adaptive variants appearing through mutation and recombination, for example, confer greater reproductive fitness in the "struggle for life." Individuals carrying these traits would leave greater numbers of offspring, so the traits would appear more frequently in subsequent generations. Those traits that reduced fitness would be selected against, their bearers reproducing less or not at all. Given sufficient time, the entire species would eventually express the new phenotype of adaptive characteristics, and the previous form would disappear, effectively becoming an extinct ancestor.

Speciation might also occur through a mode of evolution known as **cladogenesis** (also known as branching evolution). In paleontology, cladogenesis is characterized by a splitting event whereby an evolving lineage divides to form two distinct **clades**, or separate lineages (Figure 4.6). Unlike the case in anagenesis, there is no presumption of rate of change for cladogenesis, although it is often associated with a theory known as **punctuated equilibrium** (or PE for short; Eldridge and Gould 1972). The defining features of PE are long periods of phenotypic stasis in which little or no change occurs, followed by a comparatively rapid "burst" of significant morphological evolution. For this reason, PE is often referred to as "horizontal evolution," for it seems as if the new clade has materialized out of nowhere. This sudden appearance is an artifact of paleontological time scales, which tend to be quite coarse "in the ground."

Indeed, distinguishing between anagenesis and cladogenesis very much relies on the degree of resolution of the fossil record—that is, how many fossil sites are known, what time frame is covered, how complete and well-preserved are the fossils themselves, and how reliable are the

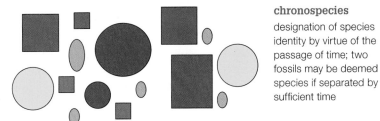

FIGURE 4.5 In paleontology, fossils are assigned to a morphospecies on the basis of a shared morphology that distinguishes them from other such groups. How many morphospecies are represented by this collection of "fossils"? Would the number change if you used only colour (or only shape) to make your decision?

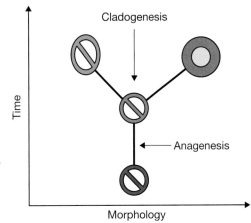

FIGURE 4.6 The linear model of phyletic gradualism (anagenesis) differs from the branching model of punctuated equilibrium (cladogenesis). The latter is defined by periods of relatively little change, with short bursts of relatively rapid change as new clades arise through a splitting of the previous lineage.

chronospecies

designation of species identity by virtue of the passage of time; two fossils may be deemed species if separated by sufficient time

tempo and mode of evolution

refers to the pace and manner of evolutionary change

anagenesis

a pattern of slow, linear evolutionary change, also known as Darwinian gradualism

phyletic evolution

an alternative term for anagenesis, with "phyletic" denoting a line of direct ancestor–descendant relationship

cladogenesis

a pattern of evolution characterized by branching, in which a single species may give rise to one (or more) "daughter" species that subsequently diverge; also known as horizontal speciation

clades

groups of species sharing a closer ancestry among themselves than any of them do with species of other clades

punctuated equilibrium

a pattern of evolution characterized by periods of stasis interrupted by rapid evolutionary change; more commonly found in small, peripheral populations on the edge of a species range

associated dates? Consider, for example, that in 1859 when Darwin published *On the Origin of Species*, a total of 56 fossil dinosaur localities were known; today that number exceeds 9,000 (Hunt 2010). As expressed by Eldridge and Gould, speciation by way of PE will most likely occur near the periphery of a species' geographic range, which is often a zone of ecological transition occupied by smaller demes, one that offers unique evolutionary opportunities.

MECHANISMS OF EVOLUTION

Whether one is speaking of microevolution or macroevolution, the question at hand is how the frequency with which a given phenotype is present in a population changes from one generation to the next. In the traditional view of Darwinism, this change is considered an outcome of natural selection. However, as we noted earlier, there are other, non-Darwinian[4] mechanisms that can exert profound changes on the incidence of different phenotypes, often over relatively short periods of time. These mechanisms act at the level of either the population (**gene flow**, **genetic drift**, and founder effect**)** or the individual (the epigenetic inheritance systems noted earlier in this chapter). In the following section we look at the different ways in which natural selection acts on population variation, and then turn our attention to non-Darwinian factors.

How Does Selection Operate to Produce Adaptation?

Adaptation may refer to a thing (e.g., the hominin pelvis is an adaptation for bipedal locomotion), a process (e.g., people adapt to increased exposure to sunlight by tanning), or a state of being (e.g., animals with stockier bodies are better adapted to conserve heat in cold environments). Natural selection is often understood as a "sorting" mechanism through which adaptive features useful for survival are favoured and less adaptive traits are found wanting. There are, in fact, several distinct patterns through which natural selection can affect trait frequencies: directional, stabilizing, and diversifying selection (Figure 4.7).

Under **directional selection**, one expression of a phenotypic character is favoured at the expense of all other forms—a pattern commonly observed in living populations. Over relatively short periods of time, directional selection can shift trait frequencies within a species, thus acting as an agent of microevolution. The peppered moth's transition from a light to a dark variety in 19th-century England (see Chapter 3) is an example of directional selection. In humans, the recent evolution of **lactase persistence** in European and African populations at some point in the past 8,000 years is an excellent example of directional selection. Lactase is an enzyme that humans require in order to convert the milk sugar lactose, a disaccharide, into two more readily digestible monosaccharides ("simple sugars"), glucose and galactose. In many populations, the

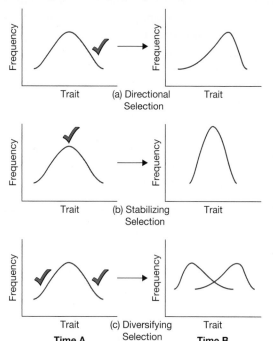

FIGURE 4.7 Over many generations, natural selection favouring some phenotypes over others (denoted by a check mark) may act to (a) shift the average phenotypic expression of a character toward a new average (directional selection), (b) increase the frequency of an already favoured phenotype at the expense of less common expressions (stabilizing selection), or (c) act against the more common expressions to favour the less typical variants (diversifying selection).

gene flow

the movement of genes with or without the movement of individuals over geographic space

genetic drift

random changes in allele frequencies in small populations, independent of selection

directional selection

a form of positive or negative selection resulting in a shift in phenotypes toward one end of the distribution, typically occurring in dynamic and changing environments

lactase persistence

in humans, the continued production past childhood of the enzyme lactase necessary for digesting the milk sugar lactose

---

4. Although designated as non-Darwinian, forces such as gene flow and genetic drift are not inconsistent with Darwinism; rather, they should be viewed as extensions or elaborations of the theory.

body loses its ability to produce lactase in early childhood (see Chapter 14). However, some human groups have evolved single nucleotide polymorphisms (SNPs) within the gene coding for the lactase enzyme, allowing for continued production of lactase into adulthood (Tishkoff et al. 2007). Notably, these populations have a cultural history of cattle herding and dairy consumption, which would have exerted positive directional selection favouring the lactase-persistent SNP.

Recent ancient DNA analysis of European Neolithic peoples indicates that the SNP associated with this geographic population, labelled T/C 13910, appeared sometime *after* the adoption of dairy farming in southern Europe, c. 8,800 years ago (Leonardi et al. 2012). This suggests that while cattle may have been herded by these early European Neolithic farmers, fresh milk was likely not a major part of their diet until after they had acquired the T/C 13910 mutation. This example also reminds us that, when it comes to looking at humans as exemplars of evolutionary processes, one needs to be cognizant of the role that culture (in this case, dairy farming) plays in shaping selective forces. This is a very important point that you should bear in mind; as we emphasize throughout this text, humans are very much a biocultural species.

Natural selection can also act to stabilize variation within a population under conditions where the average phenotype has an adaptive advantage relative to more extreme expressions of a character. Or it can disrupt one distribution of phenotypes so that two distinct distributions result. Each of these cases—**stabilizing selection** and **diversifying selection**—has particular microevolutionary and macroevolutionary implications.

An interesting example of the former is the idea that human populations have evolved a pattern of stabilized fertility around an average value below the maximum possible (Kaplan 1996). The argument here is that maximizing fertility over a woman's reproductive life span is likely to reduce survivorship for any given child, given finite access to resources. Thus, limiting the number of children per family is adaptive. Theoretically, this strategy balances the cost of raising children against their individual chances of surviving as the number of "mouths to feed" increases. However, humans are complicated biocultural creatures, and Kaplan (1996) reported that while the most common number of children in her sample was indeed stable around a relatively low level of two per family, maximum reproductive fitness as measured by the number of grandchildren was actually realized by those families having the most children (Figure 4.8). The outcome of maximizing fertility was a reduction in standard of living within the larger families; in other words, the cost was a cultural (economic) one, not necessarily a biological (survivorship) one.

Diversifying selection describes a process whereby less common variants within a population are favoured at the expense of the more frequent average phenotype. This form of natural selection has been implicated most famously in the **adaptive radiation** of "Darwin's finches" of the Galapagos Islands (Grant and Grant 2011). The 15 different finch species differ primarily in terms of beak size and shape; this reflects diversifying selection acting on an original population[5] driven by dietary adaptation to exploit different food resources defined by seed size and hardness. Abzhanov and colleagues (2004)

stabilizing selection
a form of selection favouring the most common phenotype at the expense of extreme expressions of a character

diversifying selection
a form of positive selection favouring the extremes of the distribution of phenotypes and/ or negative selection against the most common expression; may result in sympatric speciation

adaptive radiation
the opportunistic and relatively rapid diversification of new forms into new ecological zones through a series of speciation events

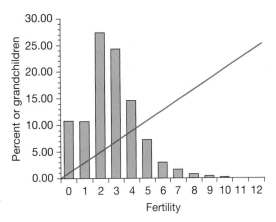

FIGURE 4.8 Reproductive fitness as measured by number of grandchildren (solid line) increases with size of family, although most families stabilize fertility around a lower value to avoid economic hardship.

From H. Kaplan (1996). A theory of fertility and parental investment in traditional and modern human societies. *American Journal of Physical Anthropology* 101 (S23): 91–135. Reprinted by permission of John Wiley and Sons.

5. Using mtDNA analysis, Sato and colleagues (2001) identified a putative ancestral species, the dull-coloured grassquit (*Tiaris obscura*), now found in Ecuador. *T. obscura* likely arrived on the Galapagos Archipelago and nearby Cocos Island about 2.3 Ma. It is certain that Darwin's finches on the Galapagos Islands are all descended from a single common ancestor, for there is greater similarity among them than exists between any of these and their continental relatives.

model organism

an extensively studied and well-understood species from which new insights into human biology and disease might be obtained; examples range from bacteria such as *E. coli* to mammals such as mice

constraint

genetic or functional limitation on the activity or expression of a characteristic

adaptationist

a perspective that commonly seeks an adaptive explanation or mechanism for the presence or form of a particular phenotypic character

biological reductionism

a method of analysis that argues that biological complexity can be explained in terms of physical laws applied to individual parts

argued that selection may have acted on developmental timing rather than beak structure per se (i.e., by modifying epigenetic pathways). Using the **model organism** *Gallus gallus* (the domestic chicken) they showed that differences in the expression of *Bmp 4* genes (coding for bone morphogenetic protein 4) could produce a range of different beak types. Interestingly, variation in beak shape within finches has been shown to affect song production (Huber and Podos 2006), which further suggests that diversification within finches may have been promoted by pre-mating isolation consistent with the recognition species concept discussed earlier.

It must be remembered that individuals are complex amalgamations of a great many phenotypic characteristics (morphological, physiological, and developmental). This raises the important issue of **constraint**, which limits selection to achieving solutions that work, as opposed to something that might be theoretically optimal. Indeed, all adaptations should be viewed as compromises—as subtle adjustments constrained by a need to retain function in related features. This raises one last important consideration: not every feature of an organism may, in fact, be an adaptation per se. Many years ago, Harvard University biologists Stephen J. Gould and Richard Lewontin (1979) argued against the **adaptationist** approach of dissecting an organism into its constituent parts—a practice known as **biological reductionism**—in order to discover a particular feature's singular contribution to fitness. Some features, they argued, may simply exist in their current form as a result of selection acting on a related attribute or as a consequence of changes in body size. The important thing to remember here is that an organism *is* greater than the sum of its parts, and a complete appreciation of its evolutionary and developmental history requires a more holistic perspective.

Beyond Natural Selection

Whenever we hear of significant political or natural upheavals (such as terrorist attacks, earthquakes, flu pandemics, and the like), we are reminded that our success or failure in the evolutionary enterprise is often determined by random events quite unrelated to the adaptive value of our unique phenotype. Sometimes we are just in the wrong (or right) place at the wrong (or right) time. Alternatively, commitment to a chosen career, a desire to explore new economic opportunities, or simply a desire to travel the world may take us hundreds or thousands of kilometres from our birthplace. As a result we transfer our particular version of the human genome from a deme with which we share many features in common to one with which we do not. Or consider the possibility that we choose to run away to a beautiful desert island with a few dozen like-minded individuals, start a cult, and eschew any contact with the world we have left behind. Most likely our little group will have brought along only a portion of the genetic variation of our former (larger) gene pool, in which case any changes (mutations) that occur within our new gene pool could have a larger impact owing to its smaller size. Each of these scenarios constitutes a force of evolution, but none were anticipated by Darwin nor do they necessarily invoke the operation of natural selection. All have had a significant impact in shaping the geographic diversity of humankind.

Gene Flow

"Gene flow" refers to the transfer of genes from one geographic location to another, but it is important to note that gene flow does not necessarily imply that an individual has moved—only his or her genes. Such exchanges of genetic information occur quite often where adjacent demes share a border; when mating crosses that border, so do alleles. That being said, we do tend to think of gene flow as the movement of individuals from place to place. When someone moves into or leaves a population, the relative proportion of alleles for any given gene necessarily changes (albeit very slightly; Figure 4.9); however, when wholesale migrations occur, the impact can be quite profound. Human history abounds with mass migrations of peoples, often through acts of force—the term "diaspora" may be familiar to you. In recent history, globalization and increasing disparities of wealth and opportunity among social classes within and between developed and developing nations have resulted in a significant increase in the movement of people. Even within countries, rural to urban migration (or vice versa) is commonplace as people look to improve their quality of life.

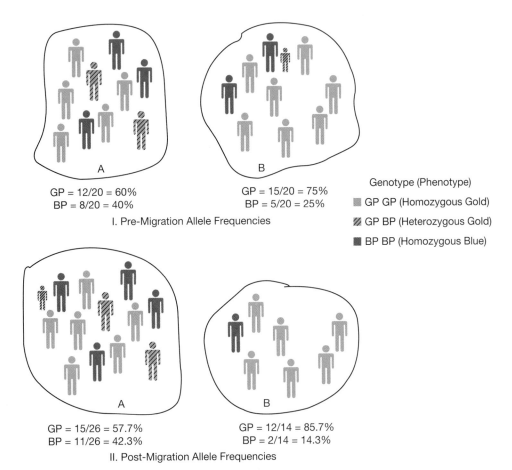

GP = 12/20 = 60%
BP = 8/20 = 40%

GP = 15/20 = 75%
BP = 5/20 = 25%

I. Pre-Migration Allele Frequencies

Genotype (Phenotype)
■ GP GP (Homozygous Gold)
▨ GP BP (Heterozygous Gold)
■ BP BP (Homozygous Blue)

GP = 15/26 = 57.7%
BP = 11/26 = 42.3%

GP = 12/14 = 85.7%
BP = 2/14 = 14.3%

II. Post-Migration Allele Frequencies

FIGURE 4.9 Gene flow alters the relative frequencies of alleles in a population. Imagine two populations having dominant (GP) and recessive (BP) alleles determining body colour. Note the impact on relative allele frequencies of migration of a family of three individuals from population B to population A.

Canada is a nation defined by over five centuries of immigration (Figure 4.10).[6] Today, people from other nations are arriving—along with their genes—as visitors, students, temporary workers, immigrants, refugees, asylum seekers, or adoptees. As of 2011, more than 1,000,000 people from around the world were awaiting approval to immigrate to Canada; in 2010, over 208,000 new immigrants arrived as permanent residents, almost 50% of whom were native to the Asia–Pacific region (Citizenship and Immigration Canada 2011), and have settled in major urban centres such as Vancouver, Calgary, Toronto, and Montreal.

The impact of such significant levels of gene flow will likely not be known for some time, perhaps several generations. Theoretically, an influx of new genetic variation is considered a good thing, conforming to a concept best known from plant studies as heterosis, or heterozygote advantage. Heterosis is the opposite of **inbreeding depression**, which argues that continued reproduction among closely related individuals leads to greater homozygosity (see Chapter 3) and an increased likelihood that harmful recessive traits will appear more frequently in the phenotype, with detrimental effects on health and survival.

Heterozygote advantage proposes just the opposite: mating among individuals with different genetic backgrounds increases heterozygosity and reduces the expression of harmful recessive characteristics. In humans, a classic example of heterosis relates to sickle cell polymorphism and malaria resistance. In regions of the world where malaria caused by the parasite *Plasmodium falciparum* is endemic, a heterozygote person carrying both the dominant normal ("HbA") and recessive sickle cell ("Hbs") hemoglobin alleles (genotypically "HbAHbs") has

inbreeding depression
reduced vigour in an organism by virtue of increased homozygosity resulting from mating between related individuals having similar DNA

6. Of course, the original immigrants to Canada were the ancestors of today's living Native peoples.

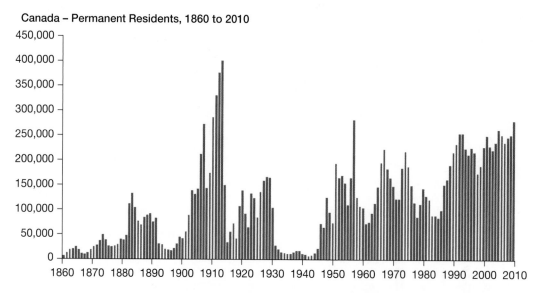

Canada – Permanent Residents, 1860 to 2010

FIGURE 4.10 Immigration has always been a major source of population growth in Canada. Declines are associated with major political and economic events, such as the World Wars I and II, the Great Depression, and changes to law (e.g., the Immigration Act).

Canada Facts and Figures: Immigration Overview Permanent and Temporary Residents 2010, Citizenship and Immigration Canada, 2011. Reproduced with the permission of the Minister of Public Works and Government Services Canada, 2013.

a fitness advantage over homozygous HbAHbA *and* HbsHbs individuals (discussed further in Chapter 14). Heterozygote advantage also accounts for patterns of variation for cystic fibrosis, or CF. CF is a genetic disorder that impairs the mucous glands of several organs and is the most common lethal single-gene disorder in European-derived populations; the incidence of CF in Canada today is approximately 1 in 3,600 live births. CF is much less frequent—indeed, sometimes unknown—in other groups.

Heterozygous carriers of the recessive allele were thought to have increased resistance to cholera and typhoid fever, although recent research combining genetic, clinical, and historical-geographic evidence now points to tuberculosis as the selective agent (Poolman and Galvani 2007). Individuals with the recessive CF allele[7] have reduced capacity to produce an enzyme, arylsulphatase B, that the TB bacterium requires in a host in order to produce its own cellular walls. Recently, Lubinsky (2012) extended this model of the geographic distribution of CF carriers to include interactions of TB with hypertension, vitamin D deficiency, latitude, and temperature. The maintenance of deleterious recessive alleles in a population as a result of heterosis is termed **balanced polymorphism**.

Founder Effect and Genetic Drift

Earlier we mentioned that the 15 species of Darwin's finches on the Galapagos Islands most likely originated from a single finch species arriving from Central or South America. As a subset of their original deme, this founding group of birds would have brought with them a limited sample of the genetic diversity present in the continental population, which explains why Darwin's finches are more similar to one another than any one of them is to the parent population. The reduction in genetic diversity and resulting phenotypic similarity associated with such events is known as founder effect (Figure 4.11) and has been well documented in human populations as a result of a long history of migration (Cavalli-Sforza 1997). For example, the complete absence of blood types A and B among the indigenous peoples of Central and South America suggests that the founding colonizers of those populations migrated from Asia carrying only the allele for blood type O.

balanced polymorphism

polymorphism means "many types" and in genetic terms denotes phenotypes established at proportions that do not require mutation to maintain their existence. Balanced polymorphism occurs when a heterozygote has a selective advantage over alternative homozygotes, thereby maintaining allele diversity within the population

---

7. Of the 1,400 identified mutations resulting in cystic fibrosis, the most common is ΔF508, estimated to be 600 generations old, which closely approximates the time frame for global endemicity for *Mycobacterium tuberculosis*.

Many founder effects of which we are aware concern pathological conditions of diverse origin, as these are the kinds of outcomes that are noticeable in society (e.g., **polydactyly** among the Amish) or otherwise of medical—and anthropological—interest (e.g., **Tay-Sachs** disease among Québécois). A study by the University of British Columbia's Genetic Pathology Evaluation Lab (Kaurah et al. 2007) investigated whether a disease known as hereditary diffuse gastric cancer (HDGC) occurred due to common ancestry or independent mutation. Their study found that in 15 of 38 families with a history of HDGC, four of them—all from the southeast coast of Newfoundland—had a novel mutation and a common haplotype, suggesting a founder effect.

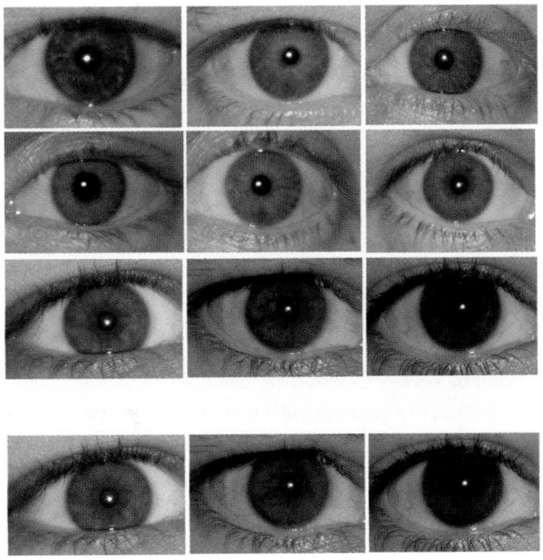

An unfortunate sidebar to this story is that, until recently (Seevaratnam et al. 2011), **genetic screening** was not very effective at identifying whether an individual carried the CDH1 gene responsible for the disease—in the Kaurah et al. (2007) study the detection rate was only 40%. Even within families that have experienced two cases of hereditary diffuse gastric cancer, it is unlikely that a family member will be diagnosed before age 50, while the disease can appear as early as the second decade of life. As a result, as-yet-undiagnosed members of families having a history of HDGC have chosen radical prophylactic gastrectomy (surgical removal of the stomach) as a preferred alternative to the possibility of developing gastric cancer.

Assuming no additional migration, increases in genetic variation within a founding population are the result of mutation. These mutations may achieve polymorphic frequencies (i.e., constitute at least 1% of all alleles for a gene) through one of two processes. One is positive natural selection, as we suspect occurred with regard to finch beak morphology. The other is through random fluctuations in allele frequency from one generation to the next. Kimura (1983) argued that most mutations are selectively neutral and are neither an advantage nor a disadvantage with respect to the bearer's fitness. The significant redundancy found in the genome supports this argument. Many single nucleotide polymorphisms code for the same amino acid in the production of proteins and thus are inconsequential. For example, the DNA sequences GAA and GAG both specify the amino acid known as glutamic acid; thus, a mutation in the third position from A to G (or G to A) has no impact—that is, it is selectively neutral. This leads us to ask: In the absence of either positive or negative selection, which we know can increase or decrease allele frequencies, how do selectively neutral mutations spread through a population?

In Kimura's model, a process known as genetic drift plays a prominent role in shaping human genetic diversity. "Drift" refers to the probability that gene frequencies will change from one generation to the next simply as a matter of chance. There are numerous factors—in humans, many of them cultural, as we have already seen in the case of the *filles du roy*—that conspire to bring potential mates together. The classic Mendelian heterozygote cross, with its hypothetical genotype frequencies (calculable in a Punnett square; see Chapter 3), is exactly that—hypothetical. The expected "AA—Aa—Aa—aa" outcome for a single-gene, two-allele trait might occur on average, but not with certainty. While less likely, two heterozygous parents could produce all aa, all AA, or all Aa children, strictly by chance. In large populations, such random deviations from expectations tend to have a negligible effect—the gene

FIGURE 4.11 Founding populations typically under-represent the degree of genetic diversity present in the parent population. In this example, in the bottom panel only three variants of iris pigmentation form the founder population.

Reprinted from *Trends in Genetics* 20 (8), Richard A. Sturm and Tony N. Frudakis, "Eye color: Portals into pigmentation genes and ancestry," copyright 2004, with permission from Elsevier Ltd.

polydactyly
a congenital condition in which an individual has more than five fingers or toes on hands or feet; one side or both may be affected

Tay-Sachs
a genetic disease affecting neurological development caused by a mutation on chromosome 15; the most common form occurs in infancy and early childhood and is fatal within the first five years of life

genetic screening
a practice in medical genetics involving identification of potentially harmful genotypes

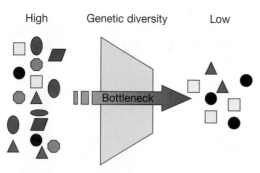

High   Genetic diversity   Low

Bottleneck

FIGURE 4.12 Genetic bottlenecks restrict the transfer of alleles, with the result that the population following the event has much less genetic diversity.

genetic bottleneck

a sudden constriction on the genetic diversity appearing in a generation, commonly associated with a reduction in population size

pool is simply too large. In small populations, random events can have greater impact. This is especially true when generation time is short and genetic diversity is low; in which case, a novel mutation can quite easily become established at polymorphic levels, or reach "fixation" (meaning that all members of the population will eventually have it).

A phenomenon combining features of both founder effect and genetic drift is known as a **genetic bottleneck** (Figure 4.12). Bottlenecks occur much as they sound: through relatively sudden constrictions on the transfer of genetic diversity from one generation to the next. Such occurrences are commonly associated with a rapid reduction in population size through increased mortality. Natural disasters, political unrest, and particularly virulent diseases are well-known causes. Recent human history is full of examples of all of these, and the differential impact of such agents within and between populations along lines of class, race, and gender is a critical element in understanding the impact of these "constricting" events (see Chapters 14 and 15). For example, Herring and Sattenspiel (2007) note that, while the Spanish influenza pandemic of 1918–19 killed at least 50,000,000 people worldwide, the geopolitical distribution of death was very uneven. In Canada as a whole, flu mortality was estimated at 0.6%, but it reached 3% for Aboriginal populations nationally, 18% among the Aboriginal population in the northern Manitoba community of Norway House, and as high as 70% in two Labrador Inuit communities. This variation in mortality reflects numerous underlying social factors, the presence of coexisting diseases (e.g., tuberculosis), and access to resources such as health care and adequate nutrition. The outcome of a bottleneck event is the loss of genetic diversity, and in this regard it mimics a founder effect. If the event also involves a significant reduction in population size, there is potential for drift to affect future genetic variance.

Is Macroevolution Simply the Sum of Microevolution?

It seems logical that we should link the small changes occurring within a population from one generation to the next with the much larger changes over protracted periods of time that result in speciation. That is, macroevolution is the sum of microevolution (or, conversely, accumulated microevolutionary change produces macroevolution). Certainly, genetic and epigenetic mechanisms exist that in theory might ultimately lead to isolation and species differentiation. However, two caveats stand in the way of this overly simplistic notion. The first is that microevolutionary (Darwinian or non-Darwinian) adjustment of allele frequencies, developmental pathways, or phenotypes is not predictive of future macroevolutionary events. There is no rule in evolutionary theory that says X amount of microevolution equals a new species! It is therefore erroneous to presume that microevolution inexorably leads to macroevolution.

Our second caveat is that the ultimate test of macroevolution in wild-living populations is the existence of pre- or post-mating reproductive isolation, which may be effected with little or no microevolutionary (genetic or epigenetic) alteration. A classic example is that of the common chimpanzee (*Pan troglodytes*) and its nearest relative, the bonobos *(Pan paniscus)*. Bonobos are thought to have become *geographically* isolated as a small founding population south of the Congo River (Myers Thompson 2003) about 1 Ma (Hey 2009). Apes as a rule avoid water, and rivers are known to impede gene flow in bonobos and chimpanzees (Eriksson et al. 2004). Although considered separate species and having interesting morphological and behavioural differences, genomic analysis (Fischer et al. 2011) shows that chimpanzees and bonobos differ very little genetically. Moreover, the range of genetic variation within chimpanzees and bonobos collectively overlaps that seen in humans, who are, of course, a single species with even greater behavioural and morphological differences than occurs in *Pan*. In other words, the species distinction between chimpanzees and bonobos is based on geographic rather than biological events.

WRESTLING WITH DIVERSITY

In Chapter 2, you learned that 18th-century Swedish botanist Carolus Linnaeus devised the first modern system for cataloguing and naming plants and animals. Classification is an essential aspect of biology, and no doubt also an essential element of the human psyche, bringing at least a semblance of order to what would otherwise appear as a chaotic assortment of living things. In the absence of classification, making comparisons among these "living things" would be at most an amusing pastime and little if anything could be said of their evolutionary relationships (phylogeny). Since Linnaeus, biological systematics has become a science in its own right; taxonomies and classifications are not created willy-nilly, but follow a particular methodology as set out under the auspices of the International Commission on Zoological Nomenclature (ICZN), including specification as to the spellings of Latin and Greek terms. Systematics also provides the basis from which hypotheses regarding evolutionary relationships among organisms can be proposed and tested.

As a group, primates have been a particularly vexatious and fascinating project for systematists, owing in part to the complicated biogeographic and evolutionary history of this group (see Chapters 5 and 7). In no small measure, the fact that humans are one of the Primate Order's more prominent and problematical members has also created some concern, although not so much with our placement in the grand scheme of things as with public acceptance of the fact of that placement. Stating that we are related to animals such as chimpanzees or bushbabies has not set well with some factions of human society since Darwin first asserted that claim (Browne 2001). As we explore in the following chapters of *A Human Voyage*, there are many reasons not just to embrace this reality but to celebrate it! But before we follow that current, it will be useful to develop a classificatory framework through which we can trace and talk about our family ties.

The Name Game

Organisms are formally identified according to genus and species, two of the four levels of relatedness developed by Linnaeus (the others being class and order). Modern Linnaean taxonomy recognizes seven major ranks (Table 4.3), and within these are "higher" and "lower" divisions (identified by the prefixes "super," "sub," or "infra," respectively). For example, between the major taxonomic ranks of order and family, one can identify the descending arrangement of suborder, infraorder, and superfamily. Such intermediary levels reflect the existence of features (biological, ecological, geographic, and/or phylogenetic) shared by taxa such that they can be "nested" into meaningful ranks within the larger framework. For example, the infraorder distinction for New versus Old World monkeys recognizes a unique evolutionary history as well as their significant separation.

The classification adopted in this text follows what is known as a **cladistic** approach, which emphasizes shared evolutionary (genetic) history, rather than a **gradistic** model, which focuses on morphological (anatomical) or ecological similarities. This view has implications for how we classify and name members of the Order Primates (see Chapter 8, Box 8.1). The related concepts of *clade* and *grade* are important to distinguish, as they factor into discussions not only of living primate diversity, but also of our evolutionary history (Wood and Lonergan 2008; see Chapter 9). While grade-level taxonomies provide meaningful heuristic models for discussing major events in primate evolution,[8] they are in the end categories whose descriptive boundaries find transitional forms such as the Southeast Asian tarsier (see Chapter 7) difficult to accommodate. A cladistic taxonomy, on the other hand, takes into account degrees of

cladistic
a taxonomic method emphasizing phylogenetic relatedness and based on the existence of *clades* composed of members of evolving lineages

gradistic
a taxonomic method that groups forms into named categories (the major units of which are termed "grades") based on similarity of form, behaviour, and/or ecology; also known as phenetics

---

8. Examples of such events discussed in subsequent chapters include the transition from prosimians to anthropoids (Chapter 7) and the development of very large back teeth in late Pliocene hominin evolution (Chapter 9).

TABLE 4.3 Classification of *Homo sapiens*

Kingdom	Animalia	Do not make their own food, but depend on intake of living food
Phylum	Chordata	Have at some stage gill slits as well as notochord (a rodlike structure of cartilage) and nerve chord running along the back of the body
Subphylum*	Vertebrata	Notochord replaced by vertebral column ("backbone") to form internal skeleton along with skull, ribs, and limb bones
Class	Mammalia	Maintain constant body temperature; young nourished after birth by milk from mother's mammary glands
Order	Primates	Hands and feet capable of grasping; tendency to erect posture; acute development of vision rather than sense of smell; tendency to large brain relative to body size
Superfamily	Hominoidea	Rigid bodies, broad shoulders, and long arms; ability to hang vertically from arms; no tail
Family	Hominidae	As above, but 98% identical at genetic level
Subfamily	Homininae	Ground-dwelling with bipedal locomotion
Genus	*Homo*	Large brain; reliance on cultural as opposed to biological adaption
Species	*sapiens*	Brains of modern size; relatively small face

*Most categories can be expanded or narrowed by adding the prefix "sub" or "super." A family could thus be part of a superfamily and in turn contain two or more subfamilies.

From Haviland. *Human Evolution and Prehistory*, 6E. © 2003 Wadsworth, a part of Cengage Learning, Inc. Reproduced by permission. www.cengage.com/permissions.

biological (evolutionary) relatedness, assessed by field observation, morphology, and analyses of molecular and DNA data.

Morphological and/or genetic traits that are shared by many related taxa reflect a deep evolutionary history. These "shared primitive" characters can be contrasted with features that have only recently evolved (called "shared derived" characters); the latter are shared by only a few closely related forms and do not extend deep into the taxonomic hierarchy. An analysis of shared primitive and derived variation results in a structure called a **cladogram** (Figure 4.13), a branching "tree" that groups forms together based on the closeness of their shared evolutionary history (Pilbeam and Young 2004; Wood and Lonergan 2008).

In examining characters held in common by different taxa, it is necessary to consider whether this similarity is due to descent or to independent evolution. Traits that exist in two (or more) groups by virtue of inheritance from a common ancestor are called **homologous traits**; those that reflect independent evolutionary histories are termed analogous traits (or more formally, **homoplasies**), and would not be found in the most recent common ancestor of those taxa. The skeletal structure of the primate arm and the pectoral fin of a whale is an oft-cited example of homology, as both derive from a (distant) mammalian ancestor (Figure 4.14a). Similarly, an often-cited example of homoplasy are the analogous wings of flying insects, birds, and bats (Figure 4.14b).

cladogram

a branching depiction of relationships among taxa based on proximity of evolutionary descent

homologous traits

referring to homology, which is similarity among characters as a result of inheritance from a common ancestor

homoplasies

analogous characters in different taxa that appear as a result of independent evolution; such a character (the singular form is "homoplasy") is not present in the last common ancestor of the taxa in question

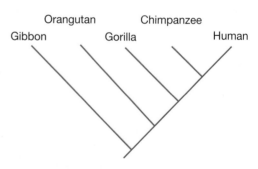

FIGURE 4.13 This cladogram, based on recent genetic analyses, shows that the human clade and chimpanzee clade are most closely related, with the gorilla clade somewhat more distant, followed by the Asian apes: orangutans and gibbons.

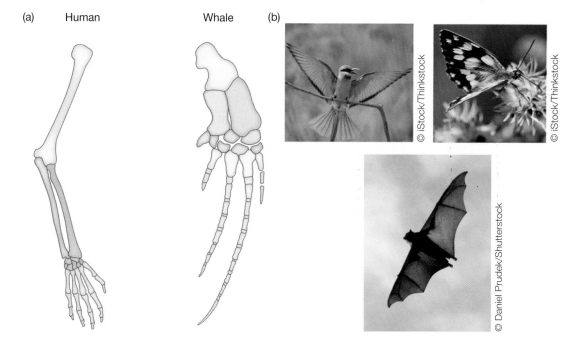

(a) Human   Whale   (b)

FIGURE 4.14 (a) *Homology* refers to traits derived from a common ancestor; while differing in size, shape, and perhaps number, our arm bones are homologous with those of the whale; (b) *homoplasy* denotes traits that have evolved independently in different taxa since divergence from a common ancestor, as in birds, bats, and flying insects.

A final important consideration: homoplasy can occur through two different evolutionary pathways, **convergence** or **parallelism**. Convergent characters appear when different structures evolve toward (i.e., converge upon) a similar end. Take the bird and bat wing example: the bones in the bird wing are analogous to those in your arm, while the bones in the wing of a bat are analogous to those in your hand. Parallelism occurs when two (or more) groups evolve similar outcomes from similar structures. For example, Begun (2007b) has argued that the anatomical similarity in forelimb structure in living orangutans, gibbons, and the fossil ape *Oreopithecus* evolved in parallel as each taxa adapted to suspending beneath tree limbs at some point in time following divergence from a common ancestor many millions of years ago (see Chapter 7). Both convergence and parallelism are forms of directional selection as an adaptive response to similar environmental/ecological challenges.

convergence

a path toward development of homoplasy: evolution acts on different ancestral structures to converge upon a similar outcome in response to similar adaptive pressures

parallelism

a path toward development of homoplasy; evolution modifies an ancestral character to achieve similar outcomes in response to similar adaptive pressures

KEY IDEAS

- Variability is the tendency of individuals in a population to differ in the expression of a genetic or phenotypic trait.

- Hardy-Weinberg Equilibrium comprises five hypothetical assumptions that, if met, indicate that trait frequencies do not change from one generation to the next.

- Neo-Darwinism emerged in the early 1940s, recognizing the roles of mutation and selection in producing and sorting variation in populations.

- Within evolutionary developmental biology, epigenetics acknowledges the important role of development and environment in the creation of novel inheritable variation.

- Species have been defined in a number of ways, most commonly in terms of reproductive isolation as the distinguishing feature of the biological species concept.

- Reproductive isolating mechanisms may act before or after mating; however, hybridization between closely related species is not uncommon.

- Fossil species are generally distinguished on the basis of morphology (morphospecies) or time (chronospecies).

- Evolutionary biologists often speak of the tempo (rate) and mode (pattern) of speciation.

- Darwin conceived of evolution proceeding slowly and in a straight line from ancestor to descendent—known as anagenesis.

- Cladogenesis is an alternative pattern of evolution, producing many branches or clades, rather than linear ancestor–descendant sequences.

- Punctuated equilibrium is one pattern of evolution in which long periods of little evolutionary change are interrupted by short bursts of rapid change, producing new species.

- Natural selection modifies population variation in several ways, including directional selection, stabilizing selection, and diversifying selection.

- Variation in populations is also modified by several processes beyond natural selection, including gene flow, genetic drift, and founder effect.

- Classification of biological diversity can follow either a shared evolution history model (cladistic) or one based on morphological and anatomical similarity (gradistic).

- Similarities among species can occur through shared common ancestry (homology) or through convergent or parallel evolution in the absence of a recent common ancestor (homoplasy).

KEY TERMS

founder effect (p. 72)

variability (p. 73)

Hardy-Weinberg Equilibrium (p. 73)

speciation (p. 74)

hybrid zones (p. 77)

morphospecies (p. 80)

chronospecies (p. 81)

anagenesis (p. 81)

cladogenesis (p. 81)

clades (p. 81)

gene flow (p. 82)

genetic drift (p. 82)

genetic bottleneck (p. 88)

homologous traits (p. 90)

homoplasies (p. 90)

convergence (p. 91)

parallelism (p. 91)

KEY QUESTIONS TO ASK MYSELF

1. Humans are really variable. Why hasn't a new species of human evolved?

2. If two species of baboon can produce hybrid offspring that can also reproduce, why are the parents not considered the same species?

3. Can I be classified as belonging to both a clade *and* a grade?

KEY CRITICAL THINKING QUESTIONS

1. The discovery of epigenetic inheritance and the role that environmental factors may play in modifying gene expression have broad ramifications for humankind, as people tend to live in diverse, complex, and often adverse environments (e.g., existing in poverty, in polluted habitats, and with poor lifestyles). What do you think are some of the implications of this reality for future human generations?

2. Our understanding of variation in nature—including that of humans—is originating more and more from the field of molecular genetics. What are the dangers for fields such as anthropology when we learn more and more about human biology from the study of DNA?

KEY THINGS TO DO NEXT

CourseMate   Visit **CourseMate** at www.nelson.com/humanvoyage2e to build your comprehension, practise your critical thinking skills, review core concepts, and explore other resources at your disposal.

5 What It Means to Be a Primate

© Travis Steffens

How like us is that ugly brute, the ape!

Quintus Ennius, 239–c. 169 BCE

OVERVIEW

In the previous two chapters, we introduced you to the biological building blocks of all life forms and the mechanisms by which organisms evolve. An understanding of our evolutionary history requires not only a good knowledge of the biological basis of human variation but also knowledge of how we compare with our closest living relatives, the nonhuman primates. This chapter introduces you to the features that characterize the Order Primates. It discusses how these features may have originated, classifies primates according to morphological and biochemical evidence, and describes their habitats, dietary adaptations, feeding strategies, and locomotor patterns. It also provides a survey of the major groups of living primates, including their distinguishing characteristics and biological and behavioural adaptations. While we share many features with our closest living relatives, we remain unique in a number of important ways.

KEY CONCEPTS

Prosimians, anthropoids, hominoids, adaptation, diversity, life history, primate genomes, primate conservation

KEY LEARNING OBJECTIVES

At the end of this chapter, you will be able to

LO1 List the ways in which primates differ from other mammals

LO2 Distinguish among prosimians, Old and New World monkeys, and apes

LO3 Apply an evolutionary perspective to understanding how primate characteristics may have evolved

LO4 Compare and contrast where primates live, how they move about, and what they eat

LO5 Evaluate the ways in which humans are unique as primates

LO6 Predict how primates might respond to human-induced changes to their habitat

PROLOGUE: THROUGH THE LOOKING GLASS

When you were a child, your parents no doubt took you to the zoo, where you found yourself pressed up against a glass window peering into the gorilla enclosure or watching intently as gibbons swung from branch to branch or baboons jostled with one another for food. Nonhuman primates, particularly the great apes, have long attracted our attention for their close anatomical and behavioural resemblance to humans. Beginning in the 1930s, Hollywood capitalized on our fascination with our primate cousins by featuring them in films such as *King Kong* (1933, 2005), the Tarzan series, former U.S. President Ronald Reagan's *Bedtime for Bonzo* (1951), and Clint Eastwood's *Every Which Way But Loose* (1978). In the 1940s, scientists recognized the potential of using nonhuman primates to test the safety of space travel for humans—in particular, the effects of prolonged weightlessness. In 1948 a rhesus monkey was launched into space, and in the years that followed, additional monkeys were rocketed into the atmosphere (see http://history.nasa.gov/animals.html). The first chimpanzee in space, a four-year-old named Ham, successfully completed a suborbital flight in January 1961; four months later, the first American astronaut, Alan Shepard, followed his path. Many thousands of nonhuman primates have been used in medical research, including the development and testing of drugs, the treatment of neurological diseases such as Alzheimer's, and immunological studies.

Of course, the fact that we can learn so much about ourselves, including our origins and biological and behavioural complexity, is but one reason to study primates. We also investigate primates because they are innately interesting, socially and behaviourally complex mammals. Moreover, many primates occupy key positions within their habitat and are thus under great pressure from human activity and habitat loss. To appreciate primates as unique members of the taxonomic Order Primates, and as models for understanding more about ourselves, we need to first be aware of what makes a primate different from, say, a gazelle or a ground sloth.

DEFINING A PRIMATE

Mammalia

the class to which all mammals belong; this includes placental, egg-laying, and marsupial mammals

Primates belong to the Class **Mammalia** and are members of the placental subgroup of mammals. All primates have a suite of characteristics that they share with other placental mammals, including body hair, mammary glands, increased brain size, a relatively long gestation period, and the ability to maintain a constant body temperature. The majority of primates are generalized compared to many other mammals, meaning that they lack specialized features—for example, hoofs (as in horses) or high, pointed cusps on the molar and premolar teeth (as in dogs).

Shared primate features reflect a common evolutionary history characterized by environmental adaptation. To date, over 300 species of primates have been identified, most of them in tropical and subtropical areas of the world.[1] Ranging in size from the pygmy mouse lemur (30 g) to the gorilla (200 kg), primates share a number of characteristics not seen in other mammals. That said, the degree of expression of these characteristics varies greatly among different species, and not all primates possess the same ones. In fact, one of the difficulties in defining primates as a group is that they have no single characteristic that distinguishes them from other orders of mammals. So what *does* distinguish them from other mammals? Primates share a combination of features that can be divided into those related to locomotion, sensory and dietary adaptations, and life history and reproduction.

---

1. The number of reported primate species is constantly changing as new species are uncovered. From 2000 to 2008, 39 species of lemurs were described in Madagascar (Mittermeier et al. 2008); an additional species of lemur, Gerp's mouse lemur (*Microcebus gerpi*), was documented on the island (Radespiel et al. 2012); and a previously unknown species of uakari monkey was identified in the Amazon region of Brazil (Boubli et al. 2008). In 2012 a new species of monkey known as the lesula was documented in the Democratic Republic of Congo (Hart et al. 2012).

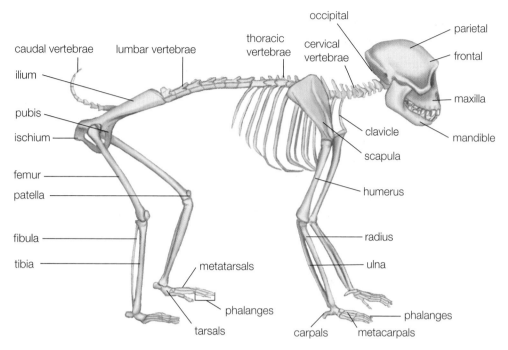

FIGURE 5.1 The basic skeletal structure of a monkey is similar to that of a human.

From JURMAIN/KILGORE/TRAVATHAN. *Essentials of Physical Anthropology*, 7E. © 2009 South-Western, a part of Cengage Learning, Inc. Reproduced by permission. www.cengage.com/permissions

Locomotory Features

Primates retain a generalized skeletal structure that resembles that of their early mammalian ancestors (Figure 5.1; see also Appendix A). Because of this generalized structure, primates have great flexibility in movement. While all nonhuman primates are **quadrupedal**, there is considerable variation in the way in which they move about, and many species use more than one form of locomotion. All primates exhibit a marked tendency toward upright posture in the upper body and have flexible shoulder joints and clavicles (collarbones). They also retain separate radius and ulna bones in the forelimb, allowing for a greater range of motion of the hands.

Like many other mammals, most primates have five functional digits on each hand and foot. What distinguishes them from other mammals, however, is their grasping (**prehensile**) hands with **opposable** thumbs, which allow for a variety of grips (Figure 5.2) and facilitate many activities. Another general characteristic of nonhuman primates is a grasping hindfoot made possible by having an opposable big toe. In addition, all primates have flattened nails and tactile pads on at least one digit, providing them with an enhanced

quadrupedal
walking on all four limbs

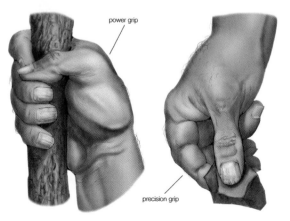

prehensile
grasping

opposable
the thumb or big toe can make contact with the tip of each of the other digits on the same hand/foot

FIGURE 5.2 Opposable thumbs allow primates to use both power and precision grips

© Universal Images Group/Getty

sense of touch and facilitating the manipulation of food and other objects; some species retain a claw on certain digits as an adaptation for feeding.

Sensory Adaptations

Primates have greater reliance on vision than other mammals. This is reflected in their forward-facing eyes, which result in overlapping fields of view, giving primates **stereoscopic vision**—that is, the ability to see things in three dimensions. Because of the importance of vision, the eyes are partly or completely enclosed in a bony orbit that provides protection. This takes the form of a **postorbital bar** in prosimians and a postorbital plate or cup in monkeys, apes, and humans (Figure 5.3). Many primate species have colour vision (Box 5.1), although most of the prosimians lack this feature as they are **nocturnal** and therefore do not need to be able to see colour. Associated with the increased reliance on vision in primates is a decreased reliance on smell, reflected in a reduction in the size of the snout and the **olfactory** areas of the brain. Strongly associated with their enhanced visual abilities is an increase in brain size. Compared to other mammals, primates have a larger brain relative to their body size, reflecting their greater intelligence. In particular, they exhibit a larger **neocortex**, that portion of the brain responsible for higher cognitive functions such as memory, problem solving, and abstract thought. This is most evident in the great apes, which have the largest and most complex brain of all nonhuman primates (see Chapter 8).

stereoscopic vision

characterized by overlapping fields of view, allowing humans and other primates to see in three dimensions

postorbital bar

the bony ring that separates the eye orbit from the back of the skull; within Primates, this feature is found among the prosimians

nocturnal

active during the night

olfactory

relating to the sense of smell

neocortex

the outer part of the brain that is involved in higher functions such as reasoning, abstract thought, and language

diurnal

active during the day

trichromatic

a condition in which an animal possesses three light-sensitive pigments in the cones in the retina of the eye, making it possible to see blue, green, and red

dichromatic

a condition in which an animal possesses two light-sensitive pigments in the cones in the retina of the eye, making it possible to see blue and green

estrus

period of sexual receptivity in females, correlated with ovulation

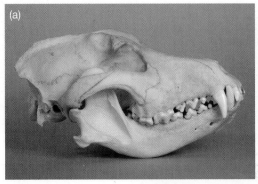

© Will Higgs

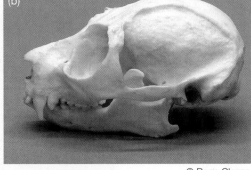

© Bone Clones, www.boneclones.com

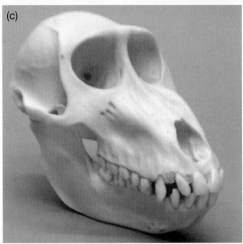

© Bone Clones, www.boneclones.com

FIGURE 5.3 Unlike other mammals such as dogs (a), primates have a postorbital bar or closure that protects the eyes. A bar is typically seen in prosimians such as lemurs and lorises (b), whereas complete closure characterizes monkeys, apes, and humans (c).

BOX 5.1

The ability to see colour varies greatly among the primates. Not surprisingly, **diurnal** species have the best colour vision, while nocturnal species have none. Humans, apes, and all Old World monkeys can differentiate among blues, greens, and reds (i.e., they are **trichromatic**), while diurnal prosimians can differentiate only between blues and greens (i.e., they are **dichromatic**). Most New World monkeys have a polymorphic system of colour vision such that both dichromatic and trichromatic individuals are present within the same species. Among the marmosets and tamarins, for example, males are dichromatic but females are either dichromatic or trichromatic (Smith et al. 2003).

Primatologist Amanda Melin has been studying the effect of colour vision on the foraging behaviour of white-faced capuchin monkeys, of whom all males and some females are dichromatic. Her field research has revealed evidence of differing foraging strategies between capuchins with differing colour vision systems. With respect to insect capture, for instance, she found that dichromats were more efficient at detecting camouflaged insects, particularly under low light, and trichromatic females spent more time visually foraging than dichromatic males and females, possibly to compensate for their reduced ability to capture camouflaged insects (Melin et al. 2007, 2010).

Similarly, Caine and colleagues (2010) found that dichromatic Geoffroy's marmosets were better at foraging in low light than trichromats, and Smith et al. (2012) observed that while trichromatic tamarins caught more insect prey overall than dichromats, the latter captured more camouflaged prey than the former. These findings suggest that selection for niche divergence may play a role in maintaining colour vision polymorphism in these primates (Smith et al. 2012).

At what point in primate evolutionary history did selection for the ability to see reds occur, and why might this trait have been selected for? It is generally assumed that all early prosimians were monochromatic or dichromatic. Andrew Smith has hypothesized that a mutation in the X chromosome allowing for the ability to see red colours likely occurred after the separation between Old and New World monkeys and probably occurred more than once. According to Smith and colleagues (2003), trichromatic colour vision would have provided an important advantage to fruit-eating primates by allowing them to spot ripe orange and red fruits. In fact, it has long been argued that trichromacy evolved as an adaptation for frugivory.

But what about trichromatic species that eat mainly leaves? Research by Dominy and Lucas (2001) on primates living in Kibale National Park in Uganda suggests that trichromacy likely evolved in order to allow them to detect more nutritious young leaves, which are distinguished by their red colour. Liman and Innan (2003), on the other hand, suggest that trichromacy may have been selected to allow males to see the reddish sexual swellings of females in **estrus**. Alternatively, it may have been selected to allow primates to determine the emotional state of their kin and enemies by being able to detect colour changes in their skin (Changizi, Zhang, and Shimojo 2006). Support for this hypothesis lies in the fact that primates with bare skin on their faces and rumps have highly evolved colour vision whereas those with fur-covered skin do not. So what is the adaptive significance of trichromacy? All of the above hypotheses are plausible, and it is likely that a variety of environmental factors selected for colour vision in primates (recall our discussion of convergent evolution in Chapter 4).

Unlike other mammals, primates also possess a unique cranial feature known as the **petrosal bulla**, a bony outgrowth on the base of the skull that houses the three bones of the middle ear. In contrast to other mammals that have a similar feature known as an auditory bulla, which is formed from the tympanic bone, the petrosal bulla derives from the petrous part of the temporal bone.

Dietary Adaptations

Primates have **diphyodont** and **heterodont** dentition consisting of two sets of different kinds of teeth that serve a variety of functions, reflecting their generally **omnivorous** diet. In adults, there are four kinds of teeth: incisors, canines, premolars, and molars. The incisors are used for cutting, the canines for piercing, and the premolars and molars for crushing and grinding. The number of each type of tooth in each quadrant of the jaw is expressed as a **dental formula**. So, for example, a dental formula of 2.1.2.3 (such as your own) means that in each quadrant of the mouth there are two incisors, one canine, two premolars, and three molars (Figure 5.4). An individual with this dental formula has a total of 32 teeth, while an individual with a dental formula of 2.1.3.3 has four extra premolars, or 36 teeth in total.

petrosal bulla

a bony outgrowth on the base of the skull that houses the three bones of the middle ear

diphyodont

having two sets of teeth: permanent (adult) and deciduous (baby) teeth

heterodont

having different kinds of teeth, e.g., molars, premolars, incisors, canines

omnivorous

eating a variety of different foods, including both plants and animals

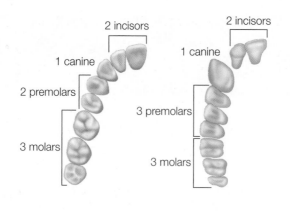

(a) Human: 2.1.2.3.   (b) New World monkey: 2.1.3.3.

FIGURE 5.4 A dental formula of 2.1.2.3 characterizes humans (a), Old World monkeys, and great apes. In contrast, New World monkeys have a dental formula of 2.1.3.3 (b).

In contrast, most early mammals possessed a dental formula of 3.1.4.3, or 44 teeth in total, so there has been a reduction in the number of teeth in primates. When dealing with fossilized remains, the number of teeth can be very useful in identifying the different taxa—for example, for distinguishing between early prosimians and anthropoids. Some primate species have unusual dental formulas. The aye-aye, for example, has a specialized dental formula of 1.0.1.3 for the upper jaw and 1.0.0.3 for the lower jaw.

Life History and Reproductive Features

Compared to other mammals, primates display longer gestation periods and a low reproductive rate, resulting in a reduced number of offspring. Unlike other mammals who give birth to large numbers of offspring at a time (**r-selection strategy**), primates follow what is referred to as a **K-selection strategy**. This is an adaptive strategy in which individuals have fewer offspring but invest greater parental care, thereby giving the offspring a greater chance of survival. With the exception of marmosets and tamarins, which give birth to twins, all primates usually give birth to only one offspring at a time. Primates also have a longer period of infant dependency, which promotes strong bonds between mothers and their offspring and allows for a greater period of learning. Finally, primates have a longer period of growth, a longer period of adulthood, and, consequently, an extended life span, ranging from less than 10 years in some tamarin species to 50 years or more in some of the great apes. The lengthened period of each stage of their life cycle (i.e., infant, juvenile, adult) again reflects the importance of learned behaviour.

THE ORIGIN OF PRIMATE CHARACTERISTICS

How did the suite of characteristics seen in primates come about? Over the years, many hypotheses have been proposed to explain the origins of primates. In the 1920s, for example, two British anatomists, George Elliot-Smith and Frederic Wood-Jones, hypothesized that primate features such as forward-facing eyes and grasping hands with nails instead of claws evolved as adaptations to an arboreal way of life. Critics of this **arboreal hypothesis** noted that other mammals such as squirrels are also well-adapted to life in the trees yet do not possess these characteristics. In response to these criticisms, primatologist Matt Cartmill (1972, 1992) proposed an alternative hypothesis to explain the origin of primate characteristics. His **visual predation hypothesis** argues that forward-facing eyes and grasping hands arose as adaptations to insect predation. According to this hypothesis, such features allowed the earliest primates, which closely resembled modern insectivores, to exploit insects in the bushy forest undergrowth in which they lived.

Randall Sussman's (1991) **angiosperm radiation hypothesis**, in contrast, argues that primate characteristics evolved as adaptations to a diet of flowers and nectar. It fails to explain, however, why such a diet would have necessitated the visual specializations seen in primates, or the fact that the molar teeth of the earliest primates do not exhibit features seen in other species known to eat nectar. Rasmussen (1990) has argued that these hypotheses are not mutually exclusive and that a combination of terminal branch feeding of fruit and nectar and the visual predation of insects may best explain how primate features came about.

More recently, a new hypothesis known as the **narrow niche hypothesis** has been put forward. Derived from studies of the foraging behaviour of Eastern gray squirrels, which lack the grasping adaptations of primates but feed and forage in terminal branches as primates do, it proposes that the suite of characteristics seen in primates evolved not only from selection pressure for fine branch feeding, but also from the relaxation of previous selection pressures (i.e., they are no longer engaged in former activities, such as terrestrial travel, due to niche narrowing) (Orkin and Pontzer 2011). In summary, while the mechanisms that led to the evolution of the defining characteristics of primates remain uncertain, there is increasing recognition that not all primate characteristics evolved together and that they likely arose at different times in response to varying environmental conditions.

CLASSIFYING PRIMATES

As you learned in Chapter 2, the science of classifying organisms is known as taxonomy. This system of classification was developed by Linnaeus, who grouped organisms together based on shared characteristics. The Order Primates has traditionally been divided into two suborders: **Prosimii**, encompassing lemurs, lorises, and tarsiers, and **Anthropoidea**, consisting of monkeys, apes, and humans. One problem with classifying organisms based on physical similarities is that groups of species that are not closely related may be grouped together. Recognizing this limitation, researchers are increasingly using biochemical evidence to examine evolutionary and biological relationships among species. For example, comparisons of amino acid sequences of various proteins, and of DNA strands from different species, have revealed that humans and chimps are more closely related to one another than either is to gorillas. Consequently, anthropologists now classify chimps and humans within the Subfamily **Homininae** (see Chapter 8 for further discussion of this classification scheme). Biochemical data have also revealed that tarsiers, formerly classified as prosimians, are actually more closely related to anthropoids. As a result, the Prosimii, excluding the tarsiers, have been reclassified as the Suborder **Strepsirhini**, and tarsiers, monkeys, apes, and humans have been grouped together in the Suborder **Haplorhini** (Figure 5.5).

narrow niche hypothesis
the hypothesis that the suite of characteristics seen in primates evolved not only from selection pressure for fine branch feeding, but also from the relaxation of previous selection pressures

Prosimii
the suborder that includes lemurs, lorises, and tarsiers

Anthropoidea
the suborder that includes monkeys, apes, and humans

Homininae
the taxonomic subfamily that includes modern humans and our earlier ancestors, as well as chimpanzees and bonobos

Strepsirhini
the suborder that comprises lemurs, lorises, and galagos

Haplorhini
the suborder that comprises tarsiers, monkeys, apes, and humans

Order	Suborder	Infraorder	Superfamily	Family	Subfamily	Tribe	Genus
Primates	Strepsirhini	Lemuriformes Lorisiformes	Lemuroidea Lorisoidea	Lemuridae Lorisidae	Lemurinae Lorisinae		
	Haplorhini	Tarsiiformes	Tarsioidea	Tarsiidae			
		Platyrrhini	Ceboidea	Cebidae Pitheciidae Callitrichidae Atelidae Aotidae			
		Catarrhini	Cercopithecoidea	Cercopithecidae	Cercopithecinae Colobinae		
			Hominoidea	Hylobatidae Hominidae	Hylobatinae Ponginae Gorillinae Homininae	Pongini Gorillini Panini Hominini	*Hylobates* *Pongo* *Gorilla* *Pan* *Homo*

FIGURE 5.5 Taxonomic classification of the living primates. (For simplicity's sake, not all scientific names have been included in this table.)

While we will be following this classification scheme in this text, it is important to note that there is no overarching consensus on primate classification, and both genetic and anatomical classification schemes have their advantages. For instance, the former allows for the examination of genetic similarities and differences among primate species and the identification of evolutionary relationships, while the latter helps us better understand the adaptive significance of various anatomical traits.

PRIMATE BIOGEOGRAPHY

Nonhuman primates are distributed in tropical and subtropical regions of the world. They occupy diverse ecological niches, ranging from the swampy forests of Borneo and Sumatra to the snowy mountains of Japan. Some species are restricted to lowland areas; others are found at higher elevations. Some species remain relatively isolated from humans; others live among them. As with many other mammals, nonhuman primates use space in different ways from day to day and season to season. The total area exploited over the course of a year is called the **home range,** which can vary in size from less than 1 square kilometre in the case of prosimians to many square kilometres in the case of monkeys and apes. Overlapping home ranges may lead to hostile encounters, and some species actively defend their **territory** against neighbouring populations. Chimpanzee males, for example, are known to participate in border patrols (Goodall 1986); these can lead to violent interactions resulting in injury and death if they come upon members of neighbouring groups. The home range is actually the sum of all of the group's **day ranges**, over which they travel from waking up until sleeping, often in search of the next available food resource. Day ranges that emphasize particular zones within the home range, and in which they spend most of their foraging time, define the **core area**.

home range

the entire area exploited by an animal or group of animals

territory

an area that is defended against conspecific members of neighbouring groups

day ranges

the geographic space through which primates move in one day

core area

the portion of a primate's home range that contains the greatest concentration of resources and that is most heavily used by a group

intermembral index

a measure of the relative lengths of the upper and lower limbs, calculated as (humerus length + radius length) × 100/(femur length + tibia length)

knuckle-walkers

primates that display a form of locomotion characterized by walking on all four limbs with the body weight partially supported by the middle phalanges of the hands

vertical clinging and leaping

a form of locomotion characterized by leaping using the hindlimbs and clinging to branches and tree trunks using the forelimbs

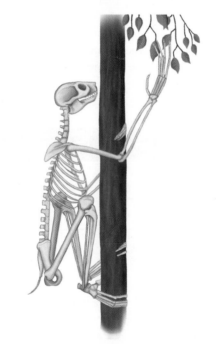

Skeleton of a vertical clinger and leaper (indri)

FIGURE 5.6 Vertical clingers and leapers have longer hindlimbs than forelimbs.

Courtesy of Stephen D. Nash

Primate Locomotion

Most primates are arboreal and spend the majority of their time in the trees. Some species have adapted to a terrestrial way of life, but no nonhuman primate species is fully terrestrial, and all of them spend at least some of their time in the trees. Gorillas, because of their large body size, are almost completely terrestrial. Primates use four different methods of locomotion, with many species using more than one form. This flexibility in locomotor patterns is possible because of their generalized skeletal structure. The basic form of primate locomotion is quadrupedalism, or movement on all four limbs, and most primates utilize this form of movement on at least some occasions. Primates that exhibit this pattern have an **intermembral index** of over 70, meaning that their forelimbs and hindlimbs are of similar length (Figure 5.1). Quadrupeds include arboreal species such as macaques, terrestrial species such as baboons, and **knuckle-walkers** such as chimps and gorillas.

A second form of locomotion, utilized by many of the prosimians, is **vertical clinging and leaping**, whereby strong hind limbs propel the body and the forelimbs grasp tree trunks and branches. Species that utilize this mode of locomotion exhibit longer hind limbs than forelimbs (Figure 5.6) and consequently have a low intermembral index. **Brachiation**, a mode of locomotion characterized by arm-over-arm movement, is seen in gibbons and siamangs. Brachiators have extremely flexible shoulder joints and longer forelimbs and shorter hindlimbs (Figure 5.7), giving them a high intermembral index. Researchers have hypothesized that these anatomical traits may have evolved to allow apes to hang from branches while feeding on fruit. Among New World primates, spider monkeys and muriquis are **semibrachiators**, meaning that they combine leaping with arm-over-arm movement. They also use their strong prehensile tails as a fifth hand. Humans are the only primates to display habitual **bipedalism,** although other primate species have been observed moving bipedally over short distances.

Skeleton of a brachiator (gibbon)

FIGURE 5.7 Brachiators have longer forelimbs than hindlimbs.

Courtesy of Stephen D. Nash

brachiation
a form of locomotion characterized by arm-over-arm movement

semibrachiators
animals that combine arm-over-arm movement with other forms of locomotion

bipedalism
moving on two legs

Feeding and Foraging

As noted earlier, primates typically have a generalized rather than specialized dentition, reflecting their mainly omnivorous diet. Teeth can, in fact, provide very useful information on diet. The cusp pattern, for example, can tell us whether a primate's diet is composed primarily of fruit or leaves, while the degree of wear on the enamel can tell us how coarse its diet is. This is particularly helpful when we are dealing with fossil remains rather than living animals. While all primates are omnivorous to some extent, most species favour certain types of foods. **Folivorous** primates rely mainly on a diet of leaves and have high, sharp molar cusps for slicing and chewing them. Most primates prefer fruit when it is available (i.e., they are **frugivorous**) and detect it on the basis of colour and scent.[2] Their molars have lower, more rounded cusps designed to crush and grind hard seeds, and some frugivores have cheek pouches for storing unripe fruits and seeds. Many strepsirhines are **insectivorous** and utilize their sharp, pointed cusps to break open the hard outer shell of their prey, and some, such as marmosets, are **gummivorous**, deriving important minerals such as calcium from gum, sap, or resin **graminivorous** primates feed on grass or the seeds of grass.

folivorous
leaf-eating

frugivorous
fruit-eating

insectivorous
insect-eating

gummivorous
gum-eating; may also consume sap or resin

graminivorous
grass-eating

With some exceptions, there is a close relationship between body size and diet, with smaller species typically being frugivore–insectivores and larger species being frugivore–folivores (Strier 2003; see Figure 5.8). The higher metabolic rate of small-bodied primates allows them to digest insects more rapidly than leaves, while the lower metabolic rate of large-bodied species such as gorillas means that digestion of their lower quality folivorous diet takes place over a longer period of time.

Some primates occasionally kill and eat small mammals, including other primates (Stanford 1999). Male chimpanzees, for example, engage in cooperative hunting and often share meat with one another and with nonhunting members of their social group, including females. Differences in hunting strategies have been observed among chimpanzees living in Gombe versus the Taï Forest. Hunting behaviour among the former, for instance, tends to be more opportunistic, and immature red colobus are the primary prey. In contrast, male

2. The presence of ethanol in fruits appears to be an important cue for detecting and selecting these foods (see Dominy 2004).

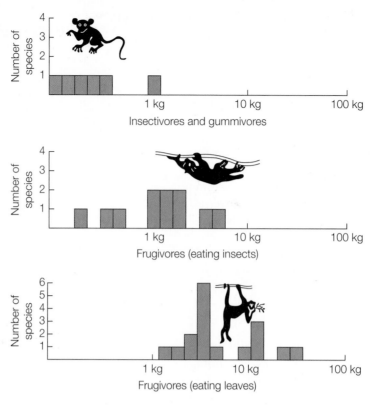

FIGURE 5.8 Frugivore-insectivores are typically smaller than frugivore-folivores.

Adapted from *Primates in Nature* by Alison F. Richard. Used with permission.

chimpanzees of the Taï Forest organize cooperative hunting parties that target mature red colobus monkeys (Boesch and Boesch 1989).

The search for food may take up 50% or more of an individual's daily activities, and the amount of time spent feeding depends largely on diet. For example, primates that rely heavily on leaves that are low in energy content and take a long time to digest typically spend more time feeding than those that rely on higher quality foods such as fruit. Colobine monkeys are unique among primates in having a **sacculated** stomach and an enlarged intestinal tract to allow for the digestion of plant material and the absorption of nutrients.

Food is particularly important to female primates, who need to feed not only themselves but also their dependent offspring, and among most primates, females have higher quality diets than males (Strier 2003). Good nutrition is especially crucial to pregnant and lactating females who have higher metabolic costs. Thus they spend a considerable amount of time feeding on higher quality foods, and those with better nutrition generally have greater reproductive success than those with a poorer diet. In many group-living primate species, access to higher quality foods is also a function of social dynamics such as rank (status within the group; see Chapter 6).

The distribution of food influences the size of a foraging group. Small groups, for instance, are typical of habitats characterized by a low density of resources such as fruits, which tend to occur in smaller patches, while larger groups are found in areas where foods are more widely distributed as in the case of leaves. Seasonal availability of food resources also affects foraging behaviour. Higher quality foods may not be available during certain times of the year, necessitating a reliance on lower quality food items and a greater range of foods. Food availability is also associated with reproductive seasonality such that births may be concentrated during particular times of the year among primates who face significant seasonal fluctuations in the availability of resources.

sacculated
divided into chambers

Complex feeding strategies have been observed among many primate species. An interesting dietary adaptation has been documented among red colobus monkeys on the island of Zanzibar. It appears to have arisen from an increase in the human population on the island and a reduction in the natural habitat of the monkeys as a result of logging. Despite living in an environment characterized by various exotic fruit trees, the monkeys appear to have taken up the habit of eating charcoal left over from the destruction of the forests. What might be the advantage of eating this substance? As it turns out, the leaves of the fruit trees on which they subsist contain toxic compounds. Eating charcoal allows the monkeys to consume the protein-rich leaves. In this way, they absorb the toxins and eliminate them from the body, at the same time retaining the vital proteins in the leaves (Struhsaker et al. 1997).

As primatologists have discovered, diet, physiology, brain size, cognition, and activity levels are all directly linked. Katharine Milton's (1981, 2009) long-term study of two sympatric New World primates, spider and howler monkeys, has revealed significant differences between the two species with respect to feeding strategies and types of foods consumed. Howler monkeys rely primarily on a diet of leaves and forage collectively in relatively small areas. Spider monkeys, in contrast, eat mainly fruits and often forage over much larger ranges in small groups or by themselves. Observations of their digestive patterns have revealed that it takes howler monkeys five times longer to digest their food than it does spider monkeys. An examination of their intestinal tracts has also revealed that howlers have considerably larger colons than spider monkeys. As a result, food remains in the gut longer in howlers, so they are able to derive energy-rich fatty acids from the fermenting masses of leaves, whereas spider monkeys with their smaller digestive tracts can process their high-energy fruit diet quickly and easily. Milton also found correlations among diet, physiology, brain size, and cognition, hypothesizing that the larger brains of spider monkeys compared to howlers are a product of their high-energy diet.

Knowledge of primate diets can also be useful in providing insight into disorders that affect humans. For example, observations of primates who appear to become intoxicated as a result of eating ripe fruit have prompted researchers to investigate how we may have developed a taste for, and ultimately, in some cases, an addiction to alcohol (Stephens and Dudley 2004).

Early field studies of primate feeding behaviour typically focused on the kinds of foods that were eaten. In recent years, however, the focus has shifted to examining the nutritional and physical properties of food, the relationship between diet and craniodental morphology, the relationship between postural behaviours and diet, and seasonal variation in diet (McGraw and Daegling 2012). Primatologists are also increasingly utilizing innovative analytical techniques to study primate diets. These include stable carbon and nitrogen isotope analysis of primate tissues such as bones and teeth (see Chapter 1), which can provide information on age- and sex-related differences in diet, dietary variability within and between primate populations and short-term dietary shifts (Crowley 2012), and the analysis of organic compounds in urine, which can be used to investigate seasonal variability in food resources (Knott 1998).

THE LIVING PRIMATES

Strepsirhini

The Suborder Strepsirhini comprises the prosimians, of which there are 7 families and roughly 85 species in the world today. This suborder is further divided into 2 infraorders: Lemuriformes, which includes lemurs, indris, sifakas, and aye-ayes, and Lorisiformes, which includes lorises and galagos, or bushbabies. Prosimians (or "pre-monkeys") are often described as more closely resembling the earliest primate forms (see Chapter 7). Their characteristics include the following:

- Small body size. They are the smallest of the primates, ranging in size from the pygmy mouse lemur (30 g) to the indri (7 kg), the latter about the size of a large housecat.
- Primarily nocturnal. This is reflected in their large eyes and lack of colour vision.

- A **tooth comb** formed by the lower incisors and canines (Figure 5.9). These teeth are joined together and protrude outward. The function of this feature varies among prosimians, with some species using it for grooming, others for feeding. The lesser galago, for example, uses its tooth comb to extract sap from tree bark.
- A **grooming claw** on the second digit of each hindfoot.
- A well-developed sense of smell, reflected by an elongated or protruding snout and the presence of a **rhinarium** (i.e., strepsirhines are wet-nosed).

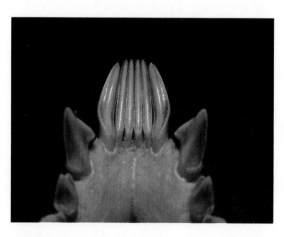

FIGURE 5.9 Tooth combs are formed by the anterior teeth and are used by strepsirhines for grooming and foraging.

William K. Sacco, specimens courtesy of Yale Peabody Museum.

Lemuriformes

This infraorder encompasses 5 families and possibly as many as 100 species of lemurs, as well as indrii, sifakas, and aye-ayes. All of these species are restricted to the island of Madagascar off the eastern coast of Africa. Among the most diversified of the primates, these animals occupy a variety of ecological niches and consequently exhibit a wide range of adaptive behaviours. Some species, such as the dwarf lemur and the aye-aye, are nocturnal, while others are diurnal. All are primarily arboreal, although some are more terrestrial than others. They use quadrupedal or vertical clinging and leaping modes of locomotion to get around, and they exhibit various forms of social organization, ranging from solitary to large groups.

The males of some species, such as ring-tailed lemurs, mark their territories with chemicals produced by scent glands in their wrists. The fat-tailed dwarf lemur is the only primate species to hibernate during the winter months, when ambient temperatures fluctuate significantly (Dausmann et al. 2005). What is the adaptive significance of this behaviour? Primatologist Kathrin Dausmann suggests that it may be a way of coping with food scarcity during the winter months by reducing the amount of energy spent on body-temperature regulation (ibid.). Another unusual member of this infraorder is the aye-aye (Figure 5.10), the only member of its genus. Occupying a similar environmental niche to woodpeckers, aye-ayes are distinct in having an elongated bony finger that they use to extract insects from trees.

FIGURE 5.10 Aye-ayes have an elongated middle finger that they use to extract insects from trees.

© Frans Lanting Studio/Alamy

Lorisiformes

This infraorder comprises two families and includes about 11 species of lorises and 20 species of galagos, or bushbabies (Figure 5.11). Found in Africa and Southeast Asia, lorises resemble lemurs in having a tooth comb and a grooming claw. Nocturnal and largely solitary, they are quadrupedal and rely on a diet of insects, fruit, eggs, snails, and lizards. Galagos are distributed over much of sub-Saharan Africa and are known for their excellent leaping abilities. Their diet includes fruit, insects, and gum from trees. Another member of the Lorisidae family is the potto. Found in the rainforests of Africa, pottos are nocturnal and arboreal.

Haplorhini

The Suborder Haplorhini includes tarsiers, monkeys, apes, and humans. More than 200 species of monkeys have been identified. These include New World monkeys (Infraorder Platyrrhini) and Old World monkeys, apes, and humans (Infraorder Catarrhini). Tarsiers, being unique in having both strepsirhine and haplorhine features, have been assigned to the Infraorder Tarsiiformes. Characteristics of haplorhines include

- Larger body size than the strepsirhines.
- Diurnal. The two exceptions are the New World owl or night monkey (*Aotus*) and the tarsier, which are nocturnal.
- A tail in most species.
- Nails on all digits (with the exception of marmosets and tamarins).
- No rhinarium.
- Decreased reliance on sense of smell and increased reliance on vision compared to the strepsirhines. This is reflected in the complete closure of the back of the orbits with a bony plate. Most haplorhines also have trichromatic vision.
- Larger brain relative to body size than the strepsirhines.

FIGURE 5.11 Galagos, also known as bushbabies, are nocturnal and are primarily insectivorous.

© EcoPrint/Shutterstock

Tarsiiformes

The five species of tarsiers (Figure 5.12) living today are restricted to Southeast Asia. As noted above, tarsiers were long categorized in the Suborder Prosimii but have recently been shifted to the Suborder Haplorhini. While they have a number of prosimian characteristics, including a nocturnal way of life, a grooming claw, and a vertical clinging and leaping mode of locomotion, they also display anthropoid features, including the lack of both a rhinarium and a tooth comb. They are also more closely related biochemically to anthropoids than to prosimians. Known as outstanding leapers owing to the mechanical advantage of elongated tarsal bones in the ankle (from which they get their name), they can jump vertically up to 4 metres (Swindler 1998, 39). They are also the most carnivorous of all nonhuman primates, relying on a diet of insects, frogs, and lizards. Their eyes are unusual not only in their very large size relative to the size of the head, but also for their inability to move. To compensate for this, tarsiers can rotate their head 180 degrees. They are generally solitary although some species are known to form social units consisting of one adult male, one adult female, and their offspring.

FIGURE 5.12 Tarsiers have huge eyes that allow them to see in the dark. Each eyeball is the size of its brain.

© Tom McHugh/Photo Researchers, Inc.

Platyrrhini

The **Platyrrhines**, or New World monkeys, derive their infraorder name from their broad, flat noses with outward-facing nostrils. Comprising over 70 species, they live in the tropical and subtropical forests

Platyrrhines
New World monkeys

of Central and South America. All are diurnal except for the owl monkey (*Aotus*). They are mainly arboreal and range in size from marmosets and tamarins (100 g) to howler monkeys (10 kg). Divided into five families (Garber et al. 2008)—Cebidae, Atelidae, Callitrichidae, Pitheciidae, and Aotidae—they display the following characteristics:

- Smaller body size than Old World monkeys.
- A prehensile or grasping tail in some species. This feature facilitates locomotion; it is also a feeding adaptation that allows monkeys to hang from branches while reaching for food.
- Dental formula of 2.1.3.3 for most species.

FIGURE 5.13 Howler monkeys are known for their loud vocalizations, which can be heard over long distances.

© david tipling/Alamy

scent markings

a form of communication characterized by the deposition of chemicals such as urine or pheromones to mark territories

FIGURE 5.14 Spider monkeys have prehensile tails that allow them to grasp branches.

© worldswildlifewonders/Shutterstock

The Family Cebidae consists of capuchin monkeys and squirrel monkeys. Occupying the rainforests of Central and South America, these primates rely on an omnivorous diet and live in social groups composed of multiple males and females. The Family Atelidae includes the howler, spider, woolly, and woolly spider monkeys. Among the largest of the New World monkeys, howlers (Figure 5.13) are known for their loud vocalizations, which serve to warn other members of their group and to help defend them against predators. Their diet consists primarily of leaves, which they spend a great deal of time eating and digesting. Spider monkeys (Figure 5.14), so named for their long, thin limbs and long, prehensile tails, are highly agile and their diet consists primarily of fruit.

As of 2013, two species of woolly monkey were listed as critically endangered due to the destruction of their habitat (see the end of this chapter for a discussion of some of the major threats to primates). The Family Callitrichidae comprises the tamarins and marmosets, the tiniest of which is the pygmy marmoset. Both of these primates use **scent markings** to claim food resources within their territories, and have claw-like nails on most of their digits, which aid in locomotion. They are also rather unusual in giving birth to twins. The Family Pitheciidae consists of the sakis, titis, and uakaris. One species of uakari is distinctive in having a red face and a partly bald head. Finally, the Family Aotidae comprises the night (or owl) monkeys, the only nocturnal anthropoid.

Catarrhini

The Infraorder Catarrhini encompasses the most widely distributed of all primates: Old World monkeys, apes, and humans.

So named for their narrow noses with downward-facing nostrils, the **Catarrhines** are divided into two superfamilies, the Cercopithecoidea (Old World monkeys) and the Hominoidea (apes and humans).

The Old World monkeys, of which more than 80 species have been identified, are grouped into one large family, the Cercopithecidae, and are further divided into two subfamilies: the Cercopithecinae and the Colobinae. Occupying a wider variety of habitats than New World monkeys, they can be found in tropical and subtropical forests of Africa and Asia, as well as savannah and grassland environments of Africa. Most species of Old World monkeys are arboreal, but some spend a considerable amount of time on the ground, where they move about quadrupedally. Features seen in catarrhines include

- **Ischial callosities**.
- Greater size range and a greater degree of **sexual dimorphism** than New World monkeys.
- Dental formula of 2.1.2.3.

Catarrhines
Old World monkeys, apes, and humans

ischial callosities
patches of hardened skin on the rear end that facilitate sitting

sexual dimorphism
differences in physical characteristics between males and females of the same species

Cercopithecinae

Included in this subfamily are macaques, baboons, and mandrills. Anatomically more generalized and more omnivorous than the colobines, they possess cheek pouches for the temporary storage of food (Figure 5.15). These pouches not only allow monkeys to grab and store food before their competition can get it, but also facilitate the digestion of this food by salivary enzymes (Strier 2003). Among the cercopithecines, the macaques are the most widely distributed, being found from Morocco to the snowy mountains of Japan (Figure 5.16).[3] All of them are both arboreal and terrestrial. Some species (such as baboons) show marked sexual dimorphism in body size and/or canine size. The females of some cercopithecines display pronounced swellings and colour changes to the genital area to signal estrus. Barbary macaques are the only Old World monkeys without tails, as well as the only wild-living nonhuman primate in Europe (Gibraltar). Mandrills live in the forests of West Africa; the males have brightly coloured swellings on their snouts that may also function to attract females.

FIGURE 5.15 Cercopithecines like this Sykes monkey possess cheek pouches that allow them to store food.

© iStock/Thinkstock

Colobinae

This subfamily encompasses the Genus *Colobus*, a group of leaf-eating species that live in the forests of Africa and Asia. As we noted earlier, colobus monkeys have specialized stomachs to facilitate the digestion of large quantities of leaves, as well as molars with sharp cusps for cutting

FIGURE 5.16 Their thick coat of fur allows Japanese macaques to tolerate very low temperatures in winter.

© Marc Veraart

---

3. One recently discovered species of macaque, *Macaca munzala*, lives at altitudes of 1,600 to 3,500 metres above sea level, higher than any other nonhuman primate species (Cachel 2006).

FIGURE 5.17 Proboscis monkeys have an unusually large nose, as seen here in an adult male.

© Smellme/Dreamstime.com

hominoids

members of the superfamily Hominoidea; they include apes and humans

and slicing leaves. These features allow them to live in high densities in forested environments. Colobines are arboreal quadrupeds and semibrachiators, and their absent or greatly reduced thumb allows them to swing quickly and easily from branch to branch. They tend to be less sexually dimorphic than the cercopithecines and to live in small groups. African colobus monkeys are frequent prey of chimpanzees, especially those of the Ivory Coast, who hunt in groups. Proboscis monkeys of Borneo are easily recognized by their large, pendulous nose (Figure 5.17), which may act as a sexual signal for females. They are also known to be very good swimmers—unusual among nonhuman primates. About 16 species of langurs occupy the forests of India, Southeast Asia, and Indonesia. One of these species, the Hanuman langur, is revered in India and is known for engaging in infanticide within its group (see Chapter 6).

Hominoidea

The Hominoidea superfamily consists of humans and the apes. It comprises two families: Hylobatidae (the so-called lesser apes, the gibbons and siamangs), and Hominidae (great apes, including humans), and three subfamilies: Ponginae (orangutans), Gorillinae (gorillas), and Homininae (chimpanzees/bonobos and humans). **Hominoids** share the following features:

- Largest of the primates (with the exception of the gibbons and siamangs).
- Diurnal.
- No tail.
- Nails on all digits.
- More complex behaviour.
- More complex brain and cognitive abilities.
- Increased period of infant development and dependency.

Hylobatidae

The eight species of gibbons and siamangs that make up this family are also referred to as lesser apes because of their smaller size compared to the other apes. Confined to the tropical rainforests of Southeast Asia, they exhibit a number of characteristics that reflect their

FIGURE 5.18 The long forearms and curved fingers of white-handed gibbons make them superb brachiators.

© Ingo Arndt/naturepl.com

arboreal way of life, including a locomotor pattern characterized by brachiation (Figure 5.18). This is reflected in their long arms relative to body size; long, curved fingers with reduced thumbs; and highly mobile shoulder joints designed for suspension and arm-over-arm movement. The most impressive brachiators of all nonhuman primates, gibbons and siamangs can move through the trees at speeds of over 50 km an hour! They rely heavily on fruit and show little sexual dimorphism. Males and females form monogamous pair bonds; males are actively involved in rearing their young, and females participate in territorial defence using distinct vocalizations, which have been described as resembling soprano opera singing (Koda et al. 2012).

Hominidae

Orangutans are found only in Borneo (*Pongo pygmaeus*) and Sumatra (*Pongo abelii*). The largest of the Asian apes, and in fact the largest living arboreal mammal in the world, they typically spend most of their time in the trees, where they move slowly using their long, narrow hands and feet to hold onto branches. On the ground, they differ from the other great apes in moving quadrupedally on their fists rather than on their knuckles. They are primarily frugivorous and solitary, and show pronounced sexual dimorphism, with females weighing less than half that of males. Dominant adult males have large cheek pads (Figure 5.19) as well as large **laryngeal sacs** that enable them to make loud vocalizations. Currently numbering less than 30,000 in the wild, orangutans are endangered and face extinction within the next 10 to 20 years.

Gorillas are the largest of the primates and inhabit the forests of western and central Africa. They are divided into two species (*Gorilla beringei* and *Gorilla gorilla*) and four subspecies: the western and eastern lowland gorilla, the mountain gorilla, and the Cross River gorilla. These subspecies differ from one another with respect to a number of features, including the colour and length of their hair and the size of their jaws and teeth. Their large body size—ranging up to 200 kg or more in males—means that they spend most of their time on the ground, where they walk on their knuckles. They are almost exclusively vegetarian and rely heavily on a diet of leaves. Mature adult males (Figure 5.20) are referred to as **silverbacks** because of the saddle of white hair across their backs. They have large **sagittal crests** on the top of their skulls that serve to anchor their powerful jaw muscles. They live in groups consisting of one or occasionally two adult males, a number of adult females, and their offspring. Western gorillas are currently critically endangered, and the remaining subspecies are at risk.

Chimpanzees (*Pan troglodytes*) (Figure 5.21), the best known of all nonhuman primates thanks to the extensive field studies of Jane Goodall and others, live in

FIGURE 5.19 Dominant adult male orangutans have large cheek pads.

© Hemera/Thinkstock

FIGURE 5.20 Primatologist Dian Fossey spent nearly two decades studying mountain gorillas in Rwanda.

Courtesy of Pascale Sicotte

FIGURE 5.21 Chimpanzees live in social groups called communities.

© Paul A. Souders/Corbis

laryngeal sac

an expanded larynx or voice box used to produce vocalizations

silverbacks

mature adult male gorillas characterized by a saddle of white hair across the back

sagittal crests

a large ridge of bone that runs along the sagittal suture of the skull; it serves to anchor the muscles involved in chewing equatorial regions of eastern, central, and western Africa. Although they are arboreal, they spend most of their time on the ground and exhibit a variety of locomotor patterns, including knuckle-walking, semibrachiation, and occasional bipedalism. They are omnivorous and eat a wide range of foods, including small game and other primates, which some groups hunt collectively. Males are larger and heavier than females, but their degree of sexual dimorphism is less pronounced than in gorillas and orangutans. They live in social groups of varying sizes, and males are typically dominant over females. Within these communities, chimpanzees move about in smaller subgroups whose membership frequently changes. Females leave the group of their birth when they become sexually mature and establish themselves in other communities, while males remain in their **natal groups.** Behavioural differences between chimpanzee communities have been well-documented, and their complex behaviour has made them popular models for early hominin behaviour (see Chapter 6).

Bonobos (*Pan paniscus*) (Figure 5.22), sometimes referred to as pygmy chimpanzees, are, in fact, similar in height to the common chimpanzee *Pan troglodytes* but are more slightly built. They also differ from chimps in having smaller heads and dark skin on their face, and less sexual dimorphism. Restricted to the forests of the Democratic Republic of Congo, they have not been as well studied as chimpanzees—owing, in part, to political instability in the Congo. They are both terrestrial and arboreal, eat a variety of foods, including fruit, leaves, seeds, and small mammals, and live in large communities from which females emigrate at or near sexual maturity. Unlike chimpanzees, bonobos tend to be less aggressive, and female bonobos are often dominant to males. Bonobos are particularly well known for their frequent use of non-reproductive sex to facilitate group cohesion and to reduce stress (de Waal 1990). Their true population size is unknown but decreasing numbers due to poaching and habitat destruction among other factors have made them an endangered species.

FIGURE 5.22 Bonobo mothers and infants form close bonds.

© iStock/Thinkstock

natal groups
the groups in which individuals are born

obligate
by virtue of necessity; our recent ancestors of the past 2–3 million years had developed a number of adaptations that effectively obliged them to adopt a terrestrial, bipedal form of locomotion

life history
the occurrence (timing, duration, etc.) of specific events and traits characteristic of a species; common life history variables include gestation length, interbirth interval, age at sexual maturity, and maximum life span

Humans and our earlier human ancestors (hominins) are members of the Tribe Hominini (see Chapter 8), a distinct taxonomic category that recognizes a number of anatomical and behavioural characteristics that distinguish us from other members of the Primate order. Unlike other primates, we live in virtually every environment on the planet, and now even off it! We eat pretty much every food available to us, and we are the only primates who are **obligate** bipeds. As such, we have some unique skeletal adaptations related to our mode of locomotion (see Chapter 8). The phases of our **life history**—which differ from those of the other primates—include a longer gestation period, a prolonged period of infant dependency, a later period of sexual maturation, and a longer life span, as well as a much longer post-reproductive phase in human females (visit the CourseMate site for a discussion of menopause in nonhuman primates). We also have a larger and more complex brain and are the only primates capable of spoken language. Our most distinctive feature is our complete reliance on material culture for survival.

Mapping Nonhuman Primate Genomes

In Chapter 3 we talked about the human genome project. The first call for an international primate genome project to map the genome of nonhuman primate species came in 2000 (McConkey and Varki 2000; VandeBerg et al. 2000). The rationale behind this initiative is the close genetic, metabolic, and physiological similarity of some nonhuman primates to humans. As such, detailed knowledge of their genome has tremendous potential to contribute to our understanding of human disease, evolution, and population genetics. The genomes of a number of nonhuman primate species, including chimpanzees (Chimpanzee Sequencing and Analysis Consortium 2005), rhesus macaques (Gibbs et al. 2007), orangutans (Locke et al. 2011), bonobos (Prüfer et al. 2012), and the western lowland gorilla (Scally et al. 2012) have already been mapped, and efforts are currently under way to map the genomes of additional species (Marques-Bonet et al. 2009).

What have the results of these studies revealed so far? There is a 4% difference between the genomes of humans and chimps with respect to the genes involved in olfaction (i.e., smell), speech, digestion, hearing, inflammatory and immune responses, and resistance to disease (Chimpanzee Sequencing and Analysis Consortium 2005; Varki and Nelson 2007). Chimpanzees, for example, have a significantly higher number of functioning olfactory receptor genes compared to humans (Varki and Nelson 2007). With respect to bonobos, their genome is remarkably similar to that of chimpanzees, and this similarity is consistent with a split between the two occurring approximately 1 Ma, after the formation of the Congo River prevented gene flow from occurring between the two populations (Prüfer et al. 2012). As for gorillas, 30% of the western lowland gorilla genome show a greater number of similarities with that of humans and chimps than the latter two share with each other, despite the fact that humans and chimps share a more recent common ancestor (Scally et al. 2012). Finally, the mapping of nonhuman primate genomes has allowed researchers to calculate the time of divergence of some of these lineages more precisely (see Chapter 7).

Breakthroughs have also been made in primate cloning, which has the potential to allow researchers to develop new medical therapies. Reports of the first primate to be cloned utilizing a method called "embryo splitting" appeared in newspapers worldwide in January 2000. Employing a technique different from that used to clone Dolly the sheep, researchers split an eight-cell embryo of a rhesus macaque into four genetically identical two-cell embryos and implanted them into surrogate mothers, one of whom gave birth to a healthy female offspring (Chan et al. 2000). Since that time, scientists have successfully derived functional embryonic stem cells from adult rhesus macaque skin cells (Byrne et al. 2007). Why are scientists so keen to clone primates? Unlike mice, on which medical treatments are typically tested, monkeys are much more closely related to humans and make excellent models for testing new drugs and other treatments. The hope is that such clones can be used to develop treatments for life-threatening diseases such as diabetes and Parkinson's. Having genetically identical monkeys would also allow researchers to evaluate more accurately their responses to different treatments.

PRIMATE CONSERVATION

In this chapter we have noted that a number of primate species face extinction in the very near future. In 2000, one subspecies of red colobus monkey known as Miss Waldron's red colobus was declared extinct in the wild (Oates et al. 2000), and many more species are on the verge of disappearing forever. In fact, more than 100 of the world's nearly 300 species of primates are now endangered. Among the most critically endangered are the Western gorillas (*Gorilla gorilla*) and the orangutans of Sumatra (*Pongo abelii*).[4] Other species in peril include the silky sifaka, the indri, and four species of lemur on Madagascar; Grauer's gorilla and two species of red colobus monkey in Africa; the pygmy tarsier, the Tonkin snub-nosed monkey, and the Eastern black-crested gibbon in Asia; and five species of New World monkeys (Mittermeier et al. 2012).

---

4. The International Union for Conservation of Nature and Natural Resources, mentioned earlier in this chapter, publishes the *Red List* annually, which identifies the 25 most endangered species.

CHAPTER 5 What It Means to Be a Primate

FIGURE 5.23 The demand for bushmeat has resulted in the slaughter of large numbers of primates.

© Karl Ammann/karlammann.com

Major threats to primates include habitat destruction in the form of deforestation, logging, and forest fires, the hunting of primates for bushmeat (Figure 5.23), and the trade in live animals for laboratories, zoos, and pets. The alteration of natural habitats due to global warming is also having an effect on primate populations (Dunbar 1998; Lehmann et al. 2010). To appreciate the impact of habitat destruction on primates, consider that about 90% of these animals live in tropical and subtropical forests. The destruction of tropical rainforests is occurring at an unprecedented rate. Countries with primate populations are losing an estimated 125,000 km^2 of forest each year (Chapman and Peres 2001). Much of the deforestation currently taking place is directly related to agriculture and resettlement. Selective logging and forest fires are also contributing to a decline in primate populations.[5] For example, in the 1980s and 1990s, a series of fires in Indonesia destroyed many of the fruit trees on which orangutans depend for food, resulting in a marked decline in the orangutan population. On Madagascar, selective logging, hunting, and agricultural practices involving the deliberate burning of forest to create agricultural fields and grazing areas have also had devastating effects on local primate populations.

An excellent case study of the impact of habitat alteration on primates is that of Kibale National Park in Uganda. Commercial logging and the clearing of land for agriculture have led to reduced food availability and increased parasitic infections among primates (Gillespie, Chapman, and Greiner 2005). As well, studies have revealed variation in the ways in which primates have responded to selective logging within the park. Chapman and colleagues (2000) investigated the long-term effects of logging on the density of five species of primates in Kibale and found that those groups living in heavily logged areas of the park experienced more significant population declines than those living in areas that were less heavily logged. In addition, populations inhabiting less heavily logged areas recovered better from habitat destruction than those living in heavily logged ones. Based on these results, Chapman and colleagues (2000) concluded that while low-intensity logging may be compatible with primate conservation, high-intensity logging is not.

Infectious diseases originating in humans are also having a significant impact on nonhuman primates, especially the great apes. Genetic similarities between apes and humans mean that they are susceptible to many of the same kinds of diseases that we are; indeed, many human diseases, such as HIV, originated in primates. The Ebola virus, which has killed hundreds of humans to date, has wrought havoc on gorilla and chimpanzee populations in the Congo. It is estimated that since 2002, 5,000 gorillas have been killed by the virus (Bermejo et al. 2006), and that up to one-quarter of the world's gorilla population has been killed by the disease in the past 10 years. In 2003 alone, an outbreak of Ebola in the Congo resulted in a 56% reduction in the gorilla population and an 89% reduction in the chimpanzee population (Leroy et al. 2004). Other diseases such as polio and anthrax have contributed to the decline in ape populations, and recent studies of chimpanzees in Tanzania and West Africa have revealed evidence of respiratory infections that appear to have been caused by human viruses (Kaur et al. 2008; Köndgen et al. 2008). Particularly alarming is the possibility that primatologists and ecotourists may have been the source of these viruses.

---

5. Selective logging is not the same thing as deforestation—the latter involves the removal of forest to less than 10% of its original level (see Chapman and Peres 2001).

Natural disasters can also take a toll on primate populations and can have a significant impact on many aspects of primate behaviour. In Madagascar, for instance, a two-year drought (1991–92) resulted in increased mortality rates and a significant decline in the population of ring-tailed lemurs living in the Beza-Mahafaly Special Reserve (Gould, Sussman, and Sauther 1999). Similarly, Hurricane Iris, which struck Belize in October 2001, had a pronounced impact on black howler monkeys living in the Monkey River region of southern Belize. This extreme weather event resulted in a significant reduction in the howler population and the complete destruction of the forest canopy. The consequences of this included the breakdown of social groups into smaller units, an increase in the number of solitary animals, a dietary shift from frugivory to folivory, and an increase in the amount of time the monkeys spent on or near the ground (Behie and Pavelka 2005; Pavelka, Brusselers, Nowak et al. 2003; Pavelka, McGoogan, and Steffens 2007).

The loss of primates has a direct impact on human food availability. A number of primates act as seed dispersers, meaning that seeds from the fruits they eat are dispersed in their fecal matter as they move about. Consequently, the loss of even one species of primate can threaten the survival of plant species. On Madagascar, for example, lemurs are the primary seed dispersers and as such play a vital role in maintaining the health of its forests. Similarly, monkeys living in the Taï Forest of West Africa are key seed dispersers; their protection therefore benefits not only them but also human populations that rely on plant resources for food (Koné et al. 2008).

While the threat of extinction looms large for a number of primate species, considerable efforts are being made to protect these animals, and many primatologists here in Canada and elsewhere are becoming increasingly involved in raising awareness of primate conservation. Through their engagement in **public anthropology**, they play a vital role in educating the public about the threats to primates and in promoting effective responses to ensure their survival. The key to designing and implementing successful conservation measures lies in identifying the factors that influence primate density in undisturbed environments and understanding how primate populations respond to, and recover from, habitat disturbance. Studies have shown, for instance, that environmental modification does not necessarily affect all primate species living in that environment in the same way. A decline in one species, for example, may result in an increase in another species.

Similarly, species vary in the ways in which they respond to the fragmentation of forest, with some species remaining within isolated fragments and others moving between them (Chapman and Peres 2001). Understanding how primates respond is therefore important for the development and implementation of appropriate conservation measures, which may include expanding the size of existing protected areas or creating new ones, and protecting or creating corridors between forest fragments (Lehman 2006). The protection of food resources on which they rely is also vital. Thus an awareness of primate diets and nutritional requirements is crucial for the construction of sound conservation plans.

Much of University of Toronto primatologist Shawn Lehman's research focuses on the conservation biogeography of African and South American primates. As the preservation of biodiversity is a key goal of conservation biology, studies of phylogenetic relationships among primates are important for determining conservation priorities. To this end, Lehman and colleagues (Lehman 2006; McGoogan et al. 2007) have analyzed **phylogenetic diversity** in Malagasy (i.e., Madagascar) and other African primates in order to develop recommendations for the preservation of these animals. Underlying this approach is the fact that the extinction of species with higher levels of phylogenetic diversity (i.e., basal taxa with few sister taxa) would mean a greater loss of evolutionary history than the extinction of species with lower levels of diversity (i.e., those with numerous sister taxa) (McGoogan et al. 2007). Applying this measure, McGoogan and colleagues (2007) ranked 55 African primate species according to their conservation priorities and found significant differences between their rankings and those of the IUCN *Red List*, suggesting that the use of phylogenetic diversity in addition to population size and the rate of population decline to assess conservation priorities may be preferable to using only the latter.

public anthropology
an emerging field within anthropology emphasizing community engagement with an aim to bring awareness to issues of inequity in the human domain, be they social, political, economic or other

phylogenetic diversity
a measure of the taxonomic distinctness of a species

Over the past few decades, a number of conservation initiatives have been launched. In 1977, the Jane Goodall Institute for Wildlife Research, Education, and Conservation was founded with the goal of increasing primate habitat conservation, expanding primate research programs, increasing awareness of primates and their relationship with their environment, and ensuring their well-being. Similarly, the Orangutan Foundation International was cofounded in 1986 by Simon Fraser University primatologist Biruté Galdikas to promote orangutan research and conservation, and rehabilitation programs designed to release ex-captive orangutans into the wild have met with some success although many challenges remain (Russon 2009). Other successful conservation measures include the construction of bridges across logging roads to assist the movement, interaction, and mating of nonhuman primates threatened by dwindling habitats. Besides this, national parks have been established, and the development of ecotourism—which promotes primates as tourist attractions—is providing funding needed for their protection. The implementation of CITES (Convention on International Trade in Endangered Species of Wild Flora and Fauna) has led to a decline in the live capture of and trade in primates. Ultimately, however, training local people in conservation and providing them with economic incentives to protect primates and their habitats are key to ensuring the long-term survival of these species.

LEARNING KEYS

KEY IDEAS

- Primates share a set of features that set them apart from other mammals.
- Primate features likely evolved due to a combination of factors, including an arboreal way of life, insect predation, a diet of flowers and nectar, and fine branch feeding.
- Most nonhuman primates live in tropical and subtropical regions of the world, and spend the majority of their time in the trees.
- Primates use a variety of different methods of locomotion, including quadrupedalism, bipedalism, brachiation, and vertical clinging and leaping.
- Primates have a primarily omnivorous diet that includes fruits, leaves, insects, and small mammals, but most species tend to favour certain types of foods.
- Strepsirhines are smaller than monkeys, possess a tooth comb and grooming claw, have a well-developed sense of smell, and are primarily nocturnal.
- Strepsirhines include lemurs, lorises, and galagos.
- Haplorhines have a larger body size and brain than strepsirhines, and are primarily diurnal.
- Haplorhines include tarsiers, New World monkeys, Old World monkeys, apes, and hominins.
- New World monkeys are smaller than Old World monkeys, most species have a dental formula of 2.1.3.3, and some species have a prehensile tail.
- Old World monkeys exhibit a greater size range and a greater degree of sexual dimorphism and possess a

dental formula of 2.1.2.3; some species have ischial callosities.
- Apes have more complex behaviour, a more complex brain, greater cognitive abilities, and an increased period of infant development and dependency compared to monkeys and strepsirhines.
- Humans are unique among primates in being obligate bipeds, having a longer gestation period, a prolonged period of infant dependency, a later period of sexual maturation, and a longer life span.
- Genetic studies have revealed the close relationship between humans and other primates, most notably chimpanzees, with whom we share most of our DNA.
- Primatologists play a key role in primate conservation by studying the factors that influence primate density in undisturbed environments, as well as the ways in which species respond to and recover from habitat disturbance.

KEY TERMS

opposable (p. 97)

neocortex (p. 98)

omnivorous (p. 99)

Strepsirhini (p. 101)

Haplorhini (p. 101)

Platyrrhines (New World monkeys) (p. 107)

Catarrhines (Old World monkeys) (p. 109)

sexual dimorphism (p. 109)

hominoids (p. 110)

obligate (p. 112)

KEY QUESTIONS TO ASK MYSELF

1. Why have primates adapted so well to life in the trees, yet other mammals such as squirrels, who also spend a great deal of time in trees have not?

2. Humans tend to find mates from within their own social group or community. Why then, do some primate species leave the group of their birth to find mating partners?

3. If meat is such a good source of protein and other nutrients, why is it that many primates prefer a diet of fruits and vegetables?

KEY CRITICAL THINKING QUESTIONS

1. Multiple species of primates coexist in a number of regions of the world. What features allow them to occupy the same habitat? Are there any advantages to sharing an environment?

2. What factors do you think best explain the diversity and success of primates?

KEY THINGS TO DO NEXT

Visit **CourseMate** at www.nelson.com/humanvoyage2e to build your comprehension, practise your critical thinking skills, review core concepts, and explore other resources at your disposal.

6 Primate Behavioural Ecology

OVERVIEW

You have now been introduced to our closest living relatives, the nonhuman primates. As you have seen, they exhibit a great deal of diversity in appearance, habitats, locomotor patterns, feeding strategies, and dietary adaptations. Similarly, their behaviours vary greatly and carry a wide range of meanings. This chapter introduces you to primate behavioural ecology—that is, the study of the ways in which primates adapt behaviourally to their environments. We begin by briefly outlining the history of primatology. We then explore what it means to live in social groups; examine aggressive, affiliative, and sexual behaviours/reproductive strategies; and consider whether nonhuman primates possess culture and language. By the end of this chapter, you will appreciate the many similarities we share with our primate cousins. At the same time, you will see that certain behaviours remain unique to humans.

KEY CONCEPTS

Behavioural ecology, dominance, altruism, kin selection, sexual selection, reproductive strategy, infanticide

KEY LEARNING OBJECTIVES

At the end of this chapter, you will be able to

LO1 Describe the different primate social groups and the benefits of living in such groups

LO2 Explain the advantages and disadvantages of studying primates in captivity versus in the wild

LO3 Apply an evolutionary perspective to understanding male and female reproductive strategies

LO4 Compare and contrast the contexts in which tool use occurs among nonhuman primates

LO5 Evaluate the strategies that primates use to maintain social stability and cohesion

LO6 Predict how primate communication might vary from one context to another

PROLOGUE: PRIMATES "R" US

The study of our nearest relatives, the nonhuman primates, is carried out as often as not by researchers in non-anthropological disciplines (e.g., psychology, medicine), and primatologists publish in journals dedicated solely to that field of study, attend meetings emphasizing primatological themes, and are members of various professional societies devoted to the science of primatology. All of that said, it is also true that primatology maintains a unique relationship with anthropology generally, and with biological anthropology in particular. The reasons are matters not simply of history, but also of pedagogy. Humans are primates, and our understanding of human origins and human patterns of social and sexual behaviour is enriched when we examine primate origins and behaviours; indeed, our understanding would be poorer without that examination. In the following pages, we explore a number of facets of nonhuman primate **behavioural ecology**. We urge you, as you read, to reflect on both the differences and the similarities—on the ways that primate behaviours are distinct with respect to our own, but also on the ways they parallel human patterns. But be aware of what has been called the "trap of the present": the diversity of primate and human behaviour that can be observed today represents millions of years of independent evolution. Thus, behavioural similarities among primate species (and ourselves) may say nothing about evolutionary connections (homology) and everything about how two (or more) species converged on the same "solution" in similar ecological circumstances (homoplasy).

behavioural ecology

the study of the ways in which primates adapt behaviourally to their environments

THE ROOTS OF PRIMATOLOGY

The first studies of nonhuman primates date back to the 17th century, when scientists dissected primates to examine their anatomical similarities to humans and other animals. While primate anatomy continued to be a major research focus well into the 20th century, studies of the behaviour of **captive** primates were also undertaken. At the same time, scientists became increasingly aware of the need to provide a constant supply of animals for medical research. This led to the establishment of colonies of **provisioned** primates, including the first major primate breeding facility in the United States, established in 1930 by psychologist Robert Yerkes in Florida,[1] and a colony of **free-ranging** rhesus macaques established in 1938 by psychologist Clarence Ray Carpenter on Cayo Santiago Island off the coast of Puerto Rico. In the early 1970s, a troop of Japanese macaques (*Macaca fuscata*) were relocated from their home range of Arashiyama, near Tokyo, to a colony in Texas. This colony, known as the Arashiyama West group, has been the focus of considerable study (Fedigan and Asquith 1991; Pavelka and Fedigan 1999; Pavelka, Fedigan, and Zohar 2002).

captive

housed in environments such as zoos and colonies where movement is restricted

provisioned

supplied with food

free-ranging

animals whose movements are not hindered by humans

FIGURE 6.1 Jane Goodall has studied the chimpanzees of Gombe Stream National Park, Tanzania, for over 40 years.

© Bettmann/CORBIS

The first field studies, which were typically only days or weeks in duration, were also initiated during this time period to document the behaviours exhibited by species in their natural habitats. Following World War II, Japanese primatologists began collecting data on *Macaca fuscata*, and their extensive studies have produced an impressive body of data on the behaviour of these animals and many other primate species. Experimental studies of primates in laboratory settings also became popular during the 1950s and 1960s. These included social deprivation experiments conducted by psychologist Harry Harlow on rhesus macaques and the attempt to teach American Sign Language to a chimpanzee named Washoe.

The 1960s also marked the launch of three extraordinary field studies: Jane Goodall's study of chimpanzees (Goodall 1986) (Figure 6.1), Dian Fossey's research on mountain gorillas

---

1. This colony has since relocated to Georgia and is now known as the Yerkes Regional Primate Centre.

(Fossey 1983), and Biruté Galdikas's study of orangutans (Galdikas 1995) (Figure 6.2). These and other long-term field studies, some of which have been carried out over several decades, allowed researchers to follow multiple generations and examine life histories, demographic shifts, the relationship between the physical environment and diet, locomotion, and social interactions, and the impact of environmental changes on behavioural patterns; they also turned upside down many of our notions about nonhuman primates. Canadian primatologists have made significant contributions to our knowledge of nonhuman primates, including variation in demography and life history in ring-tailed lemurs (Gould, Sussman, and Sauther 2003) (Figure 6.3), the impact of predation on activity patterns (Colquhoun 2006), and predictors of reproductive success in capuchins (Fedigan, Carnegie, and Jack 2008) (see Box 6.1).

There are disadvantages to studying captive primates. While they can be closely observed over many generations, their environments can be manipulated to study the effects on behaviour. Furthermore, regular provisioning means that their natural foraging patterns are not observable. Captivity may alter their activity levels so that animals normally active during the day become active at night instead. Confined spaces may alter mating patterns and increase the level of aggression within a group. Captive primates may be more prone to stress, and the incidence of abnormal behaviours may be higher than normal. The lack of seasonal changes can affect reproductive schedules so that birth rates are either increased or decreased. Captive primates, such as those imported for biomedical research, have been known to carry pathogens that can be transmitted to humans.[2]

FIGURE 6.2 Biruté Galdikas teaches primatology at Simon Fraser University and has spent the last 40 years studying orangutans in Borneo.

SFU Public Affairs and Media Relations.
Creative Commons.

FIGURE 6.3 Primatologist Lisa Gould observing a ring-tailed lemur in Madagascar.

Courtesy of Lisa Gould

There are also disadvantages to studying primates in the field. Working in remote places can be expensive and dangerous. It takes time to locate the subjects, particularly if their home range is large, and for the animals to become **habituated**.[3] It takes still more time to identify all of the individuals in a group, map out their relationships to one another, and

habituated
accustomed to the presence of humans

---

2. A well-known case occurred in 1989 and involved a research lab in Reston, Virginia, where a group of macaques imported from the Philippines was found to carry a strain of the Ebola virus. Fortunately, the virus proved to be fatal only to the monkeys.
3. Unhabituated animals are likely to run away or stop what they are doing when humans are near.

CHAPTER 6 Primate Behavioural Ecology

BOX 6.1

PROFILE ... A Brief History of Primatology in Canada

© John Addicott

The study of primate behaviour has a short but ever-expanding history in Canada. Primatology began at Canadian universities in the late 1960s and early 1970s with the arrival of Frances Burton at the University of Toronto and me at the University of Alberta. Burton began her career studying primate anatomy but soon developed what would become her lifelong interest in behavioural studies of "urban monkeys"— primates that live among humans, such as the Barbary macaques of Gibraltar and the Kowloon macaques of Hong Kong. I specialize in long-term socioecological studies of monkeys that live in large multi-male, multi-female groups, working first with Japanese macaques and then with Costa Rican monkeys. Bernard Chapais arrived at the Université de Montréal in the early 1980s with a focus on kinship and dominance in macaques, an interest that he later expanded to comparative studies of kinship across primates, including humans.

These three founders established active research and teaching programs at their institutions and soon graduated the first Canadian-trained primatologists, who went on to hold their own university positions. Anne Zeller and James Paterson trained under Burton at the University of Toronto and then launched primatology programs at the University of Waterloo and the University of Calgary, respectively. Zeller specialized in primate communication and Paterson in baboon ecology. Mary Pavelka, Colin Chapman, and Lisa Gould trained under me at the University of Alberta and went on to establish their own careers at the University of Calgary, McGill University, and the University of Victoria, respectively. Pavelka focuses on the behavioural ecology of Belizean monkeys, Chapman on the ecology and conservation of

Ugandan primates, and Gould on Malagasy lemurs. Pascale Sicotte and Paul Vasey trained under Chapais at the Université de Montréal and then set up research programs at the University of Calgary and the University of Lethbridge, respectively. Sicotte's focus has been on socioecology of African primates and Vasey's on primate sexual behaviour.

The University of Toronto is still an active centre for primate research, with the focus on lemurs and Asian macaques. This research was perpetuated after Dr. Burton's retirement by Shawn Lehman (an early protégé of Paterson's, Lehman obtained his Ph.D. at Washington University), Michael Schillaci, and Joyce Parga. I moved to the University of Calgary in 2002 and collaborated with Pavelka, Sicotte, and Paterson (the latter retired in 2005 and was replaced by Steig Johnson) to create a large and vibrant graduate program in primatology that has produced a number of young Ph.D.s who are now beginning their own careers in this discipline.

At the University of Lethbridge, Vasey was recruited by Drew Rendall (another of Paterson's early protégés, Rendall obtained his Ph.D. at the University of California, Davis). Rendall also recruited Louise Barrett and Peter Henzi (from the United Kingdom and South Africa, respectively) to create another large graduate program in primatology, the only one in Canada situated in a psychology department rather than an anthropology department. Presently, the University of Calgary, University of Lethbridge, McGill University, University of Toronto, and University of Victoria are all institutions where one can train for a career in primate behavioural studies.

Although primatologists in Canada focus on diverse species and topics, they share a common practice of collecting socioecological data and (with the exception of Bernard Chapais) study free-ranging primates in their natural habitats— that is, they do field research. Being mainly anthropologists, primatologists in Canada began with (and continue to exhibit) an interest in comparisons between nonhuman and human primates. Nonetheless, they have also broadened their lens to develop strong research programs in primate behavioural ecology, life histories, and conservation.

Source: Written by Dr. Linda Fedigan, Professor and Canada Research Chair in Primatology and Bioanthropology at the University of Calgary

recognize their various behaviours. Observing these animals can also be difficult if most or all of their activities take place high up in the trees. While field studies of unprovisioned animals can provide better information about foraging patterns, researchers working in the field may occasionally give food to their study subjects in order to more closely observe group dynamics. Interestingly, the provisioning of Japanese macaques with sweet potatoes during field studies in the 1950s resulted in the adoption and spread of a unique behaviour in which one of the animals, an adult female, began washing the potatoes to remove sand, a practice that subsequently spread to other members of the group.

Primate behavioural ecology—a field that emerged in the 1970s—has moved away from emphasizing description toward the use of standardized methods of data collection, allowing primatologists to conduct broader comparative studies and to test hypotheses about the adaptive significance of various behaviours. Increasingly sophisticated research methods are also being used to study primates, including DNA analysis to investigate mating systems and reproductive strategies, and the relationship between kinship and social behaviour (Di Fiore 2003).

Primatologists also measure hormone levels in urine, feces, and other biological samples to study the impact of hormones on behaviour (Anestis 2010), and utilize GIS (geographic information systems) to analyze spatial data. More attention is also being directed toward primate conservation, and many primatologists are actively involved in efforts to protect these animals (see Chapter 5).

SOCIAL LIVING

Primates are social animals (Figure 6.4) and exhibit a variety of different types of social organization. The size and type of their social groups are influenced by a number of factors, including the number of predators in their environment and the availability and distribution of food resources. Larger groups, for example, are typically found in areas with a greater number of predators. In contrast, smaller groups tend to be found in areas where food resources are widely dispersed. Different types of social groups have been documented within a single species. Living in a group provides a number of benefits to its members. It maximizes food exploitation, because a greater number of individuals are more likely to find food than a smaller number. This is especially important where food resources are unevenly distributed and hard to find. Primates living in social groups can share information on feeding sites and defend food resources. Social groups provide members with a greater number of mating partners, thereby increasing their reproductive fitness. Such groups offer protection from predators as well as from primates in other groups. Help in caring for offspring is available. Finally, groups allow for the transmission of behaviours from one member to another.

FIGURE 6.4 Social living provides baboons and other primates with mating partners and protection from predators, among other benefits.

Courtesy of Travis Steffens

CHAPTER 6 Primate Behavioural Ecology

According to British anthropologist and evolutionary psychologist Robin Dunbar, the cognitive demands of living in complex social groups may, in fact, explain why primates have unusually large brains for their body size. In particular, Dunbar argues that the more strongly bonded relationships (reproductive and non-reproductive) seen in primates compared to other mammals are associated with particular demands that have selected for larger brains. Support for what is now known as the **social brain hypothesis** comes from the observation that primates have more complex social systems than other mammals, and that there is a strong correlation, particularly among anthropoid primates, between social group size and brain size, most notably the size of the neocortex (Dunbar 1992, 1998b).

Despite its advantages, group living also has drawbacks. Those of you who have shared a house or apartment know that living in groups can lead to conflict. Larger groups are associated with increased competition for food and mating partners, as well as increased stress, as reflected in lower birth rates and a greater incidence of aggression.[4] Furthermore, increased group size may also facilitate the spread of infectious diseases (Genton et al. 2012).

A number of species such as gibbons and siamangs are **monogamous**—that is, they form social units characterized by one adult male, one adult female, and their immature offspring. Within these units, the adult male and female form long-term mating partnerships and there is little sexual dimorphism, reflecting the decreased need by males to compete for females. Males also tend to invest more time and energy caring for their offspring than they do in other types of social groups. **Single-male/multi-female** communities consist of a single adult male, several adult females, and their offspring.[5] This type of social group, which has a **polygynous** mating pattern, is characteristic of howler monkeys, langurs, geladas, and some gorilla populations. A less common form of social structure, seen in marmosets and tamarins, is **polyandry**, characterized by groups consisting of one adult female, several adult males, and their offspring.[6] Unlike other primate species, where females are the primary caregivers of infants, males within these social units take an active role in looking after infants during the first few months of their life.

The most common type of social group is the **multi-male/multi-female** group characteristic of species such as savanna baboons and macaques, and some colobus and New World monkeys. Comprising a number of adult males and females and offspring, these groups can number in the hundreds and are typically found in areas where predation pressure is high. Mating activity is promiscuous, and sexual dimorphism is marked. A form of multi-male/multi-female group seen among chimpanzees and bonobos is the **fission–fusion** society. The most flexible type of social group, it is characterized by fluid membership, with frequent movement of members to and from the group. Promiscuous sexual activity and moderate to high sexual dimorphism are characteristic of this type of community, reflecting the need for males to compete with one another for mating partners. Finally, several species of primates, most notably orangutans, are mainly solitary, spending most of their time foraging for food on their own and interacting with one another only occasionally for the purpose of mating.[7]

Primate social groups are dynamic entities, and adolescents often leave the group of their birth (their natal group) to join another group or form one of their own. This strategy ensures that inbreeding does not occur. Among many primate species, males emigrate while females are **philopatric**, remaining in their natal group for life. Good examples are Japanese macaques and rhesus monkeys, in which females form **matrilineal** kin groups. In contrast, female gorillas, chimpanzees, and bonobos leave the group of their birth when they reach sexual maturity to join other established groups.

---

4. One of the ways in which stress can be investigated in primates is by measuring the level of hormones such as cortisol in body fluids.

5. This type of social group was formerly referred to as a harem.

6. There may be more than one adult female in this type of group, but usually only one is sexually active.

7. Some primatologists prefer to call these species semisolitary, as females usually forage with their offspring.

In most primate societies, individuals are organized into **dominance hierarchies**. In this structure, some individuals are of higher **rank** than others. These hierarchies are more pronounced in single-male/multi-female and multi-male/multi-female groups, in which males must compete with one another for access to females, a notion grounded in Darwin's theory of **sexual selection** (discussed later in this chapter). These hierarchies serve an important function—they provide social stability and reduce conflict within a group. Dominant individuals generally have greater access to food resources and mating partners, although higher rank is not invariably associated with greater reproductive success: in species among which female choice plays an important role in mating strategies, **subordinate** males may succeed in gaining mates. Males may attain their rank through physical strength, aggression, and the ability to mobilize support within their group by forming alliances, often with related males. They may also inherit their rank from their mother, as in the case of bonobos. A female's position in the hierarchy may also be inherited from her mother, as seen in matrilineal societies such as those of baboons and macaques. Her rank may also increase as she ages and has offspring. Top-ranking individuals in a group are typically referred to as **alpha** males or females.

Separate dominance hierarchies may exist for males and females, and males are usually dominant over females. In a small number of species such as monogamous gibbons, however, the two sexes are co-dominant; in still other species—notably lemurs—females are dominant over males. Female dominance hierarchies tend to be more stable; male hierarchies can change rapidly depending on age, body size, kinship, and other factors.

Rank within a dominance hierarchy can affect an individual member's health by influencing susceptibility to stress-related diseases (Sapolsky 2005). Also, dominance rank can affect reproductive success by influencing the survival of offspring, the age at which offspring reach sexual maturity, and the rate of reproduction. Among the Gombe chimpanzees, for instance, higher ranking females were found to have higher infant survival rates, more rapidly maturing female offspring, and reduced **interbirth interval,** resulting in higher fertility rates, collectively reflecting preferential access to better foraging areas (Jones et al. 2010). An interesting example of delayed sexual maturation is exhibited by orangutans, among whom the presence of a dominant male can lead to the arrested development of subordinate males so that they fail to develop secondary sexual characteristics, such as the classic "cheek-flange" (Maggioncalda, Czekala, and Sapolsky 2002; Winkler 2005).

HUNTING AND MEAT EATING

In the previous chapter we discussed some of the feeding and foraging strategies of nonhuman primates, including the different types of diets they consume, morphological adaptations to diet, and the relationship between feeding strategies and resource distribution and seasonality. We also mentioned that some primates occasionally kill and eat small mammals, including other primates. A great deal of attention has been directed toward the hunting behaviour of chimpanzees in particular, and differences in hunting strategies have been observed between chimpanzees living in Gombe versus the Taï Forest, with the former engaged in individual opportunistic hunting of immature red colobus monkeys and the latter in cooperative hunting of mature red colobus monkeys (Figure 6.5), although there is disagreement over whether the latter behaviour is truly cooperative (Sayers and Lovejoy 2008).

A number of social and ecological hypotheses have been proposed to explain hunting among chimpanzees. The former include the "meat-for-sex" hypothesis, which argues that males hunt in order to obtain meat to give females in exchange for sex (Gomes and Boesch 2009; Stanford et al. 1994), and the male bonding hypothesis, which argues that males hunt in order to cement alliances with one another (Stanford et al. 1994). The latter include the "nutrient shortfall" hypothesis, which proposes that hunting and meat eating increase during periods of food scarcity when preferred foods, namely fruit, are unavailable (Teleki 1973), and the "nutrient surplus" hypothesis, which argues that hunting is more likely to

dominance hierarchies
social structures in which males or females hold positions of rank determined either through competition or inheritance

rank
the social position or status of an individual within a group

sexual selection
a theory proposed by Charles Darwin to explain why males of some species adopt behaviours or morphologies that may not appear adaptive in terms of natural selection, but that in fact enhance reproductive opportunities as a result of successful competition with other males and their subsequent selection by females as potential mates

subordinate
a lower ranking individual

alpha
the highest ranking individual in a group

interbirth interval
the length of time between successive births

CHAPTER 6 Primate Behavioural Ecology

FIGURE 6.5 Three chimpanzees share a red colobus monkey that they have hunted and killed, while a fourth individual begs for a share of the carcass.

© David Bygott

occur when dietary quality is high and can provide the extra energy needed for hunting (Mitani and Watts 2001). Studies evaluating these hypotheses have yielded mixed results, however, and the factors underlying chimpanzee hunting behaviour are likely complex (Gilby et al. 2006).

Hunting and meat eating have also been documented in wild bonobos, who are known to prey not only on terrestrial animals such as squirrels and antelopes, but also on other primates (Hohmann and Fruth 2008; Surbeck, Fowler, Deimel, and Hohmann 2009; Surbeck and Hohmann 1993). In contrast to chimpanzees, among which males play the dominant role in pursuing and hunting their prey and sharing meat, both male and female bonobos are involved in the acquisition of prey and the distribution of meat, and females may snatch prey away from males (Hohmann and Fruth 1993; Surbeck and Hohmann 2008).

The documentation of hunting behaviour among bonobos challenges the long-held belief that these primates are distinctly different from chimpanzees in their level of social violence (Wrangham 1999). As Stanford (1998) points out, however, apparent differences between bonobos and chimpanzees in the acquisition and consumption of food may simply reflect the small number of bonobo groups that have been studied to date. Field data suggest, in fact, that while bonobos differ from chimpanzees in terms of the type of prey and method of acquisition, they consume meat in similar frequencies (Hohmann and Fruth 2008).

The capture and eating of meat, although rare, has also been documented in Sumatran orangutans. Of the dozen or so cases of meat eating that have been recorded in these primates, all involved the capture and consumption of slow lorises by both males and females (Hardus et al. 2012; Utami and Van Hooff 1997; van Schaik et al. 2009), and meat eating appears to occur only during seasonal shortages of ripe fruit (Hardus et al. 2012).

It is important to emphasize here that despite the attention that hunting and meat eating and sharing have garnered among primatologists, particularly with respect to the use of nonhuman primates as models of early hominin behaviour (as discussed in the next section), meat in fact comprises only a small portion of the diet of chimpanzees, and hunting occurs relatively infrequently (Sayers and Lovejoy 2008). Among the Fongoli chimpanzees of Senegal, for instance, insects are an important component of the diet, and these chimpanzees consume termites throughout the year unlike their counterparts elsewhere (Bogart and Pruetz 2011). This observation supports the hypothesis that insects may have been a valuable resource among early hominins occupying similar environments (ibid.).

DO NONHUMAN PRIMATES HAVE CULTURE?

Perhaps no other primate behaviour has garnered as much attention as tool use. Indeed, the use of tools is what has made primates—the great apes in particular—such attractive models for studying early hominin behaviour (although this approach has been critiqued recently; see Sayers and Lovejoy, 2008). The first observation of tool use among primates in the wild dates back to the 1960s, when Jane Goodall witnessed Gombe chimpanzees modifying and using twigs to extract termites from mounds (Figure 6.6). Since then, numerous incidents of tool use have been recorded among both captive and wild primates, and considerable variation has been observed within and between species. For instance, chimpanzees living in West Africa typically use composite tools in the form of hammer stones and anvils to crack open nuts (Haslam et al. 2009), while those living in the savannah woodlands of western Tanzania use sticks to dig for tubers, roots, and bulbs—an activity they engage in during the rainy season, when other foods are also abundant (Hernandez-Aguilar, Moore, and Pickering 2007). In Senegal, chimpanzees have been observed fashioning spears from twigs to capture prosimians (bushbabies) in the hollows of tree trunks and branches (Pruetz and Bertolani 2007), and those in the Republic of Guinea make sponges out of leaves to soak up water (Sugiyama 1995) (Figure 6.7). The use of multiple tool sets to access a single food source has also been documented (Boesch et al. 2009; Sanz, Morgan, and Gulick 2004).

FIGURE 6.6 East African chimpanzees have been observed using sticks to fish for termites.

© Papilio/Alamy

A synthesis by Whiten and colleagues (2001) of data derived from nine chimpanzee communities revealed significant variation in behavioural repertoires among groups. More specifically, of 65 different behaviours observed in these communities, 39 were categorized as customary or habitual, and were "sufficiently frequent at one or more sites to be consistent with social transmission" (Whiten et al. 2001, 1481–1482). The transmission of novel behaviours between wild chimpanzee communities, such as the spread of "ant fishing" from one community in Gombe National Park to another, has also recently been documented (O'Malley et al. 2012). Furthermore, the transmission of cultural behaviours appears to occur primarily through females, who leave their birth group on reaching sexual maturity (Lind and Lindenfors 2010; O'Malley et al. 2012).

Archaeologist Julio Mercader of the University of Calgary conducted a fascinating study of the antiquity of tool use among chimpanzees. He and his team investigated a collection of what appeared to be stone tools recovered

FIGURE 6.7 A chimpanzee drinks water from a sponge made of leaves.

© Tom McHugh/Science Source

FIGURE 6.8 Anthropologist Julio Mercader of the University of Calgary has found evidence of chimpanzee stone tool use dating back 4,300 years.

Photograph by Ken Bendiktsen. Courtesy of the University of Calgary.

FIGURE 6.9 Orangutans have recently been observed using tools in the wild.

© Jonathan Hewitt/Alamy

from the Taï Forest (Figure 6.8). Dating to 4,300 years ago, the tools had traces of starch residue, suggesting that they had been used to process the same species of nuts favoured by chimpanzees in that region today. The data also indicate that chimpanzees transported stones from other locations to areas where they were used repeatedly (Mercader, Barton et al. 2007; Mercader, Panger, and Boesch 2002). The findings generated by this new field of "primate archaeology" (Haslam et al. 2009) have the potential to provide valuable insight into the origins of tool use among humans (see Chapter 9). For example, wear patterns on tools used by nonhuman primates can be compared to those on tools used by early hominins to identify various activities. The study of use-wear traces and residues on stone artifacts left by chimpanzees and other primates may also provide evidence of plant tool manufacture and use, of which nothing remains in the archaeological record. As Haslam and colleagues (2009, 342) point out, the recognition that nonhuman primates can produce archaeological assemblages also means that we must be cautious in interpreting such assemblages as being the sole product of hominins.

Tool use has also been observed among wild orangutans (Figure 6.9). Biruté Galdikas (1982), for example, recorded several incidents in the field during which individuals used sticks to scratch their backs or scare off wasps. More recently, primatologist Carel van Schaik observed orangutans of the Suaq Balimbing swamp in Sumatra using and modifying tools to extract fruit, honey, and insects. He and his team also documented the transmission of this behaviour to other members of the group (van Schaik et al. 2003). Interestingly, other orangutan populations in Borneo and Sumatra do not appear to use tools, leading to speculation that tool use by the Suaq orangutans may reflect their insect-rich environment. It is also possible that tool use has not yet been acquired by other orangutan groups. Whatever the case, van Schaik argues that the common ancestor of apes and humans likely used tools and that great ape cultures may have existed for at least 14 million years (ibid.). Captive orangutans have also been observed modifying and using tools (Nakamichi 2004).

Unlike chimpanzees and orangutans, which have been regularly observed to use tools in the wild, gorillas have only rarely been observed to do so. Breuer and colleagues (2005) recently documented two examples in wild western gorillas. In one case, a gorilla was observed using a stick to test the depth of a pool of water before wading through it (Figure 6.10), and in another case, a gorilla used the trunk of a small shrub as a bridge to cross a swampy area (Breuer, Ndoundou-Hockemba, and Fishlock 2005). Wild Cross River gorillas have also been seen using tools in response to interactions with humans (Wittiger and Sunderland-Groves 2007).

Incidents of tool use among wild bonobos are rare but may reflect, in part, the small number of groups that have been studied in their natural environment (Gruber et al. 2010). Wild bonobos have been observed using leaves as sponges to soak up water, throwing sticks and branches at other bonobos and at humans, and using twigs to scratch their back or fend off aggressive bees (Hohmann and Fruth 2003a). Captive bonobos, in contrast, have been found to have the same tool-using capabilities as chimpanzees (Gruber et al. 2010). One well-known individual, a male named Kanzi, acquired the ability to make and use stone tools by observing humans doing the same (Figure 6.11). Kanzi also independently developed his own technique of making tools by throwing stones against a hard surface to fracture them (Schick et al. 1999; Toth, Schick, and Savage-Rumbaugh 1993). Like chimpanzees, female bonobos engaged in a greater range of tool-use behaviours than males and used a greater diversity of tools (Gruber et al. 2010). These and other studies suggest that the potential to make and use stone tools was present in the last common ancestor of *Homo* and *Pan* (Roffman et al. 2012).

Tool use is not restricted to the great apes, and several species of monkeys have been observed using tools in the wild. For example, bearded capuchin monkeys in the forests of Brazil use stones to dig for grubs and tubers and to crack open hard food objects (Figure 6.12), as well as twigs and branches to probe for insects and honey (Fragaszy et al. 2004; Moura and Lee 2004). Capuchins also appear to be selective in their choice of stone tools (Visalberghi et al. 2009). Finally, long-tailed macaques living in coastal areas have been observed using stones to crack open molluscs and other marine prey (Gumert and Malaivijitnond 2012; Malaivijitnond et al. 2007).

Primate Medicine: Is There a Doctor in the Forest?

The observation that primates sometimes consume or anoint themselves with plants, insects, and soils that have little or no nutritional value has led to speculation that some of these items serve medicinal

FIGURE 6.10 A gorilla uses a stick to test the depth of the water.

© AP Photo/Wildlife Conservation Society, Thomas Breuer

FIGURE 6.11 Kanzi the bonobo was taught to produce flint flakes by striking one stone against another.

Courtesy of Duane M. Rumbaugh

FIGURE 6.12 Bearded capuchin monkeys use hammer stones and anvils to crack open nuts.

© The Image Bank/Getty

purposes. Self-medication by animals, also known as **zoopharmacognosy**, is attracting increasing attention among primatologists as well as other scientists searching for natural substances that could be used to develop drugs for human use. Employing plants and insects as treatments for ailments such as parasitic infections and gastrointestinal upsets has been documented in a number of primate species (Huffman 1997). Capuchin monkeys in Costa Rica, for example, have been observed rubbing themselves with oranges, lemons, and limes, which are known to contain antibacterial compounds. They have also been observed rubbing their fur with the same plants often used by local indigenous people to treat skin conditions (Baker 1996), which raises the interesting possibility that humans are adding to their own traditional knowledge by borrowing from their nonhuman relatives. Wedge-capped capuchins in Venezuela intentionally rub themselves with millipedes known to contain compounds that act as insect repellents, especially against mosquitoes that transmit botflies (Valderrama et al. 2000).

Pregnant and lactating female sifakas in western Madagascar consume greater amounts of tannin-rich plants than other members of their group. The consumption of tannins has been linked to increased body weight and increased milk secretion. In addition, tannins have antiparasitic properties (Carrai, Borgognini-Tarli, and Huffman 2003). Chimpanzees of Tanzania's Mahale Mountains National Park increased consumption of plants with known medicinal properties during the rainy season, when rates of nematode infection were higher than normal (Huffman et al. 1997), while in Uganda, chimpanzee leaf-swallowing to expel parasites has been associated with anthropogenic habitat fragmentation due to deforestation (McLennan and Huffman 2012). Similarly, bitter pith chewing[8] has been linked to parasite-related diseases in the Mahale chimpanzees (Ohigashi et al. 1994). The use of medicinal plants to treat parasitic infections and gastrointestinal upsets has been documented in bonobos and gorillas as well (Huffman 1997).

Geophagy, the intentional consumption of soil, has been observed in many primate species (including humans). This practice appears to serve a variety of functions, including neutralizing plant toxins, treating gastrointestinal disorders and diarrhea, providing nutrients, and protecting against malaria (Burton, Bolton, and Campbell 1999; Glander 1994; Krishnamani and Mahaney 2000). For example, the practice of eating soil together with clumps of leaves, documented in chimpanzees in Kibale National Park, appears to enhance the antimalarial properties of the leaves (Klein, Fröhlich, and Krief 2008). Zoopharmacognosy is a fascinating area of study, which leaves us to wonder about the antiquity and evolutionary origin of such behaviours and the degree to which they may have been practised by early hominins.

AGONISTIC BEHAVIOURS

Acts of aggression, or **agonistic behaviours**, are common in many primate communities. They occur between individuals of the same sex or the opposite sex; between related or unrelated individuals; and between individuals of different rank. The frequency of these acts depends on a number of factors, including the availability of food resources, mating partners, and space. Aggressive behaviours may take the form of threats conveyed by facial expressions and gestures, such as baring the canine teeth, or they may rise to the level of physical fighting resulting in serious injury and occasionally death. Different forms of aggression characterize males and females: males tend to have brief face-to-face encounters, whereas female encounters tend to be more prolonged.

The first observations of intergroup conflict among chimpanzees were made in the 1970s, when Jane Goodall and her colleagues observed attacks between neighbouring groups that resulted in the death of a number of individuals (Goodall et al. 1979). Initially thought to be a rarity, these acts of aggression are now known to be a common feature of chimpanzee society

---

8. "Pith" refers to the soft, spongy substance in the centre of the stems of many plants.

and to occur in the context of defending territories, food resources, and females (Wrangham and Peterson 1996). Intragroup conflict has also been documented in many primate species. In chimpanzee as well as olive baboon communities, for instance, attacks by males on females have often been recorded, and patterns of injury are known to vary by sex, rank, and age (e.g., MacCormick et al. 2012 for olive baboons). Estrous[9] females are often targeted, suggesting that males use violence and physical coercion in order to gain sexual access. Aggressive encounters associated with competition for mating partners and territory have also been documented among male orangutans. Similarly, acts of intrasexual aggression in the context of mating have been observed among wild bonobos (Hohmann and Fruth 2003b).

One of the interesting results of long-term field studies that have been conducted on gorillas has been the finding that these animals are much less aggressive than previously believed. Indeed, gorillas have long been portrayed as ferocious animals. One of the most colourful descriptions of their reportedly fierce nature comes from the account of a 19th-century American missionary named Dr. Savage, who wrote: "When confronted with a gorilla the hunter must stand his ground while listening to the horrifying cries and watching the onrushing monster, and then as the animal gets closer and closer, the courageous hunter steps forward and puts the barrel of the gun in the gorilla's mouth and pulls the trigger. If the gun fires the gorilla drops dead but if the gun does not fire, the gorilla crushes the barrel between its teeth reversing the intended order of events" (Savage 1847, 423, quoted in Swindler 1998, 13).[10]

AFFILIATIVE BEHAVIOURS

Grooming

Among primates, one of the most common **affiliative** behaviours is grooming (Figure 6.13). A type of **altruistic** behaviour, it serves a number of important functions, including removing **ectoparasites**, reducing stress, reinforcing social bonds, currying favours such as food, sex, and protection, and gaining access to infants. Grooming occurs between lower and higher ranking individuals, males and females, related and unrelated individuals, and parents and their offspring. Its frequency and duration depend on a number of factors, including group size, sex ratio, and female dispersal patterns. For example, primates living in larger groups tend to spend more time grooming than those in smaller groups,[11] whereas those living in small groups may spend very little time engaged in this activity. Interestingly, as group size increases, individuals tend to reduce the number of social grooming partners in order to reinforce alliances among a "core set" of supporters (Dunbar 2012). Females who remain with their natal group spend a greater amount of time grooming than females who leave their birth group upon maturity (Lehmann, Korstjens, and Dunbar 2007a). Rank and kinship also play an important role in the distribution of grooming within social groups (Schino 2001).

affiliative
amicable behaviours that promote social cohesion

altruistic
behaviour that benefits other members of a group but is either of no benefit to the individual engaged in it or is harmful to that individual

ectoparasites
parasites on the outside of the body (e.g., in the fur)

FIGURE 6.13 Grooming is a pleasurable activity that reduces tension and reinforces social bonds.

© AP Photo/Shuji Kajiyama

Alliances

Cooperation is a vital component of primate social groups. Primates depend on one another for their survival, and affiliative behaviour has been observed in virtually all primate species (de Waal 1990). It has been hypothesized that

---

9. "Estrous" is the adjectival form of the noun "estrus."

10. Savage believed not only that the gorilla was an aggressive carnivore, but also that it was a species of orangutan!

11. Members of large groups may spend as much as 20% of their day grooming.

kin selection

the tendency of individuals to direct beneficial behaviour toward relatives living within the same social group

this behaviour evolved indirectly through **kin selection**—that is, the tendency of primates to direct beneficial behaviour toward their relatives, thereby contributing to the survival of some of their alleles.[12] Indeed, kinship plays an important role in primate society by fostering alliances and strong social bonds. Kin selection may also explain why primates engage in altruistic behaviour such as grooming and providing care and protection for related members of their group.

Within primate societies, individuals often form alliances for the purpose of getting access to food resources and mating partners, gaining protection from other members of the group, or launching an attack against a third party. Alliances may be formed between members of the same sex, members of the opposite sex, biologically related individuals, unrelated individuals, and individuals of different ages and social ranks. Some of these alliances, such as mating **consortships**, may be short-term; others may last for years (Chapais 2011).

consortships

among primates, temporary affiliations of males and females for the purposes of mating and reproduction; in some species (e.g., chimpanzees), males may forcibly coerce females into a consortship

In some cases, predation by other animals may help forge an alliance between two different primate species. In the Taï forest, for example, red colobus and Diana monkeys peacefully coexist because they rely on different foods. When threatened by predators such as chimpanzees, however, the monkeys are drawn together. The smaller and faster-moving Diana monkeys act as guards, uttering alarm calls when they spot chimpanzees, while the colobus monkeys, who occupy higher areas in the trees, protect the Diana monkeys from birds of prey (Bshary and Noë 1997).

Female alliances typically occur in the context of food competition, although female bonobos may form alliances to dominate males. In contrast, male alliances occur in the context of competition for mates, hunting, the sharing of meat, and territorial defence. Alliances between male chimpanzees are usually interpreted as reflecting kinship, since males stay in the group of their birth while females leave their group when they reach sexual maturity. A recent genetic study of chimpanzees in Kibale National Park, however, has demonstrated that males who spend time together are not closely related to one another (Mitani, Merriwether, and Zhang 2000).

Continued conflict can be detrimental to a group, and the maintenance of group cohesion depends on cooperation among its members. In order to deal with conflicts arising within groups, primates have developed effective methods of conflict resolution. **Reconciliation** can take a number of forms, including approaching the victim of aggression after the conflict has ended and sitting beside them, making gestures such as touching, kissing, and embracing, grooming one's opponent, and vocalizing (de Waal 1990; Silk 2002).

reconciliation

the process of making peace after an altercation

SEXUAL BEHAVIOUR AND REPRODUCTIVE STRATEGIES

For most primate species, sexual activity takes place when females are in estrus, a period of sexual receptivity correlated with ovulation. For many species this is signalled by various cues, including **proceptive behaviours** such as presenting hindquarters to males, visual cues such as swelling and pink coloration of the skin in the genital region, and olfactory cues such as **aliphatic acids** secreted within the vagina, the odour of which varies over the course of the reproductive cycle (Grammer, Fink, and Neave 2005). There is considerable variation among primates in the length of the reproductive cycle and its constituent phases (e.g., menstruation, receptivity), from as few as 15 days in the common marmoset to 50-plus days for the mouse lemur. Primates differ in other aspects of reproductive timing, such as the interbirth interval (also known as birth spacing). Monogamous gibbons, for example, abstain from sexual activity for several years until a female's most recent offspring is weaned and she comes into estrus again. Galdikas and Wood (1990) found that among great apes, birth spacing varied from 45.5 ± 1.2 months for gorillas to 66.6 ± 1.3 months for chimpanzees and 92.6 ± 2.4 months for orangutans. Such differences reflect many factors, including variations in environment, social organization, and parental investment. With respect to the latter, as male investment in rearing increases, the interbirth interval decreases; male gorillas are active participants in caring for related offspring, while orangutan males offer virtually no assistance.

proceptive behaviours

actions, typically on the part of females, to initiate a sexual interaction; may include facial gestures, limb and body postures, or movements, and sounds

aliphatic acids

a group of fatty acids that, secreted by a sexually receptive female, act as chemical messengers (pheromones) to alert males to her reproductive status

---

12. The kin selection hypothesis was originally proposed in the 1960s by British evolutionary biologist William Hamilton.

The sexual behaviour of *Pan paniscus* has garnered particular attention because of the frequency, diversity, and contexts in which it occurs. Sexual activity takes place not only between males and females but also between members of the same sex, and between both related and unrelated individuals. It may be characterized by face-to-face copulation, genital rubbing, and oral–genital sex. Unlike other primate species, for which sexual activity is linked to reproduction, sex for bonobos serves many different purposes, including facilitating the female transfer between troops, reinforcing social bonds, reducing tension, and establishing power alliances.

The females of many Old World primates advertise ovulation by means of obvious physical and behavioural signs such as sexual swellings, changes in facial skin colour, and copulation calls (Clay and Zuberbühler 2011). A few species, however, such as vervet and white-faced saki monkeys, Assamese macaques, and Hanuman langurs lack conspicuous sexual signals and thus conceal fertility from males (Andelman 1987; Fürtbauer et al. 2011; Heistermann et al. 2001; Thompson et al. 2011). Hypotheses proposed to explain the latter include confusing paternity in order to reduce the risk of infanticide by males, and preventing monopolization of fertile matings by dominant males (Kappeler and van Schaik 2004).

Grammer, Fink, and Neave (2005) suggest that human females signal their ovulatory status in ways other than developing marked visual cues. These ways may include chemical signals (pheromones) to attract potential mates. Behaviours known as **mate guarding**, common among nonhuman male primates, have been shown to occur in humans when the female in a relationship is ovulating (Gangstad, Thornhill, and Garver 2002).[13]

Sexual Strategies

When Darwin proposed his theory of sexual selection in 1871, he aimed to explain two distinctions between males and females within species. First, the two sexes often differed in morphology—and in very conspicuous ways. In particular, males tended to be larger in a number of features and often sported quite flashy adornment—the male peacock with his spectacular tail comes to mind and so does the male mandrill's more colourful muzzle (Figure 6.14). Second, the two sexes employed very different strategies to solicit mates, involving distinct patterns of mate competition and mate choice (Swedell 2006). In most instances, these strategies manifested themselves as male–male competition and female choice, which Robert Trivers (1972) ascribed to the stark asymmetry between males and females in degree of **parental investment** (often calculated as the "energy cost" of reproduction). This inequity is readily apparent: a male's investment in producing low-cost sperm pales in comparison to a female's burden as entailed in egg production, gestation, birth, and lactation. According to Trivers, this imbalance leads to fundamentally different strategies employed by each sex to attain reproductive success, often dichotomized as quantity of females (male) versus quality of offspring (female).

FIGURE 6.14 Darwin's sexual selection theory accounts for conspicuous dimorphism between males and females, as seen here in the case of male (right) and female (left) mandrills.

Photograph by Gloria Rusta

Female Strategies

A female primate may employ a number of different tactics as part of an overarching strategy to maximize the quality of her offspring. She may incite males to compete through direct agonistic encounter or indirectly via sperm competition (discussed later); she may choose dominant males on the presumption that this will translate into high-quality infants; she may

---

13. Mate guarding would include greater attentiveness and vigilance, as well as proprietary behaviour on the part of the male in the relationship when the female partner was in estrus.

choose males who demonstrate affiliative behaviours, which may then translate as rearing assistance or protection of infants from other aggressive males; she may mate with multiple males so as to confuse paternity, thereby soliciting aid from males who believe the offspring is theirs (Stumpf, Thompson, and Nott 2008); she may compete with other females for access to better food resources; and she may even synchronize ovulation with other females in the group (Ostner, Nunn, and Schülke 2008), or time birth to seasons of high resource availability.

Reproductive Timing Female primates living in habitats with seasonal fluctuations in resource abundance often time conception so that birth and/or lactation occur when food is sufficient to maximize survivorship. Lewis and Kappeler (2005), for example, found that Verreaux's sifaka, a species of lemur from Madagascar, timed conception to coincide with high or declining food resources. This enabled them to store energy as fat mass. Also, they gave birth during the lean season (thus relying on the stored energy) and timed mid-to-late lactation and weaning to increasing food abundance, which facilitated the survival of the newly weaned offspring. Females within a group may synchronize their estrus cycles to coincide with seasonal variations in resources (Anderson, Nordheim, and Boesch 2006). Ovulatory synchrony would also reduce the ability of a single male in a multi-male group to sequester all receptive females. Finally, synchrony with regard to birth would reduce the likelihood of one or a few young infants being targets of harassment or even death by older (usually) males in the group (Swedell 2006).

Female Mate Choice Female choice plays an important role in the reproductive success of males, and studies of this behaviour abound in the literature. Unfortunately, identifying the factors underlying female choice of mating partners is confounded by the difficulty in distinguishing between behaviours that are merely social and those that are related specifically to reproduction (Wolfe 1991). As well, female mating choices may change over their lifetime (Strier 2003), so it has been difficult to draw solid conclusions about this aspect of reproductive behaviour. Observations of baboons and other monkeys have revealed that females may choose to mate with lower-ranking males whom they consider to be friends (Smuts 1985). These friendships appear to have several adaptive benefits. For examples, males may act as allies and provide females with protection from other members of their group or from predators. They may also defend food resources and participate in infants' care by grooming and protecting them and sharing food with them (Cords 2002; Nguyen et al. 2009; Palombit 2009; Palombit, Seyfarth, and Cheney 1997; Smuts 1985).

In multi-male/multi-female social groups, mating tends to be promiscuous, with both males and females having numerous sexual partners (although a dominant male may enjoy preferential access through consortship with an estrous female at the peak of her cycle, when she is most likely to conceive). We know that among humans, promiscuous behaviour carries the risk of sexually transmitted diseases. Does the same apply to nonhuman primates? Interestingly, an analysis of blood samples taken from healthy females representing over 40 different primate species housed in zoos revealed that, on average, the white blood cell counts of promiscuous species were 50% higher than those of monogamous species (Nunn, Gittleman, and Antonovics 2000).

An important consideration is to distinguish between female choice (an action) and female preference (a motivation or desire) (Swedell 2006). A female may prefer to mate with a particular male for a variety of reasons, but may be kept from doing so by the actions of other members of the group and thus will choose an alternative and perhaps still desirable mate. Meredith Small (1989) observed that in some species, females often prefer to mate with unfamiliar males, who may be new immigrants. This may be to avoid the negative effects of inbreeding (i.e., increased genetic homozygosity), or it may simply be a tactic to maximize partners (again with the effect of confusing paternity).

Male Strategies

The limiting factor for male reproductive success is access to receptive females, and as the majority of nonhuman primates do *not* live in monogamous pair-bonded social units, some form of intermale competition is the rule. Aggressive competition for females is part of life for a male living in single-male/multi-female or multi-male/multi-female social groups. The point of engaging in that competition is to maximize the number of females with whom he is able to mate and/or the number of copulations achieved with any given receptive female. In the latter regard, a phenomenon known as **sperm competition** can play a significant role, if the female involved is able to solicit sexual encounters from multiple males within a single estrous cycle. A number of factors comprise a male's competitive strategy, including body and canine size, dominance rank, ability to coerce females, and male mate choice. With respect to the latter, for instance, University of Toronto primatologist Joyce Parga has observed that male ring-tailed lemurs prefer females belonging to the age class with the highest fecundity (Parga 2006). As well, she found that the movement of males of the same species from their natal troop to a new one resulted in an increase in their mating success (Parga 2010). The practice of **infanticide** (discussed later) can also contribute to a given male's reproductive success.

Size Matters Some primates (e.g., hamadryas and gelada baboons, and gorillas) form single-male/multi-female (polygynous) units by actively excluding other adult males within the larger band structure, relying on features such as body and canine size to defend their harem at all times from solitary (usually young adult) males who might seek to usurp the leader. Vigilance is key and often costly in terms of energy, for it detracts from time spent foraging. Males living in multi-male/multi-female groups (e.g., savannah baboons, macaques) compete only in the presence of estrous females. Dominance hierarchies are common in such cases, with the alpha male typically attaining high rank through competitive bouts.

While a strong correlation exists between rank and reproductive success, high-status males are not always successful. Among chimpanzees and baboons (other than hamadryas), lower ranking males may form alliances to gain access to females. Using DNA genotyping in captive bonobos, Marvan and colleagues (2006) found that dominance rank was not associated with mating success; both infants tested in their study had been sired by the lowest ranking male in the group, even though the dominant male formed exclusionary consortships with the estrous females. A recent study of wild-living male bonobos, however, found a strong relationship between rank and reproductive success that was facilitated by the presence of a male's mother (Surbeck, Mundry and Hohmann 2011). As bonobo social structure is matrilineal, females can exert considerable influence over unrelated males, thereby assisting sons in gaining access to females.

Infanticide As a male reproductive strategy, infanticide occurs widely among primate species, from prosimians to apes and in both platyrrhines and catarrhines; indeed, field studies have confirmed its occurrence in 35 species (Palombit 2012). While most documented cases of infanticide involve males (van Schaik and Janson 2000), the killing of infants by females has been observed among chimpanzees at Gombe; this may reflect increased competition for resources (Goodall 1986). More recently, several cases of female-led infanticide have been documented in chimpanzee groups in the Budongo Forest in Uganda. In two of these cases, the attacks were launched by resident females against the offspring of immigrant females (Townsend et al. 2007).

Although a number of hypotheses have been proposed to account for this form of sexual conflict, the most widely applicable argument is the sexual selection hypothesis. Succinctly, male primates can increase their reproductive fitness by increasing the number of fertilizable females in a group. Since lactation suppresses menstruation, killing a female's infant initiates a new reproductive cycle. However, the sexual selection hypothesis has come under fire based on claims that there is little evidence for the intentional killing of infants among wild primates, that infant deaths are generally the consequence of more general aggression, that there is no genetic basis for this practice, and that no benefit from infanticidal behaviour has ever been demonstrated (i.e., it has not been shown that males who kill infants have greater reproductive success over their lifetime than those who do not; Sussman, Cheverud, and Bartlett 1995).

Responding to these claims, Hrdy, Janson, and van Schaik (1995) note that infanticide is, in fact, widespread and has been recorded in both captive and wild primates. Teichroeb and Sicotte (2008), for example, documented cases of infant killing among colobus monkeys living in the Boabeng-Fiema Monkey Sanctuary in Ghana. In all cases, infants were attacked by unrelated males, who consequently gained access to the mother for mating. The same pattern has been observed among other primate species. Furthermore, analyses of DNA extracted from the feces of wild Hanuman langurs have demonstrated that males were unrelated to their infant victims but were, in fact, the likely fathers of subsequent offspring

sperm competition
when a female mates with multiple partners over a short period of time, males who are able to deposit a larger volume of higher quality sperm farther into the female reproductive tract should succeed in impregnating more females; sperm competition is facilitated in multi-male social systems by large testes, large penises, longer tailed sperm, and the formation of copulatory plugs

infanticide
the killing of infants, in this context as a strategy to solicit reproductive opportunity by the adult male

(Borries et al. 1999). Hrdy and colleagues (1995) also note that among red howler monkeys, females who have lost their offspring to infanticide have shorter interbirth intervals than those who have not, increasing the likelihood that incoming males will father offspring and thus increase their reproductive success.

It should not be assumed that females respond passively to the occurrence or potential occurrence of infanticide, although active defence against an infanticidal male is unlikely to succeed due to disparities in body size. However, other counterstrategies are available (Palombit 2012). For example, because infanticide is often associated with a takeover event, the presence of a new or unfamiliar male may cause a resident female to develop post-conception sexual swellings and pseudoestrous behaviours as a means to manipulate the usurper's assessment of his paternity. Alternatively, a female may indeed permit her infant to be killed, as a "loss-minimizing" tactic, knowing that she will have opportunities to become impregnated sooner by the incoming male.

LANGUAGE AND COMMUNICATION

Communication is a vital component of the behavioural repertoire of all social animals, and nonhuman primates exhibit a rich array of gestures, vocalizations, facial expressions, and olfactory signals, all of which carry some form of meaning. The type of communication a primate uses is influenced by a number of factors, including habitat, sex, age, and rank. Primates who spend most of their time in the trees, for example, rely more heavily on auditory (vocal) signals, whereas more terrestrial species rely more heavily on visual signals, which can easily be seen by other members of their group (Dunbar 2012). Forms of communication may also differ between males and females.

pantomime
gesture that expresses meaning

Primates utilize four modes of communication: visual, auditory, olfactory, and tactile. Visual forms of communication include gestures, facial expressions (Figure 6.15), postures, eyelid flickering, lip smacking, tongue flicking, and exposing canine teeth. Gestures in particular and the meanings associated with them have attracted great interest, and those observed in some of the great apes have been likened to **pantomime** (Russon and Andrews 2011a and b). Primate vocal communication systems are equally varied, even within the same species. Howler monkeys, for example, have a vocal repertoire that includes 15 to 20 different sounds, and their loud calls, which can be heard more than a kilometre away, are facilitated by an enlarged voice box. Some species, such as gibbons, are known for their song-like territorial calls, which are produced using a vocalization technique similar to that used by professional opera singers (Koda et al. 2012). Others use a variety of calls to signal predators or food resources. Vervet and black-fronted titi monkeys, for instance, have different alarm calls corresponding to different types of predators, while chimpanzees may utter different sounds corresponding to different types of food (Cäsar et al. 2012; Slocombe and Zuberbühler 2006).

In recent years, fascinating research on vocal patterns in monkeys and apes has confirmed the existence of local "dialects" among different primate populations within species (Fedurek and Slocombe 2011). Some species also use a variety of olfactory signals to convey meaning. These may take the form of scent marking to mark territories, urine washing, and "stink fighting," seen in ring-tailed lemurs. Finally, tactile forms of communication include grooming, touching, embracing, and hand clasping. These may be used to convey interest in a mating partner, to avoid aggression, or to reconcile with a former opponent.

Given the complexity of primate communication systems, considerable debate has surrounded the question of whether nonhuman primates possess language. In this regard, particular attention has been paid to our closest relatives, the great apes. Ape language studies date back to the 1950s, when psychologists Keith and Catherine Hayes attempted to teach a chimpanzee named Vicki how to speak. Although Vicki was able to utter four human words, the experiment ultimately failed because chimpanzees, like other nonhuman primates, lack the vocal apparatus necessary for human speech. Subsequent studies focused on teaching American Sign Language (ASL) to chimps and other apes, beginning with an experiment launched in the 1960s by psychologists Beatrice and Allen Gardner to teach ASL to a young chimpanzee

FIGURE 6.15 Chimpanzees express many of the same feelings we do, but in different ways. This chimpanzee is displaying a fear grimace.

© DLILLC/Corbis

named Washoe. Not only did Washoe learn to sign more than a hundred words, but she was also able to put words together and teach signs to other chimpanzees (Gardner and Gardner 1969).

Other notable studies that followed included Francine Patterson's attempt to teach sign language to the gorilla Koko (Figure 6.16), who is reported to have mastered 1,000 signs (Patterson and Linden 1981), and Herbert Terrace's effort to teach sign language to the chimpanzee Nim Chimpsky. In the 1980s, primatologist Sue Savage-Rumbaugh taught sign language to the bonobo Kanzi, and more recently, both Kanzi and his half-sister Panbanisha were taught to communicate using a lexigram (Figure 6.17), a special board that displays symbols representing words. Orangutans have also recently become the subject of language studies (Wich et al. 2009). Among the remarkable observations that have been made during these studies include the spontaneous extension of signs as illustrated, for example, by Koko, who applied the sign "straw" not only to drinking straws but to plastic tubing and hoses (Patterson 1979), and the invention of new phrases by combining two signs, as in the case of Washoe who signed "water bird" when first seeing a swan.

Considerable criticism has been directed at many of these ape language studies, with critics arguing that while primates can learn words, they cannot form sentences and are simply reacting to prompts and mimicking their teachers (Hill 1978). Much of the debate surrounding ape language studies concerns the definition of language. Do apes, in fact, understand grammar and syntax, or are they simply learning and memorizing words and sequences? While many researchers acknowledge that apes do not have the same language skills as humans, it is clear that the line between human and nonhuman cognitive abilities is much less distinct than once thought, and the field of ape language research continues to thrive. In 2004 the Great Ape Trust was established with the goal of studying the cognitive and communicative capabilities of the great apes, and more recent studies include an examination of the similarities and differences between human and nonhuman primate vocalization in an attempt to better understand the evolution of human language (Fedurek and Slocombe 2011).

Some interesting data have also emerged on expression, representation, and symbolism among primates (Matthews 2011). A fascinating study of primate artistic expression by Anne Zeller of the University of Waterloo found some intriguing similarities between human children and the great apes in their choices of colour and pattern. In a study of over 300 paintings done by chimpanzees (Figure 6.18), gorillas, orangutans,

FIGURE 6.16 Francine Patterson (left) is signing to Koko the gorilla.

© Bettmann/Corbis

FIGURE 6.17 Kanzi the bonobo, seen here with primatologist Sue Savage-Rumbaugh, learned to communicate using a lexigram.

Courtesy of Duane M. Rumbaugh

FIGURE 6.18 The study of nonrepresentational art produced by apes, such as this chimpanzee, forms one avenue for the comparative study of cognitive development in humans and nonhuman primates.

© KIMIMASA MAYAMA/Reuters/CORBIS

and children, Zeller (2007) discovered an almost universal preference for the colour yellow as their first choice, and the frequent use of diagonal lines. These results suggest that ape drawings are not simply random scribbles but reflect conscious choices.

NONHUMAN PRIMATES AS MODELS OF EARLY HOMININ BEHAVIOUR

A number of approaches can be taken to reconstruct the behaviour of our early hominin ancestors. We can look at the behaviour of extant nonhuman primates who live in an ecological setting that is similar to that of early hominins, we can look at the behaviour of those primates most closely related to us, or we can look at a range of variables that include fossil remains, data on ancient environments, and observations of modern primates. In the 1960s, savanna baboons were popular models of early hominins because of their open grassland environment, male-dominant hierarchies, and male competition (DeVore and Washburn 1963). With the recognition of the importance of female choice in mating behaviour, however, this model declined in popularity and more recent baboon models have focused on hamadryas baboons, who share a number of behavioural traits with humans, including male kin networks, male–female pair bonding, female bonding, and a hierarchical social structure (Swedell and Plummer 2012).

For the past three decades, chimpanzees have been widely used as models of early hominin behaviour and ecology on the basis of their close evolutionary relationship to us and their complex tool use, hunting and meat eating, and cultural traditions. Based on studies of wild chimpanzees over the past five years, McGrew (2010) posits that the last common ancestor (LCA) of living apes and humans likely had large and varied tool kits that were used not only for feeding and foraging but for other purposes as well. Moreover, the LCA probably re-used tools, and exhibited inter- and intra-regional differences in material culture, had an omnivorous diet that included meat acquired through opportunistic hunting, and utilized arboreal sleeping nests.

Anthropologist Adrienne Zihlman argued some time ago that bonobos may be the best model for early hominin behaviour on the basis of their reduced canines and body proportions similar to those of our australopithecine ancestors in Africa c. 3 to 4 million years ago (Zihlman et al. 1978). Many researchers have also emphasized the distinct behavioural differences between bonobos and chimpanzees. Chimpanzee society is male dominated, males use aggression to compete for dominance rank and mating partners, and cooperatively defend their home range against intruders. In contrast, bonobos are less aggressive, engage in sexual behaviour outside of estrus and for reasons other than for reproduction, and females are dominant over males, often forming alliances with one another. As Stanford (1998) points out, however, the marked behavioural differences seen between the two species may reflect the lack of long-term field studies that have been undertaken of bonobos; they may, in fact, be more similar than we think.

The debate over the most appropriate model of extinct hominin behaviour continues, and some have argued that chimpanzees may no longer be the best choice based on the fact that many of the behaviours exhibited by these primates, such as tool use, hunting, and food sharing are also seen not only in other primate species but in nonprimates as well (Sayers and Lovejoy 2008). While we cannot assume that early hominins behaved in exactly the same way as living nonhuman primates, the behaviour of the latter nevertheless remains a valuable source of information on what we might expect to see in our earliest hominin ancestors (Stanford 2012).

KEY IDEAS

- Studying primates in captivity enables researchers to closely monitor individuals and alter their environments to suit their research objectives.

- Studying primates in the wild allows researchers to observe interactions between animals and their natural habitat and to examine seasonal changes in behaviour.

- Primates live in a variety of social groups that include monogamous, single-male/multi-female, polyandrous, and multi-male/multi-female groups.

- Group living allows individuals to share information, defend resources, gain access to mating partners, have protection against predators, receive assistance when caring for offspring, and learn and transmit behaviours from one member to another.

- Male strategies focus on access to adult females (quantity); females tend to focus on producing the best offspring possible (quality).

- Success in reproduction may reflect a variety of factors, including dominance, degree of dimorphism, female choice, and practices such as infanticide.

- Tool use has been documented among a variety of primate species and typically occurs in the context of food procurement and processing.

- Dominance hierarchies and affiliative behaviours such as grooming, establishing alliances, and engaging in conflict resolution provide social stability and serve to reduce stress and reinforce social bonds.

- Primates utilize visual, auditory (vocal), olfactory, and tactile modes of communication to convey certain meanings.

KEY TERMS

social brain hypothesis (p. 124)

monogamous (p. 124)

single-male/multi-female (p. 124)

polyandry (p. 124)

multi-male/multi-female (p. 124)

fission–fusion (p. 124)

matrilineal (p. 124)

dominance hierarchies (p. 125)

affiliative (p. 131)

altruistic (p. 131)

kin selection (p. 132)

infanticide (p. 135)

KEY QUESTIONS TO ASK MYSELF

1. If I was out foraging for food and was suddenly threatened by a predator, should I save only myself or try to warn other members of my group of the potential danger? What would be the effects of either decision?

2. Why is it that chimpanzees and bonobos behave so differently from one another and yet are biologically very closely related?

3. What might studies of primate communication tell us about the origins of language among humans?

KEY CRITICAL THINKING QUESTIONS

1. Many primate behaviours have costs and benefits in terms of their impact on reproductive success. For example, group living provides protection against predators but also means greater competition for mates and other resources. How would you go about measuring the costs and benefits of various behaviours? Can you use them to predict certain behaviours?

2. A greater degree of sexual dimorphism in body size exists in primate societies that emphasize competition among males for access to sexually receptive females. How would you account for the fact that, as a species, humans exhibit comparatively low levels of dimorphism yet still maintain relatively high levels of intermale competition for mates?

KEY THINGS TO DO NEXT

CourseMate Visit **CourseMate** at www.nelson.com/humanvoyage2e to build your comprehension, practise your critical thinking skills, review core concepts, and explore other resources at your disposal.

7 Primate Evolution

Man still bears in his bodily frame the indelible stamp of his lowly origin.

Charles Darwin (1809–1882)

OVERVIEW

This chapter focuses on the evolution of nonhuman primates. We begin by exploring how once-living primates ended up as fossils, the methods used to ascertain the age of these fossils, and what we can learn from these remains about fossil primate behaviour. We also place the fossil evidence for primate evolution in the context of the evolution of mammals and the environmental and climatic changes that accompanied the appearance and radiation of the primates. Major events in primate evolution are highlighted, beginning with the appearance of mammals directly preceding the first primates and ending with the origin of apes. The anatomical characteristics of these primates are described, and their possible phylogenetic relationships are outlined.

KEY CONCEPTS

Absolute dating, relative dating, adaptive radiation, plesiadapiforms, adapids, omomyids, anthropoids, hominoids

KEY LEARNING OBJECTIVES

At the end of this chapter, you will be able to

LO1   Describe when and where the first strepsirhines, anthropoids, and hominoids appeared and what characteristics they possessed

LO2   Distinguish among the various forms of relative and absolute dating

LO3   Apply your knowledge of extant primates to reconstruct the behaviour of extinct ones, based on their fossilized remains

LO4   Compare and contrast the hypotheses proposed to explain the origin of New World monkeys

LO5   Evaluate the factors that allowed Miocene apes to diversify into so many different species

LO6   Formulate a hypothesis to explain the lack of fossil evidence linking extinct species of primates to extant ones

PROLOGUE: THE FAMILY TREE

According to Fleagle (2000, 87), three defining periods characterize the study of primate evolution. The first began with the publication of Linnaeus' *Systema Naturae* (1735), in which humans and other primates were classified together based on physical similarities. The second began with the discovery, in the 1830s, of the first primate fossils in Europe, South America, and India, demonstrating the existence of extinct forms of this group of mammals. The third followed the publication of Darwin's *Origin of Species* (1859). As you learned in Chapter 2, implicit in Darwin's theory of evolution by natural selection was the idea that humans had evolved from an ape-like ancestor; indeed, Darwin ended his book with the comment that "in the distant future ... light will be thrown on the origin of man and his history." His strong supporter, the anatomist Thomas Huxley, demonstrated the close anatomical similarities between humans and the African great apes in *Man's Place in Nature* (1863), confirming Darwin's belief that Africa was the birthplace of humans. As we explore in this chapter, primate evolution is a vibrant field of study and has provided us with the context in which to situate our own evolutionary history, which we cover in Part III, Ancient Currents.

HOW PRIMATES BECOME FOSSILS

When we talk about the fossilized remains of extinct primates, we are typically referring to remains that have been preserved for many millions of years. Fossils can exist in different forms, but most of the evidence we discuss in this chapter consists of the remains of bones and teeth. In what circumstances are these elements preserved? Much research has been done on what happens to organisms after they die, or **taphonomy** as it is known. When an organism dies, its soft tissues begin to decompose. The rate of decomposition varies with a number of factors, including temperature, humidity, and the location of the body (e.g., whether it is buried or exposed). Once the soft tissue has decomposed completely, the exposed skeleton begins to break down and may be lost completely unless conditions are favourable for its preservation. For example, bones deposited in water and covered with sediments have a much greater chance of being preserved as fossils than those exposed to the elements and to scavengers that can scatter and destroy them.

> **taphonomy**
> the study of what happens to the remains of an organism after death

The process of fossilization occurs when groundwater carrying minerals such as iron and calcium carbonate from the surrounding sediments infiltrates the microscopic cavities in bones and deposits the minerals into them, turning the bones into stone and preserving them for millions of years. Because fossilization occurs only under very specific conditions, however, fossils are extremely rare, which means that there are large temporal and geographical gaps in the fossil record. In addition, not all elements of a skeleton may be preserved. Many fossil primates, in fact, are represented only by teeth and jaw fragments, making it difficult to draw any conclusions about locomotor patterns or body size. It is also important to keep in mind that the fate of some evolving lineages is extinction, so their remains do not make any further contributions to the story of evolution. Finally, fossils must be brought to the surface by geological activity, erosion, or some other process before we can discover them. Despite all of these limitations, paleontologists have been able to extract a tremendous amount of information from the remains that have been uncovered.

Dating Primate Fossils

> **provenance**
> the original location of a fossil or artifact

In order to explore evolutionary relationships between different fossil primates, it is necessary to establish the time frame in which these primates lived. Before this can be done, the exact location from which a fossil came—that is, **provenance**—must be identified. Once this has been established, the age of the fossil can be determined. Methods of dating fossilized remains can be divided into two categories: **relative dating** and **absolute (chronometric) dating**. The choice of method depends on a variety of factors, including the nature of the material to be dated and the geological context of the site. Chronometric dating methods are associated with a known margin of **dating error**. For example, an absolute date may be reported as 1.8 million years ± an error of 75,000 years. Another factor to consider is the precision of the particular method used. For early primate and hominin deposits, error on the order of tens or hundreds of thousands of years is typical.

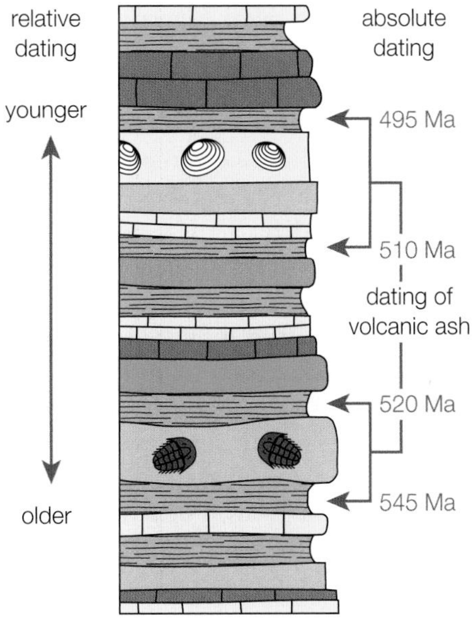

FIGURE 7.1 Relative dating involves determining whether something is older or younger than something else. Absolute dating, in contrast, involves assigning a specific age to something.

relative dating
a method of dating that identifies objects as being younger or older than other objects

absolute (chronometric) dating
a method of dating that assigns a specific age and estimated error to a fossil or site (e.g., 1.6 ± 0.23 million years)

dating error
the degree to which a date derived from an absolute or relative technique differs from the actual date

Relative Dating Methods

Relative dating methods involve determining whether a fossil is older or younger than something else without assigning an exact age to the fossil. The most common method of relative dating uses the principle of **stratigraphy** (see Figure 7.1). This method is based on the fact that within undisturbed geological deposits, strata or layers are laid down from oldest to most recent, following the Law of Superposition (discussed in Chapter 2). Thus, fossils buried in lower (i.e., deeper) strata are older than those buried closer to the surface. This method works well on sites that have not been disturbed; however, alterations in stratigraphy resulting from geological processes such as folding and uplifting can disturb a site in such a way that older layers of sediment may come to lie above younger layers.

stratigraphy
the study of the different layers (strata) that have been deposited over time

Closely related to stratigraphic dating is **biostratigraphic dating**, also known as *faunal correlation*. This technique involves dating a fossil based on associated faunal remains. For example, a primate fossil found with the remains of an extinct species of pig known to have lived between 35 and 40 Ma would, by association, be considered to fall within the same time range. **Fluorine dating** also provides relative dates based on the amount of fluorine in bones. Underlying this method is the fact that when an organism dies, its bones and teeth absorb fluorine from the surrounding groundwater. As a general rule, the longer the remains have been buried, the more fluorine they contain, so if bones found at the same site have different amounts of fluorine in them, we can conclude that those with greater amounts are older.

Finally, relative dating by **paleomagnetism** involves examining shifts in the earth's magnetic field. These shifts, which involve a reversal of the magnetic field from north to south, have occurred periodically over the millions of years of the earth's history and are recorded in sedimentary rocks. By comparing the reversals documented at one site with those from other sites that have been securely dated using methods of absolute dating, we can obtain an approximate age.

biostratigraphic dating
a method of relative dating that involves dating a fossil based on associated faunal remains that have been securely dated using other methods

fluorine dating
a method of relative dating that involves comparing the amount of fluorine that has accumulated in fossils found at the same site

paleomagnetism
a method of relative dating that involves comparing reversals in the earth's magnetic field

Absolute Dating Methods

Methods of absolute (chronometric) dating provide precise dates to fossils and sites. Some of these methods are based on the decay of radioactive isotopes of certain elements contained in organic or inorganic material. Using the knowledge that unstable **radioactive isotopes** decay into more stable forms at a constant rate, researchers can date objects by

radioactive isotopes
unstable isotopes that decay, emitting radioactivity

measuring the relative proportion of stable and unstable forms. The best-known of these **radiometric dating** methods is **carbon-14 (radiocarbon) dating**, which is based on the decay of the radioactive form of carbon-14 (^{14}C). All living organisms possess carbon-14, which they obtain from their environment. When an organism dies, it stops taking in radioactive carbon and the carbon-14 decays into stable nitrogen-14 (^{14}N). The amount of time it takes for half the ^{14}C to decay is 5,730 $\pm$ 40 years—a figure referred to as its **half-life**. Thus it takes 5,730 years for half the ^{14}C in an organism to decay, and another 5,730 years for half of the remaining amount to decay, and so on. This method is used to date organic materials such as wood, charcoal, and bone. Unlike other methods of absolute dating discussed below, however, carbon-14 dating is useful only for dating sites within the past 40,000 to 45,000 years or so. Therefore it cannot be used to date primate fossil evidence extending earlier than this date. In addition, as the proportion of the carbon-14 in the atmosphere varies over time, radiocarbon dates have to be calibrated to establish their most likely true calendar ages.

In the late 1970s, a new method of radiocarbon dating was developed called **accelerator mass spectrometry (AMS) dating**. Like the traditional method of carbon-14 dating, this technique is used on organic materials such as charcoal, seeds, pollen grains, and hair, and can provide dates ranging to 40,000 or 50,000 years ago. Unlike the traditional method, however, it has the advantage of requiring only very tiny samples of organic material (1 mg of carbon or less).

Another method of absolute dating that has been widely used to date fossil sites is **potassium-argon dating** (or K-Ar dating), which is based on the decay of the radioactive isotope of potassium-40 (^{40}K) into argon gas (^{40}Ar). As ^{40}K has a half-life of 1.3 billion years, this method can be used to date samples that are millions of years old. A related method, developed more recently, is **argon-argon dating**, which involves measuring the ratio of argon-40 (^{40}Ar) to argon-39 (^{39}Ar). While this method also requires volcanic rock, it can be used on much smaller samples than potassium-argon dating.

Other methods of absolute dating have been used to date fossils extending back millions of years. Several of these rely on the decay of one or more of the radioactive isotopes of uranium. **Fission-track dating** is based on the observation that when uranium-238 (^{238}U) in materials such as obsidian decays by fission, it produces small tracks in the rock. These can then be counted to determine the specific age of the rock, with an age range spanning millions of years. **Uranium-lead dating,** performed on zircon and other uranium-bearing minerals, looks at the radioactive decay of uranium-238 to lead-206 (^{206}Pb) and ^{235}U to ^{207}Pb, whereas **uranium-series dating** of calcium carbonate materials such as coral and shells focuses on the decay of uranium-234 (^{234}Ur) to thorium-230 (^{230}Th). These methods can be used to date material that is hundreds of thousands to millions of years old.

Several methods of absolute dating based on the accumulation of trapped electrons in certain materials have also been used to date ancient fossils. The **electron spin resonance (ESR)** technique involves measuring electrons trapped in materials such as teeth, and is based on the observation that the greater the number of trapped electrons, the older the object. **Thermoluminescence (TL)** involves measuring the amount of light produced by the release of electrons trapped in objects such as stones and ceramics when they are heated. The more light given off, the older the sample is. **Optically stimulated luminescence (OSL)** is used to determine the last time mineral grains such as quartz or feldspar were exposed to daylight by using light to measure the amount of energy trapped in the minerals' crystals. These three methods can be used to date fossils ranging from thousands (TL and OSL) to millions of years old (ESR).

Finally, a relatively new method of radiometric dating known as **cosmogenic nuclide dating** looks at the ratio of aluminum-26 (^{26}Al) to beryllium-10 (^{10}Be) in quartz sand crystals to determine how long the sediments have been buried. It has also been used to date fossils that are millions of years old (see Chapter 9).

Geologic Time Scale

When we talk about the evolution of primates, we are talking about a period of time spanning tens of millions of years, a small fraction of time compared to the earth's geologic history (Figure 7.2). The **geologic time scale** is based on temporal divisions as defined by features such as fossilized remains of extinct organisms, evidence of climatic changes, and precise radiometric dating of geological deposits (Gradstein and Ogg 2009). The interval of geologic time during which mammals, including primates, evolved is known as the **Cenozoic era** (Figure 7.3), also referred to as the "age of mammals." It is further subdivided into smaller intervals of time called **epochs**, of which there are seven: Paleocene, Eocene, Oligocene, Miocene, Pliocene, Pleistocene, and Holocene.[1]

thermoluminescence (TL)

a method of absolute dating that involves measuring the amount of light produced by the release of electrons trapped in objects such as stones and ceramics when they are heated

optically stimulated luminescence (OSL)

a method of absolute dating that involves determining the last time mineral grains such as quartz or feldspar were exposed to daylight by using light to measure the amount of energy trapped in the minerals' crystals

cosmogenic nuclide dating

a method of absolute dating that looks at the ratio of aluminum-26 (^{26}Al) to beryllium-10 (^{10}Be) in quartz sand crystals

geologic time scale

the division of the earth's geologic events into time periods such as eras and epochs

Cenozoic era

the geological era in which mammals, including primates, evolved

epoch

a measure of geologic time that partitions geologic eras (e.g., Cenozoic) into smaller units, defined with regard to major climatological/environmental events

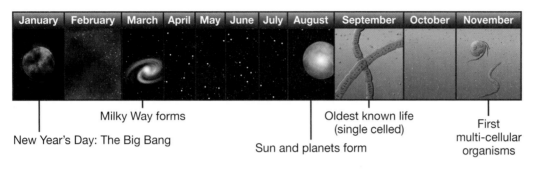

Milky Way forms

New Year's Day: The Big Bang

Sun and planets form

Oldest known life (single celled)

First multi-cellular organisms

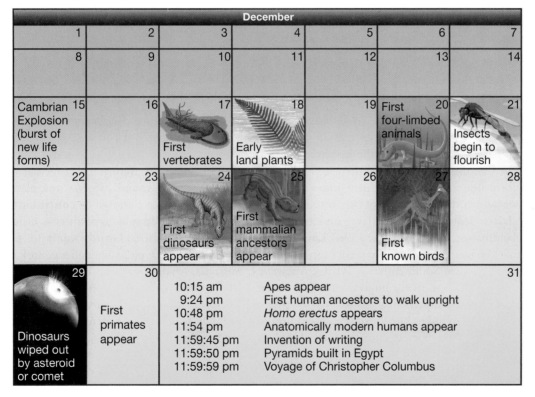

FIGURE 7.2 If the history of the universe is represented by one calendar year, primates arise on the second-last day.

---

1. The date of the Pliocene–Pleistocene boundary was changed in 2009 from 1.8 million to 2.6 million years ago, based on paleoclimatic data.

ERA	PERIOD	EPOCH	Million years ago
Cenozoic	Quaternary	Holocene	
		Pleistocene	0.01
			2.6
	Tertiary	Pliocene	5.3
		Miocene	
			23
		Oligocene	34
		Eocene	
			56
		Paleocene	
			66
Mesozoic	Cretaceous		
	Jurassic		
	Triassic		
			225
Paleozoic	Permian		
	Carboniferous		
	Devonian		
	Silurian		
	Ordovician		
	Cambrian		
			570

FIGURE 7.3   The evolution of the primates occurred during the Cenozoic era.

THE EARTH AT A GLANCE

In order to understand the conditions in which primates evolved, it is necessary to examine the geological events that were taking place during the Cenozoic era. If you were to go back in time for a moment to the beginning of the Mesozoic era (225 Ma), you would see that the continents as we know them today did not exist. Instead, they were joined together to form one giant supercontinent known as **Pangaea**. Beginning around 135 Ma, the plates on which the continents sit began to slowly move apart in a process known as **continental drift**. Floating on a fluid layer underneath, these plates eventually split to form two major landmasses, a northern one called **Laurasia** and a southern one called **Gondwanaland**. By 65 Ma, Laurasia had split to form North America and Eurasia, and Gondwanaland had broken apart to form South America, Africa, Antarctica, Australia, Madagascar, and India.

What, then, are the implications of continental drift in terms of the evolution of mammals—and primates in particular? As we will see later in this chapter, many of the early primate fossils have been found in North America and Europe. This might seem puzzling, given the northern latitudes and temperate climates of these continents today. But it is not surprising that primate fossils have been found on these continents if you consider that they were once situated much closer to the equator. Similarly, the discovery of related primate species on two different continents, as in the case of Old and New World monkeys, makes sense when you consider that Africa and South America were once closer together. The island of Madagascar is home to a huge diversity of primate species, due in part to its separation from Africa (see Box 7.1).

RECONSTRUCTING ANCIENT ENVIRONMENTS

Climate change has had a profound impact on primate evolution and has been the catalyst for a number of significant events, such as the radiation and diversification of primate species. We have heard a great deal about global warming in recent years, but fluctuations in global temperatures

Pangaea

the original landmass made up of the seven continents we recognize today

continental drift

the movement of the plates that make up the earth's continents

Laurasia

the landmass consisting of North America, Europe, and Asia

Gondwanaland

the landmass consisting of South America, Africa, Antarctica, Australia, Madagascar, and India

FOCUS ON ... Adaptive Radiation on Madagascar

The island of Madagascar, off the east coast of Africa, is distinctive for its high degree of **biodiversity**. Considered a "global biodiversity hotspot" (Conservation International 1999), Madagascar is home to a total of 105 species of mammals (Groombridge and Jenkins 1994), many of which have restricted geographical ranges. The explanation for the high degree of **endemism** seen on this landmass is still a mystery. The separation of Madagascar from Africa more than 150 Ma and its resulting isolation in part explains its rich biodiversity. The island's geographic features appear also to have played a major role in the explosive speciation that has occurred there. Based on an examination of watersheds and climate change, Wilmé, Goodman, and Ganzhorn (2006) have hypothesized that cooler and drier conditions during periods of glaciation had a more pronounced effect on watersheds with sources located at relatively low elevations, leading to greater levels of habitat isolation and speciation in those places than at higher elevations.

What about the origin and adaptive radiation of strepsirhines on the island? Several hypotheses have been proposed to explain the colonization of Madagascar by early strepsirhines, including rafting or island-hopping from the African (or possibly Indian) mainland (Martin 2000). While the date and manner of lemur colonization of Madagascar remains unclear, a recent genetic study points to a single origin for all Malagasy primates.[2] Estimates are that these animals reached Madagascar by about 54 Ma (Yoder et al. 1996).

Fleagle (1999, 91) has characterized the strepsirhines of Madagascar as "a natural experiment in evolution." Isolated on the island with no competition from other animals, these primates spread into a variety of environments in much the same way that Darwin's finches radiated across the Galapagos Islands and adapted to new ecological niches (although without flying, of course!). Recall from Chapter 5 that the Malagasy strepsirhines display a wide variety of adaptations, including several forms of locomotion and social organization, dietary specializations, and activity patterns.

have occurred numerous times in the evolutionary history of the primates. For example, the movement of the continents altered ocean currents so that warm water from tropical regions could no longer move to temperate and polar regions, leading to a reduction in global temperatures. The building of mountain ranges along the edges of continental plates affected patterns of precipitation. In turn, climatic changes resulting from these processes produced changes in vegetation, which took the form of an expansion or reduction in the size of forests, grasslands, and deserts. Changing temperatures also had an impact on the movement of mammals. Reductions in temperature, for example, led to a drop in sea levels and the consequent exposure of land bridges, which allowed mammals to migrate to other regions. Conversely, the disappearance of land bridges and the separation of continents resulted in the isolation of populations.

To understand how primates evolved, it is necessary to examine the kinds of environments in which they lived. Reconstructing ancient environments—a field of study known as **paleoecology**—is a multidisciplinary endeavour that applies techniques developed in archaeology, chemistry, biology, geology, and other disciplines. **Paleobotanists**, for example, study the fossilized remains of ancient plants in order to determine the type of habitat in which early primates lived. As you learned in Chapter 5, one hypothesis to explain the origin of primates, the angiosperm hypothesis, is based on the observation that the appearance of the earliest primates coincided with the appearance and radiation of flowering plants, as determined by analyses of fossilized plant remains. Information on plant remains can also be gathered by **palynologists**, who study the distribution of various pollen species. The analysis of faunal remains found in association with primate fossils is the focus of **paleontologists**. More specifically, the analysis of the remains of animals known to have inhabited particular kinds of habitats based on comparisons with living species can tell us a great deal about the local environment in which primates associated with those animals lived.

A number of methods can be used to reconstruct paleoclimates. The most important of these for studying long-term climate change is **oxygen isotope analysis** of ice cores taken from polar icecaps and sediment cores taken from the ocean floor. Oxygen isotope analysis is

biodiversity

variation in life forms within a given ecosystem

endemism

the state of being found exclusively in a particular place

paleoecology

the study of ancient environments

paleobotanists

specialists who study ancient plant remains

palynologists

specialists who study pollen

paleontologists

specialists who study the fossilized remains of extinct life forms

oxygen isotope analysis

the use of stable oxygen isotopes to reconstruct ancient climates; it can also be used to examine the geographic origins of organisms such as humans

---

2. The name used to refer to primates that live on the island of Madagascar.

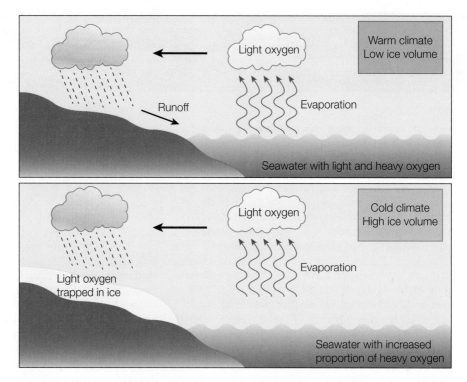

FIGURE 7.4 The ratios of the stable isotopes of oxygen, ^{18}O to ^{16}O, measured in ice cores and deep-sea sediments, provide us with valuable information on climate change.

based on the fact that the ratio of the two **stable isotopes** of oxygen in seawater, ^{18}O and ^{16}O, varies according to temperature. Because ^{16}O is lighter than ^{18}O, when water evaporates, more of the heavier ^{18}O isotope is left behind in seawater, while the precipitation that falls is more enriched in ^{16}O (Figure 7.4). During glacial periods, this precipitated ^{16}O is locked up in glaciers. As a result, ice cores that exhibit lower $^{18}O{:}^{16}O$ ratios indicate colder periods, while those that exhibit higher $^{18}O{:}^{16}O$ ratios indicate warmer periods. The reverse holds true for deep-sea cores, which represent the continuous deposition of sediment, including the remains of marine organisms that incorporate oxygen into their shells. During colder periods, the shallow waters in which these organisms once lived would have been enriched in ^{18}O, resulting in higher $^{18}O{:}^{16}O$ ratios in these organisms. As illustrated in Figure 7.5, significant climatic fluctuations have occurred over the span of primate evolution, with an overall trend of cooling and drying over time.

CLASSIFYING FOSSIL PRIMATES

Once fossil primates have been uncovered, the next step is to determine what type of taxon is represented by the fossil. This can be challenging, particularly if we are dealing with very early remains that are highly fragmented, often distorted, and incomplete. Identification of such remains as a primate depends on the presence of specific features of the skull and other bones, such as those of the hands and feet. As we noted in Chapter 5, primates share a suite of characteristics that distinguish them from other mammals, including dental morphology, forward-facing eyes, and grasping hands and feet. Nevertheless, disagreements may arise among researchers regarding the interpretation of these features.

When talking about primate phylogeny, it is also important to distinguish between a **crown group** and a **stem group** of primates. As illustrated in Figure 7.6, a crown group consists of the last common ancestor of a clade plus all of its descendants, including living members of the clade. In contrast, a stem group is composed of extinct organisms that

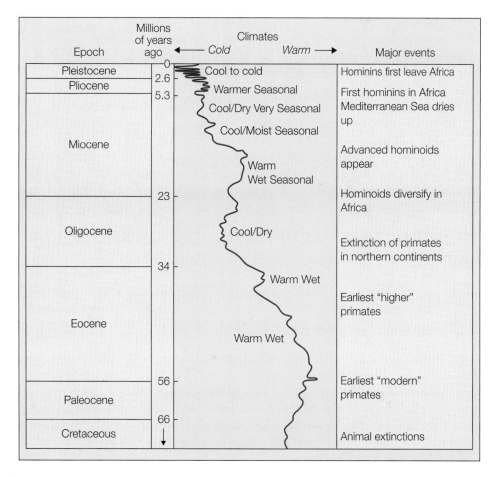

FIGURE 7.5 Major events in primate evolution and patterns of climate change during the Cenozoic era.

are not part of the crown group. If we consider the human—great ape clade, for example, humans, chimpanzees, gorillas, orangutans, and our last common ancestor would represent a crown group, and primates that predate the common ancestor would constitute the stem group.

Recall from Chapter 4 that the most widely accepted modern definition of species is a group of interbreeding organisms that are reproductively isolated from other such groups. When we are dealing with fossil remains, we obviously do not know whether early primates were able to interbreed or not. One of the ways in which species can be identified in the fossil record is by examining the morphology of fossils—size, for example—and comparing it to that of **extant** species. If the range of variation seen in the fossils falls within the range seen in similar modern species, researchers can conclude that the fossils most likely represent one species. If, on the

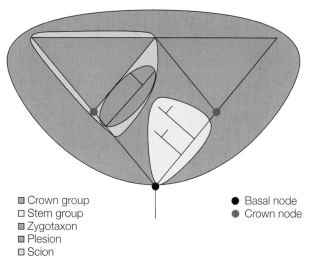

◻ Crown group	● Basal node
◻ Stem group	● Crown node
◻ Zygotaxon	
◻ Plesion	
◻ Scion	

FIGURE 7.6 Two crown groups are illustrated in red and one stem group in yellow. Together they form a larger crown group (purple) with a common ancestor (black circle).

extant

still existing; commonly used to refer to living species

other hand, the fossils exceed the range of variation exhibited by modern forms, they most likely represent more than one species.

This approach has several limitations, and there has been considerable debate over the number of primate species represented in the fossil record. For example, fossils have, on occasion, been classified as representing more than one species when in fact, they represent males and females of a single sexually dimorphic species. The choice of extant group with which to compare the fossil evidence can also lead to inaccurate classifications. We now know from the fossil record that many early primate species had no living counterparts. This raises the question of whether we can compare the degree of diversity in fossil primates with that of modern species (Begun 2004a, 501). These difficulties are compounded the further back in time you go, because the fossil finds become fewer and more fragmentary.

RECONSTRUCTING EARLY PRIMATE DIETS AND SOCIAL BEHAVIOUR

paleobiology
the study of the behaviour and ecology of fossil organisms

Within the past three decades, **paleobiology**, the reconstruction of the behaviour and ecology of fossil animals, has become an increasingly popular field of study (Sepkowski and Ruse 2009). Using data derived from biomechanical and ecological studies of living primates as well as paleoenvironmental and paleoclimatic research, primate paleontologists have been able to reconstruct many aspects of early primate behaviour, including their diet, patterns of locomotion, and social behaviour. Reconstructing the behaviour of fossil primates is a challenging task, however, and the reliability of such reconstructions can be affected by a number of factors, including the choice of extant primate with which to compare the fossil evidence. Compounding these difficulties is the fact that many behaviours are impossible to reconstruct from fossil remains, and morphological differences between living and extinct species of primates make it difficult to infer behaviours.

Dietary Reconstruction

dental microwear
microscopic wear on the enamel surfaces of the teeth, primarily due to diet

As you learned in previous chapters, extant primates are omnivorous, although some species rely more heavily on some foods than others. When it comes to examining fossil evidence, how do we go about determining what early primates ate? A variety of techniques have been used to reconstruct the diet of fossil primates. These include estimating body mass, analyzing **dental microwear**, examining molar tooth shape, and measuring enamel thickness. When we look at extant primates, for example, we can see that smaller species such as the strepsirhines tend to be more insectivorous whereas large species such as orangutans are usually folivorous. More recently, researchers have been using analyses of stable isotopes of carbon sampled from fossil enamel to reconstruct diet (Sponheimer et al. 2009). How do we estimate body mass from fossilized remains? A number of indicators have been used, including the comparative study of how body size variation in living primates correlates with variation in tooth size, tarsal bone size, long bone cross-sectional surface dimensions, and long-bone lengths (Conroy 1987; Dagosto and Terranova 1992; Strait 2001; Ruff 2003; Ruff et al. 2013). Understanding these patterns in living primates can then be used to estimate body size in fossil forms.

Information on the diet of early primates can be obtained by looking at dental microwear. The proportion of pits and scratches on the surfaces of teeth reflect the type of diet on which an animal relied. A coarse diet of leaves, for example, is reflected in a greater number of pits and scratches, while a softer diet of fruits manifests as less wear. The results of such studies have revealed evidence of a wide diversity of diets among European Miocene primates (Ungar 1996). A new method used to quantify patterns of dietary damage on teeth is dental microwear texture analysis, which uses three-dimensional surface measurements. Introduced in 2005 (Scott et al. 2005), it has been used on a number of primate fossils to reconstruct diet (e.g., Scott et al. 2009).

Diets have also been inferred from molar tooth shape, based on the observation that there is a strong correlation among living primates between the shape of the cusps and diet. Frugivores, for example, have rounded tooth cusps, whereas folivores and insectivores have more pointed cusps used for slicing through cellulose and exoskeletons, respectively. Various attempts have been made to quantify molar tooth shape differences. One such method, developed by Richard Kay (1977), involves measuring the lengths of the crests connecting unworn molar tooth cusps to calculate a **shearing quotient** (SQ), which can then be used to assess the potential of the teeth to shear foods between the edges of their crests. Folivores and insectivores, for instance, typically have higher SQ values than frugivores, reflecting their longer shearing crests and more **occlusal** surface relief relative to fruit-eaters (Ungar and Lucas 2010).

More recently, several new methods have been introduced to more accurately quantify tooth shape. These "dental topographic" methods, as they are known, include the relief index (RFI), the orientation patch count (OPC), and the Dirichlet Normal Surface Energy (DNE) technique (see Bunn et al. 2011). The details of these methods are beyond the scope of this text, but they illustrate the increasingly sophisticated techniques that are being applied to fossil primate remains to reconstruct their diet.

Finally, measurement of tooth enamel thickness can also provide clues to the diet of fossil primates (see Chapter 8). Thicker enamel observed in some hominoid species has been interpreted as an adaptation to a diet of harder or more abrasive food items; thinner enamel, in contrast, has been viewed as reflecting a diet of softer foods such as fruits. As Teaford and Ungar (2000, 13508) note, however, the correlation between enamel thickness and diet is not perfect, and there is increasing recognition that the foods primates eat have more physically complex properties than previously recognized and cannot simply be categorized as "hard" vs. "soft." So, primates that eat seeds, typically considered to be hard, may, in fact, have relatively thin enamel, while those that consume hard foods may also use their molars to process softer foods (Teaford 2006).

Social Behaviour

Fossilized remains of early primates can also provide information on their social organization and mating systems. The degree of sexual dimorphism in body size and canine teeth has been used as an indicator of social behaviour in early primates based on observations of extant primates. As you learned in Chapter 6, sexually dimorphic species tend to live in multi-male/multi-female groups (like baboons) or in single-male/multi-female groups (like gorillas). In contrast, species that lack sexual dimorphism, such as the gibbons, tend to be monogamous. Among fossil primates, sexual dimorphism in canine and/or body size of many species has been used to argue that such animals lived in social groups similar to those of baboons and gorillas (Ross 2000, 183), while the lack of sexual dimorphism in other species has been interpreted as suggesting a monogamous way of life (Swindler 1998, 224). It is important to emphasize, however, that the relationship between sexual dimorphism and social behaviour is not always straightforward, and that more than one mating system may be associated with a particular degree of sexual dimorphism (Begun 2004a). As with body size, estimation of sexual dimorphism in the primate fossil record relies on a number of techniques, and can be problematic as it requires preservation of useful morphological criteria known to reflect sexual dimorphism in living primates (e.g., canine tooth size, long-bone dimensions, pelvic differences; see Plavcan 2012b).

PALEOCENE: AGE OF THE PLESIADAPIFORMS

The first primates likely appeared during the **Paleocene** epoch, which began about 66 Ma. However, the common ancestor of primates almost certainly emerged millions of years before that. The climate during this time period was much warmer than it is today, and the landscape of North America and Europe was dominated by subtropical environments. By this time Gondwanaland had split into South America, Africa, Antarctica, Australia, India, and Madagascar.

There is a general consensus today that primates evolved from a small, insectivorous mammal that resembled a treeshrew. Radiating into new ecological niches, these early

shearing quotient
a measure of the relative shear potential of molar teeth

occlusal
the chewing surface of a tooth

Paleocene
the first epoch of the Cenozoic era, dating from about 66 to 56 Ma

BOX 7.2 PROFILE ... Understanding Primate Origins

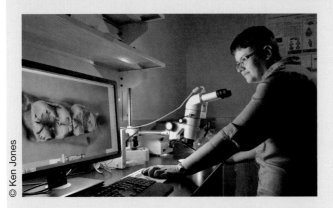

© Ken Jones

In 1993, when I was a second-year undergraduate at the University of Toronto, I took a course in Comparative Vertebrate Anatomy. One of the suggested essay questions made reference to "the earliest primates." I thought this sounded interesting and started trying to figure out who the earliest primates were. Twenty years later, I'm still trying to figure it out! For decades most researchers had considered members of a diverse group of extinct mammals called plesiadapiforms to be the earliest primates. But two papers published back to back in the journal *Nature* in 1990 called that view into question, suggesting instead that plesiadapiforms were more closely related to another order, the gliding dermopterans from Southeast Asia, than to primates. In 1993 I found these papers very convincing, and wrote an essay supporting the view that models for the early evolution of primates needed to be revised to exclude this group.

Four years later, when I was looking for a topic for my dissertation, I re-read the *Nature* papers and started questioning their conclusions. In particular, I noted that the authors had failed to consider dental traits in any detail, which seemed strange since teeth had always formed the main basis upon which plesiadapiforms had been tied to primates. I decided that for my dissertation work I would look at *all* of the evidence,

and see which hypothesis of relationships was upheld. The conclusion was clear—when the dental evidence was included, plesiadapiforms came out as stem primates.

It is important to understand that identifying the earliest primates is not just a purely semantic question. We have to answer the *who* question if we want to understand *why* primates branched off from the rest of Mammalia to take their own, unique evolutionary course. The heart of my research program is to try to understand all aspects of the origins of primates, using the fossil record. To fulfill that goal, identifying the earliest primates is key, and we are still working to refine the phylogenetic framework for primitive primates and their close kin.

I am also interested in tracing the evolutionary history of character complexes of particular importance to primates. For example, on average, members of the Order Primates have larger brains than other mammals. When and why did this evolve? I worked with undergraduate research assistants to produce the first virtual endocasts of plesiadapiforms in order to try and answer these questions. The endocasts of early primates are very primitive-looking—this was surprising, since in most ways plesiadapiforms were adaptively quite similar to living primates. Plesiadapiforms were predominantly fruit-eaters that were already well adapted for moving around in the trees. One of the main differences, however, was that they lacked specializations of the visual system such as the postorbital bar. In the brain, primitive plesiadapiforms exhibit very short cerebra caudally. Since the primary visual processing centre is located at the back of the cerebrum, I suggested that this contrast with living primates might reflect expansions to that part of the brain occurring in more derived primates. In other words, this supported hypotheses that linked the first major expansion of the brain to improvements to the visual system, but occurring after primates branched off from the rest of Mammalia.

We still have much to learn about the evolutionary context of primate origins. With the phylogenetic framework constructed by my colleagues and myself, however, we are now in a position to be asking the right kinds of questions.

Source: Courtesy of Dr. Mary Silcox, Department of Anthropology, University of Toronto

---

plesiadapiforms

a group of primate-like mammals that lived during the Paleocene epoch

procumbent

forward-projecting

primate-like mammals, known as **plesiadapiforms** (see Box 7.2), were widely distributed throughout North America, Europe, and Asia; indeed, 53 genera and 140 species have now been recognized. Once referred to as "archaic" primates because of dental similarities to later strepsirhines, they exhibit a number of features not seen in primates, including a lower dental formula of 3.1.4.3, large **procumbent** central incisors, a long snout, laterally facing orbits, claws, and no postorbital bar (Figure 7.7).

Among the plesiadapiforms known from the fossil record are *Purgatorius* and *Plesiadapis*. Recovered from early Paleocene deposits in Montana, the fossilized remains of *Purgatorius* consist primarily of teeth and jaw fragments, and a few tarsal bones. Estimated to have been the size of a mouse, this mammal had a dental formula of 3.1.4.3, and its molar teeth reflect a reliance on a diet of insects and fruit. A recent analysis of its tarsal bones has revealed that it was also an adept tree climber. *Plesiadapis,* which is represented by both cranial and postcranial remains from North America and Europe, was somewhat larger and possessed claws on all digits and non-opposable thumbs.

The plesiadapiforms were a very successful group of mammals that were adapted to a wide range of different environments. Yet by the end of the Paleocene, many of the North American representatives had become extinct, likely due to competition from rodents as well as environmental and climatic changes at the end of the Paleocene. Members of two families persisted into the middle Eocene in North America, and members of a third have been documented in Asia during the same time period. The identity of the group of plesiadapiforms that gave rise to primates remains unknown, but one species, *Carpolestes simpsoni,* found in late Paleocene deposits in Wyoming, has features that may have been present in the common ancestor of plesiadapiforms and primates, namely a foot with a nail-bearing divergent big toe (Bloch and Silcox 2006; Bloch, Silcox, Boyer et al. 2007).

Plesiadapiforms

FIGURE 7.7 Plesiadapiforms had longer snouts than primates and lacked a postorbital bar.

EOCENE: AGE OF THE STREPSIRHINES

The adaptive radiation of the first primates occurred during the **Eocene** epoch. During the early Eocene, North America was still connected to Europe, a global warming event led to a significant increase in temperatures, and tropical forests covered much of North America, Africa, and Eurasia. These conditions facilitated the appearance and spread of many new mammals, including primates. Possessing characteristics similar to those of living strepsirhines (see Chapter 5)—including forward-facing eyes, a postorbital bar, and a reduced snout—these early primates consisted of two major families: the Omomyidae and the Adapidae. Most of the fossil evidence for these primates comes from North America and Europe, where they inhabited a wide range of habitats. The common ancestor of **omomyids** and **adapids** has not yet been identified, but several possible candidates have been proposed.

The earliest known omomyid is *Teilhardina asiatica,* whose remains have been recovered from 55-million-year-old deposits in China. *Teilhardina* is hypothesized to have migrated rapidly from eastern Asia to Europe and North America soon after, possibly facilitated by an episode of rapid global warming around that time (Rose et al. 2011; Smith, Rose, and Gingerich 2006). The omomyids such as *Necrolemur* closely resembled living tarsiers in having a small body size (less than 500 g), large eyes reflecting a nocturnal way of life, and long tarsal bones (Figure 7.8). Some species were insectivorous; others relied more heavily on a frugivorous diet. Their postcranial skeleton appears to have been adapted to a vertical clinging and leaping mode of locomotion, common among living strepsirhines such as the Indriids of Madagascar.

Eocene

the second epoch of the Cenozoic era, dating from about 56 to 34 Ma

omomyids

tarsier-like primates from the Eocene epoch

adapids

lemur-like primates from the Eocene epoch

Adapids　　　　　　　Omomyids

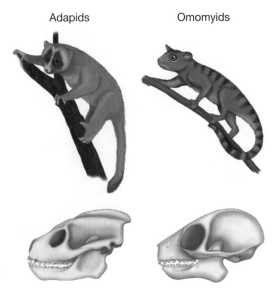

Notharctus

an Eocene primate of the family Adapidae

FIGURE 7.8　The adapids more closely resembled lemurs; the omomyids more closely resembled tarsiers.

The adapids were larger than omomyids and resembled modern-day lemurs. They also had longer snouts and smaller eyes than omomyids, suggesting that they were diurnal rather than nocturnal (Figure 7.8). Their diet consisted mainly of fruits and leaves, and their postcranial skeleton displayed features characteristic of arboreal quadrupeds. Some species had sexually dimorphic canines, suggesting a variety of mating systems. Among the best known adapids is **Notharctus**, which inhabited regions of North America between 50 Ma and 45 Ma (Gunnell and Silcox 2010).

In 2009, the remarkably well-preserved skeleton of an adapiform primate named *Darwinius masillae* was recovered from middle Eocene deposits in Germany (Figure 7.9). A small, arboreal quadruped, the taxonomic status of this fossil has been vigorously debated, with some claiming it to be a haplorhine (Franzen et al. 2009; Gingerich et al. 2010) and others a strepsirhine (Williams et al. 2010). It is an excellent example of the difficulties encountered in trying to classify fossil primates.

The Eocene was also marked by the appearance of the first anthropoids (monkeys), and there has been considerable debate regarding which of the early primates gave rise to them. The fossil record has yielded few clues to the identity of their ancestors, but some intriguing evidence has come to light in Asia that suggests that anthropoids originated on this continent and later migrated to Africa, where the earliest forms have been recovered from late middle Eocene deposits in Algeria, Egypt, and Libya (Jaeger et al. 2010). One of these Asian **basal anthropoids** is *Eosimias*, whose 45-million-year-old remains were discovered in 1994 in China. A tree-dwelling primate, it displays a number of tarsier-like features in its ankle bones, suggesting that it moved in much the same way as tarsiers (Beard et al. 1994, 1996). More recently, the dental remains of a tiny primate named *Anthrasimias* have been uncovered in India from deposits dating to nearly 55 Ma (Bajpai et al. 2008). Both these taxa have been assigned to the Family Eosimiidae. A second family,

basal anthropoids

the earliest anthropoids

FIGURE 7.9　The remarkably well-preserved skeleton of the Eocene primate *Darwinius masillae*.

Courtesy of National History Museum

Amphipithecidae, representing arboreal quadrupeds from Asia, has also been identified as anthropoids (Beard et al. 2007).

The year 2013 was marked by the announcement that yet another early primate named *Archicebus achilles* had been identified. Its nearly complete skeleton was recovered from 55-million-year-old deposits in China, and analysis of this specimen indicates that it was a small haplorhine primate that was insectivorous and possessed a combination of anthropoid-like and tarsiiform-like features (Ni et al. 2013) (see chapter opening photo for a reconstruction of this primate).

By the late Eocene, North America and Europe had separated completely, global temperatures had dropped significantly, and most of the omomyids and adapids had disappeared. Insufficient fossil evidence currently makes it impossible to identify the precise nature of the relationship between the Eocene primates and later primates, but the strepsirhine, tarsiiform, and anthropoid lineages were clearly distinct by the end of this epoch.

OLIGOCENE: AGE OF THE ANTHROPOIDS

From about 56 to 34 Ma, global temperatures declined. The transition from the Eocene to the **Oligocene** epoch was marked by a reduction in the amount of forest, the extinction of many land mammals in Europe—including the almost complete disappearance of primates from the northern hemisphere—and the appearance of primates in equatorial regions as we recognize them today. Numerous Oligocene primate fossil remains have been found. Our knowledge of primate evolution during this epoch comes primarily from fossils found in a region of Egypt known as the **Fayum**, located about 150 km southwest of Cairo. To date, this region has yielded the remains of over 17 genera, including both haplorhine and strepsirhine fossils (Kirk and Simons 2001; Simons 1995). A desert today, this area was once a warm tropical environment characterized by trees and swamps. It was home to a variety of mammals including *Moeritherium*, a genus of mammals related to the elephant (Simons 2008).

The radiation of the anthropoids continued during the Oligocene, and three families of early anthropoids have been identified in the fossil record from Fayum: Oligopithecidae, Parapithecidae, and Propliopithecidae. The earliest of these were the **oligopithecids** (34−35 Ma). Little is known about these primates, but they shared with modern catarrhines a dental formula of 2.1.2.3, and the common ancestor of all living catarrhines likely resembled them (Begun 2010a, 299).

Following the oligopithecids were the **parapithecids**. Unlike the oligopithecids, these primitive anthropoids had a dental formula of 2.1.3.3, as seen in New World monkeys, and the low rounded cusps on their molar teeth indicate a frugivorous diet. Their small eye sockets point to a diurnal way of life, and their postcranial skeleton was adapted to a quadrupedal mode of locomotion. One of the best-known parapithecids is *Apidium*, a small arboreal quadruped with strong leaping abilities (Conroy 1990), although recent 3D imaging analysis of the inner ear suggests a slower form of locomotion (Ryan, Silcox, Walker et al. 2012).[3] While *Apidium* and other parapithecids share similarities with some of the New World monkeys, they also retain a number of primitive features seen in extant strepsirhines. Current consensus is they are stem anthropoids that predate the platyrrhine–catarrhine split (Figure 7.10).

The **propliopithecids** were the largest of the Oligocene anthropoids and were more ape-like than the parapithecids. Like modern-day catarrhines, they had a dental formula of 2.1.2.3, and many species had sexually dimorphic canines. The largest and best known of the propliopithecids, ***Aegyptopithecus***, weighed 6 to 8 kg, exhibited a **Y-5 pattern** on its lower

Oligocene

the third epoch of the Cenozoic era, dating from about 34 to 23 Ma

Fayum

a fossil-rich region of Egypt once home to many Oligocene anthropoids

oligopithecids

early anthropoids from the Oligocene epoch

parapithecids

a group of early anthropoids from the Oligocene epoch

propliopithecids

the largest group of the Oligocene anthropoids

Aegyptopithecus

a propliopithecid from the Oligocene epoch

Y-5 pattern

cusp pattern formed by five cusps on the lower (mandibular) molar teeth in hominoids

---

3. The inner ear contains a structure called the semicircular canal, the shape of which determines aspects of balance important to posture and locomotion.

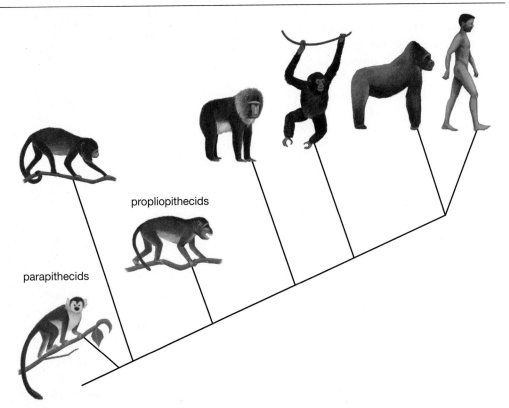

New World monkeys (platyrrhines) **Old World monkeys (cercopithecoids)** **Gibbons and siamangs (hylobatids)** **Great apes and humans**

propliopithecids

parapithecids

FIGURE 7.10 Proposed evolutionary relationships among Oligocene and extant anthropoids.

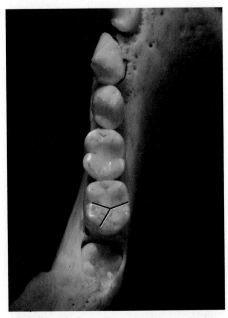

FIGURE 7.11 A Y-5 cusp pattern is seen in early catarrhines such as *Aegyptopithecus*.

William K. Sacco, specimens courtesy of Yale Peabody Museum

molars (Figure 7.11), was an arboreal quadruped, and exhibited sexual dimorphism (Figure 7.12). Despite its anthropoid status, *Aegyptopithecus* was still rather primitive, possessing a long snout, a relatively small brain, and limb bones that were relatively short and robust compared to those of living catarrhines (Begun 2010a). Based on these characteristics, this anthropoid was likely a primitive catarrhine that predated the divergence of Old World monkeys and apes (Fleagle 1999).

The Fayum region has also yielded fossil evidence of a possible ancestor of the tarsiers. An early Oligocene lower jaw fragment, identified as belonging to the genus *Afrotarsius*, has been tentatively assigned to the Family Tarsiidae, but its relationship to other early anthropoids remains uncertain (Kay 2012).

While the majority of Oligocene fossil primate evidence comes from the Fayum, the partial cranium of another catarrhine has been uncovered in Saudi Arabia. Given the genus name *Saadanius*, this specimen dates to approximately 29–28 Ma and has been identified as a medium-sized stem catarrhine that predates the divergence between hominoids and cercopithecoids, an event estimated to have occurred between 29 and 24 Ma (Zalmout et al. 2010). It also points to Afro-Arabia as being the focus of early catarrhine evolution.

Origin and Evolution of New World Monkeys

The earliest fossil evidence of New World monkeys in South America comes from late Oligocene (26 Ma) deposits in Bolivia and has been identified as belonging to the genus *Branisella* (Takai and Anaya 1996). Like extant New World monkeys, these anthropoids possessed a dental formula of

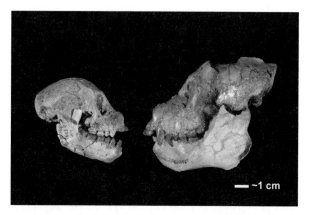

FIGURE 7.12 *Aegyptopithecus* females (left) were smaller than males (right).

Courtesy of Dr. Elwyn Simons

2.1.3.3. One of the most hotly debated questions in primate evolution concerns the origin of New World monkeys in South America. By the beginning of the Oligocene, Africa and South America were separated by a vast expanse of ocean, and North and South America were also separate continents. For the ancestors of New World monkeys to have reached South America, they had to have originated in either North America or Africa and travelled across water. While some have hypothesized that the ancestors of New World monkeys evolved from North American primates and migrated to South America, the hypothesis best supported by the fossil evidence holds that the ancestors of New World monkeys arose from an African anthropoid and spread to South America by rafting across the southern Atlantic on floating masses of vegetation (Fleagle and Gilbert 2006). While such a suggestion may seem ludicrous, lower sea levels during the Oligocene would have resulted in the exposure of numerous islands in the southern Atlantic, making travel from one continent to the other easier. Morphological similarities between African anthropoids and those found in South America provide strong support for this hypothesis. In addition, tests of the **floating island model**, which assumes an average body weight of 1 kg and the ability, based on studies of water deprivation, to survive without water for nearly two weeks, indicate that small primates could have crossed the Atlantic on floating islands in 8 to 15 days (Houle 1999).

floating island model
the hypothesis that the ancestors of New World monkeys rafted across the Atlantic from Africa to South America on floating islands of vegetation

Origin and Evolution of Old World Monkeys

Fossil evidence for Old World monkeys from the early Miocene (23 to 16 Ma) is rare. Our knowledge of these monkeys comes from fossil remains uncovered at sites in Egypt, Libya, and Kenya. As you learned in Chapter 5, Old World monkeys are divided into two subfamilies: cercopithecines and colobines. In the Miocene, the earliest Old World monkeys belonged to the Family **Victoriapithecidae**, which consisted of two genera: *Victoriapithecus*, known mainly from 15-million-year-old deposits on Maboko Island in Kenya, and *Prohylobates*. Ranging in size from 3 to 5 kg (Harrison 1989), *Victoriapithecus* possessed **bilophodont** lower molars (Figure 7.13) adapted to a diet of hard fruits and seeds, and a postcranial skeleton adapted to a quadrupedal mode of locomotion. Their facial structure resembled that of

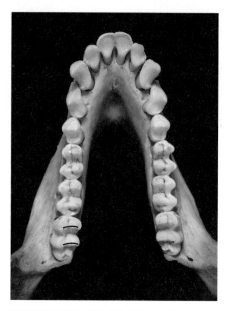

FIGURE 7.13 Old World monkeys possess a bilophodont molar pattern.

William K. Sacco, specimens courtesy of Yale Peabody Museum

Victoriapithecidae
the family to which the earliest Old World monkeys belong

bilophodont
molar teeth characterized by four cusps connected by two ridges of enamel

colobines, while their dental morphology resembled that of cercopithecines (Conroy 1990). Sexually dimorphic canines suggest that they may have had a multi-male/multi-female social organization similar to that of modern macaques (Benefit 1999). This genus represents a stem cercopithecoid and predates the split between the colobines and the cercopithecines.

By the late Miocene, *Victoriapithecus* had become extinct and a new genus of Old World monkey, *Mesopithecus*, had evolved. A member of the colobines, it became very successful and spread into many parts of Europe and western Asia. This adaptive radiation coincided with the extinction of many hominoid species in Africa and Eurasia, which may have been prompted by climatic changes that led to a reduction in forest habitat to which Miocene hominoids were adapted. We will examine these hominoids in more detail below.

MIOCENE: PLANET OF THE APES

Miocene

the fourth epoch of the Cenozoic era, dating from about 23 to 5.3 Ma

The **Miocene** epoch is commonly referred to as the age of the hominoids—that is, primates that include apes (and humans) but exclude monkeys. During this time period, significant geological, climatic, and environmental changes transformed the landscape. By this time the continents had assumed roughly the positions they have today, but the continued movement of the tectonic plates altered ocean currents, and the formation of a land bridge between Africa and Asia allowed for the movement of animals between the two continents. Temperatures increased considerably in the early Miocene, and heavy tropical forests were common. These conditions provided an ideal setting for the diversification of hominoids, and thousands of fossils have been recovered from sites in Africa, Europe, and Asia (Figure 7.14). While the evolutionary relationships of these hominoids are becoming clearer, many questions remain unanswered and there are still significant gaps in the fossil record, particularly with respect to the direct ancestors of modern apes.

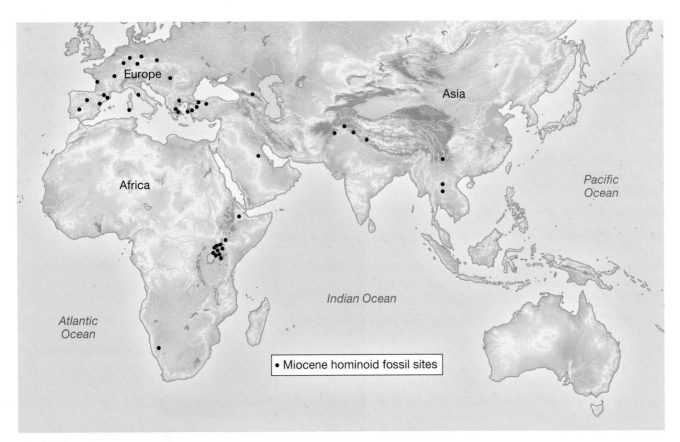

FIGURE 7.14 Miocene hominoid fossil sites.

Stanford, Craig; Allen, John S.; Anton, Susan C., *Biological Anthropology*, 2nd edition, © 2009. Reprinted by permission of Pearson Education, Inc., Upper Saddle River, New Jersey.

Early Miocene (23–16 Ma)

During the early Miocene, hominoids were restricted to forest and woodland environments of Africa. Known as **proconsulids**, these early hominoids, including the best-known genus *Proconsul*, ranged in size from about 10 to 50 kg, *and* possessed a number of derived characteristics seen in modern apes, such as the absence of a tail and a larger brain relative to body size than that of monkeys. Unlike extant apes, however, they did not have the highly flexible limbs used in suspensory locomotion; rather, their limbs more closely resembled those of monkeys, with front and hind limbs of equal length and limited wrist and shoulder mobility (Figure 7.15). Most likely evolving in Africa from an Oligocene catarrhine whose identity remains unknown, they exhibited a number of ape-like dental traits, including upper molars with a **cingulum** on the lingual (or tongue) surface and lower molars with a Y-5 pattern—a feature that distinguishes hominoids from Old World monkeys (although it is present in some propliopithecids, such as *Aegyptopithecus*). The morphology of the teeth indicates that the proconsulids were adapted to a diet of soft fruits.

Two other early Miocene hominoids are the 17.5-million-year-old *Afropithecus* from Kenya, and the 17-million-year-old *Heliopithecus* from Saudi Arabia. *Afropithecus* exhibits a combination of primitive and derived features, including a primitive-looking face that resembles that of *Aegyptopithecus* and thick tooth enamel, but a postcranial skeleton similar to that of *Proconsul* (Begun 2007a). *Heliopithecus* was morphologically similar to *Afropithecus*, and both share features with later hominoids from Europe.

proconsulids
early Miocene hominoids from Africa

Proconsul
the best-known genus of early Miocene hominoids

cingulum
a raised ridge of enamel found on the upper molar teeth

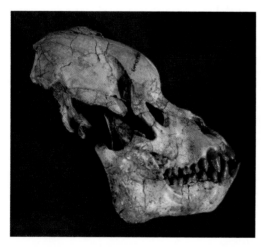 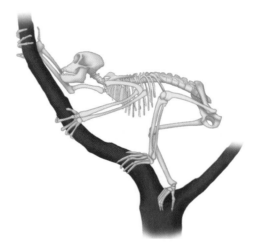

FIGURE 7.15 Early Miocene hominoids such as *Proconsul* exhibited ape-like dental features but a skeleton that more closely resembled that of monkeys.

Middle Miocene (16–12 Ma)

By the end of the early Miocene, the climate had cooled and sea levels had dropped, reducing the amount of forest and exposing a land bridge between Africa and Eurasia. This allowed many species of mammals, including hominoids, to move out of Africa into new environments, where they diversified into myriad forms (Figure 7.16). The oldest Eurasian hominoid, known from 16–16.5-million-year-old deposits in Turkey and Germany, is *Griphopithecus*, which shares a number of characteristics with African middle Miocene apes. The latter include the 15-million-year-old *Equatorius africanus* and the 13.5-million-year-old *Kenyapithecus wickeri*, a semiterrestrial knuckle-walker. While these hominoids retain features seen in the earlier proconsulids, they display a number of characteristics resembling those seen in the living apes, including robust mandibles and large, flat molar teeth with thick enamel, which enabled them to exploit new food resources, particularly hard food items. Another African hominoid was the 13-million-year-old *Otavipithecus namibiensis,* whose remains have been found in Namibia (Conroy et al. 1992), making it the first African Miocene hominoid to be found south of the equator.

CHAPTER 7 Primate Evolution

Hominoids migrate to Eurasia (ca. 16.5–17 Ma)

Early Hominoid dispersals (ca. 15–16 Ma)

Hominoids diversify in Eurasia (ca. 13–9.5 Ma)

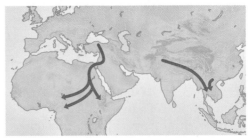

Hominoids expand south (ca. 10 Ma)

FIGURE 7.16 Maps illustrating the dispersal of the hominoids during the Miocene epoch. Between 16.5 and 17 Ma, hominoids expanded their range from Africa into Eurasia. By 13 Ma, two lineages had emerged: the hominines in Europe and the pongines in Asia. By 10 Ma, the hominines had moved back into Africa and the pongines had moved into Southeast Asia.

Adapted from Begun, D.R. 2010. Catarrhine cousins: the origin and evolution of monkeys and apes of the Old World. In CS Larsen, ed., *A Companion to Biological Anthropology*. Chichester: Wiley-Blackwell. 295–313; and C.S. Larsen, *Our Origins: Discovering Physical Anthropology*, 3rd edition. New York: W.W. Norton.

In 2002, the 12.5 million-year-old partial skeleton of a new middle Miocene ape named *Pierolapithecus catalaunicus* was discovered in Spain. While its postcranial skeleton displays a number of primitive monkey-like characteristics, including short phalanges of the hand indicating little, if any, suspensory locomotion, it also possesses modern ape-like features of the thorax, lower vertebrae, and face, suggesting that this hominoid, rather than the known middle Miocene African taxa, may have been close to the last common ancestor of great apes and humans (Moya-Sola et al. 2004). Similarities have been noted between *Pierolapithecus* and two other middle Miocene hominoids, *Anoiapithecus,* also from Spain, and **Dryopithecus**. The three may, in fact, be synonymous (Begun 2010b).

Dryopithecus

a genus of large-bodied hominoids that lived in Europe during the Miocene epoch

Late Miocene (12–5.3 Ma)

By the end of the middle Miocene, hominoids with clear affinities to the hominine and pongine clades had emerged. Climatic changes during this time period—specifically, a shift to colder and drier conditions—led to a reduction in forest environments in Europe and Asia and an increase in open grassland areas, prompting the movement of hominines into tropical regions of Africa, and of pongines south into Southeast Asia (Begun 2007a). The best-known genus of the hominine clade was *Dryopithecus*, of which three late Miocene species have been identified in the fossil record. Much of our knowledge of *Dryopithecus* comes from the work of David Begun, a University of Toronto paleoanthropologist who has been studying Miocene hominoids for 30 years. Represented by fossilized remains from France, Spain, Austria, and the Republic of Georgia, this hominoid exhibits a number of similarities to the African great apes, including a large brain comparable in size to that of chimpanzees and thin tooth enamel suggesting a soft fruit diet. Studies of its postcranial skeleton indicate that it was arboreal with highly mobile limbs and a suspensory mode of locomotion, thus more closely resembling later great apes than previous fossil apes (Begun 2010b).

klinorhynchy

downward tilting of the face relative to the cranial base

Two other dryopithecines, *Rudapithecus* and *Hispanopithecus*, have been recovered from Hungary and Spain, respectively. Dating to 10 Ma, *Rudapithecus*, whose remains come from the site of Rudabánya (Figure 7.17), possessed a skull that also displayed striking similarities to that of extant African apes, most notably **klinorhynchy**, a downward-tilting face relative to the cranial base. The cranium of *Hispano-pithecus*, whose remains also date to 10 Ma, is less well-preserved than that of *Rudapithecus*, but its teeth were chimpanzee-like and its skeleton was fully adapted to suspensory locomotion, with highly flexible mobile limbs (Begun 2010b).

A number of other late Miocene hominoids have been identified in the fossil record. *Chororapithecus* is represented by nine teeth from three individuals recovered from 10-million-year-old deposits in Ethiopia (Suwa et al. 2007). Representing a large-bodied ape, the teeth show a number of similarities to those of modern gorillas, leading researchers to suggest that *Chororapithecus* may represent a common ancestor of

FIGURE 7.17 Excavations of the late Miocene hominoid site of Rudabánya in Hungary have yielded the remains of *Rudapithecus*.

Courtesy of David Begun

gorillas and the human/chimpanzee lineage (ibid.). This claim has been met with scepticism, however, and many scientists are reluctant to accept this ape as an ancestor of later hominoids.

Remains of *Ouranopithecus* have been uncovered in Greece and date to about 9.5 Ma. Its body size is estimated to have been about 50 to 70 kg (Begun 2002), and its large jaws with broad, flat molars and thick tooth enamel were adapted for powerful chewing. Based on its similarities to other dryopithecines, it has been placed in the same tribe (Begun 2010b).

Finally, *Oreopithecus* is represented by 9 to 7-Ma-old remains found at the site of Mount Bamboli in Italy. It is rather unusual because it has a combination of both ape and monkey features. Like the dryopithecines, it has molar teeth with thin enamel and a postcranial skeleton characterized by highly mobile shoulder joints and long arms and hands, allowing for suspensory locomotion. In contrast, its dental morphology, which points to a folivorous diet requiring heavy chewing forces, resembles that of Old World monkeys. Given its unusual combination of traits, the phylogenetic position of this genus is currently unclear.

As noted above, the late Miocene was marked by the migration of not only the hominines into tropical regions of Africa, but the movement of pongines into Southeast Asia. The best-known genus of the pongine clade is **Sivapithecus**, whose fossils have been recovered from deposits in India and Pakistan dating between 12.5 and 7 Ma. Its appearance at about the same time as *Dryopithecus* suggests that the two diverged from a common ancestor sometime between 13 and 16 Ma (Begun 2010b). Its facial morphology closely resembles that of modern orangutans (Figure 7.18). Its postcranial bones, however, differ from *Pongo* in a number of respects. Specifically, *Sivapithecus* possesses a postcranial morphology characteristic of arboreal quadrupedalism but

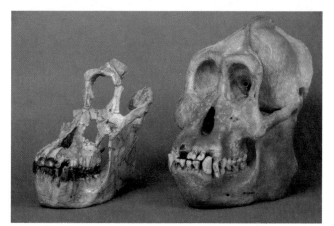

FIGURE 7.18 The face of *Sivapithecus* closely resembles that of modern orangutans.

Courtesy of Ian Tattersall

Sivapithecus

a genus of large-bodied hominoids that lived in Asia during the Miocene epoch without the suspensory adaptations seen in modern orangutans. Given these differences, *Sivapithecus* was most likely a sister clade to *Pongo* (Begun 2005).

One other late Miocene hominoid, *Gigantopithecus*, deserves mention. Known only from isolated teeth and partial mandibles found in India, Pakistan, China, and Vietnam, this pongine appears in the fossil record around 9 Ma (Ciochon, Olsen, and James 1990). Its massive teeth first came to light in the 1930s in a Chinese apothecary shop, where they were being sold for their reputed medicinal properties. Based on the size of these teeth as well as its jaws, *Gigantopithecus* is estimated to have weighed over 500 kilograms (ibid.). One species, *Gigantopithecus blacki*, was named after Canadian anatomist Davidson Black, who is best known for his identification of *Homo erectus* fossils in China (see Chapter 10).

We have introduced you to some of the more than two dozen Miocene hominoid genera that are now known to have existed. In contrast, only 5 genera of apes exist today. The relationship between late Miocene hominoids and extant apes has been the subject of intense debate, and various genera have been proposed as possible ancestors of chimpanzees, gorillas, and orangutans. Unfortunately, large gaps in the late Miocene fossil record have made it impossible to directly link fossil hominoids to extant species.[4] This gap is particularly evident in Africa, where no hominines are known from 13.5 to 10 Ma. Consequently, the relationship between late Miocene hominoids and the living apes remains unclear (see Figure 7.19 for

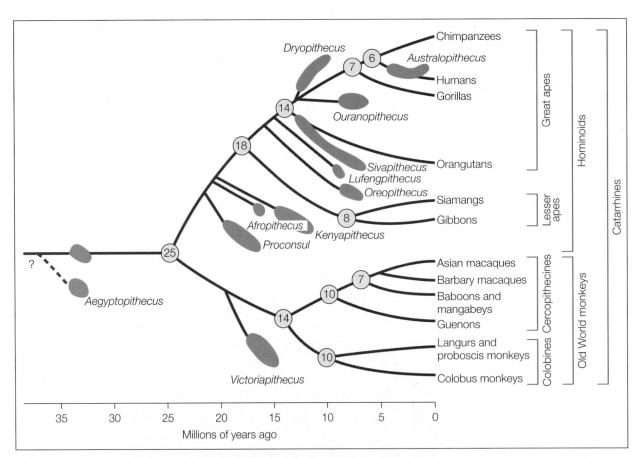

FIGURE 7.19 This phylogenetic tree illustrates possible relationships among Miocene and extant primates. The circled numbers at the nodes represent the estimated divergence dates, derived from Goodman et al. 1998.

Reprinted from *Current Biology*, Vol. 8, no. 16, Caro-Beth Stewart and Todd R. Disotell, Primate evolution in and out of Africa, R582–R588, 1998, with permission from Elsevier.

4. The first chimpanzee fossils, found in 2005 in Kenya, date back to 545,000 years ago (McBrearty and Jablonski 2005).

one possible phylogeny). As you will learn in Chapter 9, however, the recent discovery of the remains of several possible hominin ancestors attests to our rapidly expanding knowledge of this important stage of primate evolution.

MOLECULAR SYSTEMATICS

One of the most significant advances in the study of primate evolution in the past 50 years has been the development of **molecular systematics**, the use of molecular data to reconstruct primate phylogeny. Underlying this technique is the assumption that species that share similarities in their amino acid sequences and thus in their DNA most likely shared a common ancestor. Between-species comparisons have been made using amino acid sequences in a variety of proteins. For example, Sarich and Wilson's (1967) landmark comparison of serum proteins in humans and great apes demonstrated a close genetic relationship between African great apes and humans. They further estimated that the two groups shared a common ancestor as recently as 5 Ma. This conclusion was derived using a technique known as a **molecular clock**, which estimates divergence dates by comparing DNA from different living species, counting the number of genetic differences, and assuming a similar rate of change in each lineage for which a divergence date is to be estimated. The technique also requires that the clock be calibrated with a definitive date from the fossil record. Utilizing the molecular clock, divergence dates have been calculated for Old and New World monkeys, hominoids and cercopithecoids, colobines and cercopithecines, Asian and African apes, and humans and African apes (Goodman et al. 1998).

Comparisons of phylogenetic relationships derived from molecular data with those derived from the fossil record have yielded a high degree of concordance (Fleagle 2000, 89); this demonstrates the value of using molecular data to study primate evolution. There is increasing recognition, however, that estimates of divergence times may vary depending on the type of approach used. For example, Langergraber and colleagues (2012) recently dated the human–chimpanzee split to at least 7 to 8 Ma, earlier than previously estimated.

It has also been suggested that mutations may not occur at the same rate in all lineages and that some lineages may have evolved more quickly than others (Smith and Peterson 2002; Steiper and Seiffert 2012). As a consequence, calculated divergence times are not always consistent with the fossil evidence. For example, the earliest primate fossils date to approximately 55 million years ago but recent molecular studies indicate a strepsirhine–haplorhine split occurring much earlier (Wilkinson et al. 2011). Even so, molecular data, when combined with fossil evidence, has the potential to provide information about primate evolution that is not available from the fossil record alone—for example, about the relationship between late Miocene hominoids and the African great apes.

molecular systematics
the use of molecular data to reconstruct the evolutionary history of early primates and determine the time of divergence of different species

molecular clock
a concept involving the use of molecular data to estimate the sequence and timing of divergence of various evolutionary lineages

LEARNING KEYS

KEY IDEAS

- The first primates likely appeared during the Paleocene epoch.
- The earliest known primates in the fossil record include *Archicebus achilles*, *Teilhardina*, and *Anthrasimias*, all of which date to the early Eocene.
- Eocene primates exhibited a suite of characteristics seen in living primates, including forward-facing eyes, a postorbital bar, grasping hands and feet, and nails instead of claws.

- Current fossil evidence indicates that the first anthropoids appeared in Asia during the Eocene epoch and later colonized Africa.
- The earliest apes appeared in Africa between 23 and 16 million years ago.
- The dentition of the earliest apes was similar to that of extant great apes, but their postcranial skeleton more closely resembled that of monkeys.
- New World monkeys are believed to have arisen from an anthropoid ancestor in Africa that migrated to South America by island-hopping on floating masses of vegetation.

- During the Miocene epoch, apes diversified into many species, due in part to climatic and environmental changes that led to the opening up of new ecological niches and to a lack of competition from other mammals.
- The fossil evidence points to a European origin of the African ape and human clade, but large gaps in the late Miocene fossil record have made it impossible to directly link fossil hominoids to extant species.
- The study of primate fossils can reveal information about their diet, mode of locomotion, and social organization.

KEY TERMS

relative dating (p. 143)

absolute (chronometric) dating (p. 143)

geologic time scale (p. 145)

Cenozoic era (p. 145)

Paleocene (p. 151)

plesiadapiforms (p. 152)

Eocene (p. 153)

omomyids (p. 153)

adapids (p. 153)

basal anthropoids (p. 154)

Miocene (p. 158)

molecular clock (p. 163)

KEY QUESTIONS TO ASK MYSELF

1. If climate change played such an important role in the evolution of primates, should we expect the global warming that we are now experiencing to lead to changes in existing primate species?

2. Fossil evidence is increasingly pointing to an Asian origin for anthropoids, yet some researchers are reluctant to accept this conclusion. Why do we care where early anthropoids arose?

3. Why are there so many more species of monkeys today than apes?

KEY CRITICAL THINKING QUESTIONS

1. Why is it that the Miocene epoch was characterized by dozens of species of hominoids, yet only four species of great apes remain today?

2. Large gaps in the fossil record mean that we currently know nothing about the direct ancestors of the gorilla and chimpanzee. Based on your knowledge of Miocene hominoids and African apes, what might the ancestor of these apes have looked like?

KEY THINGS TO DO NEXT

CourseMate Visit **CourseMate** at www.nelson.com/humanvoyage2e to build your comprehension, practise your critical thinking skills, review core concepts, and explore other resources at your disposal.

OVERVIEW

Somewhere between 5 and 7 million years ago (Ma) the evolutionary line leading to modern humans diverged from that of the chimpanzee. The challenge for paleoanthropology has been to identify those features that are distinctive for the hominin clade. These features result from adoption of a unique form of locomotion, bipedalism; a unique type of dental anatomy, including smaller front teeth and thick molar enamel; and a brain reorganized to emphasize particular functions and larger than expected for our body size. All of these developments are linked to new ways of doing things (behaviour) in a new kind of habitat (environment); more travel over open ground, carrying objects (food, tools, babies); more cooperative group interaction (less agonistic episodes and more conciliatory behaviours); more foresight, planning, learning; and new foraging strategies. As a result of these developments, by 4 Ma hominins had arrived on the primate stage—indeed, they were becoming the principal actors.

KEY CONCEPTS

Hominin, obligate and facultative bipedalism, endurance running, nonhoning chewing complex, encephalization, obstetrical dilemma, altriciality, energetics, endocast, expensive tissue hypothesis

KEY LEARNING OBJECTIVES

At the end of this chapter, you will be able to

LO1   List the major anatomical changes in the skeleton associated with bipedalism

LO2   Describe three stages in the transition from moving on four legs to two legs

LO3   Illustrate the central features of the primate canine honing complex

LO4   Contrast two competing hypotheses for the co-evolution of brain size and bipedalism

LO5   Evaluate the meaning of encephalization as the ratio of brain size to body size

LO6   Predict the essential elements that would identify a hominin in the fossil record

PROLOGUE: A LOOK IN THE MIRROR

As the previous few chapters have illustrated, it is fairly easy to describe the major differences that set modern humans apart from our closest living relatives, although some of the genetic, morphological, and behavioural similarities might seem downright eerie. Compared

---

BOX 8.1 FOCUS ON ... Hominid or Hominin?

Before molecular genetics was applied to questions of phylogeny, classification was based on a Linnean framework in which morphologically similar forms were grouped together in inclusive and ever-broader hierarchies, from genus to kingdom (see Chapter 4, Table 4.3). In this system, all living apes (and their respective ancestors) belong to the taxonomic superfamily of Hominoidea, including separate families for hylobatids (gibbons), pongids (orangutan, chimpanzee/bonobo, and gorilla), and hominids (humans). In the past two decades, increasingly refined genetic analyses have forced a reappraisal of how close the different living apes, ourselves included, are to one another. We now know, for example, that humans and chimpanzees/bonobos are more closely related[1] to each other than either group is to gorillas, with orangutans and gibbons more distant "second cousins." These analyses have led to a revised scheme (Figure 8.1) in which the genera *Pan* and *Homo* are classified as distinct tribes (Panini and Hominini) within the subfamily of Hominine, distinct from the subfamilies of Gorilla and Orangutan.

Many authorities advocate the morphologically inspired term "hominid" rather than its genetic counterpart "hominin," arguing that the former is more pertinent historically (i.e., "hominid" is more commonly found in the older literature) or is more appropriate in discussing adaptation with respect to the fossil record. In this text we have chosen the term "hominin" for two fundamental reasons. First, it more accurately reflects our understanding of the genetic—and thus evolutionary—history of humankind with respect to our primate relatives. As a result, the label "hominin" has gained widespread acceptance among scientists in both lab and field research. Second, there is nothing in either the derivation or application of a genetic taxonomy that precludes it from being employed in discussions of morphology or adaptation (Whitcome, Shapiro, and Lieberman 2007; Wood and Lonergan 2008). Indeed, fairly recent morphological analyses agree with the genetic phylogeny, supporting the concept of a human–chimpanzee clade distinct from gorillas (e.g., Lockwood, Kimbel, and Lynch 2004).

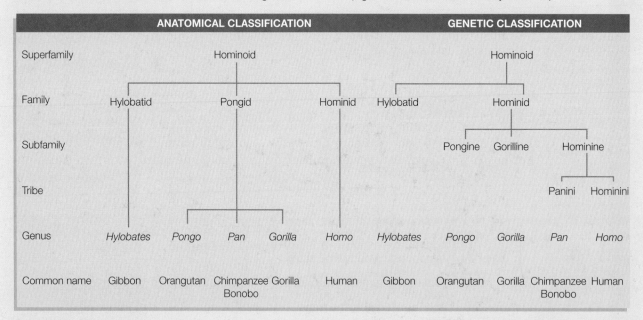

FIGURE 8.1 The genetic classification emphasizes the similarity of the greater apes within the Family Hominid, and in particular the closeness of humans and chimpanzees/bonobos. This similarity is reflected in combining these forms within the same subfamily (Hominine), with subsequent distinction at the level of tribe. The implication is that a genetic classification permits a more fine-grained approach to evolutionary relationships than does morphology.

---

1. One often sees figures of 98% to 99% similarity for shared regions of human and chimpanzee DNA; recent studies suggest that 95% commonality may be more accurate as there are important elements of the genome not shared between *Homo* and *Pan* (Wooding and Jorde 2006).

to our nearest relatives the chimpanzee and bonobos, we appear to be comparatively hairless, more or less vertical, bulbous-headed, dentally diminutive, multilingual, culturally complex, and technologically sophisticated creatures. How we got to be that way is what this book is about. But when it comes to cataloguing the fossil record of ancestors and descendants, things become less certain, and increasingly so the farther from the present we travel. With rare exceptions, the remains of our extinct forebears come out of the ground in bits and pieces, typically broken and often distorted by the pressures of soil and time. In other words, rather shoddy! This is one reason why it is both possible and logical for two different paleoanthropologists to arrive at different conclusions about how our evolutionary story unfolded. Might both be correct in every aspect? Probably not. Might both be mistaken, at least in part? Most likely yes.

Several considerations factor into deciding which of the various interpretations of hominin (Box 8.1) evolution may be "best" in the sense of being most plausible. Of course, it begins with the fossils—how do we determine whether a particular bit or piece belongs to the hominin lineage or some other? Aside from this fundamental exercise in classification (see Chapter 4), we also need to be able to situate the remains in their proper context with a good degree of confidence. By context we mean the specific features of time, geology, ecology, and behaviour, as best as they can be determined. Fortunately, the unique complex of biological adaptations and modifications alluded to above, acquired over 6 million years of hominin[2] evolution, has left some revealing anatomical signatures in bones and teeth. Scientific fields as diverse as physics, chemistry, ecology, primatology, and psychology (among others) provide valuable contextual data. When all of these multidisciplinary lines of evidence are brought together, the field of paleoanthropology is able to produce fascinating pictures of the past, even though parts of the canvas have to be repainted now and then as new discoveries come to light (Figure 8.2).

In this chapter, we explore some of the important signposts that have guided us in our attempts to reconstruct, with a fair degree of certainty, at least some parts of this human voyage. In this exploration we need to consider the biocultural impact of becoming highly **encephalized**, dentally generalized, **obligate bipeds** adapting to climate change and embarking on an extraordinary cultural and technological odyssey (Figure 8.3). It begins with an examination of those ubiquitous anatomical features that signify our adoption of bipedal locomotion. Given the fundamental nature of this transition, we explore some of these ideas in detail. We then move on to discuss dental adaptations—what teeth look like in relation to what they do. Hominins have acquired some unique dental characteristics and, given that teeth form a

FIGURE 8.2 Vignettes depicting early hominin lifeways are based on information obtained from a wide range of scientific disciplines. However, it is important to remember that new discoveries and analyses often lead to major re-interpretations of the past.

© Mauricio Anton/Science Photo Library

encephalized
"encephalization" refers to the ratio of brain size to body size; the higher this ratio for a given species, the more encephalized it is said to be

obligate bipeds
in biology, "obligate" denotes a condition of necessity; being a "biped" refers to the condition of walking on two legs; therefore, obligate bipeds walk on only two legs

considerable portion of the early hominin fossil record, their contribution to interpretations of evolutionary history is substantial. Although a somewhat later development, it also behooves us to introduce some major issues relating to increasing relative brain size (which we pursue further in Chapters 9 and 10), as reasonable arguments can be made that these evolutionary trends are inextricably linked.

2. A number of the earliest forms, dating between 4.5 and 6.5 Ma, are still ambiguous, with a mélange of hominin and panin features (see Chapter 9). Until more remains are discovered, many researchers refer to these fossils as "protohominins."

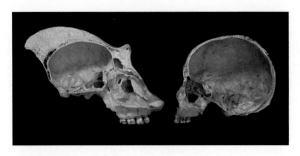

FIGURE 8.3 A capacity for reasoning reflected in an increasing brain size relative to body size is one of the hallmarks of hominin evolution. For example, compare the relative size of the brain case in the skull of a 70-kg human (right) and that of a 160-kg gorilla (left).

William K. Sacco, specimens courtesy of Yale Peabody Museum

So here we are: two legs, small teeth, big brains—a trio of seemingly innocuous changes, but each profound in its own right and even more so when considered together. No other species ever evolved on this planet having features put together in just this way. In part because of this, we are to date the only species capable of asking—and answering—why.

WHAT MAKES A HOMININ A HOMININ?

This heading might seem somewhat offhand, but it is in fact an earnest question and one that has deep historical roots. Scholars of various stripes—anthropologists, psychologists, primatologists, archaeologists, biomechanicians, and philosophers—have struggled with this question: What criterion best captures the essence of human uniqueness? What sets us apart from other primates, most particularly chimpanzees? What might have been that kernel of difference that set one group of apes on a separate evolutionary trajectory, eventually leading to you and me, somewhere in an African forest approximately 6 million years ago? Many candidates have been proposed over the years: large brains, language, culture and tool use, reproductive behaviour, bipedalism, and dental anatomy, to name a few. Some have lost prominence over time with new fossil discoveries. For example, the evolution of brains relatively larger than those of living chimpanzees, once considered the *conditio sine qua non* of hominin status, occurred millions of years after the panin–hominin divergence. Furthermore, the study of living primates has nixed the claim that only hominins fashion tools for specific purposes; in fact, modern chimpanzees arguably possess complex local cultural traditions (Luncz, Mundry, and Boesch 2012) analogous to human ethnicity (as discussed in Chapter 6). Bonobos are sexually adventurous and like ourselves engage in sexual relations for nonreproductive purposes. One famous bonobo, Kanzi, long adept at American Sign Language, has learned to vocalize words such as "milk" and "grape" (Pilcher 2005) as well as comprehend moral judgments of "right" and "wrong" (Lyn, Franks, and Savage-Rumbaugh 2008).

While many of the apparent differences between humans and our nonhuman primate relatives have become blurred in recent years, two realms have (so far) stood the test of time as hallmarks of our clade: bipedal locomotion (Stanford 2012) and dental morphology (Lucas, Constantino, and Wood 2008). Interestingly, both can be linked to a source of strong selective pressure—namely, food acquisition and processing—and it is not unreasonable to suppose that it was a shift in one or more aspects of getting and eating food that provided a fundamental opportunity for evolution of the earliest hominins.

Four Legs Good, Two Legs Better?

As you learned in Chapter 5, the most common form of primate locomotion is quadrupedalism, although many primates are quite capable of standing upright and lumbering (or dancing) around on two legs occasionally—a capacity known as **facultative bipedalism** (Figure 8.4). You also might recall that primates often sit with an upright **orthograde** posture while feeding or grooming, whether on the ground or on a tree limb. But among the primates, only humans normally and naturally move from place to place on two limbs—the obligate bipeds we referred to above. Although when you think about it, we are really bipedal only when we are *not* moving (unless we are jumping on the spot!). When humans walk

conditio sine qua non

a Latin term meaning "without which there is nothing." In this context, large brains were once thought to be the preeminent hominin feature from which all else followed. We know now that this is not the case.

facultative bipedalism

adopting a two-legged posture only under particular circumstances as an exception to a habitual non-bipedal form of locomotion

orthograde

indicating upright or erect posture, notably with regard to the trunk or run, we are actually unipeds—one foot on the ground (stance phase) and one in motion (swing phase) (Figure 8.5).[3]

The evolution of obligate bipedalism has resulted in a major restructuring of human skeletal anatomy, literally from head to toe, associated with erect posture, the effective weight transfer from trunk to legs, maintaining stability and balance, and increased mechanical efficiency (Table 8.1; Figure 8.6). The significance of having a variety of changes to anatomy resulting from bipedal behaviour distributed through the skeleton is profound, as it literally means that paleoanthropologists can find evidence for bipedalism even in the partial or fragmentary remains that are characteristic of the fossil record. Many of these changes have been quite dramatic as you can imagine—compare the human and chimpanzee pelves in Figure 8.6 for example.

FIGURE 8.4 In the wild, many apes, such as this chimpanzee from Senegal, will adopt facultative bipedal behaviour as circumstances require, perhaps to carry objects or cross open water.

© Mint Images/Getty

Other modifications have been much more subtle, such as the shape of the bony labyrinth (Gunz et al. 2012). This tiny structure, found within the inner-most part of the temporal bone situated behind your ear, contributes to our sense of hearing and balance. To assist in balance, the three semicircular canals, oriented at right angles to each other and filled with

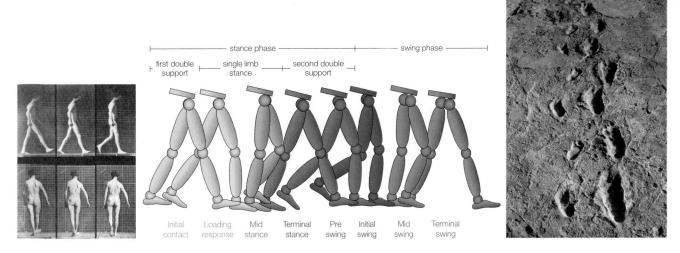

FIGURE 8.5 The analysis of human gait has a long history. In the late 19th century, Eadweard Muybridge photographed humans (and other animals) walking, running, jumping, climbing, and carrying objects from multiple angles against a standardized gridded backdrop. Modern kinematic analyses help us understand the evidence for the evolution of bipedal gaits preserved as fossilized footprints some 3.7 Ma by hominins walking over cooling volcanic ash in East Africa.

(L to R): © Eadweard Muybridge/CORBIS; Reprinted by permission of Gideon Ariel, Ph.D., Ariel Dynamics, www.arielnet.com; © John Reader/Science Photo Library

3. As running speed increases, both feet will be off the ground simultaneously, comparable to a canter or gallop in quadrupeds such as horses or dogs.

TABLE 8.1 Anatomical features associated with bipedal locomotion contrasted with chimpanzee.

Functional Objective	Trait	Human	Chimpanzee	Significance in Hominins
1. Orthograde (vertical) trunk				
A	Foramen magnum position	Beneath cranium	Back of cranium	Balance of head for forward vision
B	Shape of spine	S curve with lumbar lordosis	C curve lacking lumbar lordosis	Balance of trunk and head
C	Shape and orientation of iliac blades of pelvis	Short, wide, and curved, mediolateral orientation	Long, narrow, and flat, anteroposterior orientation	Supports trunk
2. Weight transfer				
A	Vertebral body size	Larger, esp. lumbar	Smaller	Assists weight transfer from trunk to pelvis
B	Size of hip joint	Large	Small	Assists weight transfer from trunk to legs
C	Cortical bone distribution in neck of femur	Thicker inferiorly	Even throughout	Assists weight transfer from trunk to legs
3. Balance				
A	Bicondylar angle of femur	Valgus	Absent/varus	Places lower leg closer to midline of body
B	Anterior inferior iliac spine	Present	Absent or weak expression	Attachment for strong iliofemoral ligament preventing thigh from overextending
C	Transverse and longitudinal arches of foot	Pronounced transverse arch; two longitudinal arches, one medial and one lateral	Only slight transverse arch; lateral longitudinal arch absent	Increases shock-absorbing capacity and rigidity through stance phase
D	Bony labyrinth (Semicircular canal system)	Anterior and posterior canals larger and lateral canal smaller	Shape of posterior canal oval rather than round	Stabilizes head and gaze; facilitates rapid up-down and side-to-side head movement
4. Efficiency				
A	Humerofemoral index; i.e., the ratio of arm to thigh length (also true for total upper and lower limb lengths)	Low	High	Increase in leg length relative to arm length results in greater stride length

(continued)

TABLE 8.1 (*continued*)

Functional Objective	Trait	Human	Chimpanzee	Significance in Hominins
B	Relative tarsus length in foot	Long	Short	More efficient power arm in foot
C	Relative lengths of metatarsals and phalanges	Shorter	Longer	More efficient lever arm in foot
D	Opposability of large toe	Absent	Present	Efficient "toe-off" initiating swing phase of stride
E	Midtarsal break	Rare	Present	Lack of the MT break provides for a rigid level in the foot for greater propulsion

motion-sensing fluid, detect our position and movement in three dimensions. Changes in the structure of the bony labyrinth in bipeds reflect the fact that our head, already uniquely positioned on the spine, moves quite differently walking on two legs than four—nor do we spend much time climbing and moving in trees.

A really good question is why hominins are not constantly falling over during the swing phase of bipedal walking, when only one leg contacts the ground and the other is in motion. The answer is a nifty piece of biomechanical engineering. Your pelvis differs from that of a

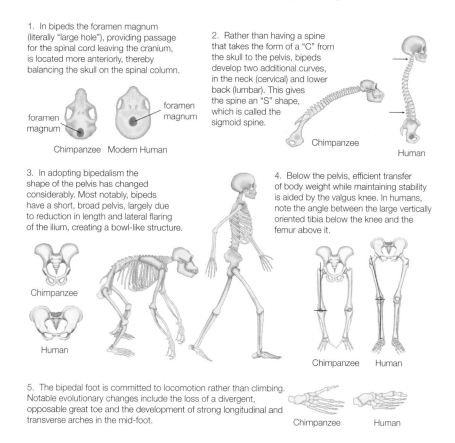

1. In bipeds the foramen magnum (literally "large hole"), providing passage for the spinal cord leaving the cranium, is located more anteriorly, thereby balancing the skull on the spinal column.

Chimpanzee   Modern Human

2. Rather than having a spine that takes the form of a "C" from the skull to the pelvis, bipeds develop two additional curves, in the neck (cervical) and lower back (lumbar). This gives the spine an "S" shape, which is called the sigmoid spine.

Chimpanzee   Human

3. In adopting bipedalism the shape of the pelvis has changed considerably. Most notably, bipeds have a short, broad pelvis, largely due to reduction in length and lateral flaring of the ilium, creating a bowl-like structure.

Chimpanzee   Human

4. Below the pelvis, efficient transfer of body weight while maintaining stability is aided by the valgus knee. In humans, note the angle between the large vertically oriented tibia below the knee and the femur above it.

Chimpanzee   Human

5. The bipedal foot is committed to locomotion rather than climbing. Notable evolutionary changes include the loss of a divergent, opposable great toe and the development of strong longitudinal and transverse arches in the mid-foot.

Chimpanzee   Human

FIGURE 8.6 Anatomical changes reflecting bipedalism are distributed throughout the skeleton, enabling researchers to infer this form of locomotion from fragments of fossil remains.

CHAPTER 8 What It Means to Be a Hominin

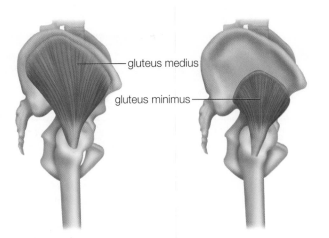

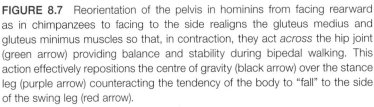

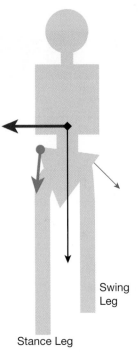

Swing
Leg

Stance Leg

FIGURE 8.7 Reorientation of the pelvis in hominins from facing rearward as in chimpanzees to facing to the side realigns the gluteus medius and gluteus minimus muscles so that, in contraction, they act *across* the hip joint (green arrow) providing balance and stability during bipedal walking. This action effectively repositions the centre of gravity (black arrow) over the stance leg (purple arrow) counteracting the tendency of the body to "fall" to the side of the swing leg (red arrow).

quadrupedal ape (see Appendix A): the large blade-like ilium, for example, is shorter and directed to the side rather than to the back. The effect of this change is to redirect the actions of the three gluteal muscles (gluteus maximus, g. medius, and g. minimus) that attach from the ilium to the thighbone (femur). In apes, a major function of these muscles is to extend the leg, pulling it rearward, but in bipedal hominins with their reoriented pelvis, these muscles act not only as extensors, but also as rotators (g. maximus) and abductors (g. medius and g. minimus)—meaning that they function not only in propulsion, but also in providing stability and balance (Figure 8.7). Importantly, contraction of the gluteus medius and g. minimus on the side of the body that is in stance phase pulls the centre of mass away from the midline of the body, thus repositioning it over the supporting limb and slightly rotating the trunk counter-clockwise. In this way, with each step, balance and stability are constantly adjusted from side to side. Think of it as an almost imperceptible mini-ballet, repeated over and over, keeping you moving forward without falling over.

What Are the Benefits of Bipedal Locomotion?

It is logical to assume that bipedalism occurred because it was adaptive, having conferred some advantages in terms of reproductive fitness to those primates who adopted the behaviour over those who did not. It must also have been the case that those benefits outweighed any negative consequences (costs) of being bipedal. And as you can also imagine, this transformation would not have occurred overnight (see Chapter 9), but rather would have developed over time as the advantages and behaviours facilitated by this unique form of locomotion reinforced the shift from facultative to obligate bipedalism.

Chimpanzees today occupy a variety of habitats, from the tropical forests of central Africa to the more open savannah woodlands of eastern Senegal. While the latter populations have received less scientific scrutiny over the years, they also occupy a habitat now viewed as most similar to that of our earliest hominin ancestors in the late Miocene. Tree cover is patchily distributed save for gallery forests following river courses and is interspersed with open grassland and brush—perfect conditions for stealthy predators such as lions and cheetahs. Surveillance has long been argued as one of the fundamental adaptive benefits of bipedal locomotion in such a habitat—being able to see farther over the grasses and low scrub within which danger might lurk. Researchers have often observed chimpanzees crossing open spaces stop and stand upright in order to reconnoitre the landscape and then, reassured of no present danger, resume traversing the ground with their classic knuckle-walking gait. Clearly, not becoming a big cat's dinner has fitness value!

Modern African apes have often been seen carrying objects from place to place. These items range from foods such as fruits or small animals to branches or stones, the latter used in displays or for cracking nuts. While an archaeological (stone tool) record of technological activity does not appear until c. 2.5 Ma, long after the advent of hominins, it is not unreasonable to suppose that object-carrying was part of the logic for a shift from four-limbed to two-limbed locomotion early in hominin evolution. Kelly (2001) proposed that this shift proceeded through an intermediate stage of **tripedalism** motivated by a need for these open-country Miocene apes to carry stones on their backs supported by one hand while moving across the ground. Kelly suggests these stones might have been used as defensive objects—that is, thrown or used as clubs (Young 2003).

While both surveillance and carrying are arguably adaptive, it is difficult to evaluate the **selective differential** of those animals consistently performing such behaviours compared to those that do so less often or not or all. A number of explanations focusing on physiological /metabolic benefits have been proposed that lend themselves to experimental tests, including thermoregulation, and **energetic efficiency**. It is possible to model predictions of these hypotheses under laboratory conditions (Sockol, Raichlen, and Pontzer 2007) or through computer simulations (Sellers, Dennis, and Crompton 2003).

Peter Wheeler of Liverpool's John Moores University has argued (Wheeler 1994) that, relative to quadrupeds, an effectively hairless, savannah-foraging bipedal hominin would have enjoyed a significant benefit in terms of managing environmental heat load because upright posture exposes much less surface area to solar radiation during the hottest time of day. Furthermore, breezes are stronger away from the ground surface, leading to increased **convective cooling**. With these advantages, a hominin walking on two limbs could search for scattered food resources at greater distances from shade or water, although access to the latter would remain a significant constraint on activity. It is not clear that this argument can account for the origins of bipedal behaviour in the earliest hominins, since they most likely evolved in a semiforested habitat (see Chapter 9).That said, thermoregulatory benefits would certainly reinforce this form of locomotion once adopted, besides facilitating exploration of equatorial savannah environments.

For some time, researchers have debated whether bipedalism was more efficient than quadrupedalism in the use of energy. In other words, are two legs metabolically cheaper than four? A comparison of chimpanzees and humans walking on treadmills found that human bipedalism was about 75% less costly in energy use than either quadrupedal or bipedal walking in chimpanzees (Sockol, Raichlen, and Pontzer 2007; Figure 8.8). Differences in anatomy and gait are implicated in this advantage. Karen Steudel-Numbers and her colleagues

tripedalism
a theoretical model proposing that early Miocene hominins may have adopted a three-limbed gait prior to bipedalism, in order to carry objects such as stones

selective differential
a measure of the probability that a given phenotype will reproduce compared to an alternative phenotype

energetic efficiency
the assessment of the relative metabolic cost of performing a given task

convective cooling
reduction of body temperature by air movement facilitating heat loss through evaporation of sweat

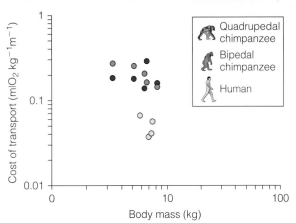

FIGURE 8.8 Experimental studies of chimpanzees indicate that they are less efficient as bipeds.

Sockol, M.D., et al. 2007. "Chimpanzee locomotor energetics and the origin of human bipedalism," *Proceedings of the National Academy of Sciences* 104: 12265–12269. Copyright 2007 National Academy of Sciences, USA.

CHAPTER 8 What It Means to Be a Hominin

(Steudel-Numbers and Tilkins 2004; Steudel-Numbers, Weaver, and Wall-Scheffler 2007) used a similar experimental model to investigate the impact of body size proportions on the energy expended in bipedal locomotion. Human subjects of varying body size and relative limb length walked or ran on treadmills, and metabolic costs (oxygen consumption and carbon dioxide production) were measured. In both scenarios, significant energetic efficiencies were achieved only for participants having legs that were long relative to body mass. Because our earliest hominin forebears were actually quite diminutive, with small bodies and short legs (Chapter 9), it is unlikely that energetic considerations played a major role in the origin of bipedalism.

Recently, Halsey and White (2012) compared estimates of energetic costs for bipedal locomotion in modern long-legged humans and a well-known short-legged ancestor, *Australopithecus afarensis* (see Chapter 9), with similar estimates for 81 quadrupedal mammals. While costs were somewhat lower for hominins, the differences were not statistically significant, leading Halsey and White to doubt that energetic efficiency provided a major adaptive advantage. Clearly there is more to explore in this ongoing debate.

Bipedalism Also Has Significant Drawbacks

While paleoanthropologists have postulated several adaptive scenarios to explain how this unique form of locomotion might have evolved, it is also true that bipedalism has entailed various costs. Many of these are associated with significant medical conditions well known to modern humans. For example, the heart has to circulate blood against gravity to a much greater degree in bipeds, contributing to the risk of heart attack and stroke. Musculoskeletal problems such as "fallen arches" in the feet, prolapse of intervertebral discs in the lower back, patellofemoral syndrome (a condition often seen in athletes resulting in chronic pain in the knee joint), and inguinal hernia have all been linked to upright posture and locomotion.

The most significant negative consequences associated with walking on two limbs relate to childbirth. The adoption of this gait entailed a fairly radical restructuring of the pelvis and a reshaping of the birth canal through which the fetus passes (Figure 8.9), producing what has come to be called the **obstetric dilemma (OD)**. Birth is actually a somewhat torturous journey for recent hominin infants, made more difficult by a fairly rigid shoulder anatomy and a larger brain. Moving from top to bottom. the human birth canal consists of three components—inlet, midplane, and outlet. The transition from one to the next sees the widest dimension of the birth canal rotate from side to side to front to back, which means that so, too, must the newborn. Indeed, a human baby enters the world facing rearward![4]

Just when this particular pattern of birth evolved is unknown, although it is likely a derived feature, first appearing in the genus *Homo*. It has been argued that earlier bipedal hominins (members of the genus *Australopithecus*) had a somewhat distinct birth pattern, resulting from a differently configured pelvis and birth canal that is a mosaic of derived and primitive characters (Lovejoy 2005). In this scenario, fetal rotation would not have been necessary for australopithecine babies, given that the pelvis was fairly wide and did not change orientation from inlet to outlet. Perhaps more important, their brains were likely not appreciably larger than in modern chimpanzees.

The obstetric dilemma faced by more recent hominin infants has led to the suggestion that birth actually occurs earlier than normally expected; in a sense, we are all born premature. The brain of human newborns is the least developed of all primates, at only 30% of its adult size. The baby is not capable of independent movement either, so all of a baby's needs for survival must be provided by its parents—most particularly the mother—for an extended period of time. This state of relative helplessness is known as **altriciality**, and is found among a number of animal species—many birds, most rodents, and cats and dogs are examples. It has been argued that human gestation length should be much longer than nine months in

obstetric dilemma (OD)

the hypothesis that evolution of larger brains competed with narrowing of pelvic structure associated with adopting a bipedal gait, resulting in babies being born in a more helpless stage of development

altriciality

a state at birth in which the newborn lacks the ability to provide for itself and receives food and care from its mother or other caregiver

---

4. Rosenberg and Trevathan (2003) argue that this form of emergence of the neonate, known medically as occiput anterior, may have led to the development of assisted birth, since the mother would be unable to "catch" the newborn, remove obstructions from the airway, deflect the umbilicus from the neck, etc. Interestingly, a recent study using video recordings of live birth in three captive chimpanzees found that in all cases the newborn chimp had rotated to a rearward facing position, with two of the infants simply landing on the ground without guided assistance from the mother (Hirata et al. 2011).

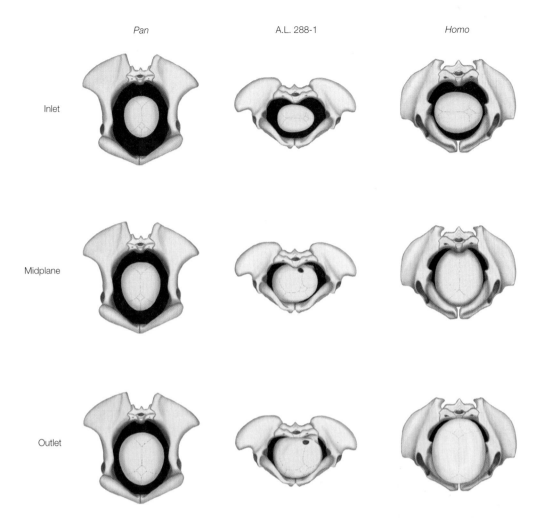

	Pan	A.L. 288-1	Homo
Inlet			
Midplane			
Outlet			

FIGURE 8.9 A combination of pelvic shape and large brain requires modern infants to rotate 90° through the midplane of the birth canal and emerge facing backward. The mosaic nature of the australopithecine pelvis as seen in AL 288-1 ("Lucy") likely resulted in a unique pattern of birth.

Lovejoy, C.O. 2005. The natural history of human gait and posture. Part 1: Spine and pelvis. *Gait and Posture* 21: 95–112. Copyright © 2004 Elsevier b.V. All rights reserved.

order to reach a stage of development resulting in a less helpless infant (Gould 1977). Thus, the OD proposes that selection pressures for bipedal locomotion with associated changes in pelvic structure competed against selection for increasing brain size—the resulting design compromise was neurologically premature birth and altricial infancy.

As we have learned throughout this text (with many more examples to follow) there may be reasonable alternative accounts to explain the same phenomena. Recently Dunsworth and colleagues (Dunsworth et al. 2012) critiqued the OD hypothesis, noting that (1) human gestation length is in fact 37 days longer than expected for a primate of our adult body size; (2) human females do not restrict fetal growth in the last weeks of pregnancy with the aim of limiting neonate size to aid delivery of the infant; (3) the broader pelvis of women compared to men does not result in less efficient bipedalism; and (4) the average dimensions of the adult human female's birth canal are actually within the range needed to successfully give birth to an infant with a brain at the same stage of development as chimpanzees—40% of adult brain size rather than 30%. If all this is true, why then are human infants born altricial, with less developed brains? As suggested by Dunsworth et al., it is not a matter of the size and shape of the female pelvis required for bipedalism, it is simply mother–infant economics —it costs a lot of energy to make a baby! The alternative they propose to the OD is the EGG hypothesis: **energetics of gestation and growth**.

energetics of gestation and growth (EGG)

the hypothesis that the evolution of larger brain size required babies to be born at an earlier stage of fetal development due to the increasing cost of gestation for the mother; in effect, it requires less energy to feed a newborn infant than to prolong gestation

What is EGG? Essentially, birth timing is established by a mother's ability to continue to provide energy, among other nutrients, to an increasingly costly fetus. How costly might this be? For the average human, the energetic costs of high levels of physical activity reach a maximum of about 2.0 to 2.5 times the **basal metabolic rate** (in energetic terms, about 12,000 to 14,000 kilojoules per day[5]). It is estimated that by the sixth month of pregnancy, a human female is already approaching this level of energy expenditure without the added cost of even minimal activity; by the end of pregnancy, the combined cost of her needs plus that of the fetus threaten to push her beyond a sustainable level. To put it bluntly, after nine months of gestation, the infant is less costly outside the womb than inside, in spite of the elevated demands of lactation. Compounding the added metabolic costs of nurturing a large-brained fetus in the evolution of bipedalism are the fundamental biomechanical consequences of carrying a couple of kilograms of baby and placenta in the upright female abdomen, although this challenge appears to have been "solved" at least by 2.6 Ma (see Box 8.2).

Whether "premature birth" is associated with an obstetric dilemma or the energetics of gestation and growth remains an open question. What we should not lose sight of in considering the question of "why" (OD or EGG?) is also the question of "what": What would have been the social and behavioural ramifications resulting from the evolution of ever-more helpless infants? We will explore this important question in Chapter 9.

Do We Know Why Hominins Adopted Bipedal Behaviour?

A very short answer to this question is "Absolutely not." But we do have some interesting conjecture regarding this fundamental development in hominin evolution. Central to this inquiry is the locomotory status of the creature commonly referred to as the **last common ancestor**[6] **(LCA)** of panins and hominins, which is as yet unknown (or at best, poorly known, as we discuss in Chapter 9). On the ground, living chimpanzees typically travel quadrupedally using a form of movement known as **pronograde** knuckle-walking (Figure 8.10). It seems logical to presume that the LCA of humans and chimpanzees was also a knuckle-walker (Begun 2004b), although this conclusion implies that knuckle-walking is a primitive trait for hominines,[7] and not one derived within the panin clade after it parted ways with hominins. Given that the more distantly related gorilla is also a knuckle-walking ape, a "primitive" assessment seems a reasonable position to adopt; Begun and Kivell (2011) have also argued that the Asian Miocene ape *Sivapithecus* may also have evolved this mode of locomotion.

FIGURE 8.10 If not carrying an object in the hand or arm, a chimpanzee engages in pronograde knuckle-walking while on the ground, with the first joint of the fingers flexed and bearing weight.

© Oxford Scientific/Getty

Others argue against this view, however. Crompton, Vereecke, and Thorpe (2008) propose that our *terrestrial* bipedality can be traced to an earlier *arboreal* bipedality present in the LCA, the two modes of locomotion sharing a common element of orthograde (upright) posture and leg extension. Using the orangutan as a model, Crompton and

basal metabolic rate
the amount of energy needed to sustain organ function while at rest and without needing to produce or lose body heat

last common ancestor (LCA)
a term designating that species from which diverging clades evolved

pronograde
a posture in which the trunk is held more or less horizontal and approximately parallel with the surface on which the animal moves

---

5. The kilojoule is the measure of nutritional energy formally used in Canada, rather than the more commonly understood calorie. 1 kilojoule is equal to 0.23901 calories.

6. There can be any number of "last common ancestors" depending on the clades contrasted: there is a last common ancestor for ourselves and chimpanzees, at some point earlier in time a different LCA gave rise to all African apes and Asian apes, and at some very distant point in the past there was a LCA leading to elephants and flatworms.

7. Remember: hominines include the gorillas, chimpanzees, bonobos, and ourselves, whereas hominins specify only the bipedal apes (humans and our ancestors), distinct from panins and gorillas.

BOX 8.2   FOCUS ON ... Babies on Board

Carrying has long been touted as one factor in the evolution of bipedalism (Robinson 1972; Watson et al. 2009), and some items are difficult if not impossible to put down. Take a fetus, for example: wherever mom goes, it goes! This reality prompted Whitcome, Shapiro, and Lieberman (2007) to ask whether the lower spine in women was somehow adapted to this increased burden and forward displacement of the centre of mass (COM) during pregnancy. As noted in Table 8.1 and Figure 8.6, a lower curve in the spine (lordosis) is normally present in humans of both sexes, facilitating positioning of the COM in line with the axis of weight transfer through the hips to the lower limbs. This curve, which develops in children in response to the shift from crawling to upright walking, is never present in quadrupedal forms such as chimpanzees.

Whitcome and colleagues found that during pregnancy, women compensate for the weight of the fetus by shifting the lower back rearward. They effectively adjust their posture so that their "pregnancy centre of mass" is aligned for appropriate weight transfer and stability (see Figure 8.11). A change in the size and shape of the three lower lumbar vertebrae in females accommodates this behavioural response. In females, these vertebrae are more wedge-shaped toward the back, with larger and stronger articulating surfaces. Interestingly, in two well-preserved lumbar spines recovered from hominin ancestors from South Africa, this adaptation is present in the one considered female (known as Sts 14), and absent in the one deemed male (Stw 431)!

After birth, of course, infant apes are not able to get around on their own. Newborn chimpanzees are almost as helpless as human babies. They do not begin to travel on their own until about age three (Pontzer and Wrangham 2006) and are usually carried on their mother's back, clinging to her body hair (Figure 8.12). This strategy would not work for bipedal hominins, whose evolution can be characterized by the loss of two necessary features: effective body hair and a grasping foot. Amaral (2008) suggests that hair loss may have evolved very early in a forested habitat to cope with heat stress associated with high activity levels. If so, this would have placed a high selective pressure, especially on females, to adopt bipedal behaviour enabling infant carrying. Alemseged and colleagues (2006) note that a 3.3-Ma juvenile hominin discovered in Ethiopia lacks a prehensile foot structure, possibly indicating a long history of infant carrying by mothers.

Wall-Scheffler, Geiger, and Steudel-Numbers (2007) note that ethnographic studies of modern human hunter–gatherers reveal that a mother typically carries her infant for the first years of life in an adjustable sling, allowing her to shift the child to different body positions (e.g., back, hip) as necessary in order to perform various tasks. They argue that devices such as slings may have been an early technological

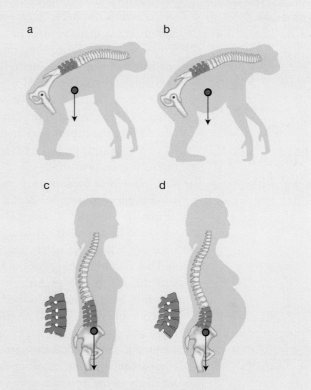

FIGURE 8.11 Lumbar lordosis is adaptive in bipeds for effective weight transfer, balance, and stability, and must be realigned in pregnant human females to offset the forward placement and weight of the fetus.

development, since arm carrying increases the energy cost of locomotion and reduces mobility by shortening stride length (i.e., we walk with longer steps if we can swing our arms). These costs are especially true for hominins with relatively narrow hips—an evolutionary development appearing around 2 million years ago (see Chapter 10). Recent experimental studies suggest that the energetic efficiency of "sling carrying" is realized only if the load (infant) is borne on the mother's front or back; an asymmetric load (hip carrying) actually consumes more energy (Watson et al. 2008).

FIGURE 8.12 While travelling, infant apes often ride on the mother's back, aided by prehensile hands and feet and the chimpanzee's coarse hair.

orthograde clamber

a form of arboreal hand-assisted bipedal loco-motion applied specifically to orangutans, involving extension at the knee, hip, and shoulder

co-workers suggest that hand-assisted extended hind–limb movement over flexible[8] branches (refer back to Figure 8.4), termed **orthograde clamber**, constitutes a behaviour lending itself to a transition from tree to ground. In support of their idea, they note that the earliest hominins predating 2.5 Ma lived in more wooded habitats and retained long, grasping arms with curved fingers (see below and Chapter 9).

Recent evidence of distinct anatomical differences in the chimpanzee and gorilla wrist (Kivell and Schmitt 2009) supports the arboreal origins model for hominin bipedalism. These authors argue that the form of knuckle-walking found in these two apes is demonstrably different, with chimpanzees having a more flexible wrist adapted to greater arboreality and the gorilla a more rigid structure reflecting its more pedestal-like forelimb posture and greater terrestriality. This model would argue for independent evolution of knuckle-walking behaviour in these closely related apes. However, David Begun and his colleagues (Begun, Richmond, and Strait 2007) are critical of the "arboreal origins" hypothesis as it does not fit neatly with a number of aspects of the comparative anatomy of either living hominoids or extinct ancestral hominins.

Leaving aside the debate as to whether bipedalism arose from a terrestrial knuckle-walking or an arboreal orthograde clamber heritage (or some other ancestral locomotive form), we are still left with a fundamental question: Why? We have considered a few of the benefits and consequences of getting around on two legs, but what behaviour(s) motivated the adoption of this unique gait? If carrying was so important to our ancestors, what were they carrying, why, and to where? If managing body temperature was a factor, in what conditions did this necessity acquire so much significance? In effect we need to ask: What was the locomotor and behavioural ecology of the last common ancestor? This is an important question. Noting that the distribution of African paleoanthropological sites associated with the emergence of hominin bipedalism are located in "topographically complex regions," Isabelle Winder and her colleagues (2013, 334) propose that facultative bipedalism appeared in the form of scrambling and climbing over rocky and rugged terrain. They suggest that a last common ancestor adapted to arboreal locomotion would in fact be pre-adapted to scrambling, as trees also offer complex topography (albeit in three dimensions!). Their model, they suggest, better accounts for many of the anatomical and behavioural changes noted earlier.

CARRYING: WHAT AND WHY?

A phrase that has long endured in any hypothesis connected to explanations for the origin of bipedalism is "freeing of the hands." Even Darwin in *The Descent of Man* (1871) invoked the idea that hands no longer committed to movement could be otherwise gainfully occupied manipulating objects. But freed for what purpose? Early views (e.g., Washburn 1960) implicated technology—the manufacture, use, and transport of tools—which is not an unreasonable proposition. However, bipedal adaptations predate the archaeological record for stone tools by several millions of years, and living chimpanzees have a rich (mostly nonlithic) technological tradition, yet remain quadrupedal. The magnitude of change involved in transitioning from a four-legged to two-legged gait is so profound that it must have involved selection favouring extended and repeated periods of upright locomotion (Harcourt-Smith 2007). Such pressures would have been rooted in ongoing environmental changes. In what is now sub-Saharan Africa, the transition from the Miocene to Pliocene epochs is marked by replacement of continuous forest cover by woodland and mixed woodland savannah. It is likely that traditionally exploited food resources became more patchily distributed, requiring a shift in food-getting strategies and/or the adoption of new foods. As a result, at least some Miocene hominoids spent increasing amounts of time travelling over more open ground, although how far and to what degree are unanswered (perhaps unanswerable) questions.

A number of hypotheses associating bipedal behaviour with food transport have been proposed, based on interpretations of the fossil and early archaeological record, comparative

---

8. "Flexible" is a central aspect of their model, since a stable branch greater than 10 cm in diameter poses less challenge (i.e., selective pressure) for travel or feeding. Orangutans are the only living great ape that lives and travels predominantly in trees.

anatomy, and primate analogy. Perhaps the most ambitious and contentious among these was Owen Lovejoy's (1981) "male provisioning" hypothesis. We say ambitious because Lovejoy attempted to synthesize aspects of behaviour, physiology, and sociology into one overarching idea, and contentious as it was proposed in the context of an emerging feminist anthropology in the 1970s and 1980s that rightly took exception to the comparatively passive role that Lovejoy assigned to females.

The male provisioning model argued that bipedalism had a selective advantage in a more open, expansive habitat in which males could range widely carrying tools and weapons and return with food (especially hunted or scavenged meat) to a **home base**. Once "home," males would share resources with a monogamously pair-bonded female and their offspring. Lovejoy argued that this bond was ensured by the evolution of **concealed ovulation** in females: since males could no longer visually identify sexual receptiveness in females, a guaranty of paternity was effectively purchased with food. The success of this arrangement was enhanced by a reduction in **birth spacing** permitted by the high energy of animal protein, which in turn allowed for fairly rapid population increase.

There are many inconsistencies in Lovejoy's 1981 account, not the least of which is that monogamous pair-bonding is rare among primates generally, and in humans in particular (although some would characterize humans as "serially monogamous," moving from one committed relationship to the next). In those animals that do bond for life, sexual dimorphism tends to be reduced, which we know is not the case for the hominin fossil record (see Chapter 9). We also know that females, hominin and panin alike, assume significant roles in nearly all aspects of social life and are not limited to a dependent existence of childbearing, childrearing, and contingent foraging (see Hager 1997).

Lovejoy (2009) has produced a refreshed, more nuanced model of early hominin life history and social behaviour following the publication of the analysis of the 4.4-Ma *Ardipithecus ramidus* remains from Ethiopia (discussed in Chapter 9), again in the context of the evolution of bipedalism. He has retained his original model's central features: bipedality associated with male provisioning of high-energy foods such as meat, concealed ovulation, and reduction of sexual size dimorphism of bones and teeth. Lovejoy links such changes to habitat expansion, cooperative foraging among males, and the advent of female choice for nonaggressive males (also seen among some living nonhuman primates).

Gavrilets (2012) more recent analysis of the evolution of pair-bonding provides some support for the male-provisioning hypothesis perhaps even predating *Ardipithecus ramidus*, with the proviso that the strategy would be most likely to evolve among lower ranking males alongside the evolution of reduced male−male aggression and female mate choice (discussed in Chapter 6). However, feminist scholars remain critical of such **androcentric** models in paleoanthropology, which often lack supporting evidence from fields such as primatology and ethnography and rely on extending estimates of sexual dimorphism determined from one or two individual specimens to entire species (Zihlman 2013).

FEEDING: HOW AND WHEN?

Food is fundamental. Second only to sex as an organizing feature of primate social structure and intragroup behaviour (Chapter 6), it ranks first from the perspective of **time allocation** and **energy budget** among most if not all primate species, including panins (Lehmann et al. 2007a). We have already seen that food is implicated in a number of scenarios regarding bipedal origins, either as an object carried, in terms of efficient travel on the ground between food resource patches or in providing energy to a female nurturing a larger-brained fetus. However, as noted earlier, energetic efficiency was probably not the selective impetus for bipedalism in the earliest hominins, and furthermore, these species retained certain forelimb characters associated with climbing or grasping in trees (discussed more fully in Chapter 9).

Some time ago Hunt (1994) proposed that habitual bipedal *walking* developed from an earlier *positional* adaptation for bipedal foraging; that is, standing upright preceded moving upright. Hunt noted that among chimpanzees at two sites in Tanzania, 80% of all bipedal

home base
an area likely associated with shelter and water to which hominins would repeatedly return from foraging

concealed ovulation
ovulation occurs during that stage in a placental female mammal's reproductive cycle (estrus) during which she is receptive to sexual intercourse (either physiologically or induced through copulation); it may be signalled with swelling and reddening of the genital area, or through chemical means such as pheromones. Thus, concealed ovulation refers to the absence of signalling, such that the male is unable to detect when a female may be likely to conceive. Some recent evidence suggests that chemical signalling still occurs between human females and males.

birth spacing
the amount of time that passes between life births, e.g., birthdate to birthdate. In primate life history, birth spacing is correlated with a number of variables, including female rank, and access to food resources is a primary determinant of birth spacing

androcentric
male-centred; the corresponding term for female-centred arguments is gynocentrism

time allocation
in the study of life history, time allocation studies document how much time is spent during a given time period (day, season, age stage, etc.) performing particular tasks

energy budget
a compendium of the sources and expenditures of energy, typically measured in calories or kilojoules

events were related to food getting (others being behaviours such as vigilance or display), and of these, 95% were postural rather than locomotory. Chimpanzees either stood erect on the ground to reach into the lower branches of trees, or they balanced on their legs, supported by one hand, while collecting fruit with the other. Hunt suggested that such behaviours in early hominins would have selected for an anatomy of the foot, pelvis, and trunk that would be "pre-adaptive" for a shift from standing to walking. In this model, then, bipedal walking was contingent on a prior phase of bipedal standing. Others have suggested that our ancestors adopted bipedal posture to exploit water-borne resources such as sedges and cane (Verhaegen, Puech, and Munro 2002)[9], as has been observed occasionally in both chimpanzees and gorillas.

Which of these various hypotheses and adaptive advantages seems most able to explain bipedalism? Bits and pieces of each is a reasonable answer. Two things are certain: bipedality did not evolve over a short period time. The required anatomical and behavioural changes are simply too profound and too extensive to argue otherwise. Evidence for bipedalism is found in protohominins as old as 6 million years (Richmond and Jungers 2008), whereas anatomy associated with arboreal climbing persists until at least 2 million years ago (Churchill, Holliday, Carlson et al. 2013).

Recent studies of modern feet and the fossil footprints found at the 3.66 Ma site of Laetoli in Tanzania suggest the presence of all of the major features associated with modern human walking (Crompton et al. 2012), including a longitudinal arch on the medial (inside) of the foot and "big-toe" push-off as our leg enters the swing phase of walking. These modern features, while present at this early date, are less expressed than in contemporary humans. Indeed, as we discuss in the following chapter, distinctive morphological features in the pelvis and limbs observed in hominin species such as the 4.4 Ma *Ardipithecus ramidus* from East Africa and the more recent *Australopithecus sediba* from South Africa (dated to c. 2.0 Ma) suggest the evolution of different "styles" of bipedalism associated with the gradual departure from foraging (and sleeping) in trees coupled with occasional terrestrial forays toward a committed lifestyle of gathering and hunting food on the ground (McHenry 2012). Indeed, different bipedal adaptations apparently existed in contemporaneous hominins species in East Africa around 3.4 Ma, as shown by a partial fossil foot skeleton discovered in Ethiopia (Haile-Selassie et al. 2012).

Interestingly, Videan and McGrew (2001) studied bipedal posture and locomotion in captive chimpanzees and bonobos and found that both species exhibited various bipedal behaviours with about the same frequency. However, there were some fascinating differences. Immature individuals in both species were more prone to bipedal locomotion than adults. Adult chimpanzees were more likely to use bipedalism for display; in bonobos it was for vigilance and carrying. Such studies tell us we should be wary of seeking a "best explanation" for the evolution of bipedalism, or that there was only ever one "kind" of bipedalism, as the behaviour clearly serves a multitude of useful purposes.

From Walking to Running

Up to this point, our discussion of bipedalism has focused on the behavioural and morphological features associated with shifting from quadrupedalism to facultative bipedalism and ultimately obligate bipedalism, with the implication that we are talking about walking. As we will see in Chapter 9, the timing of these events, and the ancestral species involved, remains a subject of debate. Facultative bipedalism may have originated as early as 6 Ma; the fossil evidence certainly indicates its presence by 4.5 Ma. The final transition to obligate bipedalism and a commitment to a terrestrial lifestyle can likely be pinned at around 2.0 to 2.5 Ma (Wood and Leakey 2011), possibly with the advent of our own genus, *Homo*, and the "co-evolution" of hands more suited to manufacture stone tools than climb in trees (Rolian, Lieberman, and Hallgrímsson 2010).

But what about running? By most accounts, the premiere track and field event today is the 100-metre sprint, with the current (as of 2013) world record held by Usain Bolt at

---

9. Interestingly, recent research (Kareklas, Nettle, and Smulders 2013) demonstrated that the tendency for our fingers to become wrinkled after water immersion enhanced our ability to grasp objects under water, suggesting that wrinkled fingers may in fact be an adaptation.

9.58 seconds. This translates to a top speed of 44.72 km/h over the 1.61 seconds it took Bolt to travel between the 60- and 80-metre marks (known as the split time). However, as impressive as this is, sprinting is not something for which humans are well adapted, according to a hypothesis suggesting that humans evolved to be efficient long-distance *endurance* runners (Bramble and Lieberman 2004). **Endurance running**, defined by Bramble and Lieberman (p. 345) as "running many kilometres over extended time periods using **aerobic metabolism**," is unique to humans among primates; indeed, it is rare in mammals generally. Nonetheless, when adjusted for body size, human runners are capable of similar speeds as many **cursorial** animals (think dogs and horses). We can also cover significant distances, which is not news to those of us who are active recreational runners.[10] Bramble and Lieberman (2004) list a total of 32 skeletal features related to ER; these features contribute to important aspects of efficient running such as head or body stabilization, thermoregulation, strength and stride length, among others. In all cases, the first appearance of these bony features is associated with members of the genus *Homo*, and can be dated to c. 2.4 to 2.0 Ma.

One possible evolutionary scenario supporting the evolution of endurance running is that it made it easier to exploit animal resources (whether scavenged or hunted is another debate!), although this hypothesis has been questioned based on paleoecological reconstructions and contemporary ethnographic analogies (Pickering and Bunn 2007; see also the rebuttal by Lieberman, Bramble, Raichlen et al. 2007). There are other arguments suggesting that greater access to high-energy foods such as meat, marrow, and brains would be adaptive, if not a necessity, for a larger brained hominin (as we discuss later in this chapter) which also pinpoint behavioural changes around the 2.0 Ma mark. Ruxton and Wilkinson (2011) updated Wheeler's models for thermo regulation as the impetus for bipedalism (discussed previously) in the context of endurance running. Their premise was that running generates considerable amounts of heat, which modern comparatively hairless humans effectively dispel through sweating. Ruxton and Wilkinson argue that endurance running would require equivalent sweating rates, with the implication that endurance running was accompanied by the evolution of hairlessness.

In conclusion, looking at the course of the evolution of bipedalism leads us to reasonably view the transition from quadrupedalism as having three components: (1) facultative bipedal walking in our earliest ancestors, (2) obligate bipedal walking in our pre-*Homo* relatives, and (3) walking/endurance running within our own genus. However, it is important to remember, as noted previously, that bipedalism may have evolved independently at different times and in different species within the hominin clade, taking on different forms of behaviour in terms of time spent on the ground, how they walked (length of stride and gait), and how they remained effective arboreal foragers. We explore these aspects in more detail in Chapter 9, remembering that hominin status hinges on fossil skeletal evidence for some form of bipedal behaviour. However, there are other important adaptive changes we can identify as hallmarks in the evolution of hominins, particularly regarding teeth and brains, to which we now turn.

TALES TOLD BY TEETH

Teeth are unique warehouses of information. The different kinds of teeth in a primate's mouth—incisors, canines, premolars, molars[11]—vary in many ways. They differ in size and shape (height, breadth, width of crowns and roots), in structure (cusp configuration, enamel thickness), and in pattern of wear (surface flattening, sharpening, damage). This variation reflects a tooth's evolutionary history as well as its function during life—its *clade* as well as its *grade* (Begun 2004b; Wood 2013; see Chapter 4 for discussion of clade and grade). And because they are extremely durable, teeth are "over-represented" in the fossil record;

endurance running
the idea that our ancestors evolved the capability for long distance, metabolically efficient running as a unique aspect of human bipedal locomotion

aerobic metabolism
the conversion of glucose to energy within mitochondria in the presence of oxygen, from sources such as carbohydrates, fatty acids, and amino acids

cursorial
pertaining to animals adapted for efficient running

---

10. Running is a hugely popular activity. Canadians spent $1.3 billion on athletic shoes between May 2012 and April 2013—one-quarter of the total amount spent on footwear; 1,694 individuals ran the full Toronto marathon in 2013 (many more ran shorter distances), covering the 42.195 km in an average time of 4 hours and 12 minutes.

11. These tooth classes are found in the adult ("permanent") dentition. Sub-adults have fewer teeth: deciduous incisors, canines, and molars. These latter teeth are replaced by the permanent premolars in the adult dentition.

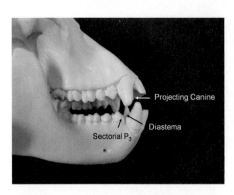

FIGURE 8.13 Diagnostic features of hominin dentition include reduction or absence of C/P3 honing mechanism with loss of the sectorial P3.

Courtesy of Richard Lazenby

historically, they have been the most commonly discovered type of fossil remains. Consequently, volumes have been written, and numerous debates engaged in, regarding what teeth tell us about hominin evolution. Often single teeth—even fragments—can alter our interpretations of fossil taxonomy and diversity, especially for early protohominins, for which we have comparatively few remnants (Schroer and Wood 2013).

Two features are often cited as distinctive of hominin versus chimp and gorilla dentitions. The first is canine size reduction and loss of the C/P3 honing mechanism and decreased canine sexual dimorphism (Figure 8.13, "C" refers to canine and "P3" to the third premolar[12]) and the second is increasing molar enamel thickness. These changes have implications for social behaviours within and between sexes as well as for dietary adaptation, in terms of foods eaten and their mechanical properties (that is, how hard and tough individual food items might be) (Lucas, Constantino, and Wood 2008) or how long over the lifespan we need to use our teeth.

Canine Honing

Primate canines are large, sharp teeth that project beyond what is known as the **occlusal plane**, where upper and lower teeth normally meet in chewing. Canine teeth serve a variety of functions, both passive (processing food) and aggressive (agonistic displays, fighting). For species in which male–male competition is a significant aspect of social life, canines tend to exhibit greater sexual dimorphism beyond that expected owing to mere differences in body size (Plavcan and Ruff 2008). These projecting canines are accommodated in the opposing (upper versus lower) jaw by a **diastema**; when the mouth is closed the large upper (maxillary) canine fits into the space (diastema) between the lower (mandibular) canine and third premolar (P3). In fact, when apes close their mouths, the **distolingual** surface of the upper canine slides along the **mesiobuccal** surface of the lower P3, effectively creating a **canine honing** (sharpening) complex, resulting in what is known as a **sectorial P3**. In hominins and some protohominins (Haile-Selassie, Suwa, and White 2004), a smaller upper canine is associated with (1) loss of the C/P3 honing mechanism, (2) reduction or closure of the diastema in the lower mandible, and (3) blunting rather than sharpening of the tips of the canines since, being smaller, they come into direct contact with the teeth in the opposing jaw. These features are important in determining the hominin status of a fossil, particularly when there is no associated evidence for bipedalism; remember these concepts, as they will return in Chapter 9.

We are not yet sure of the evolutionary timing of these dental modifications; indeed, we may have great difficulty pinpointing these (as other) transitions associated with the hominin–panin divergence (Cobb 2008; we discuss why this is so in Chapter 9). But we *can* make some inferences regarding their significance. For example, if large, projecting canines are most expressive in males living in competitive multi-male primate societies in which aggression plays an important role in establishing and maintaining rank and preferred access to estrous females—as we see in baboons today—then canine reduction suggests important changes in early hominin social organization.

It might be suggested that a behavioural hallmark of hominin evolution associated with canine reduction is decreased male–male competition and an increase in cooperation and coalition (Smith et al. 2012). Having said this, we also need to account for canine reduction in

occlusal plane

The occlusal plane refers to the orientation of the chewing (i.e., occlusal) surfaces of the upper and lower dentitions

diastema

a space between adjacent teeth in the dental row into which the protruding canine from the opposite jaw fits in a closed mouth, found in nonhuman primates and some early hominins

distolingual

the conjunction of the rearward (distal, away from the midline of the mouth) and inner (lingual, or tongue-facing) surfaces of a tooth

mesiobuccal

the conjunction of the forward (mesial, toward the midline) and buccal (outer, cheek-facing) surfaces of a tooth

canine honing

sharpening, in this instance of one tooth, the upper canine, through repeated contact with another tooth, the lower third premolar

sectorial P3

in Old World primates, a lower third premolar in which the mesiobuccal surface appears as a long, sloping surface due to contact with the upper canine

---

12. Hominins have 2 premolars in the upper and lower jaws, but they are numbered P3 and P4. This is because the very earliest primates actually had 4 premolars, but in the course of evolution most primates have lost P1 and P2.

females. Canine teeth in most female primates are not as large as in conspecific males, but they are nonetheless fairly large and projecting, and they are used as weapons in agonistic encounters with males, predators, and other females. Some time ago, Greenfield (1992) proposed a "dual selection" hypothesis to account for male and female canine reduction, in which less **intrasexual** competition and a shift to using canines as "modified incisors" to process food selectively favoured smaller canines. Others see little comparative evidence for the "dual selection" dietary explanation for female canine reduction (e.g., Plavcan and Kelley 1996), suggesting that it can be viewed as a direct outcome of fewer female aggressive encounters or as a **correlated response**— that is, a change in a supposedly independent feature (such as facial **prognathism**) produced a change in canine dimensions.

Enamel Thickness

Enamel thickness refers to the depth of the outer layer of a tooth overlying the supporting dentin relative to the size of the tooth (Figure 8.14a). As discussed in Chapter 7, enamel thickness has historically played an important role in reconstructing primate evolutionary history. For example, middle Miocene fossil hominoids such as European *Dryopithecus* have thin-enamelled molars, whereas more recent forms such as *Ouranopithecus*, discovered in Greece and dating to c. 8.0 Ma, have the thick-enamel trait seen in most hominins. However, the degree to which this classic dental attribute reflects clade (phylogeny) versus grade (function) is open to debate. Begun (2004b) notes, for example, that this feature tends to distinguish higher order taxonomic levels (i.e., genus and above) rather than species-level ones, and thus will have limited utility in pointing us in the direction of the LCA, since this creature would have been very closely related to both its hominin descendants and its panin ones.

Enamel thickness is also an indicator of dietary adaptation, with thick-enamelled species exploiting harder, more abrasive foods and thinner enamelled species exploiting softer items such as fruits. Lucas, Constantino, and Wood (2008) have suggested that the **microstructure** of thick enamel helps prevent damage to a tooth by restricting the spread of cracks from deep within the tooth to the outer surface. Among the early

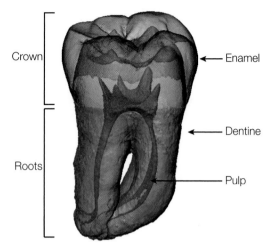

intrasexual
"intra" means *within*; thus intrasexual variation refers to differences that exist within males or females separately

correlated response
changes that occur in one feature are consistently associated with changes occurring in another

prognathism
projection of the lower face; the gnathic portion of the face contains the upper and lower jaws

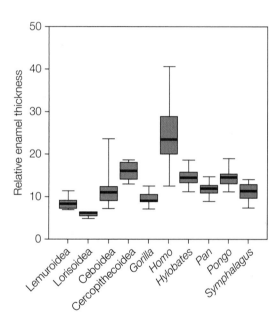

FIGURE 8.14 (a) Teeth are composed of an enamel crown (light blue) supported by an underlying dentin layer that also contributes to the roots, which are embedded in bone. Enamel thickness in hominoid teeth may be an indicator of phylogeny, but it also reflects adaptation to particular diets adopted by several taxa that may or may not be closely related. (b) The variation in enamel thickness within living primates is large, especially in ourselves. Thus, while humans on average have the greatest enamel thickness, there is overlap with other species, including panins, suggesting limited utility of enamel thickness for phylogenetic inference.

Courtesy of Matthew Skinner (top); Reprinted from the *Journal of Human Evolution*, Vol 54/2, Anthony J. Olejniczak, Paul Tafforeau, Robin N.M. Feeney, Lawrence B. Martin, Three-dimensional primate molar enamel thickness, pp. 187–195, 2008, with permission from Elsevier. (bottom)

microstructure
the arrangement of cells and their associated structures that contribute to the material properties of a tissue; usually, microstructure is viewable only with the use of instruments such as microscopes and microCT scanners

protohominins, the degree of enamel thickness varies, although generally it is always thicker than in living chimps and gorillas. Pampush and colleagues (2013) looked at enamel thickness and diet in 17 species of primates and found that thickness correlated with lifetime wear independent of presence of fractures or toughness of diet. This would caution us against assuming out of hand that thick enamel equates with a hard diet without considering the lifespan over which a tooth is used. However, studies of living primates (Olejniczak et al. 2008b; see Figure 8.14b), and humans (Smith, TM et al. 2012), suggest a greater range of enamel thickness variation than previously appreciated. Enamel thickness therefore may not be as reliable an indicator of evolutionary relationships as we once believed; however, Olejniczak et al. (2008a) have shown that the three-dimensional distribution of thickness over the entire enamel surface does discriminate among different fossil species; so what matters is not a question of how thick enamel is, but where it is thick over a tooth's surface.

WHY IS MY FOREHEAD SO LARGE?

As we discussed in Chapter 5, one of the defining features of primates among mammals is an increase in **relative brain size**. That is, primates have a higher ratio of brain mass to body mass. In the course of hominin evolution, brain/body **scaling** has been taken to an extreme, culminating in modern humans (Zollikofer and Ponce de León 2013). Although highly variable in our species, human brain volume is about three times larger than expected for a primate of our body size. In the following chapters we will be considering how these changes appear in the fossil record.

Still, there are several issues germane to distinguishing the hominin from the nonhominin brain that merit our attention at this time. The first of these is organization. It is not overall size alone that sets the hominin brain apart, but how various structures *in* the brain (both neural and vascular tissue) have changed with respect to one another. This reorganization reflects the ways in which some functional capacities of the hominin brain have been emphasized or expanded at the expense of others over time; indeed, the reorganization of the brain is a more significant aspect of its evolution than simply size alone (Smaers and Soligo 2013) and in fact occurred earlier in the course of evolution than the trend to increasing size (Holloway 2012). We also need to consider how we "feed" this ever-expanding brain—what behavioural changes would have provided for the increased energy demands of this most complex and least understood organ?

relative brain size

the absolute size of the brain adjusted to reflect the absolute size of the body of which it is a part, since we expect a larger body to have a proportionately larger brain. Primates tend to have larger brains for a given body size than other mammals

scaling

in biology, refers to the pattern of change of a part in relation to a whole; may be *isometric* (a unit of change in body size is matched by a unit of change in the part) or *allometric* (the change in a part is greater or less than the change in the whole)

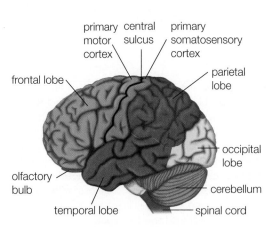

primary motor cortex · central sulcus · primary somatosensory cortex · frontal lobe · parietal lobe · occipital lobe · olfactory bulb · cerebellum · temporal lobe · spinal cord

FIGURE 8.15 The human brain is a complex arrangement of highly convoluted layers, lobes, folds, and fissures.

The Brain and Its Organization

Our brain is a multi-levelled, bilateral, lobular, and fissured mass with the consistency of unset gelatine, the outer layer of which is intricately folded (Figure 8.15). The major divisions of the brain include the hindbrain (cerebellum, pons, medulla), midbrain (tectum, tegmentum), and forebrain (cerebrum, thalamus, hypothalamus). The cerebrum is divided into two hemispheres, each further partitioned into four lobes: frontal, parietal, occipital, temporal.[13] These lobes are distinguished by folds (called gyri) and fissures (sulci). In broad evolutionary terms, the forebrain is most recent, the hindbrain most ancient—indeed, our hindbrain resembles the entire brain of creatures such

13. Lobes are named according to the bone of the cranium against which they lie; thus the temporal lobe of the brain lies under the temporal bone of the cranium.

as reptiles or birds. Among hominins, the cerebrum—also known as the cerebral cortex—is highly convoluted compared to that of panins, and even more so than monkeys or prosimians.

As we will discuss in the following chapters, hominin evolution is characterized by fundamental shifts in geography and ecology, social and cultural dynamics, technological achievement, and communication. All of these together suggest accompanying transformations in the central nervous system (CNS). It is fair to conclude that increasing social and technological complexity has placed a selective premium on those brain functions responsible for features such as fine motor control, long-term memory, reasoning/planning, and verbal/visual communication, among others (including distinctions related to gender) (Lindefors, Nunn, and Barton 2007). While the relative volume of some compartments of the neocortex, such as the frontal lobe, appears similar among apes (Semendeferi and Damasio 2000), the degree of convolution—and thus the surface area of the neocortex within lobes—shows a gradient within mammals, including primates (Zilles et al. 1988). The result is a modern human brain having the highest density of neurons—between 12 and 15 billion—of any animal (even those with absolutely larger brains, such as whales) (Roth 2012).

Brains are not bones, so you might well ask how paleoanthropologists can study brain structure in long-extinct ancestors. One approach is to examine natural or reconstructed models of fossil brains, called **endocasts**, which provide unique insights into brain evolution and form the basis for the science of **paleoneurology** (Zollikofer and Ponce de León 2013). An endocast is essentially a reflection of the internal surface of the cranium, which bears impressions of the structures adjacent to it—the various lobes and fissures of the brain, the vascular supply of arteries and veins, even the sutures of the cranium itself. While endocasts reproduce the inner surface of the bony cranium and thus only the outer surface of the cerebral cortex, they do provide a depth of information on size, shape, and structure that is becoming more and more accessible as imaging technology advances (Figure 8.16).

One of the features observable on endocasts, the **lunate sulcus (LS)**, has been the subject of considerable debate over the years, especially regarding its placement in the brains of earlier hominins such as the australopithecines (Falk 2012; Holloway 2012) compared to our primate relatives such as chimpanzees. The LS, which defines the position of the primary visual cortex on the occipital (most posterior) lobe of the brain, is readily visible in nonhuman primates but less commonly in modern humans. When it is present in the human brain, it occupies a position more to the back of the brain than in species such as chimpanzees, suggesting relative reduction of the primary visual cortex in ourselves. Adjacent areas of the brain, such as the parietal and temporal lobes, have been shown to be somewhat larger than expected in humans (Rilling and Seligman 2002). This presumably reflects an emphasis on the brain functions of these regions, such as language capacity. Holloway, Clarke, and Tobias

endocasts

impressions of the inner surface of the cranium and outer surface of the brain, which may occur naturally as "fossils" or from moulds created in the laboratory

paleoneurology

the study of the evolution of the brain and its functions

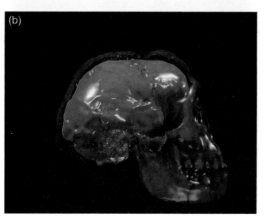

lunate sulcus (LS)

a fissure found in the anterior portion of the occipital lobe that demarcates the primary visual cortex; readily visible in nonhuman primate brains, the LS is often not seen in humans

FIGURE 8.16 Endocasts provide information about the external configuration of the brain, including relative size and position of lobes, gyri, and sulci. (a) One of the most famous natural endocasts, associated with a young *Australopithecus africanus* specimen from the site of Taung, South Africa. (b) Modern medical imaging now allows creation of virtual endocasts, such as that of the controversial Liang Bua 1 specimen from Indonesia. (Not to scale.)

© Javier Trueba/MSF/Photo Researchers, Inc. (top); Kirk E. Smith, Electronic Radiology Laboratory, Mallinckrodt Institute of Radiology, Washington University at St. Louis, MO. (bottom)

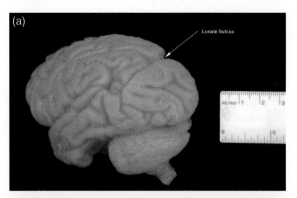

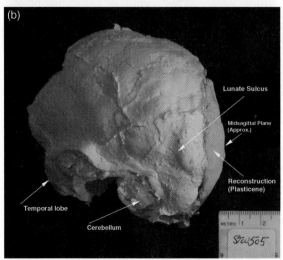

FIGURE 8.17 Comparable views of a chimpanzee brain cast (a) showing the anterior position of the lunate sulcus in relation to other landmarks and (b) an endocast of Stw 505 showing the more posterior location of the sulcus.

(2004) have observed a more posterior placement of the LS in a small-brained early hominin called Stw 505 from South Africa, dated to c. 2.5 Ma (Figure 8.17). They argue that reduction in the primary visual cortex in these (and possibly earlier) hominins would have allowed increases in adjacent areas of the brain as previously noted—areas associated with the integration and analysis of information enabling tool making and use (e.g., throwing), long-term spatial memory, facial recognition of self and others (including predators), and social communication.

Such interpretations are by their nature speculative, but they are grounded in our current understanding of brain function. All of these characteristics are present in panins to some degree, but they are most highly developed in ourselves, and the qualitative and quantitative differences could well be associated with the neural reorganization noted by Holloway and colleagues. Debate over the significance of the lunate sulcus position and its meaning continues. Falk (2012), for example, argues against the findings of Holloway et al. (2004), noting that reproduction of the sulcus on endocasts is notoriously difficult. She also points to recent magnetic resonance imaging research in living humans that suggests "there is little, if any, evidence in support of the view that contemporary humans have lunate sulci." (p. 261).

As you will discover in subsequent chapters, the very nature of the fossil record lends itself to many different interpretations, and healthy scientific debate continues.

A final aspect of the value of endocasts is worthy of mention, and returns us to the idea of the obstetric dilemma (OD) hypothesis discussed previously. Falk et al. (2012) have reported that the natural endocast of the approximately 3-year-old Taung child from South Africa, belonging to the species *Australopithecus africanus* dating to 2.5 Ma (see Chapter 9, Box 9.3), preserves evidence for the metopic suture (MS) and fontanelle, two characteristic features of young children today. In apes, both disappear through bony fusion (a normal process of skeletal aging) shortly after birth, but in humans, the MS and fontanelle typically "close" by age 2. However, not uncommonly the MS may last into adolescence or adulthood. Evidence for persistence of the MS is also seen in crania of adult australopithecines. The fact that these fossil hominins seem to follow a similar pattern of cranial fusion to ourselves suggests selection for some degree of plasticity of the head assisting in birth—the obstetric dilemma—or perhaps an accommodation for high rates of brain growth/reorganization in early childhood.

While endocasts are the richest source of information on the surface anatomy of fossil hominin brains, another avenue advancing our understanding of brain evolution more generally is primate comparative neuroanatomy. For example, paleoneurologist Carol MacLeod has applied magnetic resonance imaging and histology to compare size and complexity in the cerebellums of anthropoids, hominoids, and humans in relation to cognitive functioning (see Box 8.3).

BOX 8.3   PROFILE ... Thinking Outside the Box

Courtesy of Carol MacLeod

How does one go about studying one of the most fascinating questions about human origins—why and how humans became so smart? What is special about our brains? How are our brains different from the brains of chimpanzees, macaques, or lorises? Are our brains organized differently from the brains of our closest relatives, the great apes, or are we simply all genius chimpanzees because we have huge brains?

One way of answering these questions is to measure primate neuroanatomical structures and to compare them with one another to see if there have been significant increases in particular structures in certain taxa. Not all brain structures increase at the same rate; the neocortex and neocerebellum increase at a higher rate than earlier developing structures when these structures are regressed against whole brain volume (Finlay and Darlington 1995). Multiple regression analysis shows this exponential increase clearly and can reveal unexpected increases in some structures when the primate sample size is examined in detail.

For my research, I collected as many measures from primate brains as I could, using both magnetic resonance brain scans and preserved brains of monkeys, apes, and humans. My ape sample was large enough to analyze apes and humans against monkeys to see if there was differential expansion of some structures, reflecting a grade shift (Martin 1980) in brain proportions of hominoids to monkeys. My particular interest is the cerebellum, that cauliflower-like appendage at the base of the brain. Until recently, the cerebellum was thought to be concerned uniquely with movement and balance. This is true of the oldest part of the cerebellum, the vermis (medial cerebellum). Now neuroscientists are showing great interest in the lateral part of the cerebellum, the neocerebellum. This is important in the planning of movement, visuospatial problem solving, procedural learning (learning how to do something), working memory ("remembering" several things at once when executing a task), attention switching, and even language in humans. In other words, the lateral cerebellum participates in thinking.

I was not surprised to see that the neocerebellum was larger than expected in apes over monkeys, but I was surprised at the magnitude of this increase. The hominoid lateral cerebellum, when regressed against the vermis, is 2.7 times larger than the monkey lateral cerebellum with a vermis of the same size (MacLeod et al. 2003). The neurological structure has undergone selection, and a whole taxonomic category has acquired a new outlook on the world as a result. The skills of the lateral cerebellum noted earlier were probably important to the early hominoids as they acquired finesse in exploiting the frugivorous niche as suspensory feeders. With the increase in brain size of the ancestors to great apes and humans, these cerebellar skills were augmented, perhaps to facilitate tool using and making, as well as complex feeding strategies characteristic of the great apes and early hominins.

An intrinsic love of anatomy drives many a physical anthropologist. Collecting volumes of brain structures is time-consuming and meticulous work, but it is a pleasure for me to measure volumes from such a beautiful and complex structure as the cerebellum. There is much more to learn about its evolution in the primate order.

Source: Written by Dr. Carol MacLeod, Department of Anthropology, Langara College, Vancouver (Retired)

ENERGETICS

Physiologists studying the modern adult human brain tell us that it forms about 2.5% of our body mass yet demands 15% of cardiac output, 20% of basal metabolic rate, and 25% of glucose utilization. Comparatively speaking, our 1.33 kilogram brain is as energetically expensive as 25 kilograms of inactive skeletal muscle (Zollikofer and Ponce de León 2013). Under resting conditions (whether awake or asleep) the brain relies almost entirely on the simple sugar glucose as its energy source, and whole-brain and regional[14] studies show increases in glucose

---

14. Such studies focus on specific functions of the brain, such as motor tasks or various sensory stimulations (visual, auditory). Kemppainen and colleagues (2005) showed that as the level of physical exercise and thus brain activity increases, the brain "switches" from glucose to lactate as a source of metabolic energy.

use with normal neuronal activity. The brain "burns" approximately 4.2 kilojoules of energy per minute (about 1 calorie)—any way you look at it, the brain is not an economical organ to keep running!

Of course, size is a factor to consider in calculating brain energetics, both phylogenetically (evolution) and ontogenetically (growth). Early hominins were smaller in both body size and brain size, with the latter not much larger than those of living panins. Significant increases in body and relative brain mass have occurred only within the past 2.5 million years with the transition from the genus *Australopithecus* to *Homo* (see Chapter 10). Aiello and Wells (2002) estimate that this evolutionary development increased resting metabolic energy requirements by about 39%, more so for females than for males due to the added costs of pregnancy, gestation, and lactation (recall the EGG hypothesis). Furthermore, the costs are even greater for sub-adults (infants and children especially), for whom the brain forms a higher proportion of body mass and represents up to 70% of total energy requirements.

Growing bigger bodies and brains must have been accompanied by changes in how these larger, "brainier" hominins captured energy (e.g., by hunting) and used it for growth, maintenance, and reproduction. Possibly they shifted to higher quality, energy-dense foods, reallocated energy from one metabolic need to another, or simply changed activity levels to reduce energy requirements. Some combination of these is a reasonable if not probable conclusion. The paleontological record for these early members of the genus *Homo* indicates a continuation of the trend toward reduced jaw and tooth size, increased lower-limb length, and decreased body breadth (the adaptive value of these changes is explored in Chapters 10 and 11). These modifications imply a significant dietary change: a shift away from hard, tough foods, which require larger teeth and jaws (Lucas, Constantino, and Wood 2008), toward resources more readily digestible with a reduced gut (which would fit into a narrower trunk). In particular, this means more meat and fat, accompanied by items with high carbohydrate content such as tubers and seeds (Aiello and Wells 2002).

This dietary transition is captured by an idea proposed in the 1990s called the **expensive tissue hypothesis (ETH)** (Aiello and Wheeler 1995). This hypothesis argues that the body's essential organs bear "fixed costs"—that is, they have specific energy demands that must be met in order to maintain function. These organs include the brain, liver, heart, kidneys, intestinal tract, and lungs. Aiello and Wheeler calculated that of these, only the size of the intestinal tract was smaller than expected for an average 65-kg human. They concluded that this tradeoff—a shift of energy resources from intestinal tract size to brain size—was achieved by adopting the kind of diet described above: more meat and fewer fibrous, plant-based resources, which require a large gastrointestinal tract for processing. This would have been accomplished by a shift in foraging strategy to increase the proportion of hunted game; this in turn would have been realized most effectively by cooperative hunting facilitated by an increase in group size required to provide the necessary "hominin power."

Support for the ETH has been slow in coming (Gibbons 2007). However, over the past few years, studies of primates and other animals have confirmed the general premise of energy tradeoffs among "expensive" tissues. For example, Isler and Van Schaik (2006) did not find a negative correlation[15] for brain and gut size in birds, but they did find one for brain and pectoral (chest) muscle size. On average, pectoral muscles comprise 18% of a bird's body mass and are energy-expensive tissues, given that they must generate sufficient power for lift-off. In other words, larger bird brains mean smaller pectoral muscles.

While the ETH might apply to birds, can the same be said for primates, or mammals more generally? Among primates, capuchin monkeys in Central America have relatively large brains and small guts and eat a high-quality diet that includes insects and bird's eggs, whereas sympatric howler monkeys have relatively small brains and large guts, which they require in order to digest fruit and leaves. Navarrete et al. (2011) compared brain and organ sizes across 100 species of mammals, including 23 primate species, and *did not* find the expected negative correlation for gut and brain sizes. This led them to refute the ETH for the mammalian case. Instead, evolving

expensive tissue hypothesis (ETH)

a hypothesis accounting for the added metabolic cost of increasing brain size through the reduction of other "fixed cost" tissues; the hypothesis suggests that human ancestors reduced the cost of digestion to transfer energy resources to the expanding brain

---

15. A negative correlation exists if one variable increases in response to the other decreasing.

larger, more expensive, brains within the genus *Homo* over the last 2 million years or so could have been accomplished by either increasing energy input or changing how we use it (energy allocation).

Increasing energy input would follow from the cultural evolution of cooperative tool-assisted hunting and especially food-sharing strategies that would have the benefit of stabilizing food intake (that is, avoiding starvation). Changing the amount of energy we use can be achieved in several ways. First, we can conserve energy by limiting activity as noted earlier. Contemporary human populations adopt this strategy when resources are scarce; similarly, primates generally spend a good deal of the day resting when not feeding or travelling. However, for a mobile forager whose life depends on tracking wild game, resting is not an especially viable option.

Another option is to modulate growth rate.[16] Humans grow in three phases. From birth to about two years, growth is fairly rapid, then it drops off until puberty reducing resource needs, after which it picks up again until maturity is reached at around 18 years of age. This fast–slow–fast pattern differs from that of panins, who match humans in the first two years but then accelerate growth until just before achieving maturity at 12 years, after which growth eventually stops. These different growth trajectories result in lower energy costs for human infants and children. Chimpanzees use about 210 kilojoules (kJ) per day versus 113 kJ per day for humans during the first 10 years of life (Aiello and Wells 2002). The benefits are two-fold: brain growth continues until later childhood in humans, and reduced demand for body growth at this time means more energy can be given over to growing brains. Furthermore, children are typically not self-sufficient during this period, so lower energy demand during the first 10 years represents less of a burden for those who are providing food. Finally, as a third option, as we have discussed in depth earlier in this chapter, becoming more efficient bipeds would reduce locomotion costs.

A final wrinkle in the "expensive tissue–energy tradeoff" story of brain evolution has been argued by primatologist Richard Wrangham and his colleagues (Boback et al. 2007; Wrangham 2009). In an experimental study using Burmese pythons, they measured the **specific dynamic action (SDA)** for four different diets: intact raw beef, ground raw beef, intact cooked beef, and ground cooked beef. They found that the least costly diet in terms of digestion and best in terms of energy capture was meat that had been ground and cooked; this reduced SDA by almost 24% compared to the intact raw meal (Figure 8.18). Grinding reduces the energy required for digestion by disrupting tissue integrity; cooking reduces food toughness, which saves energy for species that chew their food. For a standard human diet including cooked food, the SDA is relatively low: about 6 to 8% of the energy ingested is used to process it.

specific dynamic action (SDA)

a measure of energy consumed in digesting, absorbing, and assimilating nutrients from a meal

In a related study, Carmody et al. (2011) fed mice diets of cooked (whole or pounded) and non-cooked (whole or pounded) organic sweet potato and organic lean beef. Greater weight gain was found for diets in which the food (starch or protein) was both pounded and cooked. They also found, in a subsequent study, that mice preferentially selected food that was processed—pounded and cooked—over raw, whole food. The implication for hominin evolution, and for encephalization in particular, is that the advent of cooking, or cooking and grinding/pounding combined, would have further enhanced the energy equation: for every unit of energy captured, less would have been required for getting nutrients into the body so that more

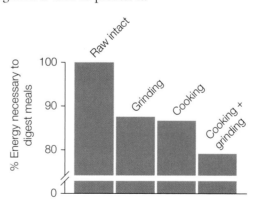

FIGURE 8.18 Cooking and grinding is the most cost-effective way to acquire nutrients from meat.

Boback, S.M., Cox, C.L., Ott, B.D., et al. 2007. Cooking and grinding reduces the cost of meat digestion. *Comparative Biochemistry and Physiology, Part A* 148: 651–656. Copyright © 2007 Elsevier Inc. All rights reserved.

16. Patterns of growth are explored in greater detail in Chapter 14.

could be used for growth of bodies and brains. Cooking with fire and the use of fire generally would have been adaptive for many other reasons (biological and social), as we discuss in Chapter 10. The open question—and a large one—is when in the past did our ancestors begin to process their food—meat in particular—in this way? That we do not yet know.

LEARNING KEYS

KEY IDEAS

- A hominin is a member of the clade (lineage) comprising all taxa leading toward humans after diverging from the chimpanzee clade.

- Bipedalism in considered the essential behavioural shift defining all hominins but may have evolved in different ways at different times in hominin evolution.

- Bipedalism likely originated in a semi-forested habitat but over time became established as a terrestrial adaptation associated with open-country foraging.

- Anatomical changes linked to bipedalism occur throughout the skeleton, literally from head to toe (position of the foramen magnum, reshaped pelvis and loss of a grasping big toe).

- Hominins are also defined by a reduction in the size of the face and teeth and an expansion of the brain relative to body size.

- The co-evolution of bipedalism and encephalization posed significant challenges for birth in hominin females, both mechanical and metabolic.

- Endocasts of fossil hominin brains show that reorganization preceded size increase.

- Brain reorganization implies changes in the importance of different brain functions that can be linked to shifts in hominin behaviour.

- The evolution of hominin anatomy with the adoption of bipedalism was accompanied by changes in physiology, social relationships, and technology.

KEY TERMS

encephalized (p. 169)

obligate bipeds (p. 169)

facultative bipedalism (p. 170)

obstetric dilemma (OD) (p. 176)

energetics of gestation and growth (EGG) (p. 177)

endurance running (p. 183)

canine honing (p. 184)

endocasts (p. 187)

expensive tissue hypothesis (ETH) (p. 190)

KEY QUESTIONS TO ASK MYSELF

1. If bipedalism is such a unique kind of adaptation why is it that almost all of the alien life forms encountered in futuristic movies are bipedal?

2. If ground cooked beef is the best option in terms of energetics, why are nutritionists so skeptical of people eating fast-food hamburgers? And why do some nutritionists promote a raw food diet?

3. The proportion of women giving birth by Caesarian section in Canada was almost 27% in 2010 (Kelly et al. 2013). How much do you think our bipedal pelvis and large brains contribute to that outcome?

KEY CRITICAL THINKING QUESTIONS

1. As you have seen in this chapter, the notion of energetics has been a key variable in a variety of explanations for hominin anatomy and behaviour. Why do you think this is the case? What are some of the important aspects of energetics that need to be appreciated in our evolutionary scenarios?

2. Significant conclusions regarding hominin evolution, such as the identification of new species, have been drawn based on relatively small amounts of evidence (e.g., a handful of teeth or fragments of bone, often separated by substantial amounts of time). Given that variation within a species may result from growth and development, health and disease, sexual dimorphism, environmental circumstances, and so forth, are such conclusions warranted?

KEY THINGS TO DO NEXT

CourseMate Visit **CourseMate** at www.nelson.com/humanvoyage2e to build your comprehension, practise your critical thinking skills, review core concepts, and explore other resources at your disposal.

9 Hominin Origins: From Ape to Australopithecine

Ancient bones from Olduvai
Echoes of the very first cry
Who made me here and why
Beneath the copper sun?

Johnny Clegg

OVERVIEW

This chapter traces the evolution of species comprising the lineage leading from the last common ancestor (LCA) that humans shared with chimpanzees to the origin of the genus *Homo*. At least 6 genera and perhaps as many as 14 species are documented in eastern, southern, and more recently west-central Africa, although the precise evolutionary relationships among them remain unclear. Although all of the species prior to the advent of *Homo* persist as relatively small in brain and body size, at least two major trends develop over these five million years of hominin evolution: (1) the exploitation of more diverse habitats, ranging from forest to savannah, facilitated by an increasingly efficient bipedal adaptation, and (2) an increasing capacity to exploit a more diverse range of food resources, processed either through the evolution of large posterior teeth (megadont) or by way of prelithic and lithic technologies, the initial evidence of the latter possibly associated with the fossil remains of *Australopithecus*.

KEY CONCEPTS

Biogeography, protohominin, divergence, hominin, australopithecine, generalized vs. derived, megadont, phylogeny

KEY LEARNING OBJECTIVES

At the end of this chapter, you will be able to

LO1   List several scientific fields for study that contribute to our understanding of hominin evolution

LO2   Explain the distinction between the terms "gracile" and "robust" as applied to our australopithecine ancestors

LO3   Illustrate the central features of the megadont adaptation

LO4   Differentiate between fossils labelled "protohominin" and "hominin"

LO5   Evaluate the evidence for the assertion that our Pliocene ancestors explored different and unique styles of bipedal locomotion

LO6   Construct a chart depicting the evolutionary timeline of hominin evolution

PROLOGUE: WE ARE ALL AFRICANS

In *The Descent of Man* (1871), Darwin pointed to the African continent as the birthplace of humanity. His reasoning was based on the similarities he perceived between humans and the African apes housed at the London Zoo. This proposition was not at all well received in Victorian England; nonetheless, it had been proven correct by the mid-20th century as more and more so-called **missing links** connecting humans with their forebears were discovered and described. The earliest hominins and their lifeways—the subject matter of paleoanthropology—are the focus of this chapter. These ancestors lived over a period spanning c. 7.0 to 2.0 million years, from the last common ancestor of the hominin and panin clades to the appearance of the genus *Homo*, encompassing the terminal Miocene and the entire Pliocene geological epochs. It is a story not only of biological evolution but also of geological and environmental transformation during which physical and ecological landscapes alike were altered.

The divergence of hominins was accompanied by significant morphological and behavioural changes (outlined in Chapter 8), and it should not be too surprising that there is considerable difference of opinion regarding the meaning and significance of these modifications. This is perhaps most evident in the various taxonomies proposed for these fossil forms, labelled as *"speciose"* versus "less speciose" (Wood and Lonergan 2008)—or more prosaically as "messy versus clean" (David Begun 2004b). Just how many ancestors have occupied our family bush since we parted ways with chimpanzees is one of the central questions in paleoanthropology, and the answer we give depends on how we interpret the variation expressed in the fossil record (see Box 9.1). Wood and Lonergan's review lists 4 (clean) to 13 (messy) different hominin taxa leading up to the origin of the genus *Homo*. Recently, Bokma et al. (2012) used mathematical models to estimate how many extinct hominin species could be expected to have occupied the "direct line to model humans" over the course of hominin evolution. Their theoretical calculations suggest that 8 hominin species appeared and disappeared (became extinct) prior to the appearance of modern humans, but the number could be as high as 27! It is important to remember that how we "split" or "lump" species in the fossil record will have a significant impact on our interpretations, not only of hominin phylogeny but also of particular aspects of the life history of the various taxa (Skinner and Wood 2006). For example, calculating the brain size or body size of a species, or the degree of sexual dimorphism represented, depends entirely on which forms you include within that taxon.

In the following pages you will be introduced to some very peculiar names representing fossils and their discovery locales. These will no doubt tie up your tongue and clog up your brain. You may well wonder how paleoanthropologists are able to piece anything together when it comes to reconstructing the fossil record (figuratively and literally!). At this point you may wish to review the section in Chapter 4, Wrestling with Diversity, since many concepts introduced there are central to appreciating some of the current arguments swirling around studies of early hominin evolution. If, at the end of this chapter, you feel a need to wash your hands of the whole thing, we have good news for you: the protohominin and hominin genera identified prior to *Homo* can be condensed to the acronym SOAAP (Table 9.1; Figure 9.1): *Sahelanthropus, Orrorin, Ardipithecus, Australopithecus,*[1] and *Paranthropus*. See, it is getting a bit easier already!

To appreciate not only why the hominin–panin divergence took place but also a host of subsequent evolutionary developments requires that we consider the context in which these events played out (Potts 2013). What was the climate like between 8 and 2 Ma? What changes in local ecologies—the limits of forest cover or structure of animal communities—can be discerned? In what ways has the geographic landscape been modified, including the size of lakes, the courses of rivers and streams, and the impact of volcanic, seismic, and tectonic activity?

---

1. We lump *Australopithecus* and *Kenyanthropus* into this category. The taxonomic status of the latter is subject to ongoing debate (see text), due mostly to a significant degree of distortion in the cranial remains recovered.

BOX 9.1

FOCUS ON ... A Splitting Headache?

When a fossil is discovered and described, one of the first goals of the researcher is to name it, thereby placing it within a framework in which species are grouped according to scientific principles of classification and taxonomy (referred to as **biological systematics**). Taxonomies enable scientists to talk about biological diversity generally and to test hypotheses regarding how this diversity may have evolved (Ohl 2007). In effect, a taxonomic classification is an explicit hypothesis about phylogeny—the name assigned to a fossil is a statement about its place in the evolutionary history of a lineage. Like all hypotheses, it is testable through observation, measurement, and comparison.

In a classic hierarchical Linnaean taxonomy, all hominins (living or extinct) are members of the Order Primates, Suborder Anthropoidea, Superfamily Hominoidea, Family Hominidae, Subfamily Homininae, and Tribe Hominini (see Chapter 4). But we do not know them by these higher-order labels; instead, we talk of "genus" and "species" and employ binomial nomenclature: *Orrorin tugenensis*, for example, or *Homo sapiens*. These names refer to specific fossil or living forms, constituting what we call the **alpha taxonomy**, and are proposed in accordance with rules laid out in the *International Code of Zoological Nomenclature*. This code requires that the designation of genus be unique; however, a species name need be unique only within the genus of which it is a member. If you discovered a new species of australopithecine, you could name this **holotype** *Australopithecus erectus* if you had reason to, even though the species *erectus* already exists within the genus *Homo*. But you could not name a new kind of giraffe *Homo camelopardalis*.

Taxonomic names are not necessarily permanent. In the middle of the 20th century, there were several more genera and species of recent human ancestors than recognized by most paleoanthropologists today: Pithecanthropus erectus, Sinanthropus pekinensis, and Telanthropus capensis, among others. These taxa have all been "sunk" into the taxon *Homo erectus*, now that additional discoveries of that ancestor have broadened our understanding of its geographic distribution, time depth, and morphological variation. If that was not confusing enough, names having been sunk can be revived. The megadont southern African australopithecines were named *Paranthropus robustus* back in 1938 when they were first described; the genus label was subsequently sunk into the taxon *Australopithecus robustus* based on similarities identified with the smaller-toothed *Au. africanus*. Today, most researchers once again see the "robust" forms as distinctive at the genus level, and as a result the taxon *P. robustus* is back in vogue.

Determining what to name an organism is no easy task, even when dealing with living species for which soft parts and reproductive behaviours can be observed. In the case of extinct forms, the difficulties are compounded, since all that (usually) remain are bones and teeth, geological and paleoenvironmental reconstructions, and inferences about unobservable behaviour. Many factors come into play. For example, how much of the original skeleton is present, and how informative are the pieces recovered? Some parts of the skeleton carry more "information content" than others. Also, what condition are they in? Fossils are typically fragmented and distorted; furthermore, they may be encrusted with mineral deposits that obscure details of morphology or, in the case of teeth, they may be worn from a lifetime of use. How old is a fossil in relation to other discoveries, and what is its context?

And, not least important, what mindset is motivating the researchers who discovered it? Considerable renown and sometimes even celebrity can be attached to naming a fossil deemed sufficiently unique to be a never-before-described species, especially if it is thought to occupy an esteemed place in a lineage (i.e., first in the line). Some scientists place more emphasis on the differences they see in a discovery when compared to known fossil species ("splitters"), and messy classifications are the outcome. Other researchers (called "lumpers") place more emphasis on similarities observed among fossils, which results in cleaner classifications with fewer members. Such a position recognizes that a single species can exhibit a lot of variation. Recent spectacular discoveries at the 1.7-Ma fossil locality of Dmanisi, Georgia (Lordkipanidze et al. 2013; see Chapter 10), have given us a new appreciation of how variable a single species of hominin can be—in this case *Homo erectus*—which may lead to a taxonomic revision for the first members of our genus. And, of course, still others are somewhere in between.

Effectively, it comes down to how one interprets biological variation and the importance of one collection of traits relative to another. These decisions require that a number of examples of a prospective taxon be available for analysis. When only one specimen is discovered, creating a new species or genus is tricky. It needs to have derived features not evident in known taxa to which it might be related, or features that lie outside the range of known variation. *Ardipithecus ramidus*, for example, was split from its original inclusion in the genus *Australopithecus* by White, Suwa, and Asfaw (1995) when they determined that size differences in some of the dental features made *Ardipithecus* more likely a **sister taxon,** and not on the direct line leading to *Homo* (a position they have since reversed).

CHAPTER 9 Hominin Origins: From Ape to Australopithecine

TABLE 9.1 Hominin diversity from the late Miocene to the advent of the genus *Homo* is considerable, although it also depends on one's approach to taxonomy and phylogeny.

Grade	Speciose Taxonomy*	Date (Ma)	Locality	Less Speciose Taxonomy
Possible or probable hominins	*Sahelanthropus (S.) tchadensis*	7.4–6.5	Toros-Menalla, Chad	*Sahelanthropus (S.) tchadensis*
	Orrorin (O.) tugenensis	6.0–5.7	Tungen Hills, Kenya	*Orrorin (O.) tugenensis*
	Ardipithecus (Ar.) ramidus	4.4	Middle Awash, Ethiopia	*Ardipithecus (Ar.) ramidus*
	Ar. kadabba	5.8–5.5	Middle Awash, Ethiopia	*As above*
Basal hominins	*Australopithecus (Au.) anamensis*	4.2—3.9	Middle Awash, Ethiopia; Kanapoi and Allia Bay, Kenya	*Australopithecus (Au.) afarensis*
	Au. afarensis	3.9—3.0	Middle Awash, Hadar and Omo in Ethiopia; Koobi-Fora in Kenya; Laetoli, Tanzania	*As above*
	Kenyanthropus (K.) platyops	3.5	Lomekwi, Kenya	*As above*
	Au. bahrelghazali	3.6	Koro Toro, Chad	*As above*
	Au. africanus	c. 3.0–2.0	Taung, Sterkfontein, and Makapansgat, South Africa	*Au. africanus*
	Au. garhi	2.5	Middle Awash, Ethiopia	*As above*
	Au. sediba	c. 2.0	Malapa, South Africa	*Au. sediba*
Megadont hominins	*Paranthropus (P.) aethiopicus*	2.6–2.3	West Turkana, Kenya	*Paranthropus (P) boisei*
	P. boisei	2.1–1.1	Olduvai Gorge, West Turkana, and Koobi Fora, Kenya	*As above*
	P. robustus	c. 2.0–1.5	Swartkrans, Drimolen, and Kromdraai, South Africa	*P. robustus*

*The accepted abbreviation of the genus name is given in parentheses; by convention and for the sake of convenience, scientists often use this form rather than the unabbreviated name (e.g., *Ar. kadabba* rather than *Ardipithecus kadabba*, or for modern humans, *H. sapiens* rather than *Homo sapiens*).

Adapted from Wood, B. A., and Lonergan, N. 2008. The hominin fossil record: taxa, grades, and clades. *Journal of Anatomy* 212: 354–376.

basal
a qualitative term distinguishing the earliest widely accepted hominins from those forms later assigned to the genus *Homo*

megadont
literally, large teeth; megadont hominins are characterized by expansion of the posterior teeth (i.e., premolars and molars)

synchronic
at the same time; thus synchronic species coexist in time

All such events, both short term and long term, establish the biogeographic framework within which evolutionary change occurs, and this is where we begin this chapter. We then ask several fundamental questions of the fossil record: (1) Can we identify the last common ancestor shared with panins, and if so, what kind of creature are we talking about? (2) What do we know about the most ancient members of our clade, the so-called protohominins living between 4.5 and 7 Ma? How confident can we be in their status as human ancestor? (3) How do we make sense of the taxonomic diversity of early hominins, at times **synchronic** and sympatric, living between 4 and 2 Ma? And (4), which of these gave birth to the genus *Homo*?

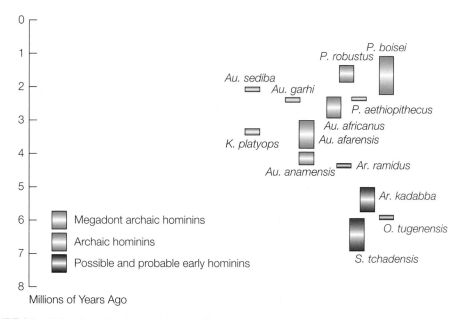

FIGURE 9.1   A timeline of early hominin evolution.

Adapted from B. Wood and N. Lonergan (2008). The hominin fossil record: taxa, grades and clades, *Journal of Anatomy* 212: 354–376. Reprinted by permission of John Wiley and Sons.

This last question is an especially important one because, even though *Homo* expanded its geographic and ecological boundaries far beyond Africa into diverse selective landscapes in Europe and Asia (see Chapters 10 and 11), it has remained the principal hominin genus living on the planet over the past 2 million years.[2] Reduction in taxonomic diversity is a characteristic feature of adaptive radiations, since proliferation of species is generally accompanied by high extinction rates (Eldridge 1989). So it is normal to proceed from many competing forms early on as the radiation "blooms," to one or two surviving branches as natural selection culls those varieties that do not quite make the grade. We will conclude this chapter by looking at different ways in which paleoanthropologists have reconstructed hominin phylogeny to reflect this process of species expansion and contraction.

A PLACE IN TIME

Recall from Chapter 1 that biological anthropology is very much a multidisciplinary and interdisciplinary field in which numerous scholars contribute different scientific expertise to understanding who and what we are as a particular kind of species. This approach is readily evident within the subfield of paleoanthropology (Begun 2012; see Table 9.2), which demands not only that fossil bones and teeth be accurately described and their variations documented, but also that they be situated in time and placed in the context of landscape and habitat. This contextual information is essential to understanding aspects of social behaviour (e.g., arboreal primates look different from terrestrial species and behave differently), diet (e.g., food resources vary by climate and vegetation), predation (e.g., different carnivores inhabit forests versus savannah woodlands), and life history (e.g., body size, longevity, fertility, and other traits are all impacted by habitat variability). As we learned in the previous chapter, to understand evolutionary change in locomotion and encephalization, we need to place these early hominins in a geological and ecological framework. In this vein, climate change has long been considered an important factor in hominoid migration, speciation, and adaptation (e.g., Bobe and Behrensmeyer 2004; Reed 2012).

---

2. As many as nine different species of the genus *Homo* have been identified, including our own, although many paleoanthropologists would opt for a smaller number, in the range of three or four. One genus of pre-*Homo* hominin, *Paranthropus*, long considered a side branch not directly ancestral to ourselves, did coexist with *Homo* until c. 1 Ma.

TABLE 9.2 Many scientific disciplines contribute to the field of paleoanthropology. Our understanding of hominin phylogeny requires a synthesis of this knowledge to interpret the evolution of species diversity, both morphological and behavioural.

Discipline	Relevant Area(s) of Expertise	Principal Applications
Skeletal biology/ functional morphology	Bone and tooth variation	Quantitative and qualitative description of fossils; functional anatomy; classification
Primatology	Behaviour and evolution of living nonhuman primates	Modelling hominin behaviour and social dynamics
Ecology	Environment–organism interactions and population dynamics	Habitat reconstruction and identification of possible food resources
Cultural anthropology	Human social and cultural interactions	Modelling hominin behaviour and social dynamics
Archaeology	Manufacture and use of technology and resource exploitation	Modelling the evolution of tools and landscape use (e.g., capture and processing of food resources)
Psychology	Comparative neuroanatomy and brain function	Encephalization, cognition, and language development
Geology/geography	Composition and structure of the planet and the processes by which it changes	Reconstruction of local, regional, and continental landscapes and paleoclimate, volcanic activity, glaciers, erosion, lakes and rivers, etc.
Chemistry	Organic and inorganic chemical properties	Isotopic reconstruction of diet and paleoenvironment; absolute dating of fossil sites; ancient DNA
Physics	Material properties, motion, energy, time	Absolute dating of fossil sites; biomechanical modelling of hominin behaviour (e.g., locomotion, mastication)
Zoology/vertebrate paleontology	Animal ecology and evolution	Predator–prey interactions, community structure, hominin diet, paleoenvironmental reconstruction, faunal dating
Botany	Plant ecology and evolution	Community structure, hominin diet, paleoenvironmental reconstruction
Statistics	Probability theory, sampling methods, hypothesis testing, and predictive modelling	Evaluation of hypotheses based on qualitative or quantitative observation of sample variation

Hominoids, Habitats, and Hypotheses

Neogene period
a geological time period comprising the Miocene and Pliocene epochs, associated with global climate change and diversification of a number of avian and mammal species, particularly open woodland and grassland forms

Scientists reconstruct paleoenvironments at various levels, from the global and continental to the regional and local (Elton 2008). Large-scale climate change is linked to planetary events such as cyclical shifts in the earth's orbit and major geographic transformations such as mountain building and continental drift. These events alter oceanic and atmospheric circulation, which in turn impacts regional and local climate and ecology, including precipitation, seasonality, vegetation, and the structure of animal communities. As discussed in Chapter 7, these changes are reflected in variation in indicators such as oxygen isotope ratios. During the **Neogene period**, spanning the Miocene and Pliocene geological epochs from c. 23 to c. 1.8 Ma, changes in the North Atlantic and Indian Ocean circulation (Cane and Molnar 2001), as well as tectonic uplift of the East African Rift system in Kenya and Ethiopia (Sepulchre et al. 2006; see Figure 9.2), were major forces in the trend toward cooler climates, **aridification**, contraction of rainforests, and expansion of woodland and grassland habitats in Africa and Eurasia. These changes began around 15 Ma and quickened toward the end of the Miocene epoch at 5.5 Ma, culminating in the series of glacial advances and retreats that have marked the last two million years of the earth's history. These transformations had profound effects on biodiversity and community ecology—and, it follows, on hominin evolution.

Migration of apes during the early to middle Miocene (23 to c. 10 Ma) occurred between Africa and Eurasia while tropical and subtropical forests were still available to support these arboreal primates. University of Toronto paleoanthropologist David Begun has hypothesized that the last common ancestor of the panin and hominin clades originated in Eurasia among a group of apes known as Dryopithecines and migrated into Africa during the later Miocene after 10 Ma as continuous forests began to disappear at higher latitudes (Begun et al. 2012).

Paleoenvironmental data from Miocene

aridification
a drying trend resulting from lower seasonal or annual precipitation levels

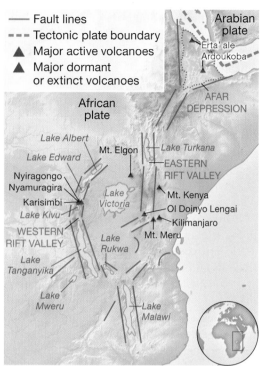

FIGURE 9.2 The African continent was transformed during the Miocene by several significant geologic events, including uplifting along a major fault recognized today as the Great Rift Valley, which extends from Ethiopia in the north to Malawi in the south. Numerous hominin fossil localities are associated with the Rift Valley.

and Pliocene fossil sites in East Africa suggest ongoing climate change. Variations in the timing and magnitude of precipitation cycles and the expansion or contraction of lakes and rivers and their subterranean water sources produced **mosaic habitats** of forest, mixed woodland, and savannah grasslands (Potts 2013). While reliable evidence indicates that large areas of grassland habitat appeared in tropical Africa possibly as early as 6 Ma (Cerling et al. 2011), it is likely that our earliest ancestors continued to rely on forest and woodland habitats for food or refuge well into the Pliocene (White et al. 2010).

mosaic habitats
areas characterized by a range of habitat types, from forest to grassland

Climate, Habitat, and Selection

The transition from closed forest to woodland/grassland was not abrupt in the late Miocene and early Pliocene; changes occurred at different times and at different rates depending on latitude and geographical features such as mountains and lakes. Given this temporal and regional variation in environment, it is important to ask some fundamental questions. What selection pressures might have been presented by these newly emerging habitats? How might they have impacted the last common ancestor (LCA) and influenced subsequent hominin evolution (Winder et al. 2013)?

In addressing these questions, we need to keep a few things in mind. First, we have very little in the way of fossil evidence for the evolution of African hominoids (gorillas, chimpanzees or even our own ancestors) c. 5–7 Ma; the bits and pieces are few and far between in both space and time and are the subject of much controversy (Begun 2013). At best we can only hypothesize what adaptations and selective forces[3] could have been paramount for the

---

3. We must also not lose sight of the possibility that non-Darwinian forces such as genetic drift or founder effect could have played a role in early hominin origins, or that certain aspects of morphology seen in fossil remains and thought to be important may be pleiotropic by-products of selection for some other characteristic.

origin of the hominin clade. Definitive statements must await discovery of additional fossils from new localities in order to clarify which features (morphological, behavioural) are derived rather than primitive, and which may be a product of homology rather than homoplasy (see Chapter 4).

Recent arguments that bipedal locomotion may not in fact be an especially useful criterion for assigning hominin status to fossil remains (e.g., Crompton et al. 2008; see Chapter 8) point to some of the difficult issues faced by paleoanthropologists studying our origins. Also, as discussed in Chapter 6, we know that living panins have fairly complex cultural behaviours; however, it is unlikely that some very significant selection pressures (e.g., predation) would have been lessened until our ancestors had developed some form of defensive technology such as stone tools, or learned to control fire (Pawlowski 2007). This means that early hominins would have been subject to the same kinds of selection pressures as other larger bodied mammals. This fact actually works in the paleoanthropologist's favour, for it strengthens the use of analogy from the lifeways of living apes such as chimpanzees and bonobos when we are trying to infer how early hominins might have lived (Stanford 2012).

Nonetheless, we can come to some fairly sound conclusions regarding the paleoenvironment and ecology of the LCA and early hominins. For example, the long-held **savannah hypothesis** proposing that hominin origins were linked to loss of forest habitat and expansion of grasslands, effectively "forcing" adoption of new lifeways (including bipedalism), is no longer tenable. First postulated in the early 20th century, the savannah hypothesis gained prominence in the decades prior to the 1970s when paleoanthropologists had little evidence of hominins much older than c. 3.0 Ma. Those fossils that *were* known had been discovered at sites suggestive of savannah-like environments. Since then—and in particular over the past 20 years—the hominin fossil record has grown in both quantity and complexity, and may extend as far back as c. 6–7 Ma (Langergraber et al. 2012). Most of these earlier sites have been found in habitats that are either woodland, **gallery forest**, or woodland–grassland mosaic. These recent developments have led to the **forest hypothesis**, which argues that hominins diverged from panins while still occupying a treed habitat. Thus the derived features of hominins (bipedalism, dental changes, etc.; see Chapter 8) likely arose in a more woody rather than open-country environment (although using analyses of carbon isotopes, Cerling and his colleagues [2011] suggest forest cover would have been less than 40% at many of these fossil localities).

It has also been suggested that early hominin divergence was not driven by the stable conditions offered by forest or savannah habitats, but rather by the increasing unpredictability of climate and environment during the late Miocene and Pliocene. This idea is captured by the **variability selection hypothesis** (Potts 2013), whose main tenet is that fluctuating conditions created a diversity of adaptive conditions to which species needed to respond. This was achieved not by acquiring habitat-specific adaptations, but by selection favouring morphologies and behaviours that would work in complex, changeable "multi-habitat" situations. The variability selection model is appealing because it accounts for the locomotory *and* dietary flexibility suggested by the fossils themselves (discussed later in this chapter); furthermore, the timing of the appearance and disappearance of fossil forms correlates with the occurrence of high climatic instability.

A PLETHORA OF PROTOHOMININS

The basal hominins immediately preceding our own genus *Homo* are known as the australopithecines, the first of which appeared about 4.2 Ma in eastern Africa. Australopithecines are themselves preceded by several earlier forms, and in this text we use the term "protohominin" to refer to these pre-australopithecine fossil taxa. Known from east and north-central Africa and dating to between 7 and 4 Ma, they include *S. tchadensis, O. tugenensis, Ar. ramidis,* and *Ar. kaddaba.* Each of these taxa exhibit morphology suggesting facultative bipedalism, but they also retain attributes that are adaptive for arboreal settings. All have dental traits linking

savannah hypothesis

the now discredited idea that the development of open savannah grassland created conditions leading to the evolution of hominins

gallery forest

dense, canopied forest found along water courses such as rivers and lakeshores

forest hypothesis

the suggestion that the hominin clade diverged from panins while still occupying a woodland/forest habitat, as suggested by paleoecological reconstruction of fossil localities

variability selection hypothesis

a model that suggests that the operating factor in hominin evolution was environmental disparity, rather than stability, which promoted adaptive flexibility in hominin traits, including locomotion, dental adaptations, and technology

them with both earlier hominoids and later hominins, and all are found in sites indicative of woodland habitat. So why do we choose to call them "protohominins"?

Recent studies of the rate at which genes mutate (Sun et al. 2012) point to a hominin–panin divergence time of 3.7 to 6.6 Ma, an event that may have been a complex, drawn-out affair (see Box 9.2). Such evidence raises some questions regarding the phylogenetic status

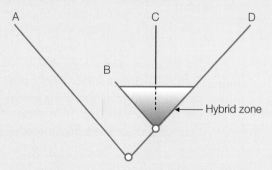

BOX 9.2   FOCUS ON ... The Long Goodbye

Depictions of speciation events tend to give the impression that they are abrupt and somewhat instantaneous (Figure 9.3). In fact, they are vague, generally clouded in mystery, and of completely uncertain duration. Fossil morphology is generally not helpful in this regard. While it can suggest that speciation occurred at some point in the past, it usually cannot tell us precisely when or over what span of time. The combination of dating error and the expectation that sister taxa will look very similar immediately following divergence constrains estimations of speciation dates. Prior to the 1970s, the origin of the hominin lineage was placed in the range of 10 to 15 Ma as a rough but educated estimate based solely on fossil remains—in particular, those of a middle Miocene Asian ape called *Ramapithecus*, which had a short face and small canines. The development of "molecular clocks" (Chapter 7) has allowed researchers to estimate divergence times for living hominoids based on accumulated differences in gene sequences and protein structures. These methods challenged that conclusion, suggesting a much more recent date for the separation of hominins from African apes, in the range of 6 to 8 Ma (Wilson and Sarich 1969). This has generated a debate between the evidence of fossil remains and that of molecular clocks. However, many paleoanthropologists are beginning to see a consensus emerging between the fossil and genetic approaches at around 5 to 7 Ma (Wolpoff et al. 2006).

Patterson and colleagues (2006) added a new wrinkle to the question of timing for the hominin–panin split. They studied close to 20 million autosomal and X chromosome base pairs of **aligned sequence** DNA data from humans, chimpanzees, gorillas, orangutans, and macaques, correcting for aberrations

such as neutral and **recurrent mutation** rate variation within the genome. Using **genetic divergence** estimates for chimpanzees and humans, they calculated a **species divergence** time of 5.4 to 6.3 Ma—which, clearly, is problematic for forms such as *Sahelanthropus*, dated close to 7 Ma, and possibly even for *Orrorin*, dated at around 6 Ma. More surprisingly, for *Pan–Homo* they found a larger than expected reduction in genetic divergence time for the X chromosome, on the order of 1.2 million years—something that was not observed in the *Gorilla–Homo* data.

What does this mean? Their "provocative explanation" (as they put it) is that the emerging hominins continued to exchange genes with panins for perhaps as long as 1 million years, and that final speciation did not occur until perhaps as recently as 4 Ma. As you learned in Chapter 4, hybridization is not uncommon between closely related species, and population genetic studies of both insects and mammals have shown that hybrid sterility is most closely associated with X-linked genes. Thus, hybrid males with their single X chromosome would be sterile more commonly than homogametic (XX) females, and natural selection would intensely select against any X-linked alleles reducing fitness. This would tend to conserve genetic divergence times for the X chromosome compared to those of the autosomes (i.e., the X chromosome remains similar between diverging species, and differences accumulate more readily in autosomes within each lineage).

Perhaps even more provocative is the authors' suggestion that later hominins may actually have emerged from *within* the hybrid zone (Figure 9.4). The implications of this argument are profound both for the early divergence hypothesis and for our interpretations of the protohominin fossil record.

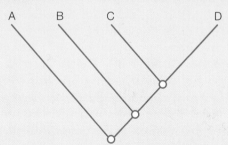

FIGURE 9.3 Although rigorously determined, graphic depictions of speciation events give the impression that they occur rather abruptly, which is not the case

FIGURE 9.4 The 2006 model of hominin origins developed by Patterson and his colleagues may be traced to a surviving hybrid population.

aligned sequence

in molecular genetics research, sequences of DNA (or RNA) derived from homologous sites within the genome are literally arranged or aligned to identify similarities and differences between species, the latter resulting from, for example, point mutations, insertions, or deletions

recurrent mutation

a mutation that tends to occur repeatedly at the same locus; a number of genetic disorders are maintained at high frequencies through recurrent mutation (e.g., Marfan syndrome in humans, leading to impaired collagen formation)

genetic divergence

an estimate of the time since two genomes diverged, based on the number of differences observed and assuming a constant rate of mutation

species divergence

an estimate of time since speciation; because genetic differences are constantly accumulating within lineages, estimates of genetic divergence time will always be older than species divergence time

alveoli

the bony sockets for teeth present in the upper and lower jaws

assemblages

the collection of all remains of plants or animals from paleontological contexts

of these "pre-australopithecines," since clearly a fossil cannot be considered a hominin if it predates that divergence! Langergraber and colleagues (2012) have argued that we need to "recalibrate" our estimates of how fast DNA might change based on new data for living chimpanzee and gorilla generation times.

As you might suspect, the rate at which changes in DNA accumulate will be a function not only of the rate of mutation within each generation, but also the length of time it takes to produce each new generation. Their analysis suggests a slower rate of change, and thus an older date for the split of the human and chimpanzee clades (c. 7.5 Ma versus 4.5 Ma). This older split date would suggest inclusion of forms such as *S. tchadensis* within the hominin lineage (Hawks 2012). Is this the final word? Not necessarily, as a new study by Fu et al. (2013), looking at mutation rates in well-dated fossils over the past 40,000 years, suggests that our previous estimates of divergence times were more accurate after all! Such differences of scientific conclusions are not uncommon—recall our discussion of the scientific method in Chapter 2—and they may be even more common in the field of paleoanthropology, characterized by very small samples and expansive time ranges. At this time, we take a somewhat conservative approach and distinguish between forms that are demonstrably hominin (skeletal and dental anatomy) and those for which some debate remains (Wood and Harrison 2011).

Protohominins exhibit a mixture of primitive and derived features, which we describe in the following sections. This mixture should not surprise you. Indeed, the closer we get to the LCA, the more we should expect to find fewer and fewer derived traits unique to the emerging hominin or panin lineages, as less evolutionary change would have occurred since their initial divergence (Cobb 2008). There is also the real possibility of hybridization between the two clades as divergence ensues (Box 9.2). In other words, gene flow and proximity in time would conspire to keep the LCA and its immediate panin and hominin descendants looking pretty much alike.

Sahelanthropus tchadensis—First Twig on the Bush?

In 2001 and 2002, several fossils were discovered at a number of sites in the Toros-Menalla area in northern Chad by members of the research team Mission Paléoanthropologique Franco-Tchadienne (MPFT), led by Michel Brunet of the Université de Pontiers, France. These were attributed to a new hominin taxon, *Sahelanthropus tchadensis* (Brunet et al. 2002a, 2005). The holotype is known formally as "TM 266-01-060-1"—more colloquially as "Toumaï."[4] Toumaï consists of a distorted yet mostly complete cranium, including fragmented teeth and **alveoli**. The remaining finds are isolated teeth or lower jaw fragments. The original late Miocene date for *Sahelanthropus* was based on faunal association with eastern African **assemblages**, including forest-dwelling pigs and elephants, as well as fish species and crocodilians, suggesting that Toumaï may well have lived in woodland or gallery forest adjacent to a lake. More recently cosmogenic nuclide dating of the fossil locality (Lebatard et al. 2008) has reinforced that conclusion, with a date of 6.8 to 7.2 Ma.

This discovery is very significant for several reasons. In the first place, it is rare to find specimens as complete as this cranium. Then there are the added factors of its early date and geographic location. Toumaï predates all previously known protohominins by as much as a million years and is found roughly 2,500 km west of the East African Rift Valley, where all previous protohominin and many hominin discoveries have been made since the late 1950s. It is even further removed from southern Africa, where australopithecines were first discovered (see Box 9.3). The addition of *S. tchadensis* to the hominin

---

4. In the local Goran language, "Toumaï" means "hope of life," a name often given to babies born prior to the dry season, when circumstances become considerably harsher and survival less certain.

BOX 9.3

RETROSPECTION ... Raymond Dart and the Man-Ape of South Africa

FIGURE 9.5 The search for human origins in Africa began with Raymond Dart's 1925 publication of the discovery of the Taung child-type specimen of *Australopithecus africanus*.

The following are excerpts from an article by Raymond Dart in the journal *Nature* in 1925, announcing his discovery of the "Man-Ape of South Africa" (see Figure 9.5).

In manipulating the pieces of rock brought back by Prof. Young, I found that the larger natural endocranial cast articulated exactly by its fractured frontal extremity with another piece of rock in which the broken lower and posterior margin of the left side of a mandible was visible. After cleaning the rock mass, the outline of the hinder and lower part of the facial skeleton came into view . . . Apart from this evidential completeness, the specimen is of importance because it exhibits an extinct race of apes intermediate between living anthropoids and man ... It is manifest that we are in the presence here of a pre-human stock, neither chimpanzee nor gorilla, which possesses a series of differential characters not encountered hitherto in any anthropoid stock. This complex of characters exhibited is such that it cannot be interpreted as belonging to any living anthropoid ... It is therefore logically regarded as a man-like ape. I propose tentatively, then, that a new family of Homo-simidae be created for the reception of the group of individuals which it represents, and that the first known species of the group be designated Australopithecus africanus, *in commemoration, first, of the extreme southern and unexpected horizon of its discovery, and secondly, of the continent in which so many new and important discoveries connected with the early history of man have recently been made, thus vindicating the Darwinian claim that Africa would prove to be the cradle of mankind.*

In this article, Raymond Dart was describing a small, ape-like partial cranium and a natural endocast of the animal's fossilized brain, discovered at the site of Taung, South Africa. The find was that of a child, between three and six years of age when it died. The proposal for a new family of primates intermediate between ape and human (Homo-simidae is no longer recognized) and for a new genus and species as a root stock from which humans evolved, stunned the still young discipline of paleoanthropology. The assertion that human origins lay in Africa and not in Asia or Europe (as had been proposed in the early years of the 20th century) was an outrageous claim. Surely, humans must have evolved from a large-brained ancestor, one capable of generating descendants able to produce Western civilization and all which that entails.

The so-called Piltdown Man, "discovered" in 1912 in England, had been contrived from fragments of a modern human cranium associated with an intentionally modified partial jaw of an orangutan; it was not exposed as a hoax until 1953 (although some scientists, notably American, were suspicious of its authenticity from the outset). But the tenacity with which Euro-centric scholars clung to its primacy in human ancestry, and the extent to which they criticized Dart's claim for *Au. africanus*, is an interesting history of politics, race, and class (Spencer 1990). To the intellectual aristocracy of Europe, it was unfathomable that "man" (i.e., White Europeans) could have his lowly origins in a geography and landscape populated by peoples they had subjugated and colonized. It was bad arithmetic that did not add up! But Dart held to his view, and the unearthing of additional australopithecine fossils from several cave sites in South Africa over the next several decades (continuing to this day) built the case for an African origin of humankind. With Piltdown exposed, and with the discovery of yet more australopithecine fossils in eastern Africa by Mary and Louis Leakey in 1959, the case was settled. Darwin and Dart had been proved right—led by a little child.

Source: *Nature* (1925) 115: 195–199.

clade means that we can identify—at present—three independent loci for hominin evolution, reflecting a geographic range larger than for any living African hominine (i.e., chimpanzee or gorilla).

Why a New Hominin and Why a New Taxon?

As to be expected for a protohominin at such an early date, *Sahelanthropus* combines primitive and derived features (Brunet et al. 2002b). On the primitive side, it has a massive browridge (relatively larger and thicker than in living gorillas) projecting from a small, chimpanzee-sized brain case, with an estimated capacity of 360 to 370 cm^3 (Bienvenu et al. 2013) and evidence of a sagittal crest on top of the vault. It also has an expansive area at the back of the head for the attachment of neck muscles. Derived features include a relatively short face—unusual for Miocene apes as well as for later hominins such as *Ardipithecus* and the australopithecines. Dental traits seen in Toumaï include small canines that wear at the tip and little in the way of a diastema in the mandible, indicating that it lacked a canine honing complex. Enamel thickness is moderate (more than in *Pan* but less than in australopithecines). Importantly, according to Brunet and colleagues (2002b), the **foramen magnum** is located closer to the face as in bipeds; it is also longer than wide, unlike the shape seen in chimpanzees. Using 3D microtomography, a very high-resolution imaging technology, Bienvenu et al. (2013) were able to reconstruct Toumaï's endocast and, while overall brain volume is small as noted earlier, features of the brainstem and occipital lobes link this fossil to later hominins.

Brunet and his colleagues argue that the presence of bipedalism[5] combined with the absence of canine honing establish Toumaï as the earliest member of the hominin clade. Recall from Chapter 8 that most paleoanthropologists regard these two features as essential criteria for hominin status. At the same time, some characteristics of the dentition and face are distinctive even compared to later forms such as *Ardipithecus* and *Orrorin*—especially the large browridge and the shape and surface relief of the upper incisors. These traits have been used to justify a new taxon. This mixture of primitive (hominine-like) and derived (hominin-like) traits, considered alongside their antiquity, suggests that *S. tchadensis* may be very close to what taxonomists refer to as the **stem hominin**.

This claim has invited skepticism. Not everyone was quick to jump on board the "*Sahelanthropus* as hominin" ship. Notably, University of Michigan paleoanthropologist Milford Wolpoff has questioned the hominin claim for Toumaï, suggesting instead that it was in all likelihood a late Miocene ape adapting to a tough diet (Wolpoff et al. 2002, 2006). Wolpoff and colleagues note that thicker enamel is in fact a primitive characteristic common to earlier Miocene hominoids (thin enamel is derived in panins), so it is not surprising to find it in Toumaï. They also argue that the foramen magnum occupies a more posterior, chimpanzee-like position, based on distance from the location of the third molar tooth. Finally, the expanded posterior brain case, the sagittal crest to which chewing muscles attach, and the massive browridge could be explained as responses to diet and posture.

However, some of these criticisms seem to have been addressed using 3D imaging technology. Using this approach Zollikofer et al. (2005) were able to "un-deform"' the original fossil cranium and produce a "corrected" version. They were able to achieve this feat because, while the cranium as a whole was distorted, the individual bones that make up the head were not. These researchers were thus able to virtually dissect and reassemble Toumaï's cranium! Analysis of this computer-generated "fossil" supports the anterior placement of the foramen magnum (among other features) and the conclusion that *Sahelanthropus* was bipedal.

So, is Toumaï hominin or hominine—human-like or ape-like? Currently, the consensus favours the former, although this issue will likely be settled only with the discovery of infracranial remains unambiguously establishing it to be a biped, like the eastern African protohominins.

Orrorin tugenensis—Sound on the Ground and at Ease in the Trees

In 2001, Brigette Senut and members of the Kenya Palaeontology Expedition described 13 new hominin fossils from the Lukieno Formation, a c. 6 Ma lacustrine (lake) and fluvial (river) deposit in the Tugen Hills near Lake Baringo, Kenya. Both dental and infracranial material was found, and a new taxon—*Orrorin*[6] *tugenensis*—was proposed (Senut et al. 2001).

---

5. Bipedalism is inferred for *S. tchadensis* from the anterior position of the foramen magnum, as no bone fide infracranial remains are known; a partial femur is claimed to have been found in association but has yet to be described in the literature.
6. In the local Tugen language, *Orrorin* means "original man."

foramen magnum

"large passage," the foramen magnum is the largest hole in the cranium, through which the brain stem passes to become the spinal cord

stem hominin

the progenitor of all later hominin species within a clade, arising from the last common ancestor

The associated fauna, including impala, elephants, and monkeys, indicate an open woodland habitat with gallery forest along the lake margins. The infracranial fossils, including the top (**proximal**) portion of several femora, the lower (**distal**) part of the right humerus, and a hand **phalanx**, suggest that *Orrorin* was an adept climbing facultative biped.

Why a New Hominin and Why a New Taxon?

Orrorin exhibits several primitive features, such as chimpanzee-like upper incisors and canines (including some suggestion of a honing complex). The lower molar is chimp-like in some respects and human-like in others. But *Orrorin* also has thick enamel, as in later hominins, and the overall size of the (molar) teeth is reduced. *Orrorin*'s status as a hominin is assured by its femoral anatomy. In an intact skeleton, the parts recovered would articulate with the pelvis, and even though no pelvic fossils have been found in this case, the bony features of the femur and the size and shape of the impressions left by the hip muscles point toward a bipedal adaptation (Figure 9.6). Compared to other hominins, the morphology of the femora most closely resembles that of the australopithecines (Richmond and Jungers 2012), albeit more primitive as would be expected given its antiquity. But *Orrorin* also retains features in its skeleton that tell us that climbing was still very much part of its locomotor behaviour. The upper arm bone (humerus) preserves **muscle markings** for forearm flexion that are more similar to that seen in chimpanzees, and the hand bone is curved, consistent with a strong grasping ability (both features are also found in australopithecines, discussed later in this chapter).

As you might have guessed, *O. tugenensis* has not been accepted without debate. Senut and colleagues (2001) have created a new taxon for these remains, arguing that it was unlike later australopithecines in having relatively small and differently shaped molar teeth and more *Homo*-like proximal femora. It also differed from *Ardipithecus* (see the next section) in having thicker enamel. However, it was their assertion that *Orrorin* was ancestral to *Homo* that caused more than a little controversy (White 2006), since this constituted a major restructuring of commonly held interpretations of hominin phylogeny on the basis of comparatively little fossil evidence. This assertion has not been generally accepted, and the suggested *Homo*-like features of the femur have been questioned (Begun 2004c). Recently, Richmond and Jungers (2008) compared the size and shape of the most complete of the *Orrorin* femora with a large sample of great apes, australopithecines, early *Homo* specimens, and modern humans, and found that *Orrorin* most likely had a bipedal gait comparable to the australopithecines but very different from *Homo*.

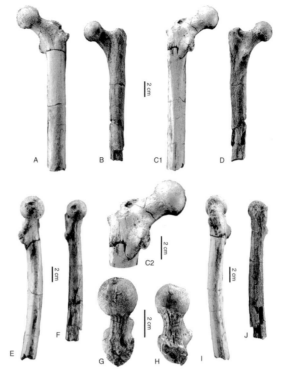

FIGURE 9.6 A comparison of the 6 Ma proximal femur of *Orrorin tugenensis* with that of 3.2 Ma *Australopithecus afarensis*.

This figure was published in Pickford, M., Senut, B., Gommery, D., et al. Bipedalism in Orrorin tugenensis revealed by its femora. *Comptes Rendus Palevol* 1: 191–203. Copyright © 2002 Académie des Sciences. Published by Elsevier Masson SAS. All rights reserved.

proximal

in skeletal anatomy, a position closer to the midline of the body (e.g., the elbow is distal to the shoulder joint); in teeth, the term refers to the tooth surface facing the back of the mouth

distal

in anatomy, a position farther from the midline of the body

phalanx

one of a series of short bones that make up the fingers in the hand or the toes in the foot

muscle markings

impressions on a bone surface that define the point of origin or insertion of a muscle; activities that build up muscles can also create more prominent muscle markings

The Ardipithecines: Hominins, Yes, But Whose Ancestor?

Ethiopia, in the Horn of Africa, has suffered a very difficult and in many ways tragic social and political history during the 20th century. Yet geographically, it may well be the womb of humankind—an irony that should not be lost on us. No other region of this planet has offered such an ancient, rich, and significant fossil record of our human voyage. Since the 1970s, Ethiopia's Afar Depression has yielded a treasure trove of fossil remains, from protohominins to early modern *Homo sapiens*, spanning several million years. Among the Afar sites, Aramis in the Middle Awash Study Area has provided evidence of the transition from the LCA to protohominins, and from protohominins to the basal hominins known as australopithecines (White et al. 2006; refer back to Table 9.1). The first of these transitions is represented by two species attributed to a new genus: *Ardipithecus kadabba* (5.8 to 5.2 Ma) and *Ar. ramidus* (White et al. 1994, 2009).[7] *Ar. ramidus* has been dated to 4.4 Ma, although a recent discovery of fossil foot remains in Ethiopia suggests that a form similar to *Ar. ramidus* was present at c. 3.4 Ma (Haile-Selassie et al. 2012).

Why a New Hominin and Why a New Taxon?

craniodental

a descriptive term referring to the hard tissues, bone, and teeth comprising the skull

Ardipithecus is represented by **craniodental** and infracranial remains exhibiting a mixture of primitive and derived traits (as we saw with *Sahelanthropus* and *Orrorin*), but also by unique attributes not present in any other known hominin. Not surprisingly, the older species *Ar. kadabba* is considered the more primitive of the two, especially in having a larger crowned and more pointed canine and a canine honing complex similar to the condition seen in smaller bodied (e.g., female) chimpanzees. However, the canine in *Ardipithecus* shows some wear on the tip, typical of later hominins, indicating its use in chewing. Predictably, this wear is more evident in the more recent species *Ar. ramidus,* whose canines are somewhat smaller. The most striking feature in both species is the presence of thin enamel on the molar teeth, unlike any other known hominin species and more like the condition seen in living hominoids (Smith et al. 2008).

In the fall of 2009, White and colleagues published a series of 11 papers in the journal *Science* describing the remains of *Ar. ramidus*, totalling 110 specimens, including a very fragmented and fragile partial skeleton that required a number of years to carefully extract from the sediments. These publications, covering all aspects of fossil anatomy, adaptation, environment/ecology, dating, geology, and behaviour garnered worldwide attention.

Most interesting are these authors' views as to *Ar. ramidus*' locomotor habits. There are indications of facultative bipedalism, such as a short, broad pelvis with realignment of the gluteal muscles for maintaining upright balance, yet the foot structure reveals a fully opposable grasping large toe (Lovejoy et al. 2009). Moreover, the limb skeleton includes curved hand bones and longer ape-like upper arms, which tell us that Ardipithecines were still efficient climbers—what White and colleagues refer to as palmigrade clambering. Missing is any indication of knuckle-walking or vertical climbing/suspensory locomotion, as seen in extant chimpanzees, a challenge for views suggesting that hominins arose from such an ancestor (Selby et al. 2013). A model of arboreal palmigrade clambering agrees well with contextual paleontological evidence (e.g., plant remains such as seeds and fossil monkeys and pigs) indicating that ardipithecines lived in more forested habitats.

This conclusion is not universally held, however. Campbell Rolian, a functional morphologist at the University of Calgary, compared limb proportions across a wide variety of species, including representatives of all living primate groups, and found that *Ar. ramidus* was somewhat unique in its locomotor behaviour, exhibiting a mixture of both palmigrade clambering and vertical climbing (Rolian et al. 2013). On the whole, though, *Ardipithecus*

---

7. In the local Afar dialect, "Ardi" means "floor," "ramid" means "root," and "kaddaba" is the term for "basal family ancestor." *Ar. kadabba* was initially identified as a subspecies of *Ar. ramidus* (i.e., *Ar. r. kadabba*) but was elevated to species status following description of additional dental remains (Haile-Selassie, Suwa, and White 2004).

showed greater affinity (similarity) to the latter, that is, the more chimp-like condition. Adaptation to both arboreal and terrestrial environments has led some researchers to suggest that chimpanzees may be appropriate analogues for drawing inferences about *Ardipithecus'* behaviour for activities such as foraging (Stanford 2012). But as we have seen before, healthy debate is a hallmark of paleoanthropology, and others take exception to the premise that chimpanzees represent a good model for putative ancestors such as *Ardipithecus* (Sayers et al. 2012), suggesting that the latter is more "human-like" in both morphology and behaviour.

THE AUSTRALOPITHECINES

The australopithecines are a diverse group of hominins, distributed across as many as ten different species and at least two (if not three) genera from 4.2 to 1.1 Ma (see Table 9.1). The best known genus, called *Australopithecus*, has pinpointed Africa as the birthplace of humankind (confirming Darwin's assertion), although not without controversy (refer back to Box 9.3). Australopithecines are distinguished for their wide geographic and environmental distribution, having been found at some 23 different sites in eastern and southern Africa (Figure 9.7). This range and habitat diversity qualifies the Australopiths as **eurytopic** (Behrensmeyer and Reed 2013), suggesting that these hominins possessed a high degree of adaptability (both biological and behavioural). Although several hundred fossils assigned to the various australopithecine species have been discovered, the evolutionary relationships among them and later hominins (genus *Homo*) are still the subject of considerable debate.

A number of developments characterize australopithecine evolution. First, although overall body size does not increase appreciably—they remain about the size of common chimpanzees (40 to 50 kg; McHenry and Coffing 2000)—australopithecines are notable in that the various species fall into one of two morphological variants, one more slightly built (thus the term "gracile") and the other somewhat larger (hence more "robust"). Second, the differences between the **gracile** and **robust** variants are most pronounced in the craniodental remains (face, skull, teeth), earning the robust variant the label of megadont hominins. This significant increase in the size of the posterior teeth (premolars and molars) is taken to an extreme in the more recent robust form, *Paranthropus boisei*. Third, the sample size for several australopithecine species, including the earliest forms, is sufficiently large that we can document variation in sexual dimorphism in both body and canine size, although the degree to which such dimorphism reflects australopithecine mating behaviour and/or competition (as known for living hominoids) is not clear (Plavcan 2012b).

The fourth development to note is that canine reduction continues, resulting in the complete absence of a C/P3 honing complex and no diastema in more recent australopiths. Fifth, although still comparatively small-brained, the trend toward increasing encephalization (brain size scaled to body size)—which as you learned in Chapter 8 was a defining feature of hominin evolution—begins with *Australopithecus*. Sixth, while the protohominins *Sahelanthropus, Orrorin,* and *Ardipithecus* were at least facultative bipeds, and the early australopithecines retain a facility for climbing in trees, the transition to obligate bipedalism likely occurred among later members of the gracile lineage c. 3.0 to 2.5 Ma, presaging the arrival of our own genus, *Homo.* And finally, the production of stone tools with cutting edges around 2.4 Ma, attributed to the gracile species *Australopithecus afarensis*, marks a momentous development in technology and challenges the assertion that *Homo* was the earliest maker of **percussive stone tools**.

Australopithecine Origins

From 4.2 to 3.0 Ma, two gracile australopithecine species are recognized from eastern Africa: *Au. anamensis* and *Au. afarensis,* which have been argued to form a **phyletic sequence** originating in *Ar. ramidus* (White et al. 2006), although this is by no means conclusive

eurytopic

organisms that are able to live in diverse habitats and geographic ranges; the prefix "eury" means "broad, wide" and the affix "topic" refers to "place"

gracile

small or slightly built; among australopithecines, refers to those species lacking the skeletal and dental features associated with the megadont adaptation

robust

rugged or strongly built; several australopithecine species possess skeletal and dental features associated with large chewing muscles and crushing and grinding of hard foods

percussive stone tools

implements fashioned by purposefully striking one stone against another to produce a cutting edge

phyletic sequence

an unbroken lineage of ancestor–descendant species

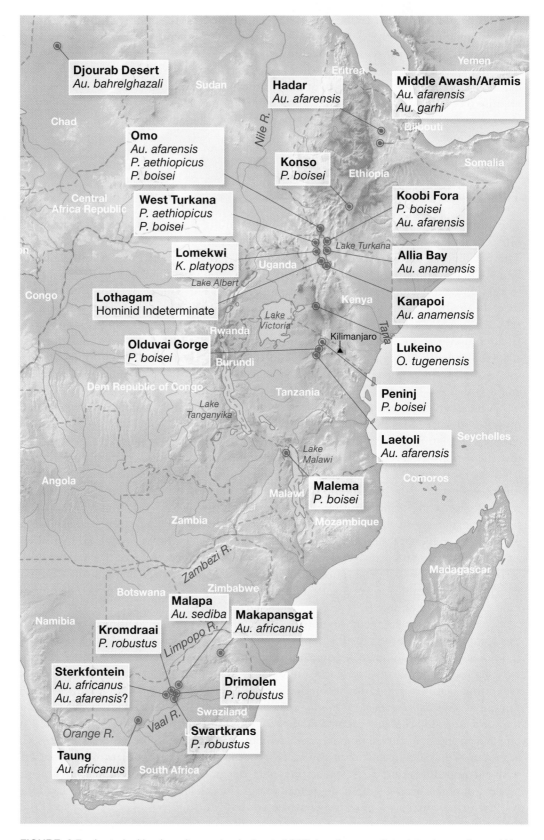

FIGURE 9.7 Australopithecine sites extend about 5,000 km from northeastern to southern Africa, although comparatively little research has been conducted between Tanzania and South Africa.

From Ann Gibbons. 2002. "Becoming human: In search of the first hominids," *Science* 295: 1214–1219. Reprinted with permission from AAAS.

(Alemseged 2013). These speciation events are thought to be tied to ecological niche expansion and diversification, with accompanying changes in diet to include plants and animals eating more grasses and sedges—that is, more open-country foods—as shown by carbon isotope studies (Sponheimer et al. 2013). Earlier protohominins (before 4.2 Ma) occupied closed forest or woodland habitats, and a fundamental australopithecine adaptation seems to have been exploitation of more open savannah grasslands, bushlands, and aquatic fringes in addition to woodland and gallery forest zones. This broadening of habitat use does not seem to be linked to any major change in climate, habitat, or mammalian species turnover (White et al. 2006), all of which are believed to have had an impact on the later evolution of *Homo*, and Cerling et al. (2011) have shown that woodland remained a significant proportion of our hominin ancestors' habitat prior to the appearance of *Homo*. Just why the first australopithecines decided to venture into more diverse habitats than had been exploited by protohominins remains an unanswered question, in spite of considerable volumes of paleoecological research (Behrensmeyer and Reed 2013). If we adopt a speciose classification, the ensuing million years of australopithecine evolution (from 3.0 to 2.0 Ma) witnessed a profusion of species, including branching events leading to additional gracile and robust forms evolving in both eastern and southern Africa. It is thought that one of these gracile branches, possibly represented by *Au. garhi,* gave rise to the genus *Homo* c. 2.3 Ma.

The origin of australopithecines has been dated to c. 4.2 Ma with the discovery of *Australopithecus anamensis*[8] at the sites of Kanapoi and Allia Bay on the shores of Lake Turkana, Kenya (Leakey et al. 1995; Figure 9.8). Additional remains attributed to *Au. anamensis* occur at two localities in Ethiopia—Asa Issie and Aramis (also dated to c. 4.2 Ma). These latter discoveries extend both the range and the habitat diversity of this species, as the Ethiopian environment comprised more closed woodland than the Kenyan sites. White and colleagues (2006) argue that *Au. anamensis* evolved from *Ar. ramidus* over a span of only 200,000 years—an event they term **punctuated anagenesis**, in which a slowly evolving lineage is suddenly marked by a rapid speciation event. These authors suggest that a shift toward increasing tooth size in *Australopithecus* led to a rapid "ecological breakout"—that is, an opportunistic expansion into more diverse savannah woodland habitats. The fossil remains suggest that *Au. anamensis* had clear affinities to the earlier *Ar. ramidus* and to later *Au. afarensis*. At Asa Issie, *Au. anamensis* canine shape is broadly similar to that of *Ar. ramidus*, while a proximal femur fragment bears resemblance to that of the more recent *Au. afarensis* in terms of shaft curvature and muscle attachment sites. *Au. anamensis* craniodental traits associated with upper and lower jaw form

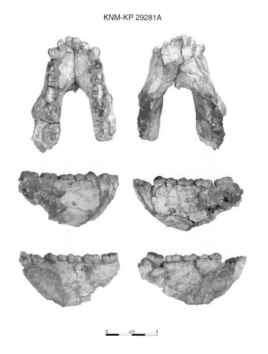

KNM-KP 29281A

FIGURE 9.8 *Au. anamensis* from East Africa, including this fragmentary mandible, is the first of a number of basal hominin species.

Fossil image: Ward, C.V., Leakey, M.G., and Walker, A. 2001. Morphology of *Australopithecus anamensis* from Kanapoi and Allia Bay, Kenya. *Journal of Human Evolution* 41: 255–368. Copyright © 2001 Academic Press. All rights reserved.

punctuated anagenesis

speciation has two tempos, slow and gradual (anagensis) or rapid followed by stasis (punctuated equilibrium); punctuated anagenesis combines these into a pattern of rapid change within a continually evolving lineage; the possibility of punctuated anagenesis is not universally held among evolutionary biologists

---

8. In the local Turkana language, "anam" means "lake"; all of the initial *Au. anamensis* finds are associated with a lacustrine (lake) environment.

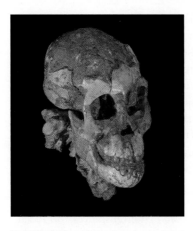

FIGURE 9.9 The discovery of the fossils of a three-year-old at the site of Dikika, Hadar, Ethiopia, was embraced by the media as "Lucy's Child," in reference to the famous partial skeleton nicknamed "Lucy" that was discovered in 1974.

© Zeresenay Alemseged/Photo Researchers, Inc.

and the C/P3 complex show changes that would be predicted if *Au. anamensis* were ancestral to *Au. afarensis* (Kimbel et al. 2006).

It seems that *Au. anamensis* had barely arrived on the evolutionary stage before it gave way to *Au. afarensis*, the earliest evidence for which occurs around 3.9 Ma. *Au. afarensis* is known principally from major fossil localities in Tanzania (Laetoli and the Afar Depression [Hadar]). These two regions have yielded numerous remains of this species, sampling over 300 individuals of various ages, including the most ancient hominin child yet discovered—a three-year-old found at the Dikika locality in Hadar and dating to 3.3 Ma (Figure 9.9).

The relationship of *Au. anamensis* and *Au. afarensis* remains somewhat cloudy due to a paucity of fossil materials in the half-million-year gap between the two forms, although the recent discovery of dental (tooth and jaw) and fragmentary postcranial remains from the site of Woranso-Mille, Ethiopia, offers some intriguing clues (Haile-Selassie et al. 2010). This locality has been dated 3.57 to 3.8 Ma, and the dental remains show affinities with the older *Au. anamensis* forms as well as some derived features found in the later *Au. afarensis* material. The Woranso-Mille fossils are, unfortunately, too sparse and fragmentary to support a definitive taxonomic assignment to either of these species; however, their transitional morphology supports the argument that *Au. anamensis* and *Au. afarensis* comprise an ancestor–descendant lineage. In fact, Haile-Selassie and colleagues suggest that these two forms may not represent separate species.

FIGURE 9.10 Early hominin tracks found at Laetoli, Tanzania, provided tantalizingly early evidence for bipedalism.

© John Reader/Science Photo Library

Among paleoanthropologists, Laetoli and Hadar have garnered as much controversy as celebrity. The older Laetoli site is best known for the rare preservation[9] of hundreds of animal trails, from insects to elephants—and, remarkably, for the 24-metre-long tracks of two (possibly three) bipedal hominins (Figure 9.10). The Laetoli trails have been studied intensely and debated hotly since they were discovered in 1978 (Leakey and Hay 1979). At that time they were the oldest record of hominin bipedalism. Debate swirled around whether these tracks had been produced by *Au. afarensis* or a more modern (*Homo*) species, and how similar the bipedal adaptation of the track makers was to that of modern humans in terms of posture, foot structure, and locomotory biomechanics (e.g., stride length and walking speed).

A more recent comparison of the Laetoli imprints with impressions in wet sand made by modern humans and chimpanzees (Berge, Penin, and Pellé 2006) has concluded that the Laetoli hominins shared

---

9. The Laetoli tracks are preserved in carbonatite, a rare igneous rock of volcanic origin. Presently, the East African Rift Valley is home to the only active carbonatite volcano in the world, known as Ol Doinyo Lengai ("Mountain of God" in the local Maasai language), which dominates the Tanzanian landscape. Carbonatite volcanoes are unusual in releasing very low-temperature lava, which cools quickly, preserving excellent detail, although it is also quickly weathered when exposed to the elements. The Laetoli tracks were produced by the now-dormant Sadiman volcano, about 20 km distant. The fine detail of their preservation is owed to their having been rapidly covered with further layers of volcanic ash. Since their exposure, they have been the subject of major conservation efforts.

locomotor features in common with both humans and chimpanzees but were much more like the former than the latter. Details of arch structure and weight-transfer pattern (determined from heel and toe impressions), the relatively short stride length, and the narrow foot gap (i.e., distance between left and right foot) clearly align the Laetoli trails with a human-like pattern of relatively slow walking with heel strike and toe-off. In an experimental study in which study subjects walked over wet sand in a "human" and "chimpanzee-like" gait, Raichlen and colleagues (2010) found that the Laetoli trails were likely produced by hominins walking with a human-like extended knee. What is generally accepted within the paleoanthropological community is that the fossil tracks were produced by hominins, most likely from the *Au. anamensis–Au. afarensis* lineage,[10] but with a bipedal adaptation not yet like our own in some respects.

The Hadar locality in Ethiopia made headlines worldwide when an almost 40% complete skeleton of an approximately 1.1-m-tall hominin (Figure 9.11) was discovered in November 1974 by members of the International Afar Research Expedition (IARE), led by the French geologist Maurice Taieb and paleoanthropologists Donald Johanson and Yves Coppens. Nicknamed

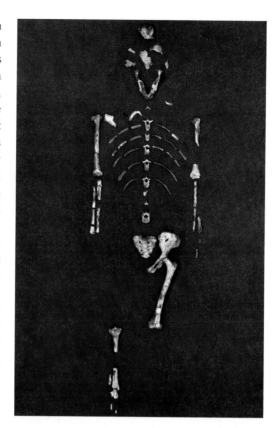

FIGURE 9.11 Lucy is perhaps the best-known hominin outside the field of paleoanthropology. The completeness of her skeleton challenged many long-held interpretations of early hominin evolution within the field.

Courtesy Institute of Human Origins, Arizona State University

"Lucy" (more formally designated AL 288-1),[11] this fossil discovery and other startling finds made soon after (including 333 fossil pieces from 13 individuals thought to have perished together) challenged then-accepted views of hominin evolution. Lucy was an old (3.2 Ma), small-brained (about 380 cc), bipedal hominin with reduced canines—an unexpected combination of traits for human ancestors as we understood them in the early 1970s. Until then, based on known species such as the 1.9 Ma ER 1470 cranium of *Homo rudolfensis* from Kenya (see Chapter 10), the belief was that hominin evolution had been initiated with brain expansion, followed by features such as bipedal locomotion. Preservation of the sacrum and the left half of Lucy's pelvis as well as her knee joint established this species' status as an obligate biped. In 2000, a fossil foot bone assigned to *Au. afarensis* was discovered at Hadar dating to 3.2 Ma and preserving evidence of human-like transverse and longitudinal arch structures (see Table 8.1), further evidence of a creature adapted to habitual bipedalism (Ward et al. 2011). Lucy's skeleton also generated much speculation concerning other life history attributes, such as childbirth (discussed in Chapter 8).

---

10. Foot bones from a South African gracile australopithecine, *Au. africanus*, named "Little Foot" (STS 573), have been suggested as a good match for the kind of foot structure possessed by the Laetoli hominins (Clarke 1998). The circumstances of discovery make the dating of Little Foot problematic, but a recent claim of over 4 Ma has been made (Partridge, Granger, and Caffee 2003; see the text for discussion).

11. The well-known anecdote has it that "Lucy" acquired her name from the 1967 Beatles song *Lucy in the Sky with Diamonds*, which was played frequently in the IARE camp. Formally, AL 288-1 refers to Afar Locality 288, with "Lucy" being the first discovery at that site. Lucy was not an inappropriate moniker, as the morphology of the pelvic bone identified AL 288-1 as female.

More Skeletons in the Australopithecine Closet

A number of other australopithecine species have been identified from the middle to late Pliocene, although except for *Au. africanus* in South Africa, all are known from single localities and one or only a handful of fossil remains (refer back to Figure 9.7). For example, *Au. bahrelghazali*, discovered at the site of Koro Toro in Chad in 1993 and recently dated to c. 3.6 Ma by cosmogenic nuclide dating (Lebatard et al. 2008), consists of a partial mandible with seven teeth, including canines and premolars. Many paleoanthropologists see *Au. bahrelghazali* as a western version of *Au. afarensis*, although Guy, Mackaye, and Likius (2008) have shown that the cross-sectional shape of the **mandibular symphysis** can discriminate taxa among living hominoids (including humans) and that this trait confirms *Au. bahrelghazali's* status as a new species. Caution must be exercised, however, until more remains of this form are discovered.

Another contemporary of *Au. afarensis* was described by Meave Leakey and colleagues (Leakey et al. 2001) from the c. 3.5 Ma site of Lomekwi, west of Lake Turkana in Kenya. These fossils, given the name *Kenyanthropus platyops* ("flat-faced man from Kenya"), consist of a number of isolated teeth, mandibular and cranial fragments, and—most important—a nearly complete albeit distorted cranium. Leakey and colleagues argue that the small-crowned molar teeth and **orthognathic** features of this fossil are evolutionarily derived with respect to *Australopithecus* (whose lower faces protrude from under the nasal region), justifying its attribution to a new genus. However, *K. platyops'* brain size is similar to *Au. afarensis*, and other dental traits such as enamel thickness are comparable with *Au. anamensis*. Given the significant distortion of the cranium, some paleoanthropologists are reserving judgment, considering *K. platyops* a variant of *Au. afarensis*.

The discovery of a new australopithecine species, *Au. garhi*,[12] from the site of Bouri in Ethiopia (Asfaw et al. 1999) represents a significant addition to the story of hominin evolution in eastern Africa, as it is situated both chronologically (at c. 2.5 Ma) and morphologically between earlier *Au. afarensis* and later *Homo* species. Compared to the previous million years, the pre-*Homo* fossil record of gracile hominins after 3.0 Ma is rather sparse, although it is of critical importance in untangling that most central of questions: Which species gave rise to the genus *Homo? Au. garhi* in part answers that question. Cranial, dental, and infracranial remains representing more than one individual are known, including a partial skeleton with upper and lower limbs and foot bones. While distinguished from *Au. afarensis* by absolutely larger posterior teeth, it does not share the suite of derived craniodental features of the megadont complex (see the next section) characteristic of *Paranthropus*, a sister clade not considered ancestral to later hominins. Cranial capacity is still small and comparable to *Au. afarensis*, at around 450 cc. Asfaw and colleagues (1999) remark that while the infracranial material cannot be attributed to this taxon with certainty (none were found with the craniodental remains), they exhibit both human-like and *Au. afarensis*-like features.

As significant as *Au. garhi* may be in terms of hominin phylogeny, its putative behavioural and technological adaptations are equally so. Bouri is located in the Middle Awash study area which, as noted earlier, is associated with an open woodland and lakeshore grassland habitat. Fossil remains of catfish, suids, and bovids occur in the Bouri deposits, and bones of the latter show evidence of cutmarks and intentional breaking made by stone tools. A few stone artifacts have been located near the discovery site, apparently having eroded out of the hominin-bearing sediments. Artifacts belonging to the earliest known lithic technology (the Oldowan; see Chapter 10) have been reported at the 2.6 Ma Gona site just 96 km north of Bouri, although these lack association with hominin remains.[13]

More recently, McPherron and colleagues (2010) have described faunal remains (a femur and rib from a medium and large-sized grazers) with cutmarks and percussion

---

mandibular symphysis
the midline of the lower jaw, where the left and right sides of the dental arcade meet

orthognathic
"ortho" refers to vertical or flat, and "gnathic" to the jaws; thus, "orthognathic" means "flat face"

---

12. In the local Afar language, "garhi" means "surprise."

13. Remains of *Ar. ramidus* have been found in the Gona study area, but east of the archaeological deposits and c. 1.8 million years older.

damage related to stone tool use (cutting, scraping, and pounding). These remains were found at the nearby Dikika site and date to c. 3.4 Ma (Figure 9.12). The implication from these discoveries at Bouri and Dikika is that the original user of lithic percussive technology was not *Homo*, as has always been presumed, but *Au. afarensis* followed by *Au. garhi*. No apparent tools were found at Dikika, so it is not possible to determine if the hominins were making tools, or simply using stones with sharp, natural breaks.

Although eastern Africa has provided a wealth of Pliocene remains of gracile australopithecines,[14] the original discoveries of this variant were made in southern Africa beginning in 1925. Several sites have yielded remains of this hominin, known as *Au. africanus*, including Taung, Sterkfontein/Jacovec Cavern, and Makapansgat (refer back to Figure 9.7). In many

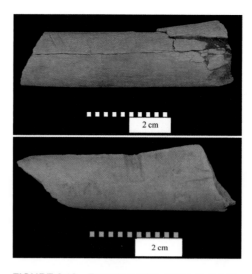

FIGURE 9.12 Faunal remains dating to 3.4 Ma show clear evidence of butchering and hammering to acquire meat and bone marrow.

Photo by C. Marean, copyright Dikika Research Project

respects, *Au. africanus* resembles *Au. afarensis* from eastern Africa in being a small-bodied, bipedal, thick-enamelled hominin. Other features appear more derived, however, including a slightly larger average brain size (452 cc vs. 438 cc; McHenry and Coffing 2000), a less prognathic face, and slightly smaller teeth. *Au. africanus* has generally been viewed as having originated as a population(s) of *Au. afarensis* that migrated south toward the end of the Pliocene, and dates of between 3.0 and 2.0 Ma are often cited.

Dating has long been an issue for the South African sites, which consist of sedimentary dolomitic limestone cave deposits—a geological context in which the classic radiometric methods used in eastern Africa (e.g., ^{40}K/^{40}Ar or ^{40}Ar/^{39}Ar; see Chapter 7) are not applicable. Sites such as Sterkfontein, from which more than 500 hominin fossils have been recovered, have historically been dated using biostratigraphic (faunal) association with eastern African localities whose antiquity has been determined using radiometric techniques (Partridge et al. 2003). Recent development of methods such as cosmogenic nuclide dating, which tracks the decay of ^{26}Al and ^{10}Be (isotopes of aluminum and beryllium) in buried quartz sand crystals, have allowed researchers to obtain absolute dates for cave deposits. Using this approach, Partridge and colleagues (2003) have obtained a date of c. 4.0 Ma for the partial skeleton StW 573[15] ("Little Foot") and for remains attributed to *Australopithecus sp. indet.* from Jacovic Cavern, which include a partial cranium, two proximal femora, and isolated teeth. (The label "species indeterminate"—or *sp. indet.*—is used when researchers are confident in assigning a fossil to a particular genus, but are not sure to which species it should be assigned.) The Jacovic fossils appear to sample both "gracile and robust" (a distinction we discuss below) australopithecine species. The proposed early date for these remains is remarkable and would suggest that the southern African species are descended from either *Ar. ramidus* or *Au. anamensis*, not *Au. afarensis*. However, Walker and colleagues (2006) dated deposits above and below the sediments in which Little Foot was recovered using the radiometric method ^{238}U/^{206}Pb and obtained a date of only c. 2.2 Ma. This may be a more reasonable estimate for the antiquity of this fossil, as the uranium (U)–lead (Pb) dates agree well with the biostratigraphic *and* paleomagnetic records of the deposits, and the method requires fewer assumptions regarding depositional history than cosmogenic nuclide dating.

14. Recently Crevecoeur et al. (2014) have described a single tooth from the Central African site of Ishango dating to between 2.6 and 2.0 Ma. This specimen is tentatively assigned to *Australopithecus* and, if confirmed, would extend the geographic range of this taxon currently known only from East and South Africa, and from Chad in Northern Africa.

15. "StW" stands for "Sterkfontein West," the locality within the Sterkfontein complex where remains of Little Foot were discovered.

Australopithecus sediba— A Study in Mosaic Evolution

Every now and then in the field of paleoanthropology a discovery is made transforming our understanding of the evolutionary pathways explored by our hominin forebears. Such is the case with *Australopithecus sediba*, a new species of australopithecine discovered at the c. 2.0 Ma site of Malapa, South Africa (Figure 9.13), a fossil-cave locality not far from the well-known hominin sites of Sterkfontein and Swartkrans, both of which have yielded numerous examples of gracile and robust australopithecines over the past nine decades. Indeed, the region is so rich in hominin fossil remains that it has been aptly named "The Cradle of Human-kind" (designated a UNESCO World Heritage Site in 1999). To date, over 200 complete and fragmentary remains derived from at least four individuals have been recovered: an adult female, an adolescent male, and two juveniles, collectively providing insights on skeletal morphology and behaviour across the life span. The likelihood that these individuals fell into the cave and were subsequently rapidly buried without interference from predators led to excellent preservation of the remains, including the unique occurrence of fossilized skin (discussed later in this chapter).

FIGURE 9.13 View of the Malapa site in 2008, shortly after discovery of the *Au. sediba* fossil, MH2 (Malapa hominid 2).

Photo courtesy of Lee Berger and the University of the Witwatersrand

Au. sediba represents an exciting find for many reasons. It dates to a time of transition from the genus *Australopithecus* to *Homo*, and indeed presents a mixture of primitive and derived morphological traits. Such a mixture results from evolution acting independently on different aspects of an organism's biology (anatomy or behaviour), retaining some features over long spans of time and adapting others to suit new circumstances (Berger 2013). For example, long upper limbs, a broad conical rib cage, and high shoulders are more reminiscent of other australopithecines and living apes. This anatomy is conducive to arboreal climbing, yet aspects of its hand (longer thumb and short fingers) are more *Homo*-like and adapted to fine motor skills and precision grips possibly related to tool production (Kivell et al. 2011; see Box 9.4). While fully bipedal, its lower limb anatomy suggests that *Au. sediba* had a unique and somewhat peculiar gait (DeSilva et al. 2013) described as "hyper-pronated." In essence, the sole of *Au. sediba*'s foot was turned slightly inward, so initial contact with the ground would have been made with the outside of the foot; in order to effect weight-transfer and "toe-off" into the swing phase of its stride (refer back to Chapter 8 for a description of the mechanics of bipedal walking) the foot would then have to roll over with each step. The resulting ambling gait would also require changes in other aspects of the skeleton, such as the lower spine, in order to maintain balance. Such a novel pattern of walking—seen in at least one member of *Au. sediba*—affirms what we had suggested in Chapter 8: our Pliocene hominin ancestors were effectively experimenting with different forms (styles) of bipedal locomotion.

The mosaic dental and jaw anatomy of *Au. sediba* further attests to its unique place in our ancestral bush, sharing similarities with the south African gracile *Au. africanus* (but not the earlier East African *Au. afarensis*), as well as later *Homo* species (Irish et al. 2013). Even more perplexing in some respects is the suggestion that the diet of *Au. sediba*, reconstructed from plant remains and carbon isotope analyses, consisted of tree leaves, bark, grasses and sedges, similar to modern chimpanzees and *Ar. ramidus* but not contemporary gracile australopithecines or later early *Homo* species (Henry et al. 2012).

breccia

a rock formation composed of stone fragments embedded within a fine-grained cement-like matrix

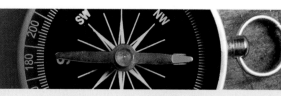

BOX 9.4 PROFILE … Holding Hands with Our Ancestors

Courtesy of Dr. Tracy Kivell

© Peter Schmid

FIGURE 9.14 Bones of the almost complete *Au. sediba* hand emerge from the limestone breccia in which they were found.

When the *Au. sediba* fossils were being first excavated out of the **breccia** in 2009, a beautifully preserved right humerus, radius, and ulna "disappeared" into a large block of sediment. Given the completeness of the rest of the forelimb, it was likely that there would be hand bones preserved as well.

Beginning with my Ph.D., my research has focused on the evolution of the human and nonhuman primate hand, starting with the development of the wrist bones in living and fossil humans and other hominoids, leading to experimental studies on the functional loads experienced by the hands during locomotion, and now focusing on the internal bony structure of hand bones in a variety of different extant primates and fossil hominins. The hand is a direct link to our environment, be it through locomotion or manipulation, and thus can offer unique insight into behaviour in the past. Therefore, when it became clear that at least a few hand bones were associated with the *Au. sediba* adult female skeleton, Prof. Lee Berger (University of the Witwatersrand—nicknamed "Wits") and head of the *Au. sediba* excavations) and Professor Steven Churchill (with whom I worked at Duke University) asked me to be a part of the *Au. sediba* team. Of course, I was honoured and delighted to say yes!

In June 2010 I travelled to Johannesburg, South Africa, to conduct the initial analysis of the *Au. sediba* hand bones. When I arrived, all of the bones were still in the breccia, but a few metacarpals, phalanges, and carpal bones were exposed (Figure 9.14). The hard-working and patient fossil "prep team" at Wits worked tirelessly to remove and clean each fossil from the sediment. Each day, new fossils would be brought to me in the lab and, in the end, we had almost a complete hand; we were missing only three wrist bones and the distal phalanges of the fingers (Figure 9.15). This made the *Au. sediba* hand the most complete early hominin hand available for study (the hand of another South African australopithecine known as "Little Foot" appears equally complete but is not yet fully excavated).

Over the next year, I worked hard with a team of researchers —including Professor Churchill and Dr. Job Kibii—to describe, quantify, and compare the new fossils to those of humans, other apes, and as many other hominin fossils as possible. Like the rest of the *Au. sediba* skeleton, the hand is a mosaic of primitive and derived features. Because the bones are associated not only with a particular species but also with a specific individual— both of which are very rare for postcranial fossils—it allows us to say a lot more about overall hand function than one can say from isolated elements.

The *Au. sediba* hand revealed features that were in many ways still like that of earlier hominins and African apes, such as slightly curved phalanges that have well-developed flexor sheath ridges, which suggest arboreal locomotion and strong flexion of the forearm and hand. In contrast, the thumb is remarkably long compared with the length of the fingers— even longer than that of modern humans!—which would have enabled thumb-to-finger precision grips that are used during stone-tool use and tool-making. This was a remarkable combination of features that, as a paleoanthropologist who has been studying the hand for several years, would not have thought could have existed within a single species, let alone a single individual. My ongoing research—as we wait for more hand bones to be excavated from the site of Malapa—now looks at the internal structure of the hand bones to better re-construct how *Au. sediba* may have been using her hand during life.

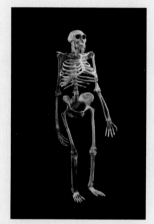

FIGURE 9.15 *Au. sediba* (here shown as a composite of three individuals recovered at Malapa) represents one of the most complete hominin ancestors ever discovered, including the unique presence of fossilized soft tissue.

Photo courtesy of Lee Berger and the University of the Witwatersrand

Source: Contributed by Dr. Tracy Kivell, School of Anthropology and Conservation, University of Kent, Canterbury, UK and the Department of Human Evolution, Max Planck Institute for Evolutionary Anthropology, Leipzig, Germany

As noted earlier, the circumstances under which the Malapa hominins were entombed in the cave deposits resulted in exceptional preservation, including rarely found intact and undistorted skeletal elements. Recently, Keeling and Berger (2013) reported on the possible preservation of organic tissue on two of the *Au. sediba* specimens. Employing several investigative techniques, including CT-scans and molecular imaging, they found suggestive evidence that a brownish substance adhering to the cranium of MH1 and mandible of MH2 may in fact be remnants of skin. While such finds are not unknown in paleontology, it would mark the first example of such a discovery in the hominin fossil record.

Au. sediba presents us with fascinating insights into a dynamic phase of hominin evolution, opening doors to many new questions regarding adaptation and taxonomic relationships with earlier and later hominins, including our own genus. Much more work needs to be done before we are able to make conclusive statements regarding the phylogenetic significance of the Malapa hominins. Having said that, it seems evident that they represent a distinct group of southern African gracile australopithecines, with arguably the clearest connection to subsequent members of the genus *Homo*, which overlap in time with Malapa.

Robust Australopithecines and the Megadont Adaptation

The jaws and teeth of the australopithecines provide crucial data in sorting out the phylogenetic relationships of these various species (Irish et al. 2013). As you might imagine, teeth can also tell us lots about how these hominins may have lived day to day: interactions between males and females, competition, and diet, although such interpretations must be framed in a good understanding of the ecological context of the species in question. For example, while female–male differences in canine tooth size has been shown to be a good measure of sexual selection acting on body size in living primates (as discussed in Chapter 6), in australopithecines smaller canines (and smaller body size) in females may reflect less access to resources compared to males (Gordon 2013). The size and shape of teeth and jaws can also be highly informative about what an animal typically eats, and how diet may have changed through evolutionary time (Delezene et al. 2013). One of the most salient features of the craniodental complex related to dietary habits within australopithecines is a trend toward post-canine megadontia, which is taken to an extreme in that group known as the robust australopithecines.

Three species of robust australopithecines are known, belonging to the genus *Paranthropus*.[16] These include *P. aethiopicus* and *P. boisei* from eastern Africa (2.6 to 1.1 Ma) and *P. robustus* from southern Africa (2.0 to 1.5 Ma; refer back to Figure 9.7). Widely presumed to have become extinct by 1.0 Ma and not to be ancestral to later hominins, the origins of *Paranthropus* are somewhat more ambiguous. Some researchers link all robust species to a still unknown eastern African progenitor (possibly *Au. afarensis*); others see separate origins for the eastern and southern African lineages, the latter derived from *Au. africanus*. This view would suggest that the megadont adaptation evolved independently in these two geographic locales. Differences do exist between the two eastern African species, as well as between the more recent (post-2.3 Ma) eastern and southern African species of *Paranthropus*. For example, the earlier form *P. aethiopicus* has a more **prognathic** face, larger incisors, and a smaller mandible than *P. boisei* (Wood et al. 1994), and as a rule the eastern African robust species are exceptional in the degree to which they express the major craniodental features defining this clade (Wood and Chamberlain 1987). In spite of these distinctions, it is reasonable to see them as geographic variants sharing a common ancestor.

prognathic
refers to the degree to which the lower face projects forward

---

16. Considerable debate exists regarding the systematics of the robust forms. *Paranthropus* was the original taxon created by Robert Broom in 1938 for the South African species *P. robustus*. However, when similar forms were discovered in East Africa—originally called *Zinjanthropus boisei* by the Leakeys—they were later assigned to the genus *Australopithecus*. Some researchers consider the megadont adaptation and the behaviour implied by it to be sufficient to indicate an adaptive shift worthy of a generic distinction, and refer all robust species to *Paranthropus*. This is the position taken in this text. Collectively, however, all of the Plio-Pleistocene hominins not ascribed to *Homo* are casually referred to as "australopithecine."

Although comparable in body size to their gracile "sisters" such as *Au. afarensis* and *Au. africanus* (about 30 to 45 kg for females and males), robust australopithecines are exceptional for having massive post-canine teeth, estimated between 600 to 700 mm^2 in occlusal (chewing) surface area, in contrast to 450 to 500 mm^2 in gracile forms (McHenry and Coffing 2000). This of course is the source for the label "megadont." The transition to the megadont pattern is associated with a number of cranial modifications that accommodate a substantial muscle mass providing large chewing forces, including well-developed sagittal and nuchal crests and expansive cheekbones . Researchers initially concluded that this anatomy reflected an adaptation to a diet of tough, fibrous foods, which earned *P. boisei* the nickname "Nutcracker Man" when the first cranium was discovered by Mary Leakey in 1959.

The craniodental features are so derived relative to the earlier gracile australopithecines that scientists quite naturally viewed the robust species as dietary specialists living in open grassland habitats and surviving on hard-to-chew foods as a result of ecological factors or possibly through **competitive exclusion** vis-à-vis tool-using australopithecines or early species of *Homo*. However, paleoenvironmental reconstruction of robust australopithecines locales indicates habitat diversity, from open, arid grassland to lakeshore margins to closed, wet woodlands.

Ungar, Grine, and Teaford (2008) studied dental microwear on the molar teeth of several *P. boisei* specimens from various sites and time periods and found that the pattern of wear was not consistent with a constant diet of tough, fibrous foods. This finding challenges the notion of dietary specialization and points to an interesting discrepancy between what an animal's morphology suggests it *could* eat based on biomechanical considerations and what it may *actually* have eaten as revealed in tooth wear patterns. In biology, this is known as **Liem's Paradox**: a species may evolve a specialized phenotype in order to access secondary **fallback foods** when preferred resources are less available. At the same time, this adaptive morphology in no way impedes its ability to consume more easily processed preferred foods when they are available. What this line of thinking suggests is that *Paranthropus* may have been more of a dietary generalist, able to eat pretty much anything, and not a specialist at all. Interestingly, Ungar and colleagues (2008) also found that *P. robustus* in southern Africa had a dental microwear pattern more in keeping with biomechanical expectations; that is, this species most likely relied more heavily on fallback foods than eastern African *P. boisei*. When it comes to wear on teeth, diet is only one consideration. Recent experimental studies by Lucas et al. (2013) indicates that grit adhering to plant tissue would contribute to wear to a much greater degree than the food source itself.

The robust australopithecines were for the most part contemporaries with members of early *Homo*, including the species *H. habilis* and *H. ergaster*. Neither of these forms exhibits a megadont adaptation, but both are likewise associated with a varied range of habitats. As we explore in the following chapter, exploitation of diverse food resources by early *Homo* (including fallback foods) was made possible not by teeth, but by tools.[17] A review of models for the extinction of this last-surviving member of the australopithecine clade (Wood and Strait 2004) also tested the presumption that *Paranthropus* was too much of a dietary specialist to survive the regime of climate change (cooling and drying) in eastern and southern Africa established in the late Miocene. These authors examined 11 different criteria providing direct (e.g., dental wear, carbon isotope analysis) and indirect (e.g., paleoecology, tooth size and shape) evidence for specialization, principally regarding diet. Their results were not sufficiently compelling to conclude that *Paranthropus* was more specialized than the earliest members of the genus *Homo*. Thus, while it is clear that extinction was the ultimate fate of this enigmatic genus, the factors that led to the disappearance of *Paranthropus* remain a mystery.

competitive exclusion

a phenomenon in which two species closely related in phenotype and ecology come into direct competition for resources. In these cases one species will either become extinct or adopt a new phenotype (morphology and/or behaviour), allowing it to exploit other resources

Liem's Paradox

a model in biology that describes the apparent paradox between a specialized phenotype and a generalized behaviour; the paradox is resolved if the specialized phenotype does not restrict an organism from nonspecialized behaviours

fallback foods

resources on which a species relies when its preferred, more easily acquired and processed foods are unavailable

---

17. Some paleoanthropologists have argued for many years that *Paranthropus* had sufficient manual dexterity to fashion Oldowan-type tools. Research of the internal structure of a hand bone attributed to this species (Lazenby et al. 2008b) suggests that while it is human-like in some respects, *Paranthropus* may have had limited dexterity.

FROM BUSH TO BRANCH: RECONSTRUCTING PLIOCENE HOMININ PHYLOGENY

If nothing else, this discussion of early hominin evolution should convince you that paleoanthropology is a complex discipline in which fieldwork, fossil data, analysis, and personalities produce competing interpretations. For example, sound arguments can be made that *Sahelanthropus, Orrorin,* and *Ardipithecus* are all members of the hominin lineage. However, even though they comprise a temporal sequence, their morphological differences make it unlikely that they form an evolutionary sequence, and each discoverer has claimed that "their fossil" is the most likely stem hominin species. Unravelling the earliest history of the human lineage is further complicated by several realities.

First, molecular data place the hominin–panin divergence somewhere within the 2-million-year time frame occupied by these protohominins, although as noted above perhaps toward their earliest appearance around 6 to 7 Ma. Second, many of the most significant discoveries (such as *Sahelanthropus*) are fairly recent, and analyses are still in early stages. As analysis progresses, considerable revision to existing interpretations is likely to occur. Third, the discipline is plagued by a still extremely poor late Miocene/Pliocene fossil record for African hominoids (e.g., ancestors of chimpanzee and gorilla). Finally, returning to our opening discussion of taxonomic lumping versus splitting, the similarities and differences among fossils that we rely upon to "sort things out" may exist by virtue of function rather than genetics—a condition Collard and Wood (2007) refer to as **homoiology**. Two fossils with similar cranial morphology may be biologically related (i.e., belong to the same species) or they may just have similar diets to which the bones for the head and face adapt to during life (i.e., be separate species)! These challenges will be overcome only by further fossil discoveries in the 4- to 7 Ma time range and by continued cooperation and sharing of data among researchers.

It is not much easier to untangle relationships among the diversity of hominin species between 4 and 2 Ma (Figure 9.16). Prior to 3 Ma, the lineage *Ar. ramidus–Au. anamensis–Au. afarensis* is the only game in town assuming, of course, that we reject both *Kenyanthropus* as a valid genus and the possibility that an as yet undiscovered form links *Ardipithecus* and

homoiology

similarities that occur among organisms by virtue of a bone's ability to respond to existing mechanical forces; similar behaviours will reproduce such forces and thus the associated morphology, which may be confused with genetic relationships

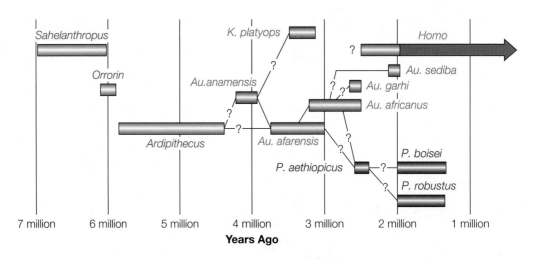

FIGURE 9.16 Depiction of one possible reconstruction of Pliocene hominin evolutionary relationships. The complexity of hominin morphological and behavioural diversity is such that one could contrive a number of different models, none of which may be correct. Note that in almost every instance, the line connecting two forms is presented with a question mark, reflecting the uncertainty inherent in deriving phylogenetic reconstructions. In this depiction, *K. platyops* is retained as a separate genus, although at this time most paleoanthropologists would suggest placement of this form within *Au. afarensis*.

Au. afarensis. The rest of it remains a bit of a muddle. Is *Homo* derived from *Au. garhi, Au. africanus,* or possibly *Au. sediba?* Are the robust eastern African forms linked phyletically (by linear descent) or cladistically (branching evolution) with *Au. afarensis* and/or *Au. africanus?* Do the eastern and southern African robust species form a sister clade, or do they belong to separate and geographically isolated lineages? These are all important and as yet unanswerable questions. It may be that the reality is something quite different from any of these alternatives. The take-home message here is that the volumes of data we have about our early hominin forebears remain small compared to what we do not yet know. The problem is that we can never *know* what we do not know. Nonetheless, our understanding of the major events in early hominin evolution is clearer now than it has ever been, although still not nearly clear enough. This confusing picture reflects the fact that paleoanthropology is a highly active and deeply fascinating field of study.

LEARNING KEYS

KEY IDEAS

- Variation in completeness, preservation, and dating makes the naming of fossils a complicated and at times controversial endeavour, contributing to debates on the number of ancestors present and their evolutionary history.

- Interpreting the fossil hominin record (How many species are there? How are they related?) requires consideration of both morphology—what they looked like, anatomically—and ecology—the context of where and how they lived. Scientists from many different fields—from archaeology to psychology to physics—contribute to this understanding.

- Hominin evolution in the Pliocene was fuelled by significant changes in African climate and habitat, with increasing dryness and reduction of tropical forest habitat, favouring species with anatomical and behavioural adaptations conferring flexibility.

- The earliest members of our lineage termed "proto-hominins," known as *Sahelanthropus, Orrorin,* and *Ardipithecus,* predate 4.0 Ma and offer a mix of primitive and derived traits as would be expected the nearer we approach divergence of hominins from the last common ancestor shared with panins.

- The protohominins were at least facultative bipeds, although postcranial remains of *Orrorin* and *Ardipithecus* show clear adaptations for arboreal climbing; such remains are lacking for *Sahelanthropus.*

- The australopithecines are the first true hominins, from c. 4.2 to 1.0 Ma, and can generally be ascribed to either a gracile or a robust form.

- Among many of the gracile forms (such as *Au. afarensis* and *Au. sediba*) anatomical evidence for retained climbing ability is found.

- Several australopithecine species (such as *Au. afarensis, Au. africanus,* and *Au. sediba*) are represented by numerous fossil remains, including partial skeletons from single individuals, providing valuable evidence for differences between sexes and across the lifespan.

- Australopithecines are widely distributed in eastern and southern Africa, allowing finely detailed reconstruction of habitats, lifeways, and dating.

- Marks on animal bones indicating the use of stone tools to acquire animal protein and fats (meat and marrow) is clearly associated in time and space with australopithecines, most likely *Au. afarensis* in eastern Africa (Ethiopia) at c. 3.4 Ma.

- The robust australopithecines, known by the genus name *Paranthropus,* represent a side branch (sister clade), having adopted a distinctive lifeway of hard-object feeding reflected in the megadont adaptation in dental and cranial features.

- Some paleoanthropologists suggest an evolutionary lineage leading from *Ar. ramidus* to *Au. afarensis* to *Au. garhi* to *Homo,* although this is by no means universally accepted; others have argued that *Au. sediba* likely represents that most likely ancestor to the genus *Homo.*

KEY TERMS

speciose (196)

alpha taxonomy (196)

megadont (198)

mosaic habitats (201)

variability selection hypothesis (202)

foramen magnum (206)

stem hominin (206)

eurytopic (209)

gracile (209)

robust (209)

phyletic sequence (209)

prognathic (218)

competitive exclusion (219)

fallback foods (219)

KEY QUESTIONS TO ASK MYSELF

1. I wonder what would it have been like to have been the first hominin to make a stone tool?

2. It seems like every time there is big new discovery in the field of paleoanthroplogy, our picture of hominin evolution just get murkier. Why is that?

3. The pattern seems to be one of hominins spending more and more time on the ground, moving around, using different kinds of tools, eating new kinds of foods, and evolving bigger brains. These things must be related, but how?

KEY CRITICAL THINKING QUESTIONS

1. In reconstructing hominin phylogeny, paleoanthropologists consider what fossils look like as well as when and where they were found. How much emphasis do you think each of these factors should be given in sorting out the fossil record of ancestor–descendant relationships?

2. The argument has been made that hominins such as *Ar. ramidus*, *Au. afarensis* (both from eastern Africa), and *Au. sediba* (from southern Africa) evolved different kinds of bipedal locomotion with retention of the ability to climb trees. How would you explain this in terms of adaptation, taking into account ecological circumstances and evolutionary relationships through time?

KEY THINGS TO DO NEXT

CourseMate Visit **CourseMate** at www.nelson.com/humanvoyage2e to build your comprehension, practise your critical thinking skills, review core concepts, and explore other resources at your disposal.

10 The Emergence of the Genus *Homo*

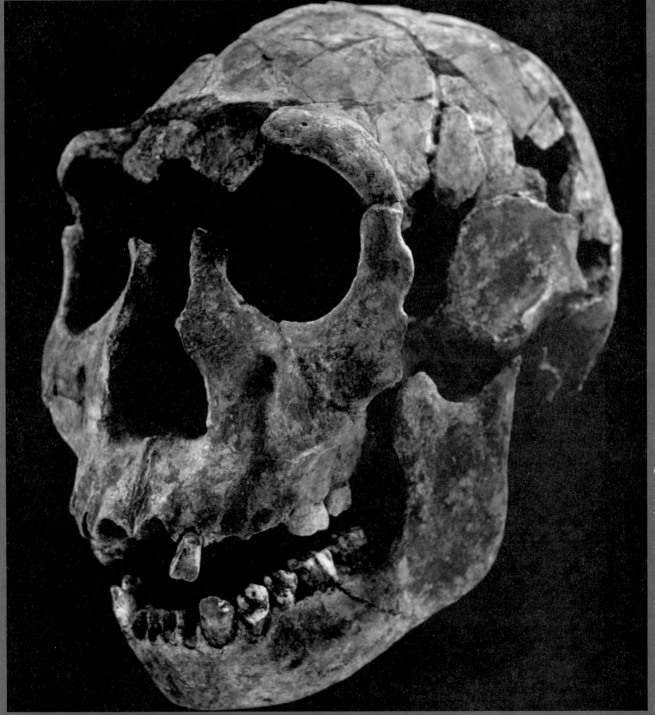

> *I was taught that the human brain was the crowning glory of evolution so far, but I think it's a very poor scheme for survival.*
>
> Kurt Vonnegut (1922–2007)

OVERVIEW

As you learned in the previous chapter, a number of different species of hominins coexisted in eastern and southern Africa during the late Pliocene epoch. Around 2.5 million years ago, one of these species gave rise to the first members of the genus *Homo*, hominins that possessed a larger brain and body size than their predecessors, had more sophisticated stone tool technology, hunted large game, and used fire. One of these species was the first to leave Africa and disperse to other regions of the Old World, where it endured for well over a million years. This chapter reviews the fossil evidence for these hominins, examines their anatomical characteristics, explores the ways in which they adapted behaviourally to their environments, and addresses some of the debates surrounding the taxonomic status and phylogenetic position of members of this genus.

KEY CONCEPTS

Experimental archaeology, bioenergetics, life history, stable isotope analysis, Oldowan, Acheulian, migration, hunting

KEY LEARNING OBJECTIVES

At the end of this chapter, you will be able to

LO1   List the ways in which early members of the genus *Homo* differed morphologically and behaviourally from the australopithecines

LO2   Explain the methods used to reconstruct the diet of early *Homo*

LO3   Apply your knowledge of the australopithecines to justify the designation of early *Homo* fossils as representing a new species of hominin

LO4   Compare and contrast the anatomical characteristics of *Homo erectus* with those of *Homo habilis* and *Homo rudolfensis*

LO5   Evaluate the evidence for separate African and Asian *Homo erectus* species (i.e., *Homo ergaster* and *Homo erectus*)

LO6   Formulate a hypothesis to explain why *Homo erectus* endured for such a long period of time with few morphological changes

PROLOGUE: 35% MAKES ALL THE DIFFERENCE

Is a 35% increase really meaningful? If you were talking about the annual change in your investment portfolio or home heating bill, it certainly would be! But perhaps not so meaningful in the case of the price of a single iTunes download or the number of unmatched socks in the family laundry bin. However, in the history of our genus it turns out to have pretty significant import, as 35% is the difference between the average brain size for early *Homo* compared to *Au. africanus*, and slightly more when compared to that of *Au. sediba*. What explains this dramatic increase, which took place over as little as half a million years and is still the subject of much debate (as we discussed in Chapter 8)? Diet is certainly implicated and so are various aspects of sociality and spatial organization (i.e., group living and movement). Brain expansion is by many accounts the defining feature of the transition from australopithecine to *Homo*.

The one demonstrable event that can be situated within the time frame of brain expansion is the development of an established stone tool industry. Even though the very earliest occurrence of these Oldowan-type tools predates the first appearance of the forms we ascribe to the genus *Homo*, it is certain that this new mode of interacting with the environment (more specifically, killing and/or butchering animals) became a large part of the behavioural niche carved out by our lineage. The implications are nothing short of profound (we can say this retrospectively with much confidence!). The development and evolution of a percussive stone tool technology has been linked to functional asymmetry (handedness), neural asymmetry, language development (including grammar and syntax), foresight, elaboration of the frontal cortex and its executive functions (including recognizing future consequences of current actions; see Semendeferi et al. 2002), and eventually, migration out of Africa. As we will see in this chapter, the advent of the genus *Homo* was accompanied by accelerating changes in morphology, technology, subsistence, life history, and social behaviour. Humankind had entered a new adaptive milieu unlike that experienced by any of our ancestors (or known from living hominoids, for that matter)—one that would forever, and unrelentingly, chart the course for all subsequent human evolution—the ascendancy of material culture.

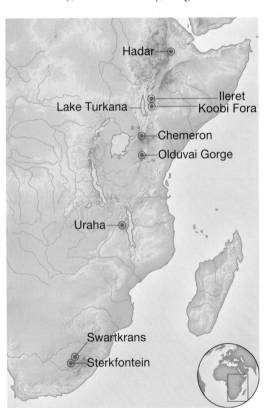

FIGURE 10.1 Early *Homo* sites in Africa.

Adapted from/Based on Schrenk, F., Kullmer, O., Bromage, T. 2007. The earliest putative Homo fossils. *Handbook of paleoanthropology*, edited by Henke, W. and Tattersall, I. Berline: Springer Verlag, p. 1613; Jurain, R., Kilgore, L., Trevathan, W. 2005. *Introduction to Physical Anthropology*, 10e. Belmont, Calif: Wadsworth, p. 189.

OUR ANCESTORS COME TO LIGHT

The first fossils attributed to early *Homo* were discovered in 1960 when excavations by Louis Leakey and his team at Olduvai Gorge (Figure 10.1) uncovered hominin fossils consisting of a nearly complete left parietal bone, a partial right parietal bone, a partial mandible, 14 teeth, and a number of hand bones. The age at death of this individual was estimated to have been 12 to 13 years, based on the degree of eruption of its teeth. Dating between 1.8 and 1.6 million years ago, the remains were recovered from the same deposit as the *Zinjanthropus* ("Zinj") fossil (now recognized as *P. boisei*) discovered by Mary Leakey in 1959. Given the catalogue number OH 7 for Olduvai Hominid 7, its large cranial capacity (680 cc) compared to Zinj prompted Leakey and his colleagues to assign it the taxonomic name *Homo habilis* ("Handy Man"), reflecting their belief that it had made the stone tools found nearby. Six additional specimens representing adults, adolescents, and juveniles were also recovered during this excavation (Leakey et al. 1964). More recent finds include a cranium (OH 24, Figure 10.2), a maxilla with a complete set of teeth (OH 65), and a partial female skeleton (OH 62).

The initial reaction from many people was that the hominins represented by these fossils were not significantly different from the australopithecines to warrant identification as a new species. Hindering acceptance of these fossils as distinct from earlier hominins was the fact that the sample size was small, the remains were very fragmentary, and there were few postcranial bones. This view changed in the early 1970s, however, with the discovery of additional early *Homo* fossils in the Koobi Fora region on the eastern shores of Lake Turkana[1], and more recently at Ileret, Kenya. Dating between 1.9 and 1.4 Ma, these remains, which include a nearly complete skull known as KNM-ER 1813 (Figure 10.3), resemble those from Olduvai, and many are currently interpreted as representing *Homo habilis,* although the taxonomic status of some of these fossils has been questioned (discussed later). In more recent years, the *Homo* lineage in East Africa has been extended to 2.3 Ma with the discovery of a maxilla (Au.L. 666-1) from Hadar, Ethiopia (Kimbel et al. 1996). A number of early *Homo* fossils have also been found in South Africa, including a fragmentary skull (Stw 53) at the cave site of Sterkfontein (Tobias 1991).

The Anatomy of Early *Homo*

The key defining feature of the genus *Homo* is its larger brain relative to body size compared to the australopithecines (Leakey, Tobias, and

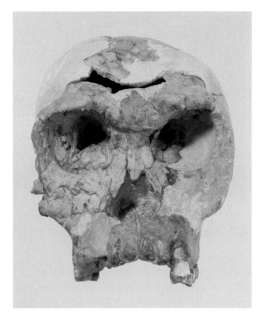

FIGURE 10.2 This fossil of Olduvai hominid 24, also known as "Twiggy," was found in Olduvai Gorge and represents *Homo habilis.*

© John Reader/Science Photo Library

FIGURE 10.3 KNM-ER 1813 dates to 1.9 Ma and has a cranial capacity of 510 cc.

© Human Origins Program, Smithsonian Institution

Napier 1964; Tobias 1991; Figure 10.4). The cranial capacity of *Homo habilis* ranged from 510 cc, only slightly less than that measured in some *Australopithecus* fossils (e.g., 521 cc for *P. boisei,* and 530 cc for *P. robustus*), to 750 cc, with an average of 629 cc (Antón 2012). Besides a larger brain, *Homo habilis* had a more rounded braincase, and its face was smaller and less projecting than that of the australopithecines. Its dental characteristics included a parabolic dental arcade (palate), large incisors, large canines relative to the premolars, and smaller molars than those of some australopithecines, although some early *Homo* fossils had relatively large molars.

---

1. These fossils were labelled KNM-ER for "Kenya National Museum East Rudolf," indicating that the site is located on the east side of Lake Rudolf (renamed Lake Turkana in 1975).

CHAPTER 10 The Emergence of the Genus *Homo*

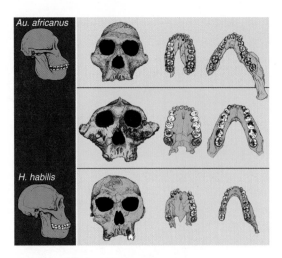

FIGURE 10.4 Compared to *Au. africanus* (top), *Homo habilis* (bottom) had a larger cranial capacity, a more rounded braincase, a smaller and less projecting face, and smaller molars.

Our knowledge of the postcranial anatomy of early *Homo* comes from studies of only a small number of preserved postcranial skeletons. Early *Homo* limb proportions reflect both ape-like and more human-like features (Haeusler and McHenry 2007). An analysis of the relative limb strength of OH 62 indicates that *Homo habilis*, while fully bipedal when on the ground, engaged in frequent arboreal locomotion (Ruff 2008). Similarly, analysis of the left foot of OH 8, originally uncovered in 1960, has revealed that while *Homo habilis* was an obligate biped, it retained some features characteristic of arboreal adaptation (Susman 2008).[2] Body mass estimates for these hominins range from 33 kg to 48 kg (Antón 2012); stature estimates range from 118 cm to 145 cm (Antón 2012).

As noted above, the first *Homo habilis* fossils were found in deposits that also yielded stone tools, and it is generally agreed that they were the makers of these tools, an assumption based primarily on their larger brain. Hand bones have been recovered from Olduvai, although uncertainty remains regarding whether they belonged to *Homo habilis* or *P. boisei* (Tocheri et al. 2008). Morphological studies of these bones have revealed a combination of primitive and derived features, suggesting that these hominins did not manipulate objects in the same way that we do (Tocheri et al. 2003).

FIGURE 10.5 KNM-ER 1470 has a cranial capacity of about 750 cc and is thought by some to represent *Homo rudolfensis*.

One Species or Two?

Fossils discovered in the early 1970s at Koobi Fora were initially interpreted as representing *Homo habilis* based on similarities with fossils found at Olduvai. One of the most complete skulls (KNM-ER 1470; Figure 10.5), however, stood out as having a larger cranial capacity (750 cc) than other early *Homo* fossils from Koobi Fora and elsewhere. This led to speculation that more than one species of *Homo* was represented in the fossil record from East Africa, and this specimen was subsequently classified as *Homo rudolfensis* (Groves 1989; Wood 1991, 1993).[3] Additional fossils have since been assigned to this taxon based on their larger cranial capacities and other features (Schrenk et al. 2007 summarize this evidence). While the majority of *Homo rudolfensis* fossils uncovered to date come

---

2. This fossil has more recently been identified as belonging to the same individual as OH 7 (Susman 2008).

3. The name *rudolfensis* was coined by Russian paleontologist V.A. Alexeev, who identified KNM-ER 1470 as *Pithecanthropus rudolfensis* (Alexeev 1986).

from Koobi Fora and date to approximately 1.8 Ma, fossilized remains of this species, including the body of a mandible (UR 501) found in a "corridor" known as the Malawi Rift (Schrenk et al. 1993) and a temporal bone (KNM-BC 1) uncovered at the site of Chemeron in Kenya (Hill et al. 1992; Prat et al. 2005), extend its time range back to nearly 2.5 Ma. While the taxonomic status of KNM-ER 1470 remains uncertain, the analysis of three newly discovered fossils from Koobi Fora dating between 1.78 and 1.95 Ma confirms the presence of two contemporaneous species of early *Homo* in early Pleistocene East Africa (Leakey et al. 2012).

BEHAVIOURAL ADAPTATIONS

The First Stone Tools

As noted earlier in this chapter, *Homo habilis* was so-named because its remains were first found in a deposit that also yielded stone tools. Representing the **Oldowan industry**, the earliest of these **Lower Paleolithic** tools come from the 2.6-million-year-old site of Gona in Ethiopia (Semaw et al. 2003). Consisting of pebble tools and choppers made of quartz, chert, or flint (Figure 10.6), their method of manufacture was by percussion, which involved striking one stone with another to make a cutting edge. Flakes chipped off during this process were also used as tools.

To an untrained eye, some of these implements look like any other rock or pebble. Indeed, naturally shaped stones have often been mistaken for tools. To the trained eye, however, a number of clues indicate that these stones were, in fact, modified and used by hominins. While we do not know for certain whether these hominins were australopithecines or *Homo habilis*, stone tools have been found elsewhere in East Africa in association with early *Homo* remains, for example, in the Hadar region of Ethiopia (Kimbel et al. 1996). At other sites such as Olduvai, dense concentrations of stones suggest that human activity such as food processing or tool manufacturing may have taken place at these locations. Some of these sites have been interpreted as home bases, to which hominins returned repeatedly with tools and carcasses (Isaac 1978). In addition, tools made of stone not local to the area suggest that hominins intentionally transported the material from elsewhere, indicating planning and foresight. **Quarrying sites** characterized by a large number of stone tools have been identified archaeologically in East Africa.

Oldowan industry
the earliest stone tool industry, characterized by pebble and chopping tools made and used by early hominins

Lower Paleolithic
the period associated with the Oldowan and Acheulian stone tool industries

quarrying sites
sites from which hominins obtained raw materials to make stone tools

FIGURE 10.6 These Oldowan chopping tools were found in Olduvai Gorge.

© Lithic Casting Lab/Peter Bostrom

Using **experimental archaeology**, attempts have been made to determine how these tools were used. More specifically, paleoanthropologists have endeavoured to make and use stone tools in order to understand how early hominins may have done the same. Louis Leakey himself butchered animals using tools he had made (Jones 1980). Also, microscopic wear on the cutting edges of tools has been examined to assess tool use. Such studies suggest that Oldowan tools were likely used to process carcasses and to extract marrow from the bones of animals that had been either hunted or scavenged. At some butchering sites tools have been found in association with animal bones exhibiting cut marks.

Unfortunately, our knowledge of the role of tools in food acquisition and processing is limited, as tools made of perishable materials such as wood have not been preserved in the Lower Paleolithic archaeological record (Ungar et al. 2006a, 219). Based on our observations of modern great apes, however, early hominins would almost certainly have used such tools for acquiring and processing food. Perhaps they also used sticks to fish for termites or capture small mammals, as some chimpanzees do today.

Dietary Adaptations

Hunting and the consumption of meat have long been viewed as playing a significant role in human evolution. In the 1960s and 1970s, hunting models emphasizing the role of males were pervasive in the literature (see Chapter 8). Such models presented scenarios in which the introduction of stone tools led to the increased consumption of meat. This in turn resulted in the expansion of the brain and, consequently, more sophisticated tool kits, more efficient hunting techniques, and further expansion of the brain. We have already mentioned that Oldowan tools have been found with animal bones at a number of early *Homo* sites, pointing to the consumption of meat, a practice that (as noted in Chapter 9) was introduced likely with *Au. afarensis* c. 3.4 Ma.

As you learned in Chapter 6, chimpanzees in the wild today form intentional hunting parties and capture a variety of small mammals, including other primates. Similarly, archaeologists have long assumed that hominins obtained animals through hunting. Microscopic studies of animal bones found at early *Homo* sites, however, have revealed evidence consistent with scavenging in the form of hominin-made cut marks superimposed on carnivore tooth marks, and cut marks located on bones that would have yielded little meat (i.e., those left behind by carnivores) (Shipman 1986).

Challenges to the "Man the Hunter" model have also come from studies of modern-day hunter–gatherers. Among such groups, a greater proportion of their diet consists of plant foods than meat, and most of these plant foods are gathered by women. This observation has prompted researchers to develop alternatives, termed "Woman the Gatherer" models, which emphasize plant consumption among early hominins. O'Connell and colleagues (1999), for example, have argued that underground plant resources such as roots and tubers[4] may have been a key component of the diet of early *Homo* and would have been more abundant over the last 2.5 million years. Similarly, Wrangham and colleagues (1999) argue that plants would have been a vital food resource, especially in times of food shortages, as fallback foods.

Direct evidence for what early *Homo* actually consumed comes from the fossils themselves. In Chapter 7 we talked about the various ways in which the diet of fossil primates can be reconstructed. These include examining molar tooth shape, enamel thickness, and dental microwear. As noted above, early *Homo* had larger incisors and smaller molars than the australopithecines. These differences suggest that their diet involved greater use of the anterior teeth and the consumption of foods that required lighter chewing forces, although this dental trend is difficult to evaluate without larger sample sizes and more precise estimates of body weight (Ungar et al. 2006a, 219). Tooth shape—more specifically, the amount of relief on the chewing surfaces (i.e., **occlusal relief**)—can also provide information on the types of foods consumed. Species that rely on tough foods such as leaves, for example, tend to have greater

---

4. Tubers are also known as "underground storage organs."

occlusal relief (i.e. more jagged teeth with higher cusps) than those that rely on hard foods such as nuts and seeds.

Tooth shape can be examined using **dental topographic analysis**. This technique involves using a laser scanner to generate 3D models of teeth and geographic information system (GIS) software to measure features on the surface of those teeth. The application of this method to the teeth of *Au. afarensis* and early *Homo* has revealed that the latter had greater occlusal relief than the former, suggesting that early *Homo* relied on tougher, more elastic (i.e., deformable) foods than their predecessors (Ungar 2004).

The use of dental microwear to reconstruct diet (see Chapter 7) is based on the observation that the consumption of hard objects such as nuts and seeds tends to produce large pits on the enamel surfaces, whereas the consumption of tough foods such as leaves tends to result in smaller pits and more striations. In contrast, species that consume soft fruits tend to have microwear patterns that fall somewhere in between (Teaford 1988; Teaford and Walker 1984). Ungar and colleagues (2006b) examined dental microwear in a sample of 18 early *Homo* teeth from East and South Africa, and compared it to that seen in five extant primate species and two protohistoric human foraging groups. Their analysis revealed that the early *Homo* specimens had a higher prevalence of intermediate microwear pits than the other groups, pointing to the consumption of a more varied diet.

Chemical analysis of early *Homo* fossils has also pointed to a generalized diet for these hominins. One type of analysis that has been used to reconstruct the diet of past populations, including hominins, is **stable isotope analysis** of the carbon and nitrogen atoms in bones and teeth (Sponheimer et al. 2013). In contrast to traditional sources of dietary information such as faunal remains, which provide information on the range of animal foods available, stable isotope analysis of **collagen** and **apatite** provides direct evidence of the types of foods that were actually eaten. This technique is based on the fact that the **isotopic signatures** of foods consumed are reflected in the tissues of the consumer and thus provide a record of their dietary intake over a period of time. More specifically, isotopic analysis of collagen provides information on an individual's intake of dietary protein over a period of 10 years or more, whereas isotopic analysis of carbonate provides a profile of the carbon isotopes in the total diet (i.e., fats, proteins, and carbohydrates).

Underlying the use of stable carbon isotope analysis to reconstruct diet is the fact that the ratio of the stable carbon isotopes ^{13}C and ^{12}C, expressed as a $\delta^{13}C$ value in parts per thousand, or per mil (‰), differs among different types of plant foods (Figure 10.7). Individuals who consume primarily C_3 plants (most temperate region plants) have lower $\delta^{13}C$ values than those who consume a diet rich in C_4 plants (e.g., maize and millet). In addition, individuals who rely primarily on terrestrial resources have lower $\delta^{13}C$ values than those who consume a predominantly marine diet. In contrast, dietary reconstruction using stable nitrogen isotope analysis looks at the ratio of the stable isotopes ^{15}N to ^{14}N,

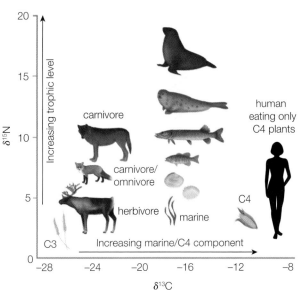

Stable carbon and nitrogen isotopic composition of different organisms

FIGURE 10.7 Reconstructing the diet of past populations involves comparing isotope values measured in humans with those derived from a range of plants and animals from the environment in which those humans lived.

Documenta Praehistorica 25 volume 1998 (p 205). Used with permission.

dental topographic analysis

a method of analysis that involves using a laser scanner to generate 3D models of teeth and GIS to measure features on the surfaces of those teeth

stable isotope analysis

a type of chemical analysis that looks at stable isotopes of certain elements in bones and other tissues of the body; it can tell us something about the diet and residential history of an individual

collagen

a type of protein that forms the main organic component of bone

apatite

the major inorganic component of bones and teeth

isotopic signatures

refers to the ratio of stable isotopes of a particular element, for example, $^{13}C/^{12}C$; this is expressed as $\delta^{13}C$ in per mil (‰)

expressed as a $\delta^{15}N$ value in per mil (‰). These values principally reflect trophic level, or the position of an organism in the food chain. Thus carnivores have higher $\delta^{15}N$ values than herbivores. Also, humans who obtain most of their dietary protein from high trophic-level marine foods (large fish, seals, etc.) have higher $\delta^{15}N$ values than those who rely primarily on terrestrial protein sources (Figure 10.7). With respect to early *Homo*, stable isotope analyses of tooth enamel taken from East and South African specimens have revealed a predominantly C_3 diet that may have included fruits, nuts, leaves, and animals that feed on these foods, with the addition of some C_4 foods such as grass-eating vertebrates and insects—a pattern also seen in *P. robustus* but distinct from *P. boisei* (Lee-Thorp et al. 2000; van Der Merwe et al. 2008).

In summary, data derived from the fossil and archaeological record point to increasing dietary versatility with the appearance of *Homo* (Ungar et al. 2006a). This observation is consistent with paleoenvironmental reconstruction of East and South Africa during the early Pleistocene, which indicates climatic changes leading to the spread of grasslands and an associated increase in grassland-adapted mammals. Exploitation of this broader range of food resources would have been facilitated by the use of tools made of stone and other materials.

HOMO ERECTUS: ENIGMA OR ARCHETYPE?

An Anatomy for All Occasions

The early Pleistocene marked the emergence in Africa of a third species of *Homo* that possessed a larger brain and body and a more modern-looking postcranial skeleton than *Homo habilis* and *Homo rudolfensis*. Known as *Homo erectus*, this species had a cranial capacity ranging from about 700 to 1,200 cc, with an average of 900 cc, an increase of more than 30% over *Homo habilis* (Figure 10.8). This larger brain was housed in a skull that was uniquely

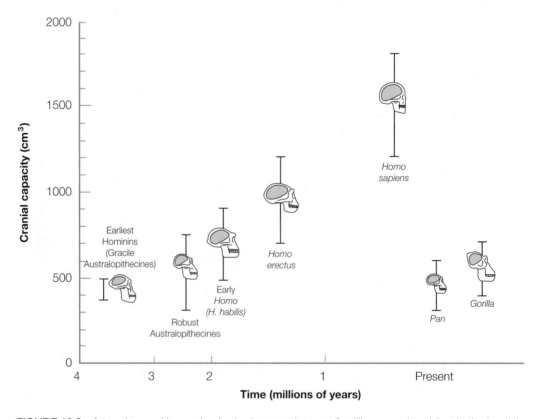

FIGURE 10.8 A trend toward increasing brain size over the past 2 million years is evident in the hominin fossil record.

Homo erectus. Cranial characteristics included a long, low vault, a low sloping forehead, a pentagonal shape when viewed from the rear, a somewhat projecting face, a heavily built jaw with smaller incisors and smaller molars than *Homo habilis*, **shovel-shaped incisors**, a **sagittal keel**, a heavy **supraorbital torus** or browridge, and an **occipital torus** that served to anchor large neck muscles (Figure 10.9).

Far fewer postcranial remains belonging to *Homo erectus* have been recovered than crania, so our knowledge of the postcranial anatomy of these hominins comes mainly from only a handful of specimens. These suggest that *Homo erectus* had a significantly larger body than earlier hominins, as well as modern body proportions with longer legs that would have allowed them to expand their foraging range and cover greater distances more efficiently. Body mass estimates range from approximately 40 kg to 65 kg (Antón 2012); stature estimates range from 155 cm to 179 cm (Antón 2012). This transition to a larger body size occurred rapidly and likely reflects a shift to a more nutritious diet that included even greater amounts of meat than eaten by previous hominins.

Homo erectus in Africa

Homo erectus fossils dating between 1.9 and 1.0 Ma have been recovered in both East and South Africa (Figures 10.10–10.12 and Table 10.1). Fossilized footprints, found in 1.5-Ma-old sediments at Ileret, Kenya, and representing the earliest evidence of an essentially modern foot, may also belong to *Homo erectus* (Bennett et al. 2009).

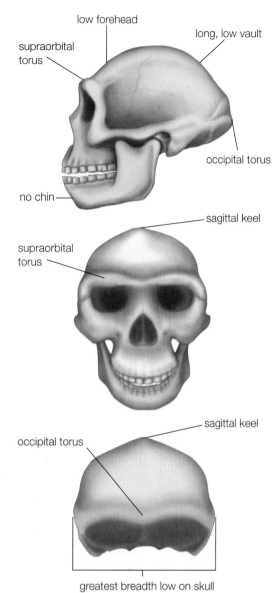

shovel-shaped incisors
front teeth with marginal ridges of enamel on the lingual (tongue) surface

sagittal keel
a raised area of bone running along the sagittal suture

supraorbital torus
a ridge of bone running across the top of the eyes; also referred to as the browridge

occipital torus
a horizontal ridge of bone running across the occipital bone

FIGURE 10.9 *Homo erectus* had a larger cranial capacity than earlier hominins as well as cranial features that included a large supraorbital torus, a sagittal keel, and an occipital torus.

The best-known African *Homo erectus* fossil found to date is the nearly complete skeleton (KNM-WT 15000)[5] of an adolescent male estimated to have been 11 to 12 years of age or possibly younger when he died (Figure 10.13). Found at the site of Nariokotome on the western shore of Lake Turkana, the skeleton, nicknamed "Turkana Boy," has been dated to 1.6 Ma, making it among the oldest *Homo erectus* fossils found to date in Africa (Walker and Leakey 1993). Besides being in an excellent state of preservation, a particularly striking feature of this individual at the time of his discovery was his stature; he was estimated to have been around 160 cm tall when he died and would have reached 185 cm had he lived to adulthood (Ruff and Walker 1993) (but see the next paragraph). Also, the body proportions of this individual more closely resemble those of later *Homo.* In particular, a lengthening

---

5. KNM-WT denotes Kenya National Museum West Turkana.

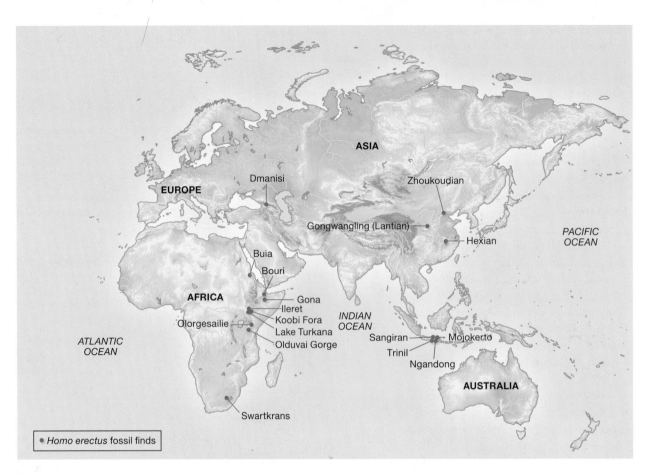

FIGURE 10.10 Locations where *Homo erectus* fossils have been found.

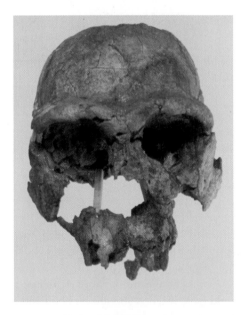

FIGURE 10.11 KNM-ER 3733 dates to approximately 1.8 Ma, making it one of the oldest *Homo erectus* fossils in the world.

© John Reader/Science Photo Library

FIGURE 10.12 The calvarium of Olduvai hominin 9 resembles that of Asian *Homo erectus* in having a pronounced supraorbital torus.

© John Reader/Science Photo Library

TABLE 10.1 Partial list of *Homo erectus* fossils found in East and South Africa.

Fossil ID	Bone	Location	Date (Ma)
KNM-ER 2598	Occipital fragment	Lake Turkana	1.89
KNM-ER 3733	Skull	Koobi Fora	1.8
BSN49/P27	Pelvis	Gona, Ethiopia	1.8
KNM-ER 992	Mandible	Koobi Fora	1.5
KNM-ER 42700	Cranium	Ileret, Kenya	1.5
SK 847	Cranium	Swartkrans	1.5
"Daka"	Cranium	Bouri, Ethiopia	1.0
UA 31	Cranium	Buia, Eritrea	1.0
OH 9	Cranium	Olduvai Gorge	1.5

of the lower limbs points to a more efficient striding gait, meaning that *Homo erectus* would have been able to cover long distances more efficiently as increased lower limb length decreases the energy costs of walking and running. The long, linear body build and increased surface area from which to dissipate heat (see Chapter 14) also indicate that *Homo erectus* was well adapted to the hot African climate and may have been more active during the midday.

The discovery of the Nariokotome skeleton also provided scientists with a rare opportunity to study the life history of *Homo erectus*. An analysis by Dean and colleagues (2001) of the timing of formation of the anterior tooth crowns of this adolescent revealed a rate of growth closer to that of great apes than to modern humans, suggesting that this individual developed more rapidly than we do. Similarly, Smith's (2004) examination of skeletal and dental indicators of growth in the skeleton, including the length of the **diaphyses**, the degree of fusion of the **epiphyses**,[6] and the degree of formation of the teeth, revealed a marked difference between the skeletal and dental age of this individual, also pointing to a more rapid rate of development than that seen in modern humans. A subsequent study has confirmed that this individual followed a pattern of growth and development that was different from that of modern *Homo sapiens*. More specifically, his adolescent growth spurt (which modern humans associate with puberty) was determined to have been of shorter duration and lesser magnitude than that of modern humans. As a result, he would have reached an adult stature of only about 163 cm (5 feet, 4 inches), not 185 cm (6 feet, 1 inch) as previously estimated (Graves et al. 2010).

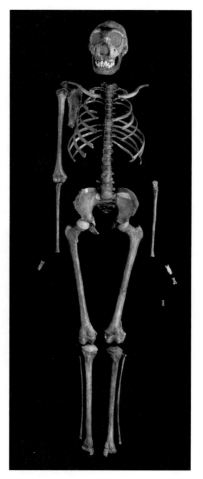

FIGURE 10.13 KNM-WT 15000 is remarkable for its state of preservation and degree of completeness.

Artifact credit: National Museums of Kenya, Nairobi. Copyright protection notice: © 1985 David L. Brill\Brill Atlanta

diaphyses
the shafts of the long bones

epiphyses
the caps at the ends of the long bones; bone growth ceases when the epiphyses fuse to the diaphysis

---

6. The growth of the long bones occurs in the region between the epiphysis and the diaphysis. Once the epiphysis fuses to the diaphysis, growth ceases.

CHAPTER 10 The Emergence of the Genus *Homo*

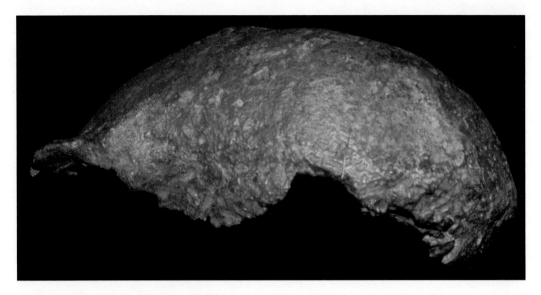

FIGURE 10.14 This skull cap was discovered by Eugène Dubois near the village of Trinil on the island of Java.

Homo erectus in Indonesia

The discovery of *Homo erectus* fossils in Indonesia dates back to 1891; indeed, in the history of fossil discoveries they are among the first hominin fossils to be found. At that time a young Dutch physician named Eugène Dubois came to Java to look for the remains of early humans, whom he believed had originated in Asia. His excavations near the village of Trinil on the Solo River (refer back to Figure 10.10) yielded a skullcap (Figure 10.14) with a low, sloping forehead and a heavy browridge, as well as a modern-looking femur that he thought belonged to the same individual. In 1894 he announced his new species, *Pithecanthropus erectus* ("erect ape-man"), more popularly known as Java Man. The Trinil fossils were subsequently classified as *Homo erectus* (Mayr 1950).

The earliest *Homo erectus* remains in Asia come from the site of Mojokerto, which has yielded a juvenile cranium dating to 1.8 Ma (Swisher et al. 1994).[7] Other early *Homo erectus* fossils, including the most complete cranium found in Java, have been uncovered at the site of Sangiran (Figure 10.15), from deposits dating between 1.7 and 1.0 Ma. The site of Ngandong, first excavated in the early 1930s, has also yielded a rich array of *Homo erectus* fossils, including twelve crania initially labelled *Homo soloensis*. Their remarkably late date, ranging from 46,000 to 27,000 years ago (Swisher et al. 1996) suggests that *Homo erectus* survived in Java long after they had disappeared elsewhere in Asia, perhaps due to their relative isolation and differing subsistence base.

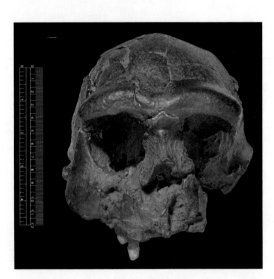

FIGURE 10.15 This cranium, known as Sangiran 17, is the most complete *Homo erectus* skull that has been found in East Asia. It exhibits a long, low cranium and large supraorbital torus.

7. Originally classified as *Homo mojokertensis*, this specimen is now recognized as *Homo erectus*.

Homo erectus in China

The earliest Chinese fossils identified as *Homo erectus* come from the site of Gongwangling in Lantian county, Shaanxi province (refer back to Figure 10.10), and date to 1.2 Ma, although the discovery in northern China of stone tools and butchered bones may extend the range of *Homo erectus* to nearly 1.7 Ma (Zhu et al. 2004). Later *Homo erectus* fossils include the Hexian cranium, with an estimated age of approximately 412 kya (Grün et al. 1998).

The largest and best-known sample of *Homo erectus* fossils comes from the site of Zhoukoudian (also referred to as Choukoutien) near Beijing. First excavated in 1921, the site has yielded the remains of approximately 40 individuals and more than 100,000 stone tools and other artifacts spanning hundreds of thousands of years. Detailed studies of the fossil assemblage were made by Canadian anatomist Davidson Black, who assigned the taxonomic name *Sinanthropus pekinensis* to the fossils (Black 1931b; Box 10.1). These studies were continued by his successor, the eminent German anatomist Franz

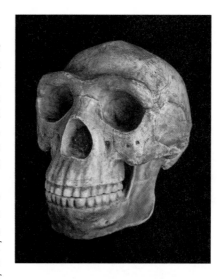

FIGURE 10.16 This *Homo erectus* skull, recovered from the site of Zhoukoudian, was reconstructed in 1937 by anatomist Franz Weidenreich.

© The Natural History Museum/Alamy

Weidenreich, who produced a series of superb descriptions and casts of the fossils (Figure 10.16). The deposits in which the Zhoukoudian remains, commonly referred to as "Peking Man," but later reclassified as *Homo erectus*, were found have been dated from about 300,000 to 600,000 years ago using electron spin resonance, paleomagnetism, and biostratigraphy. While the *Homo erectus* crania from China resemble those from Indonesia with respect to vault size and shape, differences are evident in the shape of the supraorbital torus and the degree of facial prognathism. Specifically, the Chinese specimens possess supraorbital tori that are straighter when viewed from above and less prognathic faces (Antón 2003).

One of the greatest mysteries in paleoanthropology concerns the disappearance of the Zhoukoudian fossils prior to the outbreak of World War II. The Japanese invasion of China in 1937 prompted researchers to pack up the fossil remains in preparation for shipping them to the United States for safekeeping. Somewhere along the route, however, the precious cargo disappeared, and their whereabouts remain unknown to this day. Fortunately, the detailed descriptions, drawings, and casts made by Weidenreich of all of the original *Homo erectus* fossils found at the site have enabled continued study of this material. Still, the mystery has been the subject of great speculation as well as fodder for popular culture.[8]

Homo erectus in Georgia

Early *Homo erectus* remains dating to 1.8 Ma have been recovered from an early Pleistocene site lying below medieval ruins at the site of Dmanisi in the Republic of Georgia (refer back to Figure 10.10). These include five crania, four mandibles, and postcranial remains (Gabunia and Vekua 1995; Gabunia et al. 2000; Lordkipanidze et al. 2013; Vekua et al. 2002). Thousands of faunal bones and a large number of Oldowan-like stone tools have also been found at this site. Resembling early *Homo erectus* specimens from Africa, the Dmanisi fossils exhibit cranial capacities ranging from 546 to 730 cc and large prognathic

---

8. Canadian writer Robert J. Sawyer won Canada's top science fiction award for his 1996 short story "Peking Man," which links the disappearance of the fossils to Bram Stoker's *Dracula*.

BOX 10.1   PROFILE ... Davidson Black

Courtesy of Julie Cormack

Davidson Black (Figure 10.17) was born on July 25, 1884, in Toronto. As a young man he was a keen naturalist, spending many hours exploring and later working (with the Hudson's Bay Company) in the lake districts north of Toronto, or wandering the forests and valleys of the city's hinterlands identifying and collecting zoological specimens, especially birds. He was a skilled artist, having earned three drawing certificates from the Provincial Art School—a talent that prepared him well for his eventual training in medicine and later for a career in anthropology. He suffered from the same congenital weak heart as his father (who died at age 49, when Davidson was two years old), an ailment that became further stressed one winter when Davidson contracted rheumatic fever. During his extended convalescence, he realized that his career path would be medicine and not the family profession—law—that his mother wished for him.

FIGURE 10.17 Canadian anatomist Davidson Black.

Courtesy of the Becker Medical Library, Washington University School of Medicine.

In 1906 he graduated from the University of Toronto with a bachelor's degree in medicine (M.B.). He immediately returned to that university to acquire a Bachelor of Arts (B.A.) degree, which he was awarded in 1911 (after a slight delay because he had not completed his German language classes). Before graduating, Davidson accepted a post as lecturer at Western Reserve University in Cleveland, Ohio, where he taught neurology. During a sabbatical visit to Europe, just as the clouds of World War I were beginning to darken, he had the pleasure of handling the newly discovered Piltdown Man fossils from southern England, today known to be forgeries (a human cranium with an orangutan lower jaw). That experience convinced him that anthropology, not medicine, would be an exciting field to pursue. In 1918 he was offered a teaching post at the newly established Rockefeller-funded Peking Union Medical College (PUMC) in Beijing, China, and he and his wife left Canada for an unknown future. Black had been hired as Professor of Embryology and Neurology but quickly found himself engrossed in the analysis of numerous human skeletal finds made by his Swedish colleague, J.G. Andersson. He was slowly leaving behind his medical teaching responsibilities in order to explore local caves in search of human remains. In 1922 he joined Roy Chapman Andrews's Central Asiatic Expedition to Mongolia.

Since 1919, animal fossils had been found at limestone quarries in the Western Hills southwest of Beijing. Within a couple of years, Andersson had arranged a small excavation there. Three teeth were found, and Black, as the resident anatomist, was asked to identify them. He recognized them as "human," and with a German-American geologist, Amadeus Grabau, he assigned them the name *Sinanthropus pekinensis* ("China Man from Peking"). The discovery of human fossils and (later) thousands of stone artifacts and animal bones placed the Zhoukoudian caves on the world's anthropological map. Black was responsible for identifying and publishing descriptions of the Zhoukoudian human remains, today known as our 500,000-year-old direct human ancestor—*Homo erectus*.

Black was very comfortable with the Chinese community, and he collaborated with Chinese scientists such as Wong Wenhao and Ding Wenjiang of the National Geological Survey of China to establish the Cenozoic Research Laboratory (the foundation of the present-day Institute of Vertebrate Paleontology and Paleoanthropology). Black was also the administrative liaison between the Rockefeller Foundation that funded the Zhoukoudian program and the international multidisciplinary research team (of Chinese, Swedish, French, Austrian, and Canadian experts) that was responsible for excavation and scientific analyses.

But Black's contributions were cut short: on March 15, 1934, at the height of his work at Zhoukoudian, he died at age 49 of congenital heart failure. Within a year, his position at the PUMC had been taken up by a German-American anthropologist, Franz Weidenreich. Then in 1937, during the Japanese invasion of Manchuria, excavations stopped. In 1941, with hostilities worsening, attempts were made to transfer the Peking Man fossils out of the capital. After leaving the PUMC's vaults, they vanished. Their location remains unknown to this day. (For further details, see Cormack 2000, 2003; Tobias et al. 2000, 2001).

Source: Written by Julie Cormack, Mount Royal University, Calgary.

faces (Figure 10.18). Their postcranial remains, which include the partial skeleton of an adolescent and the remains of three adults, exhibit a combination of primitive and derived features, including small body size (a primitive trait) and modern human-like limb proportions and lower limb morphology (derived traits) (Lordkipanidze et al. 2007). An analysis of the locomotor mechanics of the Dmanisi hind limb has revealed that it was functionally similar to that of modern humans, reflecting improved walking and running performance compared to earlier hominins (Pontzer et al. 2010). As the authors of this study point out, this finding is consistent with the hypothesis that among early *Homo*, hunting, scavenging, or both selected for increased efficiency in walking and running.

The morphological heterogeneity of the Dmanisi assemblage has resulted in a lack of consensus—even among those who have excavated and studied them—regarding the taxonomic status of these fossils. Similarities between these specimens and those from the Turkana Basin in Kenya prompted Gabunia and colleagues (2000) to label them *Homo ergaster*, and later *Homo georgicus* (Gabunia et al. 2002).

FIGURE 10.18 This cranium (D-2700), found in 2001 at the site of Dmanisi in the Republic of Georgia, has a cranial capacity of about 600 cc and resembles some African *Homo erectus* specimens.

© Guran Tsibakhashvili

A subsequent analysis revealed some resemblance to *Homo erectus* fossils from Sangiran, suggesting that the Dmanisi hominins may belong to this taxon (Rightmire, Lordkipanidze, and Vekua 2006). The recent analysis of a complete cranium recovered from the site expands the range of variation seen in these hominins and points to the existence of a single evolving lineage of early *Homo* (Lordkipanidze et al. 2013, 326).

One Species or Two?

Homo erectus was remarkable not only for its significantly larger brain and body compared to earlier hominins, but also for the fact that it was the first hominin to leave Africa for other parts of the Old World (discussed later in this chapter). Given the widespread geographic distribution of *Homo erectus*, it is not surprising that considerable regional variation is evident in the fossils that have been found to date. Some paleoanthropologists (e.g., Jacob 2001) have argued for the identification of *Homo erectus* fossils from Africa as a separate species, *Homo ergaster* (Groves and Mazek 1975), distinct from *Homo erectus* in Asia (Wood 1991), based on morphological differences between the two. As noted above, however, the addition of the Dmanisi fossils strengthens the argument for a single evolving lineage of early *Homo* rather than multiple species (Lordkipanidze et al. 2013).

BEHAVIOURAL ADAPTATIONS

Technological Leaps and Bounds

The earliest *Homo erectus* fossils are associated with Oldowan tools. However, about 1.5 Ma, a new Lower Paleolithic stone tool industry known as the **Acheulian** appears in the African archaeological record. This industry was characterized by a greater variety of artifact types, notably **bifacial tools**, meaning that flakes were removed from both sides of the tool, resulting in more "cutting edge" than the earlier Oldowan tools had. The principal

Acheulian
a Lower Paleolithic stone tool industry usually associated with *Homo erectus*

bifacial tool
a stone tool that has had flakes removed from opposite sides to produce a cutting edge

FIGURE 10.19 Acheulian stone tools included hand axes and cleavers. The reproduction hand axe seen here measures approximately 12 cm in length.

Courtesy of Anne Keenleyside

Courtesy of Anne Keenleyside

hand axe
a teardrop-shaped stone tool characteristic of the Acheulian industry

Acheulian tool was the **hand axe** (Figure 10.19), a teardrop-shaped tool whose functions may have included butchering animals, digging roots, cutting wood, and processing plants. Some researchers have also posited that hand axes were thrown at animals to kill them. The Acheulian toolkit also included cleavers and scrapers, which may have been used to butcher carcasses and remove meat from the bones.

We noted in the previous section that considerable regional variation is evident in the *Homo erectus* fossils that have been found to date. Similarly, technological differences also characterized this species. For instance, simple Oldowan-like choppers and flake tools, such as those found at Zhoukoudian, tend to occur more frequently at *Homo erectus* sites in Asia, while Acheulian hand axes are more common in Africa. Some paleoanthropologists have viewed this difference as indicative of cognitive differences among *Homo erectus;* others see it as more likely reflecting environmental differences. For instance, the presence in the Far East of dense forests of bamboo, which may have been made into tools (Pope 1989), might explain the smaller number of Acheulian hand axes in this region compared to Africa.

The more advanced cognitive abilities of *Homo erectus* compared to earlier hominins are also reflected in their presumed presence on islands separated from the mainland by large bodies of water. Stone tools and faunal remains dating between 800,000 and 880,000 years ago have been recovered from deposits on the island of Flores. At that time, the island would have been separated from the mainland by at least 19 km of water. This suggests that these hominins must have had some type of watercraft in order to reach Flores (Morwood et al. 1998).[9]

9. The ability to make and use watercraft has generally been attributed to modern humans, who are believed to have used them to colonize Australia some 40,000 to 60,000 years ago.

Finally, *Homo erectus* appears to have been the first hominin to use fire, although the evidence for this at some sites has been debated. Early reports of the archaeological excavations at Zhoukoudian in China, for instance, noted the presence of ash deposits and interpreted them as evidence for the use of fire (Black 1931a). Subsequent analyses of these deposits, however, revealed that while there is evidence of fire at the site in the form of burned bones, there is "no direct evidence for in situ burning" (i.e., hearths) by hominins (Weiner et al. 1998, 253).[10] Thermally altered patches of clay, stone artifacts, and/or animal bones have been found at Koobi Fora (Bellomo 1994), Chesowanja (Gowlett et al. 1981), and Swartkrans (Brain and Sillent 1988), suggesting the use of fire by *Homo erectus* by 1.6 Ma, but again critics have argued that either the burned remains are not in their original context or were the result of bush fires naturally ignited by lightning strikes or volcanic activity (Roberts and Bird 2012; Roebroeks and Villa 2011).

More compelling evidence in the form of burned bone and plant remains has been found in 1-million-year-old sediments at the site of Wonderwerk Cave in South Africa, analyzed using both microscopic and molecular techniques (Berna et al. 2012), and at the Acheulian site of Gesher Benot Ya`aqov in Israel, where burned seeds, wood, and flint suggesting the repeated use of fire have been found in deposits dating to nearly 790,000 years ago (Goren-Inbar et al. 2004). There is no archaeological evidence, however, that *Homo erectus* had the ability to make fire, and we do not see any evidence for the habitual use of fire until much later in time, after the appearance of Neandertals and early modern humans (Roebroeks and Villa 2011; see Chapter 12).

Fire would have had numerous benefits for *Homo erectus*. It would have provided them with light, heat, and protection from predators; it would also have allowed them to cook their food. This has important implications in terms of morphological and behavioural changes (see Chapter 8). Because cooking makes it easier to digest food, it increases the body's net energy gain and may have contributed to an increase in brain size and a reduction in tooth and gut size among *Homo erectus* (Aiello and Wheeler 1995; Wrangham and Carmody 2010). It may also have allowed these hominins to expand the range of plant foods in their diet (Wrangham et al. 1999, 568). For later hominins, fire would have facilitated the hafting of stone artifacts as well by allowing adhesives to be heated (Roebroeks and Villa 2011).

The First Big-Game Hunters?

The evolution and dispersal of *Homo erectus* has long been linked to big-game hunting. Archaeological evidence commonly cited as proof of hunting by these hominins is the association of stone tools with the remains of large animals, many of them with cut marks. At the 600,000-year-old to 1-Ma-old site of Olorgesailie in Kenya (Figure 10.20), for example, concentrations of Acheulian tools have been found together with the bones of baboons, elephants, hippos, and other mammals, suggesting that *Homo erectus* used these tools to kill and butcher these animals. Some of the evidence for big-game hunting prior to 500,000 years ago has been re-evaluated, and taphonomic alterations and/or hominin scavenging appear to account for some of the assemblages seen at these sites. Nevertheless, evidence for the importance of meat in the *Homo erectus* diet is certainly more compelling than it is for *H. habilis* and *H. rudolfensis*, and meat would have provided some of the calories needed to fuel the larger brain and body size of these hominins. As noted in the discussion of "Energetics" in Chapter 8, however, high-carbohydrate foods such as tubers and seeds would likely have comprised additional sources of energy, and dental studies of early *Homo erectus* specimens from Africa and Georgia indicate a broader diet compared to that of australopithecines, one that persisted relatively unchanged as *Homo erectus* expanded into Eurasia (Pontzer et al. 2011; Ungar 2012).

---

10. Chemical analysis of the so-called ash layers revealed no evidence of silica particles that would be found if wood had been burned (Weiner et al. 1998).

FIGURE 10.20 At the site of Olorgesailie in Kenya, dozens of Acheulian hand axes and other tools were found in association with the butchered remains of elephants, hippos, baboons, and other animals.

© Carolina Biological/Corbis

The First Voyager: Hominins Out of Africa

It is widely assumed that *Homo erectus* was the first hominin to leave Africa. This is based on features that would have allowed it to migrate out of Africa, including long limbs, modern body proportions, and a larger brain than earlier hominins. The discovery of *Homo erectus* fossils in the Republic of Georgia and in Indonesia dating to 1.8 Ma indicates that this migration occurred far earlier than previously thought and that these hominins dispersed rapidly across Asia (Figure 10.21). Dispersal rates have been calculated for *Homo erectus* based on demographic and reproductive variables derived from extant mammals and fossil taxa (human and nonhuman) from Europe, Africa, and Asia (Antón, Leonard, and Robertson 2002). Among mammals, a strong correlation exists between body size, diet, and home range size, such that larger body size and greater consumption of meat are associated with a greater home range. The latter, in turn, is related to dispersal capability. A computer simulation model points to rapid multiple dispersals from Africa prior to 1.7 Ma and to rapid colonization of Southeast Asia by 1.6 Ma (Mithen and Reed 2002). The periodic advance of glaciers in the northern hemisphere during the Pleistocene meant that the sea level would have been significantly lower than it is today, allowing these hominins to walk to Java from the mainland via exposed land bridges.

Factors that may have precipitated this dispersal have been debated, and it is now generally believed that technological advances are unlikely to have been the catalyst, as the migration of *Homo erectus* out of Africa predates the emergence of Acheulian tools, suggesting that the first migrants would have relied on an Oldowan toolkit (Antón, Leonard, and Robertson 2002). Instead, biological and ecological factors—including fully developed bipedalism and a global cooling trend that resulted in the eastward migration of mammalian fauna and the opening up of new ecological niches for hominins and other animals to exploit—appear to have played a more important role.

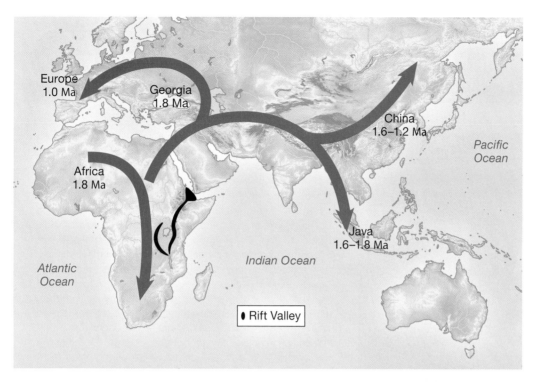

FIGURE 10.21 Map showing possible routes of dispersal taken by *Homo erectus*.

Based on Mithen, S. and Reed, M. (2002). Stepping out: a computer simulation of hominid dispersal from Africa. *Journal of Human Evolution*, 43 (4). pp. 433–462; Larsen, C. (2013). *Essentials of Physical Anthropology*. New York: W.W. Norton.

THE HOBBITS OF FLORES ISLAND

In 2003 a remarkable discovery was made in a limestone cave on the island of Flores in eastern Indonesia. The partial skeleton of a tiny adult female hominin (LB1) (Figure 10.22), nicknamed the "Hobbit" because of her small body size and large feet but formally known as *Homo floresiensis*, was uncovered from deposits that have been dated to between 95 and 17 kya. The site also yielded a variety of stone tools and animal bones representing Komodo dragon and a dwarf species of stegodon.[11] What is so striking about this skeleton is its unique combination of primitive and derived features never before seen in any hominin. Its cranial capacity, estimated at only 380 to 410 cc,[12] falls within the range of early australopithecines. Similarly, its small stature (estimated at only 1 m), its body proportions, and its primitive wrist resemble those of *Australopithecus* (Tocheri et al. 2007; see Box 10.2). Yet the shape of its brain, as revealed by three-dimensional reconstructions, resembles that of *Homo erectus*, suggesting that it possessed higher cognitive abilities than *Australopithecus*

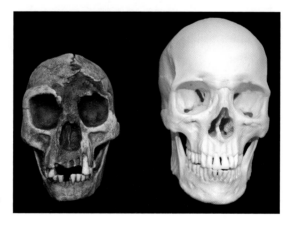

FIGURE 10.22 *Homo floresiensis* cranium (left) compared to that of *Homo sapiens* (right).

© Sabena Jane Blackbird/Alamy

11. The stegodon is an extinct mammal similar to an elephant.
12. The cranial capacity of LB1 has recently been recalculated to have been 426 cc (Kubo et al. 2013).

CHAPTER 10 The Emergence of the Genus *Homo*

BOX 10.2   PROFILE ... The Hobbits

Courtesy of Matthew Tocheri

When I was working toward my undergraduate degree in anthropology at Lakehead University during the late 1990s, I had no idea of the adventure that awaited me within a few years. After graduating from Lakehead, I headed to Arizona State University (ASU) to begin my new life as a physical anthropology graduate student. Although I went to ASU with a focus on bioarchaeology, I soon found myself more interested in research about human evolution and functional morphology. These new interests led to my doctoral dissertation research, which focused on the evolution of the wrist in hominids (humans and great apes), especially in relation to the evolution of behaviours involving tools in hominins (humans and our close fossil relatives).

Through my research, I learned that modern humans and Neandertals have differently shaped wrist bones compared to great apes and other primates. Even the handful of wrist bones from early hominins, such as *Australopithecus* and *Homo habilis*, show more similarities to African apes than they do to us and Neandertals. But just as I was preparing for my doctoral defence, something extraordinary and unexpected happened. I suddenly found myself in the same room as casts of wrist bones from *Homo floresiensis*—the so-called "Hobbits" of human evolution discovered on Flores, Indonesia, in 2003. The Hobbit remains had sparked a huge controversy in paleoanthropology, and the debates over them both at professional meetings and in the literature were extremely intense and volatile. Some researchers considered the Hobbit remains to represent a tiny species of human that went extinct roughly about 17,000 years ago; others were adamant the

remains represented nothing more than modern humans with some sort of pathology or growth disorder.

As I slid the lid off the container that held the casts, little did I realize that I was about to be transported figuratively into "Mordor" and literally into the centre of one of the biggest and most heated debates in human evolution for more than a century. What I saw inside the container is illustrated below (Figure 10.23). It was obvious: these wrist bones did not belong to a normal or pathological modern human; instead, they resembled the bones of African apes and "Lucy" (*Australopithecus afarensis*)—exactly like you would expect the wrist bones of a primitive human species to look like. The Hobbits were for real: another human species that had survived at least until 17,000 years ago, sharing this world with us as close evolutionary cousins. So there I was, joining a fellowship with a Hobbit. In return for promising to tell a part of her species' story as I now understood it from her wrist, she would help emphasize the importance of the wrist for understanding the recent evolutionary history of our own species.

This unexpected meeting soon led to a comparative study of the Hobbit wrist bones, published in *Science* (Tocheri et al. 2007; see also Larson et al. 2009). Those bones provided a key piece of evidence to support interpretations that *Homo floresiensis* was a human species distinct from modern humans and Neandertals. About a year and a half after we published our research, I travelled to Jakarta with Professor William Jungers (Stony Brook University) to work with our

Chimpanzee   Hobbit (LB1)   Modern Human

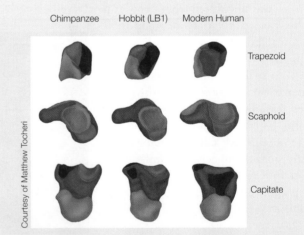

Courtesy of Matthew Tocheri

Trapezoid

Scaphoid

Capitate

FIGURE 10.23 A visual comparison of three of the Hobbit's (LB1) wrist bones scaled to the same size as those of a chimpanzee and a modern human. The colours indicate the anatomically comparable articular and nonarticular bone surfaces (see Tocheri et al. 2007 for details).

Source: Written by Matthew Tocheri, Human Origins Program, Department of Anthropology, National Museum of Natural History, Smithsonian Institution, Washington, D.C.

Indonesian colleagues at the National Center of Archaeology in Indonesia. During that visit, we searched through thousands of unidentified bone fragments recovered from the same sediments that had yielded many of the bones attributed to *Homo floresiensis*. That search recovered three additional wrist bones, all of which clearly belonged to a slightly smaller second individual but displayed the same distinctive shapes observed in the first skeleton (Orr et al. 2013).

Overall, the evidence continues to build in support of *Homo floresiensis* as a human species distinct from *Homo sapiens*, and one that likely evolved in isolation on Flores from an earlier hominin species. Recent discoveries of stone tools on Flores suggest that hominins were already present on this oceanic island as early as 1 million years ago (Brumm et al. 2010), long before *Homo sapiens* first appeared in Africa around 200,000 years ago (McDougall et al. 2005; White et al. 2003).

I look forward to returning to Indonesia soon to work with my Indonesian, Australian, and American colleagues as we continue to piece together the fascinating evolutionary history of *Homo floresiensis*. Without doubt, we are in for more surprises and debates as far as the Hobbits are concerned. I can hardly wait!

(Falk et al. 2005). Its facial morphology and dental characteristics also link it more closely to *Homo* than *Australopithecus*. Its pelvis, lower limb bones, and feet indicate that it was fully bipedal but possessed a mosaic of primitive and derived features pointing to biomechanical differences in its gait compared to modern humans. In particular, LB1's foot was long relative to her femur and tibia, and it lacked a well-defined medial arch (Jungers et al. 2009).

A variety of interpretations have been proposed to explain the unique mosaic of features seen in LB1. Claims that it represents a modern human with **microcephaly** or a modern pygmy have been rejected by most researchers, and detailed analyses of the fossils support the identification of this hominin as a new species (Argue et al. 2006; Brown et al. 2004). Its unique morphology has prompted Brown and colleagues to suggest that it evolved from an ancestral *Homo* population that became isolated on the island and subsequently underwent a process known as **insular dwarfism**. This process, which occurs when a founding population becomes reproductively isolated in a small environment such as an island, has been documented in a number of mammalian species. The reduction in body size that results from this isolation is believed to be the result of decreased availability of food resources (smaller bodies require less food) and fewer predators (large size is advantageous in coping with predators).

Other researchers have argued that it is unlikely that all of the primitive traits seen in the LB1 cranial and postcranial skeleton were a consequence of insular dwarfism, and posit that *Homo floresiensis* may have descended directly from a primitive small-bodied hominin that arrived on the island alongside or at a different time than *Homo erectus* (Jungers et al. 2009). In addition to its uncertain ancestry, it remains a mystery how such a population was able to survive alongside *Homo sapiens* as recently as it did. Unfortunately, the archaeological record provides no clues to the nature of the interaction between *Homo floresiensis* and *Homo sapiens* (Morwood et al. 2004). To date, the remains of fewer than 10 individuals have been recovered from Liang Bua, and studies of these remains support the hypothesis that the lineage leading to *Homo floresiensis* likely originated prior to the divergence of Neandertals and modern humans (Orr et al. 2013).

microcephaly
a congenital condition characterized by an abnormally small head

insular dwarfism
a process by which a founding population becomes isolated in a small environment such as an island and consequently undergoes a reduction in size

ANOTHER PIECE OF THE PUZZLE, BUT WHICH PIECE?

By now you are probably feeling rather overwhelmed by all the various fossils we have introduced you to in this chapter. You are not alone: the taxonomic status of early *Homo* and its relationship to other Pleistocene hominins is one of the most contentious issues in paleoanthropology today. Among the questions that have yet to be resolved is whether *Homo habilis* is indeed a valid taxon. Early analyses of *Homo habilis* remains emphasized the resemblance between this hominin and later humans. Within the past decade, however, the emphasis has shifted to highlighting the similarities between *Homo habilis* and the australopithecines. These similarities have prompted some paleoanthropologists to call for the inclusion of this species within the genus *Australopithecus* (Wood and Collard 1999). Further support for this argument comes from analyses of the rate of dental development in early *Homo*, which more closely resembles that of fossil and extant African apes than later humans (Dean et al. 2001).

Also unresolved is the number of species represented by the early Pleistocene fossil record. As you learned in Chapter 4, the identification of fossil species is based on the degree of morphological variation seen in the fossil record (i.e., morphospecies) and the amount of time separating various fossil forms (i.e., chronospecies). With respect to Pleistocene hominins, considerable debate has surrounded the interpretation of morphological variation seen in fossils identified as *Homo habilis*. Some experts view this variation as representing a single polytypic species, with variation representing sexual dimorphism or differences due to growth and development; others view it as evidence for more than one species. Complicating the identification of *Homo* in the fossil record is the fact that at least one gracile australopithecine species in southern Africa, *Au. sediba*, coexisted with early *Homo* c. 2.0 Ma. In eastern Africa, *Au. gahri* may also have lived alongside the very earliest members of our genus.

Paleoanthropologists today agree that *Homo* evolved from *Australopithecus* or *Australopithecus*-like ancestor in East Africa but disagree on which species was the most likely ancestor. According to some paleoanthropologists (e.g., Leakey et al. 2012; Spoor et al. 2007), the fossil evidence points to the existence of multiple lineages of early *Homo* in early Pleistocene East Africa. Based on the argument that the degree of variation seen in early *Homo* crania exceeds what one would expect to see in a single species, as many as four separate species have been identified: *Homo habilis, Homo rudolfensis, Homo erectus,* and *Homo ergaster*. Disagreement remains concerning these taxonomic classifications, however, and it is still unclear which of the first two (*H. habilis* and *H. rudolfensis*), if either, gave rise to the latter two. Given that *Homo habilis* and *Homo erectus* appear to have coexisted in East Africa for nearly 500,000 years, it has been argued that *Homo habilis* cannot have been ancestral to *Homo erectus*, at least in this particular geographic region (Spoor et al. 2007). This view has recently been challenged, however, by the statistical analysis of a large sample of crania from East Africa and Georgia dating between 1.9 and 1.5 Ma (Van Arsdale and Wolpoff 2012). The results of this analysis are consistent with a single, evolving lineage encompassing a large amount of variation, some of which may be explained by sexual dimorphism (ibid.).

LEARNING KEYS

KEY IDEAS

- Early members of the genus *Homo* had a larger brain; a more rounded brain case; a smaller, less projecting face; and smaller molar teeth than the australopithecines.

- Much like the last gracile australopithecines, limb proportions in the earliest members of the genus *Homo* exhibited a mosaic of ape-like and human-like features, and analyses of their limb and foot bones indicate that while they were fully bipedal on the ground, they also engaged in frequent arboreal locomotion.

- Early *Homo* may have consisted of two separate species, *Homo habilis* and *Homo rudolfensis*.

- These hominins made and used stone tools known as Oldowan tools, which were used to process carcasses and plants.

- Compared to the australopithecines, early *Homo* consumed a more varied diet that included plant resources such as roots and tubers, and meat.

- *Homo erectus* had a larger cranial capacity and body size than *Homo habilis/rudolfensis*, thick cranial bones, a heavily built jaw with small molars, a sagittal keel, a supraorbital torus, and an occipital torus.

- Some argue that African representatives of early *Homo erectus* should be placed in a separate species, *Homo ergaster*, but the morphological variation seen in the fossil evidence from Africa, the Republic of Georgia, Indonesia, and China increasingly points to the existence of a single, evolving lineage of early *Homo*.

- The long-term success of *Homo erectus* may be linked to their larger brain and increased intelligence, their more sophisticated Acheulian tool technology and control of fire, their increased reliance on meat, their larger body size, and their modern limb proportions, which enabled them to adapt to a wide variety of environments.

- A third more recent species of hominin known as *Homo floresiensis* shows similarities to earlier *Homo* species, and may have descended from a primitive small-bodied hominin.

KEY TERMS

Oldowan industry (p. 229)

Lower Paleolithic (p. 229)

experimental archaeology (p. 230)

stable isotope analysis (p. 231)

shovel-shaped incisors (p. 233)

sagittal keel (p. 233)

supraorbital torus (p. 233)

occipital torus (p. 233)

Acheulian (p. 239)

hand axe (p. 240)

KEY QUESTIONS TO ASK MYSELF

1. Why is it that some members of the genus *Homo* were tall and others short?

2. Given their small brain size, why have the "Hobbits" been classified as members of the genus *Homo*? Is a large brain not the quintessentially human characteristic?

3. Why is it not surprising to see morphological and behavioural variability among *Homo* erectus?

KEY CRITICAL THINKING QUESTIONS

1. Based on your knowledge of the australopithecines gained in Chapter 9, do you agree that the early *Homo* fossils warrant a new taxonomic designation? Why or why not?

2. If we accept that several species of early *Homo* lived in eastern Africa between 1.9 and 1.6 million years ago, what factors might have allowed these species to evolve, let alone coexist?

3. Considerable morphological variability has been observed within and among *Homo erectus* fossil assemblages from Africa and Asia. What might this mean in terms of their evolutionary history?

4. Why do you think *Homo erectus* was able to survive in parts of Indonesia until as recently as 27,000 years ago, a time when modern humans had already made their appearance?

KEY THINGS TO DO NEXT

CourseMate Visit **CourseMate** at www.nelson.com/humanvoyage2e to build your comprehension, practise your critical thinking skills, review core concepts, and explore other resources at your disposal.

11 The Advent of Humanity

OVERVIEW

As you learned in the previous chapter, *Homo ergaster* was the first hominin to leave Africa and migrate to other regions of the Old World. This chapter explores the next stage in our evolutionary history: the emergence of Middle and Late Pleistocene hominins in Africa, Europe, and Asia. We examine the fossil evidence for these individuals and explore their anatomical and behavioural characteristics. We introduce you to the most famous Late Pleistocene hominins, the Neandertals,[1] and highlight their distinctive cranial and postcranial morphology, patterns of growth and disease, and behaviours. As you will learn, aspects of modern human behaviour were evident in these hominins, hence our decision to use the word "humanity" in the title of this chapter. We conclude with an examination of the genetic evidence for these hominins and the reasons for their ultimate demise.

KEY CONCEPTS

Archaic hominins, Neandertals, thermoregulation, Mousterian, zooarchaeology, symbolic behaviour, language

KEY LEARNING OBJECTIVES

At the end of this chapter, you will be able to

LO1 Describe the morphological characteristics of Neandertals and other archaic hominins

LO2 Summarize the genetic evidence for the position of Neandertals in our evolutionary history

LO3 Apply a biocultural perspective to explain the adaptive significance of Neandertal cranial and postcranial morphology

LO4 Compare and contrast the anatomical characteristics of archaic hominins with those of *Homo erectus* and modern humans

---

1. We use the spelling *Neandertal* here, but the alternative spelling, *Neanderthal*, is also commonly used in the literature. "Thal" in German means "valley." The "h" was dropped in the early 20th century to make the spelling consistent with the German pronunciation, which has no "th" sound.

LO5 Evaluate the argument that the demise of the Neandertals was the result of being out-competed by anatomically modern humans

LO6 Predict how climatic conditions might have impacted the biological and behavioural adaptations of archaic hominins

PROLOGUE: SKELETONS IN THE CLOSET

Neandertals

a group of Late Pleistocene hominins who lived in Europe and western Asia between approximately 130,000 and 30,000 years ago

In 1911 the French novel *La Guerre du Feu (Quest for Fire)* was published. Set in Europe 80,000 years ago, it tells the story of a violent confrontation between a primitive tribe representing *Homo erectus* and a group of **Neandertals**, as the former attempt to steal a burning ember from the latter. Having lost their valuable flame, three Neandertals set out in search of fire, and their journey brings them face to face with a group of *Homo sapiens,* who possess the ability to make fire. A series of hostile encounters follows. The story ends with the lead character, a Neandertal named Naoh, in a moonlit embrace with his paramour, the anatomically modern Ika. More than 40 years later, British author William Golding, best known for his novel *Lord of the Flies,* published *The Inheritors* (1955), a book about the last Neandertals and their extinction at the hands of anatomically modern humans. In both of these novels, Neandertals are portrayed as anatomically and behaviourally inferior, and this theme has been woven into many subsequent books and films on human evolution. More than 50 years later, the academic debate on the distinctiveness of Neandertals is as lively, and as dramatic, as ever. Were these creatures a separate species? Did they contribute to the genome of modern European and Near Eastern populations? Or were they summarily dispatched by encroaching Upper Paleolithic modern forms? Recent archaeological, paleontological, and, most provocatively, molecular discoveries are shedding new light on these questions.

THE EMERGENCE OF ARCHAIC HOMININS

archaic hominins

hominins that show a mosaic of *Homo erectus* and modern human traits

By 500 kya, our human voyage had embarked on a new direction with the appearance of what are often referred to as **archaic hominins** because of their combination of features seen in earlier *Homo erectus* fossils and those seen in anatomically modern humans. These included smaller teeth, a significantly larger cranial capacity (averaging 1,350 cc), and an associated change in the overall shape of the skull from a pentagonal-shaped vault to a more parallel-sided vault with a maximum breadth located more toward the crown of the skull than the base. We will examine the fossil evidence for archaic hominins from each of the three main geographic regions of the Old World and discuss their taxonomic status and phylogenetic relationships.

African Archaic Hominins

Fossils of archaic humans have been found at a number of sites in East and South Africa (Figure 11.1). One of the earliest of these was a partial cranium recovered from the site of Bodo in Ethiopia. Possibly dating to about 600,000 years ago, it exhibits a combination of *Homo erectus* and modern features—a low vault, a heavy browridge, and thick cranial bones typical of *Homo erectus,* but at the same time having a cranial capacity of 1,250 cc, within the range of modern humans. This cranium also has cut marks indicating defleshing, although the purpose of that act (cannibalism? mortuary ritual?) remains unknown (White 1986). One of the most complete Middle Pleistocene crania ever found comes from the site of Broken Hill (Kabwe) in Zambia (Figure 11.2). Dating to at least 125,000 years ago, it resembles the Bodo cranium and other African archaic specimens in possessing the low vault, sloping forehead, and heavy browridge seen in *Homo erectus;* but it also has a cranial capacity that exceeds the range for this species.

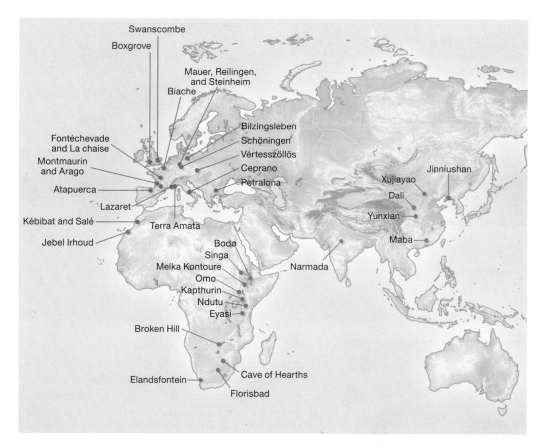

FIGURE 11.1   Archaic sites in Africa, Europe, and Asia.

European Archaic Hominins

Archaic hominins are best known from Europe, represented by that most distinctive group, the Neandertals, whom we will discuss later in this chapter. Like their African counterparts, non-Neandertal European archaic hominins possessed thick cranial bones, a heavy browridge, a pronounced occipital torus, and a cranial capacity similar to that of modern humans. Early archaic specimens include a mandible recovered from the site of Mauer (Figure 11.3) near Heidelberg, Germany, a tibia and some teeth from the site of Boxgrove in southern England, a partial cranium from the site of Arago in France (Figure 11.4), a partial cranium from the site of Swanscombe in England, a nearly complete cranium from Steinheim in Germany (Figure 11.5), and a cranium from Petralona, Greece (Figure 11.6).

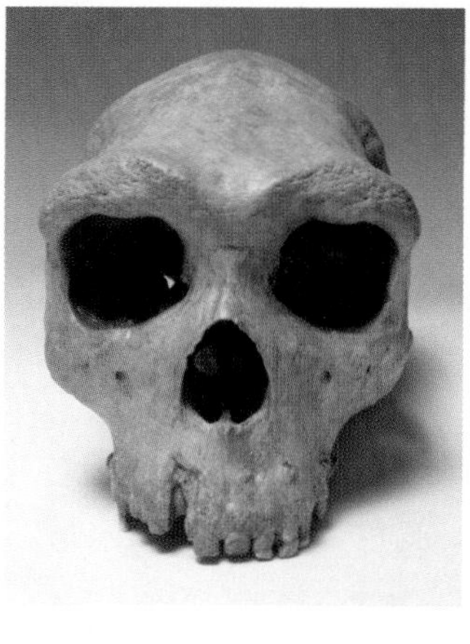

Over the years a number of Middle Pleistocene fossils have been labelled the first inhabitants of Europe. These include a **calvarium** discovered at the site of Ceprano in Italy,[2] the 500,000-year-old Boxgrove fossils, and the Mauer jaw, recently re-dated to 609 ± 40 kya (Wagner et al. 2010). In 1994, however, excavations at the site of Gran Dolina in the Atapuerca region

FIGURE 11.2 This cranium from Kabwe exhibits the heavy brow-ridges, sloping forehead, and low vault seen in archaic *Homo sapiens*.

© John Reader/Science Photo Library

calvarium

the skull, excluding the facial bones and mandible

---

2. This specimen was initially dated to 800,000 to 900,000 years ago but has more recently been re-dated to 430,000 to 385,000 years ago (Manzi et al. 2010).

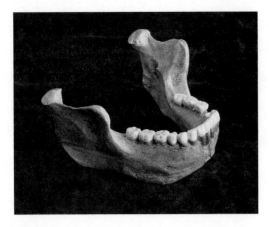

FIGURE 11.3 Mauer jaw.

© Neanderthal Museum

FIGURE 11.4 Arago cranium, left pelvic bone, and mandibular fragments.

© John Reader/Science Photo Library

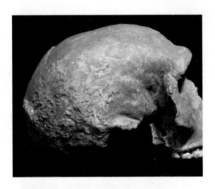

FIGURE 11.5 Steinheim cranium.

© Universal Images Group/Getty

FIGURE 11.6 Petralona cranium.

© DEA/A. DAGLI ORTI/Getty

of northern Spain yielded a remarkable collection of even older bones belonging to at least six individuals, together with stone tools resembling Oldowan tools as found in early Pleistocene Africa, and faunal remains. Recovered from the lowest layer of the site, known as the Aurora stratum, these fossils have been dated by electron spin resonance and paleomagnetism to more than 780,000 years ago (Figure 11.7). Even more tantalizing, the bones of all six individuals—two adults, two adolescents, two infants—display cut marks in a pattern identical to that seen in the faunal remains, prompting claims that the occupants of the site engaged in or were victims of cannibalism (Fernández-Jalvo et al. 1999).

The unique combination of cranial and dental traits displayed by these fossils—including a fully modern midfacial region, slightly enlarged mandibular anterior teeth, reduced posterior teeth, and a gracile mandible—have led Spanish paleoanthropologists to classify them as *Homo antecessor*, a species that they believe probably originated from *Homo erectus/ergaster* in Africa and may represent the last common ancestor of modern humans and Neandertals (Bermúdez de Castro et al. 1997). Not everyone accepts this new taxon, however, as its holotype is the cranium of a 10-year-old child, so the rather slight and modern appearance may reflect age rather than species-level distinctions.

One of the largest collections of European archaic fossils comes from the site of Sima de los Huesos ("Pit of Bones"), also in Atapuerca. Representing a minimum of 28 individuals, these remains have been dated to over 300,000 years ago and exhibit a number of Neandertal features that are notably absent in archaic fossils from Asia and Africa, as well as the more ancient remains attributed to *Homo antecessor*, including a projecting face and arched browridges (de Castro et al. 2004; Figure 11.8). These features suggest that the Neandertal lineage was likely established in Europe by at least 300,000 years ago.

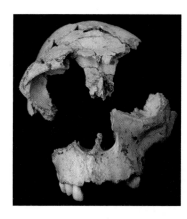

FIGURE 11.7 Partial skull of a child identified as belonging to *Homo antecessor*.

© Javier Trueba/MSF/Science Photo Library

FIGURE 11.8 This skull, identified as Atapuerca 5, exhibits a combination of *Homo heidelbergensis* and Neandertal features.

© Javier Trueba/MSF/Science Photo Library

In 2008, paleoanthropologists announced the discovery of yet another archaic fossil consisting of a partial mandible and some teeth. Uncovered at the site of Sima del Elefante in Atapuerca, these remains have been dated to 1.1 to 1.2 Ma and have tentatively been assigned to *Homo antecessor* (Carbonell et al. 2008). More recently, an even earlier specimen consisting of a hominin molar from the site of Barranco León in southern Spain has been described (Toro-Moyano et al. 2013). Dating to approximately 1.4 Ma, it is reported to represent the oldest known hominin from western Europe, indicating that this region was colonized soon after hominins expanded out of Africa.

Archaic hominin fossils have also been recovered from sites in Central and Eastern Europe. Among them are a human mandible recovered from Pleistocene deposits in the Mala Balanica Cave, Serbia. The discovery of such fossils in this region points to the Balkans as a potential migratory route from western Asia into Europe (Roksandic et al. 2011) (see Box 11.1).

Asian Archaic Hominins

Early archaic fossils in Asia (refer back to Figure 11.1) also display a mosaic of *Homo erectus* and modern features, although smaller, flatter faces in some of the crania point to regional differences between these specimens and those of Africa and Europe. One of the best-known fossils, a nearly complete skull dating to approximately 200,000 years ago, comes from the site of Dali in China. It displays the low vault and massive browridge typical of *Homo erectus*, but it also has facial features that more closely resemble those of modern humans. A partial skeleton from Jinniushan in China, dating to more than 200,000 years ago, has a cranium with a pronounced browridge and sloping forehead but a cranial capacity that exceeds that of *Homo erectus* (Tiemei, Quan, and En 1994). The early dates for this and other archaic specimens are close to those obtained from the latest *Homo erectus* fossils, suggesting that the two species may in fact have coexisted in China (Tiemei et al. 1994), although some paleoanthropologists favour a scenario of continuity between *Homo erectus* and archaic hominins in this region (see Chapter 12). Archaic hominin remains in the form of a partial cranium and postcranial remains dating from the Middle to Late Pleistocene have also been found in the Central Narmada Valley in India. Their morphological features have been interpreted as indicating the presence of two types of archaic hominins in the region during this time period (Sankhyan et al. 2012).

One Species or Several?

The transitional nature of the archaic fossils described above makes it difficult to classify them, and there has been considerable debate concerning the number of species of archaic humans that existed during the Middle and Late Pleistocene. Some paleoanthropologists prefer to lump all fossils into one category, which they refer to as archaic *Homo sapiens*;

BOX 11.1

PROFILE... Not "Just Another Neanderthal"

Courtesy Mirjana Roksandic

One very cold February afternoon in Winnipeg, a phone call to my home from Serbia made me jump up and down, to the great amazement and merriment of my family and house guests. I managed to scramble together enough funding to fly to Serbia and exchange the "balmy"–30C for the more moderate clime and blooms of early March in Belgrade. There, Dr. Dusan Mihailovic, my best friend from the undergraduate years at the University of Belgrade and currently a professor in the very same department, invited me to examine the specimen he had recently excavated from the Balanica cave in Southern Serbia. Thankfully, I was left alone in the lab for a sufficiently long time to contain my excitement at the prospect of cleaning, restoring, and describing a fossil human mandible that came to be known as BH-1. In our first—on record—discussions, Dusan and I decided that it could be 250,000 years old, based on the combination of morphology and stratigraphy and his understanding of the archaeological sequence. Well aware that morphology is not a good indicator of age, especially in poorly researched areas, we were very cautious in our assessment. The chronological framework for Serbia was non-existent at the time, even when it came

to more abundant archaeological and paleontological finds. Recently, we have dated the specimen as being half a million years old, making it the oldest human fossil in Eastern Europe.

I did one of my many graduate degrees (D.E.A., or in a really grand translation: Diploma of Profound Studies) in Professor Vandermeerch's laboratory at the University of Bordeaux—one of the best schools in Neanderthal studies of all times. Incidentally, it was there that I discovered burial archaeology and I was bound forever to switch between these two fascinations: evolution and mortuary ritual. When I moved to Canada and started my Ph.D. at Simon Fraser University, I decided to follow my fascination with sedentary hunter–gatherers of Lepenski Vir and their burial rituals, and proceeded to work in Portugal and now in the Caribbean on similar questions.

I never abandoned my fascination with Neanderthals and I have yet to find my own Neanderthal specimen. Balanica mandible (the BH-1 specimen) is not a Neanderthal; it is best regarded as *Homo erectus* in a very general sense, and could potentially be more closely related with non-European fossil humans. For all its small size, Balanica mandible looms large in our understanding of human evolution in Europe. Because of its Middle Pleistocene age, the time where our understanding of the exact evolutionary trajectories of African and Asian populations and their relationships with the European fossils is not yet clear—the famous "muddle in the middle"—it opens up different possibilities for interpretation and a promise of more to come from this part of the world.

Source: Written by Mirjana Roksandic, Department of Anthropology, University of Winnipeg, Canada.

others recognize the existence of at least two species. In 1908 the Mauer mandible was given the species name *Homo heidelbergensis* based on its robusticity and lack of a chin (Schoetensack 1908). Since that time, many of the archaic fossils described above (e.g., Boxgrove, Arago, Steinheim, Swanscombe, Petralona) have been assigned to this taxon. The picture that is emerging is one of archaic populations arising from their *Homo erectus* ancestors at different times in Europe, Africa, and Asia. Regional and temporal variability is evident in these fossils, with the earlier specimens more closely resembling *Homo erectus* and the later specimens more closely resembling modern humans (as one would expect). The origin of *Homo heidelbergensis* remains unclear, as does its relationship to later hominins (Stringer 2012). Paleoanthropologists who accept *Homo heidelbergensis* as a valid taxon see this species as ancestral to Neandertals in western Eurasia and the earliest *Homo sapiens* in Africa (Rightmire 2007; see Figure 11.9a). In contrast, others view *Homo ergaster* as being ancestral to Neandertals in western Eurasia and *Homo sapiens* in Africa (Figure 11.9b). The taxonomic status of archaic hominins in Asia and their connection with modern Asians remains unresolved. Similarities between the Chinese specimens found at Dali and Jinniushan and those from Africa and Europe raise the possibility that these late Middle Pleistocene humans represent an eastward expansion of *Homo heidelbergensis* (Rightmire 2007). It is hoped that the discovery of additional archaic fossils from China will clarify this issue.

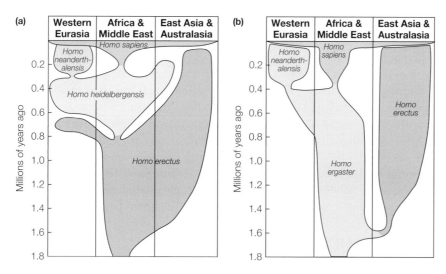

FIGURE 11.9 Two possible phylogenies are illustrated here. In the first one, (a) *Homo heidelbergensis* gave rise to Neandertals in western Eurasia and anatomically modern humans in Africa. In the second one, (b) *Homo ergaster* gave rise to Neandertals in western Eurasia and modern humans in Africa.

"Figure 12.37" from *How Humans Evolved*, Fifth Edition by Robert Boyd and Joan B. Silk. Copyright © 2008, 2006, 2003, 2000, 1997 by W.W. Norton & Company, Inc. Used by permission of W.W. Norton & Company, Inc.

BEHAVIOURAL ADAPTATIONS OF ARCHAIC HOMININS

In Chapter 10 you learned about the Oldowan stone tool industry associated with *Homo habilis* and possibly the australopithecines, and the Acheulian industry associated with *Homo erectus*. Early archaic hominins continued to make and use Acheulian tools, including bifaces and flake tools, but archaeological evidence indicates that these tools were more finely made than those attributed to *Homo erectus*. There was also considerable geographic variability in tool types, with hand axes being common in Africa and Europe and almost non-existent in Asia. In addition to stone tools, archaic hominins also made tools from wood, as indicated by three remarkably well-preserved wooden spears found at the 400,000-year-old site of Schöningen in Germany (Thieme 1997; Figure 11.10). Unfortunately, organic materials such as these are rarely preserved in the archaeological record; in this case we owe their preservation to the anaerobic environment and the presence of tannic acids in the bog in which they were deposited. Evidence for hafted tools in the form of modified stone points excavated from the site of Kathu Pan 1 (KP1) in South Africa, however, indicates that spears with hafted stone points were being utilized as early as 500,000 years ago (Wilkins et al. 2012). Blade tools, typically associated with anatomically modern humans (see Chapter 12), have also been recovered from Kathu Pan 1 (Wilkins and Chazan 2012) and from contemporaneous deposits in the Baringo Basin of Kenya (Johnson and McBrearty 2012).

FIGURE 11.10 Archaeologist Hartmut Thieme examines a 400,000-year-old wooden spear found near Schöningen, Germany.

© Kenneth Garrett/National Geographic Creative

Archaic hominins probably lived in some sort of shelters, but archaeological evidence for these is almost non-existent. Oval or circular arrangements of stones found at the sites of Terra Amata in France and Bilzingsleben in Germany suggest some form of structure, while a linear arrangement of large rocks found in Lazaret Cave in southern France may have supported the poles of a tent (de Lumley 1969). The remains of plants, small and large mammals, birds, and fish have been found at various Middle Pleistocene sites, and some of these resources may have been part of the diet. Faunal remains recovered from several sites have been used to argue for big-game hunting, although other activities might also account for the association of these bones with stone tools. Among the most convincing evidence are the remains of mammals found in association with *Homo heidelbergensis* fossils at Boxgrove (Roberts and Parfitt 1999). The association of the Schöningen spears with stone tools and butchered animal bones further bolsters the argument that archaic hominins successfully hunted large game.

THE APPEARANCE OF NEANDERTALS

When Darwin published his "Big Book" in 1859, very little fossil evidence for earlier humans had been uncovered. Neandertal fossils had been found in 1830 in Belgium and 1848 in Gibraltar, but neither was recognized at the time as representing an earlier human form. In 1856, what was to become the Neandertal-type specimen was recovered from the Feldhofer cave in the Neander Valley in Germany, from which the name of these hominins derives.[3] Consisting of the top of a skull, some ribs, parts of a pelvis, and some limb bones, it was initially believed to be a modern human with some type of pathological condition. In the decades that followed, however, additional Neandertal fossils uncovered from sites in western and central Europe confirmed their status as ancient humans. Spanning the period from about 130,000 to 30,000 years ago, thousands of Neandertal fossils have been unearthed to date, and their geographic range is now known to have extended as far south as the Levant in the Middle East and as far east as the Altai mountain region of central Asia (Krause et al. 2007; see Figure 11.11). No other group of fossil hominins has been more thoroughly studied.

In 1911, French paleontologist Marcellin Boule undertook a reconstruction of the skeleton of an elderly male found in 1908 at the site of La Chapelle-aux-Saints in France (see chapter opening photo).[4] In doing so, he ignored several important features, including the large cranial capacity of this individual (1,620 cc) and several pathological conditions affecting his skeleton. Consequently, he portrayed this individual as ape-like in appearance, with stooped posture, bent knees, and a long, low cranium reflecting what Boule believed to be low intelligence. Boule's reconstruction, which relegated Neandertals to a separate species that eventually became extinct, was widely accepted and gave rise to the stereotypical image of Neandertals that has long been accepted in popular culture (Figure 11.12).

Neandertal Morphology

classic Neandertals

Neandertals of western Europe that exhibited the most pronounced morphological characteristics of this group of hominins

Descriptions of Neandertal morphology typically refer to that of the **classic Neandertals** of western Europe and it is important to emphasize that Neandertals living in the Near East did not exhibit many of the extreme morphological features seen in their European counterparts. To appreciate the morphology of European Neandertals, it is useful to examine the environmental conditions in which these hominins lived. Classic Neandertals emerged in Europe at the beginning of the last interglacial period, about 130,000 years ago, when the climate was noticeably warmer than during the previous glacial period (Figure 11.13). About 115,000 years ago, however, climatic conditions deteriorated once again, ushering in the last and most recent glacial period in Europe. Sheets of ice covered much of northern Europe, and most of western and central Europe

---

3. This site was revisited in 1997, and excavation of cave sediments discarded in 1856 yielded dozens of artifacts and faunal remains and over 60 human bone fragments, including several that belonged to the original specimen excavated in 1856 (Schmitz et al. 2002).

4. The age at death of this individual was estimated as 40 years; this would have been considered elderly for Neandertals, most of whom died before this age (Trinkaus 1995).

FIGURE 11.11   The geographic range of Neandertals, determined from fossil and mtDNA evidence, spanned western Europe to central Asia (see Krause et al. 2007).

Based on K. Havarti, (2007). *Neanderthals and their contemporaries, Handbook of Paleoanthropology*, edited by Henke, W. and Tattersall, I. Berline: Springer Verlag, p. 1720.

and Eurasia consisted of tundra. Isolated by these glacial conditions for a considerable period of time, the Neandertals developed a distinctive morphology that has made them unique among hominins.

Classic Neandertals possessed the following: a large skull with a low vault and a low, sloping forehead; a cranial capacity that in some cases exceeded that of modern humans (average 1,500 cc); a rounded feature at the back of the cranium known as the **occipital bun**; small mastoid processes; **midfacial prognathism**; a large nasal cavity; large rounded orbits; prominent arched browridges; and no distinct chin. Their dental characteristics included relatively large incisors, relatively small molars, a **retromolar space** reflecting the forward shift of the teeth relative to the skull vault, and **taurodontism** (Figure 11.14).

FIGURE 11.12   This image of a Neandertal, based on Marcellin Boule's reconstruction of the skeleton from La Chapelle-aux-Saints, reflected the widely held belief that these hominins were ape-like in appearance.

The Granger Collection, New York

occipital bun

a bulge on the occipital bone of the skull that projects posteriorly, typical of Neandertals

midfacial prognathism

forward projection of the nasal region of the face

retromolar space

a gap between the third molar and the ascending ramus of the mandible

taurodontism

enlargement of the pulp cavity in molar teeth, a characteristic of Neandertals

paranasal sinuses

a group of four pairs of air-filled spaces located on both sides of the nasal cavity, above and between the eyes, and within the sphenoid bone

temporomandibular joint

the location on the skull base where the mandible articulates with the temporal bone

As suggested above, the unique cranial morphology of classic Neandertals has long been viewed as an adaptation to cold temperatures. Researchers have hypothesized that a forward-projecting face would have kept the nasal cavities—and thus the incoming cold air—farther away from the temperature-sensitive brain, while the large nasal cavities and **paranasal sinuses** would have provided greater surface area for warming and humidifying the cold dry air. More recently, biomechanical explanations have come to dominate the literature. Proponents of the "anterior dental loading" hypothesis (Brace 1964; O'Connor, Franciscus, and Holton 2005; Rak 1986) have argued that the large, prognathic face and large incisors of Neandertals were adaptations to heavy biting forces resulting from the use of the teeth as vises in producing tools. Support for this hypothesis comes from the heavily worn incisors seen in Neandertal fossils as well as degenerative changes to the **temporomandibular joint**.

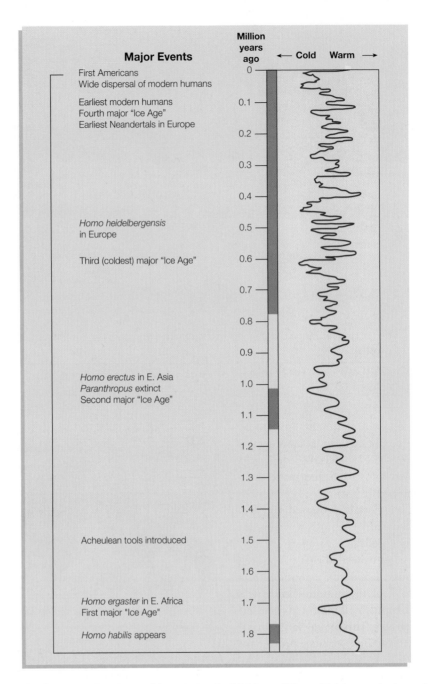

FIGURE 11.13 Changing climatic conditions during the Middle and Upper Pleistocene had a major impact on archaic hominins, including Neandertals.

masticatory

related to mastication (chewing)

O'Connor and colleagues (2005) tested the anterior dental loading hypothesis by assessing the ability of the Neandertal **masticatory** system to generate heavy occlusal loads (i.e., bite force), using modern humans as a comparison. Their results revealed that compared to modern humans, Neandertals were not capable of generating significantly higher levels of anterior bite force, and that their larger, more heavily worn anterior teeth might instead reflect repetitive use of their teeth. More recently, Clement and colleagues (2012) tested the anterior dental loading hypothesis using a new method of examining tooth wear in Neandertals, Middle and Upper Paleolithic modern humans, and recent hunter–gatherers from the Canadian Arctic, and found that all individuals in their sample had heavily worn anterior teeth relative to their

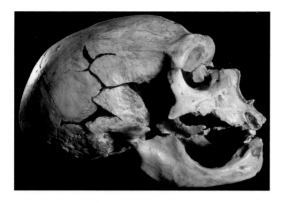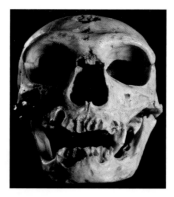

FIGURE 11.14 The classic Neandertal cranium had a long, low vault, pronounced browridges, midfacial prognathism, a large nasal aperture, and an occipital bun.

posterior teeth. This finding suggests that all Late Pleistocene hominins, not just Neandertals, habitually applied heavy forces between their front teeth (ibid.).

The adaptive significance of the width of the Neandertal nasal opening and the size of their paranasal sinuses has also been re-examined. If the Neandertal face was cold-adapted, one would, in fact, expect the nose to be narrower, as seen in modern populations who inhabit colder regions. Consequently, their sinuses should also be smaller; instead they have been found not to differ significantly from those of more recent *Homo sapiens* living in temperate regions (Rae et al. 2011). Thus the evidence for the Neandertal face being cold-adapted remains unconvincing, and their unique craniofacial morphology was likely the result of a variety of factors, including mechanical loading as noted above as well as the possibility of genetic drift due to relatively small population sizes (Weaver et al. 2007).

Arguments have also been made for the Neandertal postcranial skeleton being cold-adapted based on the fact that it has similar body proportions to that of modern cold-adapted populations such as the Inuit. Compared to anatomically modern humans, Neandertals were shorter and stockier, with more robust, heavily muscled, and slightly curved long bones and large, barrel-shaped chests (Figure 11.15). Stature estimates based on long-bone lengths average 158 cm in females and 166 cm in males (Churchill 2008), and their limb bones were shorter than those of most modern human populations. These body proportions resemble those seen in cold-adapted living populations and are designed to conserve heat in cold environments by reducing the amount of surface area from which heat may be lost (see Chapter 14). When evaluating the impact of body size and shape on thermoregulation, however, it is important to obtain accurate estimates of body surface area of fossil hominins such as Neandertals (Cross and Collard 2011). Research by Simon Fraser University anthropologists Alan Cross and Mark Collard has, in fact, revealed that while Neandertals would have lost less heat than modern humans overall, they would have lost less heat from their upper arms but more heat from their legs (visit the CourseMate site for a discussion of thermoregulation and Neandertals).

The marked robusticity of Neandertal limbs has also been interpreted as reflecting high activity levels and a physically demanding lifestyle. Researchers have investigated activity levels in Neandertals using a number of approaches, including taking external measurements of limb bones and examining musculoskeletal stress markers. More recently, research on functional adaptation in Neandertals has shifted to examining the **cross-sectional geometry** of their bones. In one such study, a comparison of upper- and lower-limb robusticity in Neandertals, early modern humans, and recent humans using measurements taken from the midshaft of long bones revealed similarities between Neandertals and modern foragers such as the Inuit, suggesting that they shared a similar pattern of mechanical loading

cross-sectional geometry

the mass and distribution (shape) of cortical bone viewed in a plane perpendicular to the long axis of a tubular bone, such as the femur or metacarpal

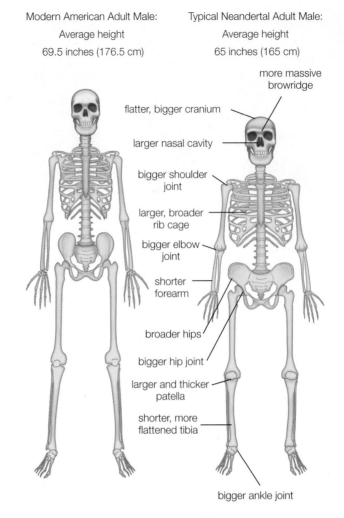

Modern American Adult Male:
Average height
69.5 inches (176.5 cm)

Typical Neandertal Adult Male:
Average height
65 inches (165 cm)

more massive
browridge

flatter, bigger cranium

larger nasal cavity

bigger shoulder
joint

larger, broader
rib cage

bigger elbow
joint

shorter
forearm

broader hips

bigger hip joint

larger and thicker
patella

shorter, more
flattened tibia

bigger ankle joint

FIGURE 11.15   Compared to that of modern humans, the Neandertal skeleton was shorter and more robust and had short limbs and a barrel-shaped chest.

(Pearson, Cordero, and Busby 2008). Analyses of Neandertal hand bones have revealed that these hominins, like modern humans, had the ability to produce and use complex tools, as also indicated by the tools themselves (discussed later in this chapter). A three-dimensional comparison of Neandertal hand morphology with that of modern populations has indicated that Neandertal hands were adapted primarily for power, whereas those of modern humans were adapted to more frequent precision manipulation (Niewoehner 2008).

Detailed studies of the Neandertal pelvis have revealed that compared to a modern human, a Neandertal had a longer and thinner **pubic ramus**. Initially thought to reflect differences between the two groups in the length of gestation (Trinkaus 1984), this difference is now believed to be more likely related to locomotion and posture-related biomechanics (Rak and Arensburg 1987).

pubic ramus

the portion of the pubic bone of the pelvis that extends medially

Neandertal Growth and Development

Neandertals appear to have buried their dead (discussed later in this chapter). As a result, a large number of well-preserved skeletons of infants, children, and adolescents have been recovered from Neandertal sites. These remains have enabled researchers to compare the growth and development of these hominins with that of anatomically modern humans.

Compared to other primates, humans have longer periods of infant and childhood growth, allowing for a greater period of learning. The question of whether Neandertals also had prolonged growth has been addressed using a variety of methods. Computer tomography (CT) has allowed researchers to reconstruct Neandertal skeletons and compare their morphology with that of modern humans. Ponce de Léon and colleagues (2008), for instance, used CT scanning to reconstruct the remains of a Neandertal newborn found in Mezmaiskaya Cave, Russia, and two infants found in Dederiyeh Cave in Syria. Their study revealed that Neandertal babies were born with brains as large as those of modern human infants but that their brains grew more rapidly than ours during the first few years of life.

Studies of Neandertal dental development have yielded seemingly conflicting results. Ramirez Rozzi and Bermúdez de Castro's (2004) analysis of a sample of Neandertal and anatomically modern human teeth revealed that Neandertal tooth enamel was deposited more rapidly, suggesting that they reached maturity earlier than modern humans. A similar conclusion was reached by Smith et al. (2010), who examined dental development in Neandertals and modern humans. In contrast, other studies (e.g., Guatelli-Steinberg et al. 2005) have found Neandertal tooth development to fall within the range of variation seen in modern populations. As Guatelli-Steinberg (2009) emphasized, interpreting the rate of dental development among Neandertals hinges on knowing the range of variation in dental development exhibited by modern humans. Furthermore, the rate of dental growth seen in Neandertals may not be an accurate reflection of their overall growth rate. She recommends a multi-faceted approach in which dental development is examined in conjunction with the development of other systems such as the skeleton.

A small number of studies have addressed Neandertal **ontogeny** by examining both dental and skeletal growth. Thompson and Nelson (2000), for example, examined data on dental maturation and femoral growth from four Neandertals, five Upper Paleolithic *Homo sapiens* from Europe, and two modern samples, and found that the Neandertal growth trajectory differed from that of the other samples, suggesting either advanced dental development or slow femoral growth compared to modern humans. More recently, an investigation by Martín-González and colleagues (2012) of growth rates in Neandertals and modern humans revealed slower growth rates in the former after the age of five months. This difference may be linked to elevated metabolic costs associated with the harsh climatic conditions in which these hominins lived, and/or nutritional stress associated with weaning (Martín-González et al. 2012), which, in one Neandertal, appears to have occurred relatively early as indicated by the chemical analysis of a tooth from this individual (Austin et al. 2013). What is also clear from some of the more recent studies of growth and development is that well-developed Neandertal morphological characteristics such as a more robust mandible than that seen in modern humans were present early in life (Crevecoeur et al. 2010).

ontogeny
the development of an organism from embryo to adult

Reflections of a Hard Life

Neandertals suffered from a variety of ailments, including traumatic injuries, nutritional deficiencies, and joint disease. Trauma has been documented in many Neandertal skeletons, and a number of these injuries have been interpreted as signs of interpersonal violence. These include the remains of a young adult Neandertal from St-Césaire, who displayed evidence of sharp-force trauma to the cranium (Zollikofer et al. 2002), and of an adult from Shanidar, who exhibited a cut mark on the ninth left rib (Trinkaus 1983). In their review of Neandertal trauma, Berger and Trinkaus (1995) noted the high frequency of traumatic lesions in Neandertal remains and the fact that the healed or partially healed nature of many of them indicates survival of the injury. Interestingly, their examination of the anatomical distribution of these traumatic lesions revealed a pattern similar to that seen in modern-day rodeo riders, and they posited that this high prevalence of head and neck injuries may have resulted from frequent close encounters with large prey animals, as might occur in attempts to hunt them with spears at close distances (Berger and Trinkaus 1995).[5] More recently, however, they acknowledge that other factors besides hunting methods, such as interpersonal violence, likely also contributed to the anatomical pattern of trauma

5. In the 1980s, Dr. Valerius Geist, Professor Emeritus of Environmental Science at the University of Calgary, proposed that Neandertals were "close quarter hunters"; see his 1981 paper "Neanderthal the Hunter" in *Natural History* 90(1): 26–36.

seen in Neandertals (Trinkaus 2012), and in fact, the pronounced right-dominant bilateral asymmetry seen in Neandertal humeri and widely linked to close range hunting with spear thrusting may, instead, have resulted from scraping activities such as hide preparation (Shaw et al. 2012).

Neandertals also experienced episodes of nutritional stress, as revealed in their teeth, many of which exhibit defects known as **linear enamel hypoplasia** (Figure 11.16). These nonspecific indicators of stress, which result from a disruption in enamel formation, provide a permanent record of stress episodes during childhood. A number of studies have revealed high rates of enamel hypoplasia in Neandertals, suggesting that they suffered from high levels of nutritional deficiencies (Ogilvie, Curran, and Trinkaus 1989). A recent comparison of the prevalence of enamel hypoplasia in Neandertals and Alaskan Inuit, however, found that Neandertals were no more stressed than the latter (Guatelli-Steinberg, Larsen, and Hutchinson 2004).

Joint diseases recorded in Neandertal skeletons provide further evidence of a hard life. Osteoarthritis, or degenerative joint disease, has been recorded in a number of Neandertal remains, including the skeleton from La Chapelle-aux-Saints discussed earlier. Another joint disease, diffuse idiopathic skeletal hyperostosis (DISH), has also been diagnosed in a Neandertal skeleton (Crubézy and Trinkaus 1992). Characterized by excessive bone growth on the vertebrae, the condition is more common in males and in older adults. While its etiology remains unknown, genetics and diabetes have been implicated, among other factors.

Documentation of debilitating conditions such as traumatic injuries and joint disease has led to speculation that such individuals would have required considerable care from other members of their group. One of the best-known examples is Shanidar 1, an adult male Neandertal estimated to have been 30 to 45 years of age at the time of his death. Examination of his skeleton revealed that he had suffered multiple fractures, including an injury to the right humerus that had resulted in paralysis leading to atrophy of the bone (Trinkaus 1983). Solecki (1971) concluded from this that he would have been dependent on others for care. Similarly, healed injuries in other Neandertals have been interpreted as evidence of care and compassion (Trinkaus and Zimmerman 1982). Dettwyler (1991) has challenged the assumption that the survival of disabled individuals is evidence of compassion and support, arguing that skeletal remains tell us nothing about the degree to which an individual was "handicapped" by his or her disability, or the way in which that individual was treated. It is hard to imagine, however, how a Neandertal incapacitated by injury or disease would have survived for any length of time without help.

NEANDERTAL BEHAVIOURAL ADAPTATIONS

Technology

In Europe, Neandertals are most often associated with the **Mousterian** stone tool industry (Figure 11.17), named after the site of Le Moustier in France. This **Middle Palaeolithic** industry was characterized by a number of methods of manufacturing, including the **Levallois**, or prepared core technique, which involved preparing disc-shaped cores from which flakes

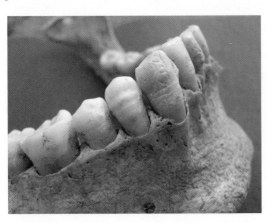

FIGURE 11.16 Linear enamel hypoplasia, defects in the surface of the tooth enamel that result from episodes of nutritional or disease stress during childhood, have been documented in Neandertal remains. They are seen here in modern human mandibular teeth.

Courtesy of Anne Keenleyside

linear enamel hypoplasia

horizontal defects in tooth enamel that represent episodes of physiological stress that occurred while the teeth were forming

Mousterian

a Middle Paleolithic stone tool industry generally associated with Neandertals

Middle Palaeolithic

the period dating from about 250,000 to 40,000 years ago and associated with Mousterian tools

Levallois

a tool-manufacturing technique of the Middle Paleolithic that involved making tools from a prepared core

FIGURE 11.17 The Mousterian stone tool industry was characterized by a greater variety of tool types than the Acheulian industry. These included scrapers and points such as those seen here.

Courtesy of Anne Keenleyside

were knocked off and made into tools. In contrast to Acheulian assemblages, Mousterian toolkits encompassed a greater variety of tool types, and the variability in these toolkits has led to considerable discussion and debate about their significance. In the mid-20th century, the well-known French archaeologist François Bordes identified five major types of assemblages, hypothesizing that they represented different cultural groups (Bordes 1961). In contrast, archaeologist Lewis Binford interpreted them as indicating different behavioural complexes—that is, different toolkits used for different functions (Binford and Binford 1966). As Mellars (1996) points out, however, other factors such as temporal changes in stylistic attributes perhaps contributed to this variability. This debate reminds us that it is important to consider the interaction of multiple factors when attempting to explain the diversity seen in Middle Palaeolithic assemblages. More recent Neandertal sites such as Saint-Césaire and Arcy-sur-Cure in France, are associated with a tool industry known as the **Châtelperronian**, which consisted of blade and bone tools and personal ornaments.

A particularly interesting artifact, interpreted as the oldest musical instrument in the world, came to light in 1995 in a cave in Slovenia. Dating between 82,000 and 43,000 years ago, it consisted of the partial femur of a cave bear that had been punctured on one side with four holes, forming what appeared to be a small flute (Turk 1997; Figure 11.18). This interpretation has not been accepted by everyone, however, and the holes may have been made by carnivore teeth (Chase and Nowell 1998).

A variety of behavioural strategies enabled Neandertals to cope with the cold climate in which they lived. These included the occupation of caves and rock shelters and the use of fire, as indicated by deposits of ash and charcoal at a number of sites. They also likely wore clothing made from animal hides. There is no evidence in the archaeological record of sewing implements, but heavy anterior tooth wear and wear patterns on some of their stone tools may point to the preparation of hides for clothing and/or shelters.

Châtelperronian
an Upper Paleolithic tool industry associated with late Neandertals

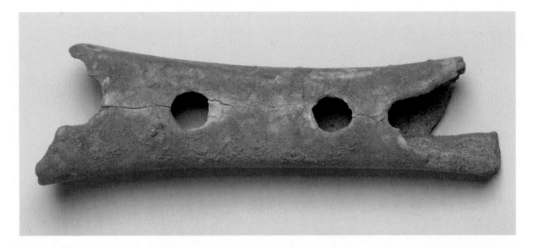

FIGURE 11.18 This perforated long bone fragment has been interpreted as a flute made and used by Neandertals.

© National Museum of Slovenia, photo Tomaž Lauko

There has been considerable debate about the range over which Neandertals roamed during their lifetime, with some researchers arguing for a limited range and others for longer distances. Most of our information on Neandertal mobility comes from raw materials, some of which have been found to originate from locations over 100 km away from the site in which they were found (Mellars 1996), although the majority come from distances of less than 5 km. Recent strontium isotope analysis (see Chapter 14) of a Neandertal third molar from the 40,000-year-old site of Lakonis in Greece points to the movement of this individual over a fairly wide geographic area (over 20 km) during his or her lifetime (Richards et al. 2008).

With respect to their social organization and settlement patterns, Hayden (2012) has argued that Neandertals may have formed local bands consisting of 12 to 25 members, based on the distribution of raw materials and the amount of meat consumed at kill sites, among other factors. These bands interacted with one another on a smaller scale than anatomically modern humans did, and likely moved about frequently within relatively small areas (Mellars 1996).

Diet and Subsistence Practices

Like their *Homo erectus* ancestors, Neandertals and other archaic hominins exploited a variety of food resources, including large and small terrestrial game, birds, marine resources, and plants. Stable isotope and dental microwear analyses have both been used to investigate Neandertal diet. Stable carbon and nitrogen isotope analyses of Neandertal skeletal remains recovered from several sites have revealed that in Europe at least, they derived almost all of their dietary protein from meat (Bocherens et al. 1999, 2005; Fizet et al. 1995; Richards, Pettitt et al. 2000; Richards and Schmitz 2008). Furthermore, their $\delta^{15}N$ values are higher than those measured in contemporaneous carnivores such as cave hyenas, suggesting that these hominins were top predators (Bocherens et al. 2005) (Figure 11.19). These findings are consistent with **zooarchaeological** evidence obtained from Neandertal sites, which points to a heavy reliance on medium to large herbivores such as reindeer, red deer, bison, and horse.

The question of whether Neandertals hunted or scavenged has long been the subject of debate, although it is now widely recognized that Neandertals were capable of hunting a variety of game, while also likely scavenging on occasion. In general, archaeological evidence for scavenging consists of faunal assemblages containing primarily cranial and foot bones, the presence of carnivore tooth marks on the bones, and a lack of cut marks on fleshier parts of the skeleton (Marean 1998; Marean and Kim 1998). Archaeological evidence for hunting

zooarchaeological

nonhuman, typically used to refer to animal bones

includes a focus on one or two species of large mammals, evidence of butchery in the form of cut marks on bones that would have yielded a considerable amount of meat, and the presence of weapons such as spears. At Combe Grenal, for instance, the faunal assemblage consists of predominantly horse and bison remains, greater representation of meat-bearing upper limb bones than lower limb bones, and clear patterns of cut marks on the limb bones—evidence consistent with hunting (Chase 1986). A number of other Neandertal sites have also yielded the remains of large game. For instance, reindeer were hunted during the fall and winter and butchered at the rockshelter site of Chez-Pinaud Jonzac (Niven et al. 2012).

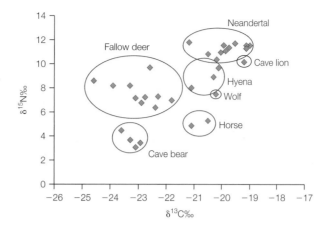

FIGURE 11.19 Stable isotope analyses of the remains of Neandertals and animals that would have been available to them indicate that Neandertals consumed a large quantity of meat (data from Bocherens et al. 1999; Richards and Trinkaus 2009).

Reports of the postmortem modification of Neandertal remains, possibly for the purpose of consumption, date back to 1899 when excavations at the site of Krapina in Croatia uncovered a large number of broken, burned, and cut bones scattered around fire pits. More recently, a Neandertal skull with broken cranial base was recovered from the Guattari cave in Italy and was interpreted as reflecting removal of the brain for consumption. Subsequent reanalyses of the Guattari and Krapina fossils has since revealed that the observed damage is more consistent with post-depositional processes, including scavenging by carnivores and the postmortem preparation of bodies for burial (see the next section, as well as Russell 1987; Trinkaus 1985; White and Toth 1991). The cannibalism theory has been revived, however, by the discovery of cut marks on the bones of six Neandertal skeletons recovered from the site of Moula-Guercy (Defleur et al. 1999). Neandertal remains and deer bones found at the site exhibited similar cut marks, and the bones of both species had been broken open, presumably to extract the marrow. Cut marks on the lingual (inner) surface of a juvenile Neandertal mandible suggest that its tongue had been cut out (ibid.). While this evidence is certainly convincing, the question remains as to why Neandertals engaged in this activity in the first place.

Ritual and Symbolic Behaviour

Neandertals are often referred to as the first humans to practise intentional burial. Indeed, numerous Neandertals have been found buried in caves. Archaeological evidence commonly cited as proof of deliberate burial includes articulated skeletal remains, an unusual positioning of the body, the presence of presumed grave goods such as tools and animal bones, and the presence of floral and burned remains possibly reflecting funerary rituals. For example, the site of La Ferrassie in France is often cited as strong evidence of purposeful burial based on the interment of eight individuals of varying ages, a number of them very well preserved, in what some have interpreted as a possible family burial plot. An infant burial in the Amud Cave in Israel has also been cited as evidence of a deliberate burial (Rak et al. 1994). Its articulated skeleton was found lying on its right side with the maxilla of a red deer leaning against its pelvis.

As critics point out, good preservation and articulation of skeletal remains may also occur as a result of natural depositional processes in caves and rock shelters (Gargett 1989, 1999). At the Kebara Cave site in Israel, for instance, anthropologist Rob Gargett has argued that a partially disarticulated incomplete skeleton of a Neandertal (Figure 11.20), interpreted by some

FIGURE 11.20 This Neandertal skeleton, found in the Kebara Cave site in Israel, has been interpreted by some as evidence of intentional burial.

© Javier Trueba/MSF/Science Photo Library

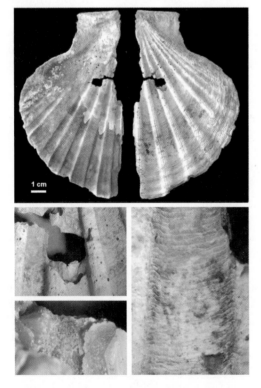

FIGURE 11.21 These perforated marine shells were recovered from a Neandertal site in Spain.

Zilhao et al. 2010. Symbolic use of marine shells and mineral pigments by Iberian Neandertals. Proceedings of the National Academy of Sciences 107(3): 1023–1028.

as evidence of purposeful burial in a "pit," is more consistent with "slow decomposition and natural burial" (Gargett 1999, 69) based on the fact that it is surrounded by sediments that are indistinguishable from those above it, other pits of similar size containing no human remains are present below the skeleton, and the pattern of disarticulation is what would be expected following decomposition and disturbance.

Similarly, Simon Fraser University archaeologist Dennis Sandgathe and his colleagues have challenged the status of the Roc de Marsal Neandertal child as a case of deliberate burial (Sandgathe et al. 2011) based on stratigraphic, geological, and archaeological data, arguing that the depression containing the skeleton was likely naturally formed, the artifacts associated with the remains were not distinct from those found in other layers of the site, the position of the body suggests no special treatment, and the high level of intactness of the skeleton could occur if, for example, the individual died during the winter and froze quickly. As for the pollen discovered in the famous Shanidar burial from Iraq and interpreted as evidence of burial with wildflowers, it may have blown into the cave or been carried into the grave by burrowing rodents (Sommer 1999). Despite these criticisms, many researchers today believe that at least some Neandertal burials are real and that they reflect deliberate actions.

Other Neandertal behaviours considered to be symbolic in nature include the use of red ochre, now dated to as early as 200,000 to 250,000 years ago (Roebroeks et al. 2012), the extraction of feathers and modification of skeletal remains of large raptors (Finlayson et al. 2012; Morin and Laroulandie 2012), and the manufacture of objects such as pendants (Figure 11.21; Caron et al. 2011; Zilhão et al. 2010), although the association between some of the latter artifacts and Neandertals has been challenged based on a re-dating of their archaeological context (Higham et al. 2010).

Neandertal Language Capabilities

We have not yet considered the language capabilities of our hominin ancestors. As spoken language among all primates is unique to humans, the origins of language has been a topic of great interest, and researchers have attempted to determine when speech first appeared in our evolutionary history based on morphological and behavioural features of earlier hominins. As you will recall from Chapter 6, nonhuman primates lack the ability to speak because they lack the vocal apparatus necessary for human speech. Inferences have been made, however, from the fossil evidence of early *Homo*. Some scholars have argued, for instance, that endocranial cast asymmetry in the form of enlargement of the left hemisphere, as seen in some fossil specimens, points to the development of rudimentary language in early *Homo* and *Homo erectus* (Broadfield et al. 2001; Holloway 1999). Such claims have been disputed however, and some researchers believe that language as we know it today did not emerge until later in human evolution, coinciding with the appearance of anatomically modern humans some 150,000 to 200,000 years ago (see Chapter 12).

Two other anatomical features have also been used to make inferences about speech capabilities in earlier hominins. A low **larynx** and large **pharynx**, for example, have long been considered "anatomical prerequisites for producing the full range of human speech" (Lieberman and Crelin 1971, 220). Sound generated in the larynx, or voice box, is modified by the pharynx, the cavity above the larynx in which our familiar vowel sounds are produced. The position of the larynx and the size of the pharynx can be inferred from the degree of flexion of the base of the skull (**basicranial flexion**; Figure 11.22). Based on

larynx

an organ in the neck responsible for the production of sound; also known as the voice box

pharynx

part of the neck and throat located superior to the larynx that modifies sounds made by the larynx

basicranial flexion

the degree of angling of the base of the skull from which the position of the larynx and size of the pharynx can be inferred

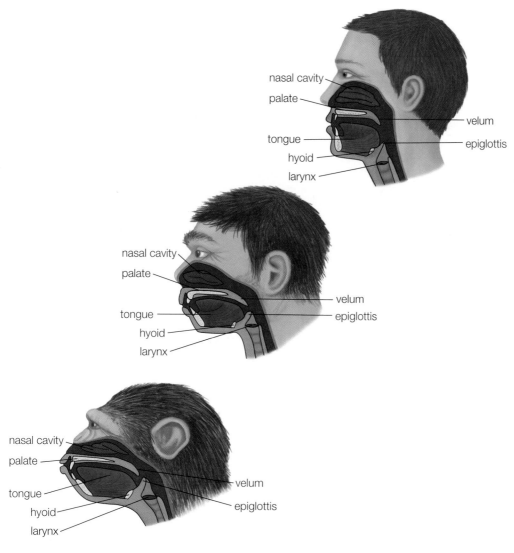

FIGURE 11.22 Compared to chimpanzees (bottom), Neandertals (middle) have a lower larynx and a longer pharynx, as indicated by the angle of the base of their skull.

their reconstruction of the vocal anatomy of Neandertals—most notably, a higher positioned larynx and smaller pharynx compared to modern humans—Lieberman and Crelin (1971) concluded that they were incapable of making the full range of sounds made by modern humans.

The accuracy of this reconstruction has been questioned, however, and a recent study has revealed that the Neandertal **vowel space** was comparable in size to that of modern humans, suggesting that they could potentially have made the same range of sounds we can (Boë et al. 2002). The 1988 discovery, in the Kebara Cave in Israel, of a 60,000-year-old Neandertal **hyoid bone** almost identical in size and shape to that of modern humans has also been used to argue that Neandertal vocal capabilities were very similar to our own, based on the claim that the position of the larynx to which this bone is connected was also similar to that of modern humans (Arensberg et al. 1990).

New genetic evidence has provided additional clues to Neandertal language capabilities in the form of a genetic variant called *FOXP2*, which is found in modern humans and which plays a role in speech and language.[6] Initially thought to have originated in modern humans less than 200,000 years ago (Enard et al. 2002), this variant has been detected in two Neandertal specimens from Spain dating to approximately 43,000 years before present (Krause et al. 2007), supporting the argument that Neandertals possessed language abilities similar to those of modern humans.

DECIPHERING THE NEANDERTAL GENOME

The taxonomic status of Neandertals and their relationship to modern humans has been the topic of some of the most heated debates in paleoanthropology. On the one hand, many have argued that the Neandertals were morphologically too specialized to have contributed to the modern human gene pool and that they represent a different species, *Homo neanderthalensis*. This view is supported by some of the growth studies that were discussed earlier in this chapter. Opponents, however, argue that Neandertals were not so distinct from modern humans and should therefore be classified as a subspecies, *Homo sapiens neanderthalensis*. As you will learn in Chapter 12, skeletal remains exhibiting a mosaic of Neandertal and modern human features have in fact been found in Portugal, lending support to the argument that the two groups interbred.

Within the past decade, genetic data have provided a new means of addressing the position of Neandertals in our evolutionary history. In 1997, scientists announced that they had sequenced mitochondrial DNA from the Neandertal-type specimen discovered in the Neander Valley 1856 (Krings et al. 1997). To verify the results, the mtDNA was extracted and analyzed at two different labs, one in Europe and one in the United States. Comparison of the Neandertal mtDNA with that of modern humans revealed that the Neandertal sequence showed three to four times the number of differences than are typically seen among living humans. On this basis, Krings and colleagues (1997) concluded that Neandertals and modern humans were separate species who last shared a common ancestor sometime between 550,000 and 690,000 years ago.

Critics of these results were quick to point out that the mtDNA used in this study was extracted from only one individual and that the degree of difference between the Neandertal mtDNA and that of modern humans is less than what is seen between humans and our closest living relatives, the chimpanzees. Since then, however, mtDNA has been extracted from more than a dozen additional Neandertal skeletons (Beauval et al. 2005; Briggs et al. 2009; Caramelli et al. 2006; Green et al. 2008; Krings et al. 2000; Lalueza-Fox et al. 2005; Orlando et al. 2006; Ovchinnikov et al. 2000; Schmitz et al. 2002; Serre et al. 2004.). All sequences have been found to fall outside the range of variation seen in modern humans, suggesting that Neandertals contributed few if any of their genes to the modern European gene pool.

vowel space

The space within the oral cavity in which vowel sounds are created by altering the relative position of tongue and pharynx

hyoid bone

a bone in the neck that supports the tongue and provides attachment for muscles that connect to the larynx

---

6. People with mutations of this gene have impaired speech.

The analysis of mtDNA has also extended the geographic range of Neandertals to the site of Okladnikov in Siberia (Krause et al. 2007).

Studies of nuclear DNA have yielded interesting results as well. We noted the *FOXP2* gene above, and Lalueza-Fox and colleagues (2007) identified a variant of the *MC1R* gene associated with pigmentation in a 43,000-year-old specimen from Spain, suggesting that this individual had fair skin and red hair. The sequencing of nuclear DNA from a 38,000-year-old Neandertal fossil recovered from the Vindija Cave in Croatia demonstrated its distinctiveness from that of modern humans and suggested that the two groups shared a most recent common ancestor approximately 700,000 years ago (Noonan et al. 2006). Four years later, a draft sequence numbering 4 billion nucleotides of the Neandertal genome was published (Green et al. 2010). The researchers conducting this study recovered genomic DNA from four sites spanning the geographic range of Neandertals in Europe (most of the sequence was prepared from three individuals sampled from Vindija Cave, Croatia). This sequence was then compared to "libraries" of the modern human and chimpanzee genomes, as well as to data from five selected human individuals from Europe, west and southern Africa, China, and Oceania.

These comparisons point to a number of significant outcomes. While Neandertals and modern humans are estimated to have diverged between 270,000 and 440,000 years ago, any given human currently shares between 1% and 4% of his or her genome with Neandertals, but collectively—as a species—modern humans may share between 20% and 30% of our genome with our cousins (see Box 11.2).[7] Furthermore, gene flow seems to have occurred between Neandertals and early modern humans in Europe, but not in Africa. Green and colleagues hypothesized that this admixture would have taken place in the Near East shortly after modern humans left Africa, thus explaining the lack of Neandertal nuclear DNA in Africans. Subsequent studies have confirmed admixture between Neandertals and Eurasians (Yotova et al. 2011), but one recent study has revealed evidence of admixture between Neandertals and North Africans (Sánchez-Quinto et al. 2012). As researchers point out, greater sampling of African populations and a better understanding of African genetic diversity are needed in order to determine exactly when and where admixture occurred (Hodgson et al. 2010).

A remarkable new discovery was announced in March 2010 in the form of a mitochondrial DNA sequence obtained from a small finger bone excavated in 2008 from Denisova Cave in the Altai Mountains of southern Siberia. Much to the surprise of the researchers conducting this study, the bone, dating from 48,000 to 30,000 years ago, yielded a mtDNA sequence that was distinctly different from that of both Neandertals and early modern humans who lived in the area, suggesting that a third hominin lineage may have been present in this region at the same time (Krause et al. 2010; Figure 11.23). Furthermore, the study revealed that the Denisova hominin shared a common ancestor with Neandertals and anatomically modern humans approximately 1 Ma, while the latter two shared a common ancestor approximately 466,000 years ago. The retrieval of a nuclear genome sequence from the same bone indicated that while

FIGURE 11.23 Sequencing of mtDNA from a finger bone excavated from the Denisova Cave in southern Siberia revealed a lineage distinct from that of Neandertals and anatomically modern humans.

7. This low level of admixture reflects a low rate of interbreeding between Neandertals and Eurasians, possibly due to mating avoidance, a low reproductive fitness of hybrids, or both (Currat and Excoffier 2011).

CHAPTER 11 The Advent of Humanity

BOX 11.2   FOCUS ON ... Humans 'R' Neandertals

Molecular anthropological approaches to understanding our recent evolutionary history have made amazing strides in the past few years. As noted in the text, several studies in the past decade have recovered both mitochondrial and nuclear ancient DNA from isolated Neandertal individuals and skeletal elements. These discoveries point to a number of interbreeding events during the last 100,000 years between Neandertals, their "sister" group from Denisova, and more recently ancestral modern humans in Europe, East Asia and North Africa. Now, two studies published in early 2014 using modern human DNA have shed even more startling insights into our past liaisons with Neandertals.

Using different analytical methods, teams from the University of Washington (Vernot and Akey 2014) and Harvard University (Sankararaman et al. 2014) sought evidence of Neandertal genes represented in the modern human genome that had been sequenced as part of the 1000 Genomes project (www.1000genomes.org). Their research focused on genetic variation in single nucleotide polymorphisms and haplotype length (shared allele sequences), which they then compared with the Altai Neandertal nuclear genome map (Prüfer et al. 2014). What they found and, importantly *did not find*, gives us reason to reconsider both the social and biological relationships among these various early hominins roaming Europe and Asia during the Upper Paleolithic.

One important outcome of these studies was the considerable agreement in their results, even though methods differed. For example, both studies found Neandertal DNA in our DNA that is associated with a gene involved in the production of the protein keratin (a component of hair, skin, and nails). Keratin plays an important role in skin pigmentation, sensitivity to heat and cold, "waterproofing," and as a barrier to bacterial infection. These researchers hypothesize that the Neandertal genes may have adapted modern humans to the particular climates they encountered in Europe and East Asia. However, they also found other Neandertal genes that may have increased risk for certain diseases common among modern

populations, including type 2 diabetes, Crohn's disease, and primary biliary cirrhosis (a degenerative liver disease). These negative outcomes probably did not occur in Neandertals, but—this research suggests—may be due to an unfavourable interaction with the modern human genome. That is, in some cases, Neandertal and modern human DNA are not compatible.

A surprising outcome of these studies is that the distribution of Neandertal genes in the modern genome is not uniform. In some parts of our genome, Neandertal ancestry may be as high as 62% to 64% (Sankararamann et al. 2014), while in other locations, both teams of researchers found virtual "deserts" (to use their description) of Neandertal DNA, occurring at less than 0.1% of the modern genome. This is particularly evident in regions of the X chromosome, and for genes related to testicular function in males. To be blunt: Neandertal DNA seems to not be compatible with modern human sexual function. The obvious question is why?

The answer seems to be that men belonging to *Homo sapiens* who happened, by virtue of parentage, to carry Neandertal genes for testes function were less likely to reproduce themselves—in Darwinian terms, they were less fit. As one of the Harvard team, David Reich, stated in an interview: "A massive process has removed at least one-third of the Neandertal ancestry that initially came into the modern human genome" (Gibbons 2014). In fact, biologists are quite familiar with such an outcome, having observed it experimentally in species that reproduce quickly compared to ourselves (mice, rabbits, fruit flies, and such). We now know that hybrid male sterility signals incipient speciation (refer back to Chapter 4 regarding isolating mechanisms). At the same time, modern human females—having two X chromosomes and of course not limited by impact on testes function—might remain fertile in any encounter with a Neandertal male. Which raises the interesting question: Have modern humans inherited more Neandertal DNA from "Mom" than from "Dad"?

Neandertals interacted with the ancestors of present-day Eurasian populations and contributed their genes to them, the Denisovans did not. Rather, the latter contributed 4 to 6% of their genes to present-day Melanesians (Papua New Guineans) (Reich et al. 2010; Figure 11.24). Further analysis has revealed that gene flow between Denisovans and the ancestors of modern Melanesians occurred within Southeast Asia, indicating a very widespread population of Denisovans (Reich et al. 2011).

Significant advances continue to be made with respect to our knowledge of Late Pleistocene hominins. A recent analysis of a Neandertal toe bone recovered from the Denisova Cave has indicated that interbreeding occurred among a number of distinct hominin populations, including an unknown hominin group (Prüfer et al. 2014). Genetic data are also being used to investigate Middle Pleistocene hominins. Recall our earlier discussion of the fossils recovered from Sima de los Huesos (the "Pit of Bones") in Atapuerca, Spain. The retrieval of a

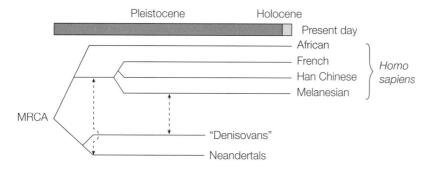

FIGURE 11.24 Genetic evidence indicates that Neandertals interbred with Eurasians and Denisovans with Melanesians.

mitochondrial DNA sequence from one of these individuals demonstrates that it more closely resembles that of Denisovans than of Neandertals, a surprising finding given that these fossils display a number of Neandertal features (Meyer et al. 2013). This observation raises the possibility that the Sima de los Huesos hominins were related to the population that gave rise to both Neandertals and Denisovans, or that their mtDNA derives from another hominin population (Meyer et al. 2013). Whatever the case may be, these findings add another layer of complexity to our understanding of human evolutionary history in Middle and Late Pleistocene Eurasia.

The Fate of Neandertals

Radiometric dating indicates that Neandertals disappeared from western Asia around 45,000 years ago and from most of Europe by 30,000 years ago, although one site in Gibraltar suggests that Neandertals may have survived in this area until at least 28,000 years ago (Finlayson et al. 2006). Until recently, the popular explanation for their demise was that they were supplanted by modern humans who possessed a more effective technological and cultural repertoire, including better clothing, shelter, and hunting technology, more diverse subsistence strategies, enhanced mobility, and larger social networks. In other words, they were out-competed. This argument was based largely on evidence indicating substantial behavioural differences between Neandertals and modern humans. In recent years, however, it has become increasingly apparent that the technology, subsistence strategies, and symbolic behaviour of Neandertals was not markedly different from that of early anatomically modern humans (D'Errico 2003) and that the transition from the Middle to Upper Palaeolithic, discussed in more detail in the next chapter, was one of mosaic evolution rather than cultural revolution (McBrearty and Brooks 2000).

There is growing consensus that no single factor can account for the disappearance of Neandertals and that a variety of factors—including deteriorating climatic conditions and diminishing food resources—may have contributed to their decline. Paleoclimatic records reveal unstable conditions between 40,000 and 25,000 years ago, with the most severe and prolonged period of climatic stress occurring around 30,000 years ago. These unstable conditions may have precipitated the extinction of the large herd animals on which the Neandertals depended for food (Stringer 2008; Stringer et al. 2004). Archaeologist Eugène Morin of Trent University analyzed the faunal remains from Saint-Césaire and found that as the temperature declined, the proportion of reindeer in the Neandertal diet increased while the proportion of horses, bison, and red deer decreased. Heavier reliance on reindeer—a species whose populations are known to fluctuate widely—would have placed Neandertals at increased risk of famine and led to decreased population densities, ultimately contributing to their demise (Morin 2008). Finally, an estimated tenfold increase in the population of anatomically modern humans, calculated based on archaeological evidence (stone tool densities, meat-weight densities, and occupation areas) from western Europe, may also have played an important role in the demise of the Neandertals (Mellars and French 2011).

LEARNING KEYS

KEY IDEAS

- Archaic hominins possessed a combination of features seen in earlier *Homo erectus* fossils, as well as those of anatomically modern humans.

- Archaic hominins had a significantly larger cranial capacity, a more rounded skull, and smaller teeth than *Homo erectus*, but some retained a large supraorbital torus and a receding forehead.

- One species of archaic hominin, classified as *Homo antecessor*, has been identified in the fossil record from Spain, and may have originated from *Homo erectus/ergaster* in Africa.

- The origins of a second species of archaic hominin, classified as *Homo heidelbergensis*, remain unclear, but some consider it to be ancestral to Neandertals in western Eurasia and the earliest *Homo sapiens* in Africa.

- The most well-known archaic hominins, Neandertals, possessed a large skull with a low vault and low, sloping forehead; midfacial prognathism; a large nasal cavity; large, rounded orbits; prominent arched browridges; and an occipital bun.

- Neandertals were short and stocky, with robust, heavily muscled, and slightly curved long bones, and a large, barrel-shaped chest.

- Neandertals' large prognathic face, large nasal cavities, heavily worn incisors, and short, stocky body build are likely the result of a combination of factors, including adaptation to cold temperatures, heavy chewing stresses resulting from the use of the teeth as tools, and a physically strenuous lifestyle.

- Neandertals used Mousterian tools, hunted large game animals, practised cannibalism, occupied caves and rock shelters, used fire, wore clothing made from animal hides, practised intentional burial, and produced items that can be considered art.

- Pathological lesions on Neandertals' skeletons point to a hard life characterized by traumatic injuries due to accidents, interpersonal violence, nutritional deficiencies, and joint disease.

- The extraction and sequencing of nuclear DNA from Neandertal remains indicate that these hominins contribute to the modern human gene pool.

- A third hominin lineage referred to as the Denisovans has also been revealed through genetic analysis of fossil remains, and appears to have shared a common ancestor with Neandertals and modern humans.

- Neandertals disappeared from western Asia around 45,000 years ago and from most of Europe by 30,000 years ago.

- Factors that may have contributed to Neandertals' demise include a less effective technology than that of modern humans, deteriorating climatic conditions, and diminishing food resources.

KEY TERMS

Neandertals (p. 250)

archaic hominins (p. 250)

occipital bun (p. 257)

linear enamel hypoplasia (p. 262)

Mousterian (p. 262)

Middle Paleolithic (p. 262)

Levallois (p. 262)

zooarchaeology (p. 264)

KEY QUESTIONS TO ASK MYSELF

1. Why have Neandertals been portrayed so negatively for such a long time?

2. What might have prompted Neandertals to interbreed with modern humans, or avoid interbreeding with them?

3. Were biological or cultural adaptations more important for hominins such as Neandertals who lived in cold climates?

KEY CRITICAL THINKING QUESTIONS

1. Neandertal body size and proportions are often compared to those of modern Inuit in attempts to explain their significance. Is this an appropriate comparison? Why or why not?

2. Neandertal remains that have been found to date include a number of sub-adult skeletons. Why might it be more difficult to estimate the age at death of fossilized remains such as these than of modern human remains?

3. Why do you think there has been such a heated debate regarding whether Neandertals interbred with modern humans?

KEY THINGS TO DO NEXT

CourseMate Visit **CourseMate** at www.nelson.com/humanvoyage2e to build your comprehension, practise your critical thinking skills, review core concepts, and explore other resources at your disposal.

12 The Emergence of Anatomically Modern Humans

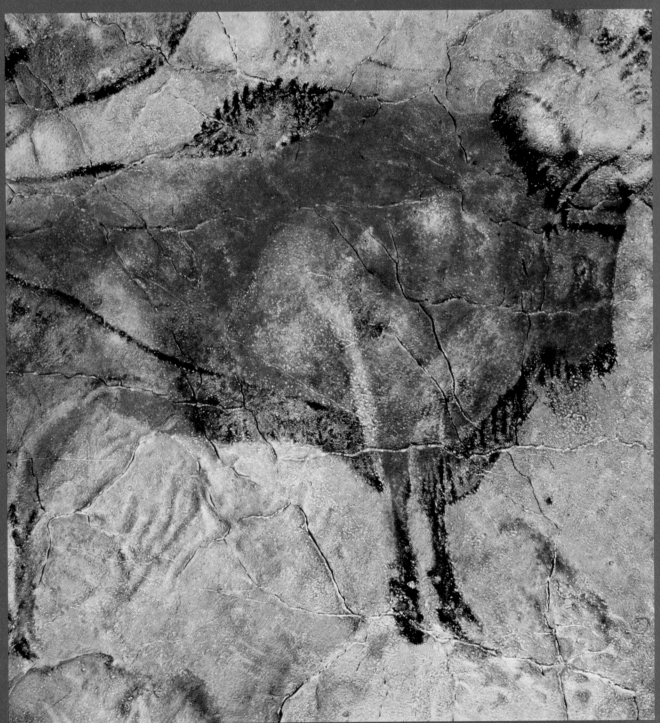

*Alone among all creatures, the species that styles itself wise,
Homo sapiens, has an abiding interest in its distant origins,
knows that its allotted time is short, worries about the future
and wonders about the past.*

John Noble Wilford, Journalist

OVERVIEW

This chapter examines the emergence and spread of anatomically modern *Homo sapiens* and their morphological and behavioural characteristics. Most paleoanthropologists now agree that fully modern humans first evolved in Africa from archaic hominins but continue to disagree on exactly how they came to occupy other regions of the Old World and what their relationship was to earlier hominins in these regions. We introduce you to several models for explaining the origins of modern humans, and examine each model with respect to the fossil and genetic evidence. We review the cultural and behavioural adaptations of *Homo sapiens* and assess the ongoing debate concerning the emergence of modern human behaviour. Finally, we examine the evidence for the initial human colonization of Australia and the Americas.

KEY CONCEPTS

Out of Africa, multiregional evolution, transitional fossils, replacement, hybridization, assimilation, last common ancestor, behavioural modernity

KEY LEARNING OBJECTIVES

At the end of this chapter, you will be able to

LO1 List at least four ways in which the earliest modern humans differed anatomically from archaic hominins and Neandertals

LO2 Summarize the fossil and genetic evidence for modern human origins

LO3 Apply your knowledge of the archaeological and genetic evidence for the peopling of the Americas to assess the timing, route, and number of migrations

LO4 Compare and contrast the behavioural adaptations of modern humans with those of archaic hominins

LO5 Evaluate the models that have been proposed to explain the origins of anatomically modern humans

LO6 Predict how early modern humans may have varied physically based on the environmental conditions in which they lived

PROLOGUE: DANCING WITH NEANDERTALS?

It is possible that one of the questions that prompted you to take this course is a simple one: "Where did I come from?" Or something similar—perhaps "Am I *really* related to chimpanzees?" By now we hope you realize that, while the question is simple, the answer is frightfully complicated. This is true even though we have not only *more* evidence than ever before, but more *lines* of evidence, including several varieties of molecular data. Given that modern *Homo sapiens* has been around for less than 5% of our 6.5-million-year evolutionary story as hominins, one would think that having such a wealth of information relating to recent events would settle the matter. Far from the truth, as this chapter will attest.

There are, in fact, a number of interrelated questions when it comes to the appearance of those hominins collectively referred to as "anatomically modern *Homo sapiens*" (intentionally, to distinguish them from something less anatomically modern, e.g., archaic forms such as Neandertals). Succinctly put, the issues are these: Where did we come from, where did we go, and what did we do when we got there? Or more bluntly: origin—migration—behaviour. Our interests here are several. We are, after all, talking about *us*—our most immediate ancestors, who by and large (and for want of a shower or a shave) could be sitting next to you as you read this. We are also talking about our ancestors who colonized the most remote parts of the planet—namely, Australia and the Americas, North and South from Nunavut to Patagonia. And—not least especially—we are talking about the advent of so much of ourselves that we presently take for granted: art, symbolism, and **signification**. Hence the complications!

As you will see in this chapter, it comes down to "sharing and caring." How much of the genome, morphology, and behaviour of our anatomically modern relatives will we find among the archaic hominins (e.g., Neandertals)? Was contact sociable or violent? Did we mingle, murder, or both?

signification

a sign (a character, a word, an image) that identifies an entity or assigns meaning to a situation; for example, a red light at an intersection or a dollar sign

MODERN HUMANS TAKE THE STAGE

Anatomically modern *Homo sapiens* began to appear sometime between 150,000 and 200,000 years ago. Compared to their predecessors, they possessed a higher, more rounded cranium, an average cranial capacity of about 1,500 cc, a more vertically oriented forehead with relatively small browridges, a smaller and flatter face, smaller teeth, and a well-developed chin (Figure 12.1). The first anatomically modern humans also possessed a more lightly built postcranial skeleton with straighter, less robust limb bones than earlier hominins.

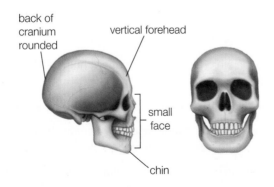

FIGURE 12.1 Compared to archaic hominins, anatomically modern humans had a higher and more rounded skull, a vertical forehead, smaller browridges, a smaller, flatter face, smaller teeth, and a projecting chin.

back of cranium rounded

vertical forehead

small face

chin

THE ORIGINS OF ANATOMICALLY MODERN HUMANS

Considerable debate surrounds the origins of anatomically modern humans. While we know that archaic hominins evolved into modern *Homo sapiens*, we are less certain about where and when this occurred. Three models have been proposed by anthropologists to explain the origins of modern humans: (1) the recent out-of-Africa model, (2) the assimilation model, and (3) the multiregional evolution model. We will review these models and consider the fossil and genetic evidence for each.

Recent Out-of-Africa Model

The recent out-of-Africa model (Figure 12.2) proposes that modern humans first evolved in Africa between 150,000 and 200,000 years ago, then spread to Europe and Asia, replacing pre-existing archaic populations in these regions with little or no interbreeding (Stringer and Andrews 1988). It holds that Neandertals and other archaic populations were separate species that were either wiped out or driven to extinction by modern humans. This model makes several predictions: (1) that the earliest anatomically modern human fossils are found in Africa and that modern humans found in Europe and Asia are more recent; (2) that archaic and anatomically modern humans overlapped more or less briefly in areas of the Old World into which the latter moved; (3) that the archaeological record shows a sudden change in technology and behaviour during the replacement event; and (4) that genetic evidence reveals distinct differences between archaic and modern humans—that is, the genes of all modern humans in Eurasia are derived only from populations that lived in Africa 150,000 to 200,000 years ago.

Assimilation Model

The assimilation model (Figure 12.2) proposes that modern humans first evolved in Africa and spread from there to other regions of the Old World, where they interbred with small archaic populations, genetically swamping them (Smith, Jankovic, and Karavanic 2005; Trinkaus 2005, 2007). Predictions from this model are that (1) the earliest anatomically modern human fossils are found in Africa; (2) the fossil evidence points to interbreeding between archaic and modern humans; (3) the archaeological record shows a diffusion of technological and stylistic traits between archaic and modern populations; and (4) the genetic evidence shows little or no evidence of Neandertal and other archaic genes in modern populations due to assimilation by a larger, more genetically diverse population.

The Multiregional Evolution Model

The multiregional evolution model (Figure 12.2) proposes that archaic humans evolved into modern *Homo sapiens* in several regions of the Old World and that extensive gene flow between regions maintained these populations as a single species (Thorne and Wolpoff 1992;

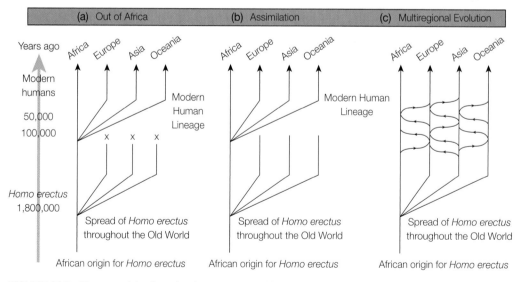

FIGURE 12.2 Three models of modern human origins: (a) recent out-of-Africa; (b) assimilation; (c) multiregional evolution.

Adapted from Tryon, C. & Bailey, S. (2013) Testing Models of Modern Human Origins with Archaeology and Anatomy. *Nature Education Knowledge* 4(3):4; Stoneking, Mark, "Human Origins: The Molecular Perspective," *EMBO Reports*, Vol. 9, Special Report, 2008.

Wolpoff, Zhi, and Thorne 1984). At the same time, regional differences emerged because of different local selective pressures. It predicts that (1) the fossil record from Africa, Europe, and Asia shows continuity in the form of transitional fossils possessing morphological characteristics of both archaic and modern humans; (2) the archaeological record shows continuity in technology and behaviour; and (3) the genetic data show lineages emerging from several different regions of the Old World, as well as evidence of gene flow between these regions.

What Do the Fossils Tell Us?

Fossil evidence for early modern humans has been uncovered in Africa, Europe, and Asia (Figure 12.3). There is considerable uncertainty with respect to the dating of some of these specimens, especially those from East Asia, and disagreements have surrounded the interpretation of this evidence. As you will see, some of the same fossils have been used to support more than one model of modern human origins.

With respect to the recent out-of-Africa model, the fossil evidence meets the first prediction—namely, that the earliest evidence for anatomically modern humans comes from Africa. The oldest fossils are represented by a partial skeleton recovered from the site of Omo and dated to approximately 195,000 years. based on argon-argon dating of the deposits in which it was found (McDougall, Brown, and Fleagle 2005). The partial remains of three individuals, including a cranium dating to 160,000 years ago, have been recovered from the site of Herto in Ethiopia. Modern features of this cranium include a high, rounded vault; a vertical forehead; and a small face (Figure 12.4; White et al. 2003). Other sites that have yielded the remains of fully modern humans are Aduma in Ethiopia, which yielded cranial

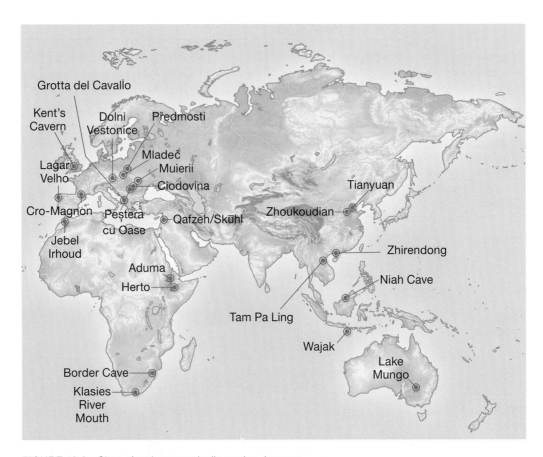

FIGURE 12.3 Sites of early anatomically modern humans.

remains dating from 105,000 to 70,000 years ago (Haile-Selassie et al. 2004a); Klasies River Mouth, a cave site on the coast of South Africa from which fragmentary remains, including a mandible with a distinct chin dating to more than 100,000 years ago (Feathers 2002) have been recovered; Border Cave, South Africa, from which a partial cranium dating to 90,000 years ago has been found (Grün and Beaumont 2001); and Jebel Irhoud, Morocco, from which remains dating to approximately 160,000 years ago have been excavated (Smith et al. 2007).

The earliest anatomically modern humans in the Near East are currently represented by several well-known specimens. These include crania from the cave sites of Qafzeh and Skhūl (Figure 12.5) in Israel, dating to between 110,000 and 90,000 years ago. In contrast, the appearance of anatomically modern humans in Europe is much more recent, post-dating 45,000 years ago. Among the earliest sites with human remains are Grotta del Cavallo in southern Italy (45,000 to 43,000 years ago; Benazzi et al. 2011), Kent's Cavern in the United Kingdom (44,000 to 41,000 years ago; Higham et al. 2011), Peștera cu Oase (35,000 years ago), Muierii Cave (30,000 years ago), and Cioclovina Cave in Romania (29,000 years ago), Mladeč (31,000 years ago) (Figure 12.6), Dolní Vestonice (26,000 years ago) (Figure 12.7), and Předmostí in the Czech Republic (27,000 to 24,000 years ago), and Cro-Magnon in southwestern France (28,000 years ago) (Figure 12.8). The expansion of modern humans across Europe appears to have occurred rapidly, and the overlap between modern humans and Neandertals may have been as short as 1,000 to 2,000 years in some places (Mellars 2006).

The fossilized remains of anatomically modern humans do not appear in China until about 40,000 years ago (Shang et al. 2007), although a partial mandible from Zhirendong (Zhiren Cave), dated to approximately 100,000 years ago, may be the oldest early modern human to be found in East Asia (Liu et al. 2010). A partial skeleton recovered from Tianyuan Cave dates to approximately 40,000 years ago (Shang et al. 2007), and several anatomically modern crania recovered from the Upper Cave at Zhoukoudian have been dated to 29,000 to 24,000 years ago. (Suzuki and Hanihara 1982). A partial cranium dating to at least 46,000 years ago has also been recovered from the site of Tam Pa Ling in Laos, indicating that modern humans had reached mainland Southeast Asia by about 50,000 years ago (Demeter et al. 2012). A date of 45,000 to 39,000 years ago has been assigned to modern human fossils from Niah Cave in Borneo (Barker et al. 2007), and human bones from Wajak, Indonesia, have recently been dated to between 37,000 and 28,000 years ago (Storm et al. 2013). Similarly, securely dated fossils from Australia indicate the presence of anatomically modern *Homo sapiens* by 40,000 years ago (see below).

The fossil evidence appears to meet the second prediction of the recent out-of-Africa model, as well—namely, that archaic and anatomically modern humans overlapped briefly in

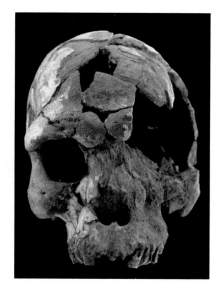

FIGURE 12.4 This anatomically modern skull from Herto is estimated to be about 160,000 years old.

Fossil credit: © 2000 David L. Brill, Brill Atlanta

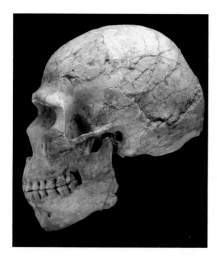

FIGURE 12.5 Recovered from the site of Skhūl in Israel, this 100,000-year-old cranium exhibits many modern features, including a high vertical forehead and a distinct chin.

Fossil credit: Peabody Museum, Harvard University. Copyright protection notice: © 1985 David L. Brill\Brill Atlanta

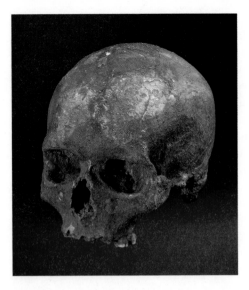

FIGURE 12.6 The Mladeč Caves in the Czech Republic have yielded early modern human remains, including this approximately 30,000-year-old cranium.

© Wolfang Reichmann, Naturhistorisches Museum, Wien

FIGURE 12.7 The cranium of this individual from Dolní Vestonice exhibits features of anatomically modern humans, including a high, rounded vault; a non-projecting face; and a distinct chin.

© Pascal Goetgheluck/Science Photo Library

FIGURE 12.8 This skull, known as Cro-Magnon 1, was discovered in 1868 and was among the first fossils to be recognized as belonging to *Homo sapiens*.

© John Reader/Science Photo Library

areas of the Old World into which the latter moved. More specifically, a number of sites in Europe and the Near East have yielded Neandertal remains that are contemporaneous with or postdate those of modern humans, suggesting that they coexisted in these regions for thousands of years.

What about the assimilation model? Several sites in Europe have yielded early modern human remains displaying a mosaic of modern features and Neandertal traits such as an occipital bun. These include specimens from Peştera cu Oase (Rougier et al. 2007; Trinkaus et al. 2003) and the Muierii and Cioclovina Caves (Soficaru, Dobos, and Trinkhaus 2006; Trinkaus 2007). One European fossil in particular, the skeleton of a four-year-old child (Figure 12.9), has gained considerable attention for its "hybrid" status. Excavated from the site of Lagar Velho in Portugal and dating to 24,500 years ago, this skeleton exhibits the lower-limb robusticity and length typical of Neandertals, while at the same time possessing a distinct chin, dental proportions, and pubic ramus length characteristic of early modern humans (Duarte et al. 1999). The fact that this individual is a juvenile, however, makes it difficult to draw conclusions about its adult morphology, especially given that very little is known about the range of morphological variation in children during this time period. As Tattersall and Schwartz (1999, 7119) remark: "The probability must thus remain that this is simply a chunky Gravettian child."[1]

---

1. "Gravettian" refers to a specific technological tool industry identified for the European Upper Paleolithic dating to 28,500 to 21,000 years ago.

What about the multiregional evolution model? The fossil record provides some support for its first prediction—namely, that continuity is evident in Africa, Europe, and Asia in the form of transitional fossils possessing morphological characteristics of both archaic and modern humans. For example, moderately heavy browridges and facial prognathism seen in the *Homo erectus* cranium from Sangiran in Indonesia are also found in some of the early modern human specimens recovered from Australia (Thorne and Wolpoff 1992; Wolpoff et al. 1984). Continuity is also evident in the fossil record from China, suggesting a gradual transition from *Homo erectus* to modern *Homo sapiens* in this region (Wu 2004).

What Does the Genetic Evidence Tell Us?

The first genetic studies to investigate modern human origins involved the use of mitochondrial DNA (mtDNA) derived from living populations. As you will recall from Chapter 3, mtDNA is inherited only from females, while nDNA comes from both mother and father. In 1987 a group of researchers from Berkeley attracted international attention when they published genetic data supporting an exclusively African origin for modern *Homo sapiens*. The team, led by Rebecca Cann (Cann, Stoneking, and Wilson 1987), took mtDNA samples from 147 modern women representing five different ethnic groups from Africa, Asia, Europe, Australia, and New Guinea. Comparisons of these samples revealed little genetic variation, indicating that these women shared a common ancestor relatively recently. The team's analysis also revealed that the mtDNA of the African women exhibited the greatest amount of variation, as would be expected if they had more time to diverge or accumulate genetic differences; thus, they represented the oldest population of anatomically modern humans. The researchers concluded from these findings that the last common ancestor of all modern humans, dubbed "mitochondrial Eve,"[2] originated in Africa sometime between 90,000 and 180,000 years ago.

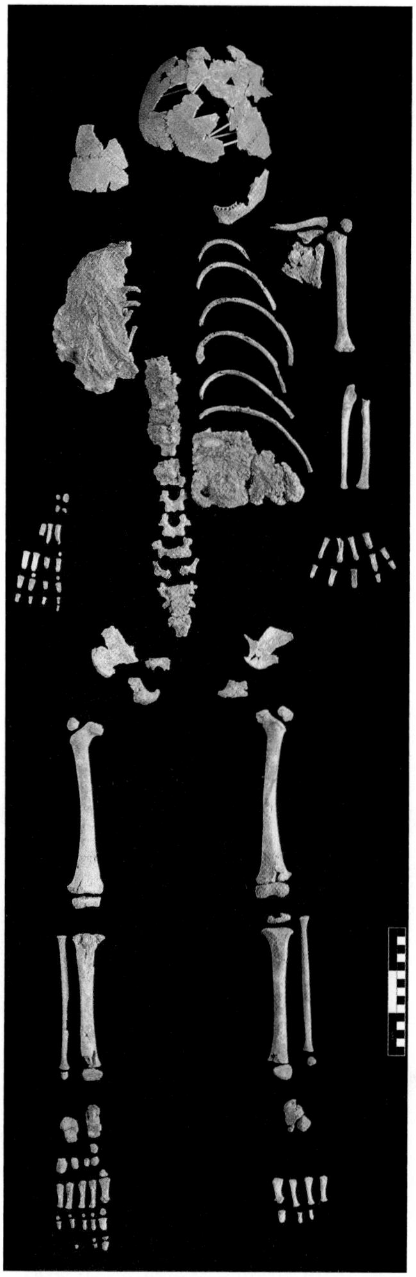

Underlying the use of mtDNA from living humans to calculate the date at which anatomically modern humans emerged are these four assumptions: (1) the genetic variation measured in modern samples represents the total amount of variation derived from the common ancestor; (2) the rate of mutation has been constant; (3) random mating has occurred; and (4) the particular mitochondrial DNA sequence used in the analysis is selectively neutral. Critics of the Berkeley

FIGURE 12.9 This child's skeleton, found at the site of Lagar Velho in Portugal, exhibits a combination of Neandertal and anatomically modern features.

Lagar Velho child © José Paulo Ruas, Direção-Geral do Património Cultural/Arquivo de Documentação Fotográfica

---

2. This is a widely used but misleading term. It does not mean that she was the mother of all who came after her, but simply the last common ancestor whose mitochondrial DNA is present in all living humans. So, while she tells us something about our common mitochondrial ancestor, she tells us nothing about the rest of our genome.

CHAPTER 12 The Emergence of Anatomically Modern Humans

study were quick to point out flaws in the evidence presented by Cann and her colleagues, including errors in the way in which they analyzed their data and their assumption that the rate of mutation of mtDNA was constant. Their detractors claimed that additional analyses of the same data could result in many different genetic trees, not all of which point to an African origin for modern humans. The low genetic variability exhibited by the mtDNA could, they argued, be equally consistent with a much older origin for modern humans if, in fact, there was sufficient movement of people and therefore genes between populations to maintain low genetic diversity (recall from Chapter 4 that gene flow between two populations reduces the amount of variability between those populations, thereby making them more similar to each other). As well, Africans may possess the greatest amount of genetic diversity simply by virtue of having been the largest population for most of human prehistory and therefore having experienced less genetic drift than would be the case for a small population (Relethford and Jorde 1999). Thus the data is compatible with both the recent out-of-Africa and multiregional evolution models. More recent mtDNA analyses have confirmed an African origin for modern humans sometime between 100,000 and 200,000 years ago (Ingman et al. 2000).

Studies of Y chromosome DNA have provided additional support for an African origin for modern *Homo sapiens*. As noted in Chapter 3, this chromosome does not undergo recombination with the X chromosome except at its tip, and its DNA therefore passes from father to son largely unchanged. Research by geneticist Michael Hammer and colleagues on a small section of DNA on the Y chromosome called Yap (for "Y Alu insertion polymorphism") revealed the presence of five Yap haplotypes, or clusters of genes, in 60 populations worldwide, with African populations showing greater haplotype diversity compared to those from other regions (Hammer et al. 1997).

Analyses of other regions of our genome have provided further confirmation of a modern human lineage arising in Africa. At the same time, however, they have revealed lineages emerging in Asia as well, suggesting admixture between archaic and modern populations. Harris and Hey's (1999) study of genes found on the X chromosome, for instance, yielded evidence of two separate founding populations emerging some 200,000 years ago, one African and the other non-African. Similarly, an analysis of the beta-globin gene, one of the hemoglobin genes, has revealed evidence for an Asian lineage dating back more than 200,000 years, and gene flow between Asian and African populations (Harding et al. 1997). Subsequent studies of X-linked and autosomal DNA regions have provided additional support for admixture between anatomically modern humans and archaic populations of Eurasia (Garrigan et al. 2005; Plagnol and Wall 2006), thus refuting the recent out-of-Africa model.

Geneticists have also examined DNA sequences in fossil *Homo sapiens* from both Europe and Asia (Fu et al. 2013a and 2013b). With respect to the European material, mtDNA has been extracted from the remains of seven late Upper Paleolithic *Homo sapiens* fossils from Europe, two from southern Italy (Caramelli et al. 2003), two from the Czech Republic, and three from France (Serre et al. 2004). All exhibited sequences that are distinct from those derived from Neandertal samples, suggesting that Neandertals contributed few if any of their genes to the modern European gene pool. As Relethford (2001a) points out, however, the absence of Neandertal mtDNA in modern Europeans does not necessarily mean complete replacement without interbreeding (Relethford 2001a), as predicted by the recent out-of-Africa model. Furthermore, if there was considerable gene flow between geographic regions over time, as predicted by the multiregional evolution model, we may not *expect* to find evidence of regional affinities in mtDNA (Relethford 2001b). As you learned in Chapter 11, the Neandertal genome data (Green et al. 2010) have, in fact, revealed the presence of Neandertal genes in modern humans, pointing to regional contributions to later human evolution outside of Africa. Thus the genetic evidence for modern human origins is not inconsistent with the multiregional evolution or assimilation models.

The relatively low level of genetic diversity in modern humans has long been interpreted as resulting from a **population bottleneck**. Various hypotheses have been proposed to explain the occurrence of this bottleneck. Stanley Ambrose (1998), for instance, has posited that massive environmental change following the cataclysmic eruption of the Toba volcano

population bottleneck

an evolutionary event in which a population is reduced in number, resulting in the loss of genetic variation on the island of Sumatra approximately 70,000 years ago reduced the world's population to about 10,000 individuals. A subsequent decline in global temperatures then forced survivors of this disaster to seek refuge in tropical areas of Africa, where they rapidly differentiated into the diverse populations that we see today.

Premo and Hublin (2009) have challenged the view that low genetic diversity in modern humans resulted from a recent bottleneck. Citing genetic evidence indicating that the **effective population size** of the human lineage has been low for more than 500,000 years, they hypothesize that a primitive form of what they term "culturally mediated migration" may have acted to maintain low genetic diversity in modern humans, Neandertals, and our last common ancestor. More specifically, gene flow between different groups of individuals may have been constrained by cultural barriers (e.g., mating practices) to migration, thereby mimicking the effect—at the genetic level—of a population bottleneck.

effective population size

a measure of reproductive potential based on the likelihood that individuals in a population of a given size contribute genes equally to succeeding generations

THE EMERGENCE OF MODERN HUMAN BEHAVIOUR

The transition from the Middle to the Upper Paleolithic in Europe around 40,000 to 35,000 years ago is commonly portrayed as characterized by significant cultural and behavioural innovations in the form of more sophisticated tool technologies, changes in subsistence practices, and greater expressions of symbolic and ritual behaviour. These innovations have been interpreted by some as representing a "cultural revolution" resulting from a genetic mutation that stimulated the modern human ability to innovate (Klein 2008, 271–272). This hypothesis has been challenged, however, and it is becoming increasingly apparent that **behavioural modernity** emerged in Africa and Eurasia long before modern humans first appeared in Europe (McBrearty and Brooks 2000). As you learned in the previous chapter, aspects of behavioural modernity such as intentional burial and artistic expression were evident among Neandertals as well.

behavioural modernity

having the attributes of modern human behaviour (e.g., cognition, language, symbolism, social relationships)

Technology and Subsistence

Lithic assemblages recovered from **Middle Stone Age** sites in Africa and the Near East indicate that the earliest anatomically modern humans continued to make tools using the Levallois technique. At the same time, they began to make and use more sophisticated implements in the form of **blade tools** made by striking multiple blades from a single prepared core using a hard or soft hammer. These blades were then fashioned into a variety of different tools (Figure 12.10), including **micro-liths**, small flaked tools that were likely hafted onto wooden shafts to form **composite tools**. An early advanced stone tool technology dominated by the production of microliths has been documented at the 71,000-year-old Pinnacle Point site in South Africa. This technology would have given early modern humans a substantial advantage over archaic populations, including increased success at hunting (Brown et al. 2012).

Early modern humans—and, as we noted in the previous chapter, late Neandertals as well—also made tools from materials other than stone, including needles of bone and antler, presumably for sewing clothes from

Middle Stone Age

the period spanning 250,000 to 40,000 years ago in Africa; it is associated with archaic and anatomically modern humans

blade tools

tools made of long, parallel-sided flakes struck from a prepared core

microliths

small, flaked tools made from blades or parts of blades

composite tools

tools consisting of two or more components; for example, stone tools hafted onto wooden spear shafts

FIGURE 12.10 Blades were fashioned into a variety of tools, such as these Upper Paleolithic tools from Israel.

Photo by J. Shortell, courtesy of the Wesleyan University Archaeology and Anthropology Collections

FIGURE 12.11 The meaning of the incisions on this piece of ochre from Blombos Cave is unknown, but it may represent a primitive calendar.

Courtesy of the Blombos Cave Project

hides, and bone points and harpoons, such as those recovered from the Middle Stone Age site of Blombos Cave in South Africa, dating to nearly 80,000 years ago (Henshilwood et al. 2001a) and the site of Katanda in the Republic of Congo, also dating to 80,000 years ago (Feathers and Migliorini 2001). In addition, early *Homo sapiens* made elaborate items of personal adornment, including jewellery manufactured from exotic materials that would have originated hundreds or thousands of kilometres away, pointing to long-distance exchange networks. Blombos Cave, for example, has yielded a remarkable collection of pierced shell beads (Henshilwood et al. 2004). Other forms of creative expression uncovered at Middle Stone Age sites include pieces of incised ochre from Blombos Cave (Figure 12.11) (Henshilwood et al. 2002), 82,000-year-old shell beads covered in red ochre from the site of Grotte des Pigeons in Morocco (Bouzouggar et al. 2007), and ochre-stained shells from 92,000-year-old deposits in Qafzeh Cave (Bar-Yosef Mayer et al. 2009).

Archaeological evidence recovered from Middle Stone Age sites in South Africa points to a broad subsistence base that included terrestrial herbivores such as antelope and zebras as well as, at some coastal sites, marine resources such as shellfish and tortoises. At Klasies River Mouth, for instance, modern humans appear to have relied heavily on the eland antelope, but they also consumed other food resources such as fish and shellfish. The remains of marine foods have also been recovered from Katanda (Yellen et al. 1995), Blombos Cave (Henshilwood et al. 2001b), and Pinnacle Point (Marean et al. 2007). In addition, the presence of grindstones at some Middle Stone Age sites suggests the processing of plant foods (McBrearty and Brooks 2000).

LATER STONE AGE/UPPER PALEOLITHIC

Later Stone Age
the period of time spanning 40,000 to 10,000 years ago in Africa

burins
stone tools used to shape bone, wood, antler, and ivory into other tools

The transition from the Middle to the **Later Stone Age** in Africa around 40,000 years ago was associated with the appearance of a greater number and variety of blade tools, including microliths and **burins**, and more sophisticated flaking techniques. The production and use of tools made from materials other than stone also increased.

In Europe, the Upper Paleolithic is typically divided into four main cultural periods associated with anatomically modern humans: (1) Aurignacian, (2) Gravettian, (3) Solutrean, and (4) Magdalenian. The Aurignacian (37,000 to 28,500 years ago) is characterized by a variety of blade, bone, and antler tools as well as figurines. The Gravettian (28,500 to 21,000 years ago) is marked by more elaborate blade technology and the production of figurines and cave paintings (discussed later in this section). Tool manufacturing techniques reached a pinnacle in the Solutrean period (21,000 to 18,000 years ago), best known for its exquisite leaf-shaped Solutrean blades (Figure 12.12). Finally, the Magdalenian period (18,000 to 10,000 years ago) was dominated by elaborately worked tools of bone, antler, and ivory.

As noted earlier, evidence for the use of marine resources has been uncovered at a number of Middle Stone Age coastal sites. Greater reliance on marine foods is evident in the Later Stone Age, and middle to late Upper Paleolithic populations in Europe also relied on a broader spectrum of resources, which included fish and waterfowl, as indicated by faunal evidence and stable isotope analysis (Richards et al. 2001, 2005). These populations also utilized a variety of strategies to obtain their food. Finely made harpoons were used to catch fish, and large game animals were driven into bogs or over cliffs where they could be easily dispatched. Successful procurement of these animals was facilitated by specialized hunting equipment such as **atlatls** (Figure 12.13). These implements extended the arm of the thrower, making it possible to throw darts and spears faster and farther.

atlatl
a device fashioned from bone, antler, or wood that increases mechanical advantage in spear-throwing, increasing distance and force

FIGURE 12.12 A remarkable level of skill is reflected in these exquisitely made Solutrean points.

© Lithic Casting Lab/Peter Bostrom

Archaeological evidence for symbolic and ritual behaviour in the Later Stone Age and later Upper Paleolithic is much more plentiful than in earlier times. Among the many cultural achievements during this period was cave painting. Cave and rock art sites have been found in Europe, Africa, and Australia, and among the most famous of these are Lascaux and Chauvet in France and Altamira in Spain (see opening chapter image). Dating to more than 30,000 years ago, the cave site of Chauvet contains more than 300 paintings, many of them depicting large game animals (Figure 12.14). So spectacular are some of these sites that increasing numbers of tourists have necessitated the construction of "replica" caves in order to preserve the original paintings from the damaging effects of humidity from human breath. Natural pigments such as red ochre and manganese were used to create the paintings, and experiments have demonstrated that some of these pigments may

FIGURE 12.13 Native hunter throwing a dart with an atlatl. The atlatl acts as a third element to the arm, extending the mechanical advantage in throwing a dart or a spear. This advantage increases both velocity and distance, making for an exceptionally lethal hunting weapon.

Donald Monkman illustration, © The Manitoba Museum, Winnipeg, MB

CHAPTER 12 The Emergence of Anatomically Modern Humans

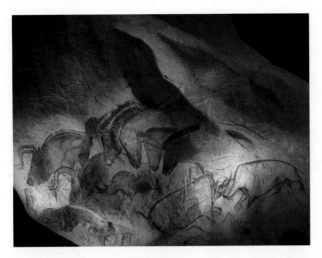

FIGURE 12.14 The Chauvet cave paintings depict animals such as cave bears, deer, bison, lions, rhinos, and horses.

© Javier Trueba/MSF/Science Photo Library

entoptic

images that arise from within the eye during altered states of consciousness

have been spit, blown, or stencilled onto the wall by the artists rather than painted on with a brush (Lorblanchet 1991). The fact that many of these paintings are located at great heights or in deep recesses of caves, necessitating the use of torches and some form of ladder to create them, suggests that they were meant to be seen by only a small number of people.

Anthropologists have long pondered the significance of cave art. Some have suggested that the paintings had magical significance and were created to protect hunters, ensure a successful hunt, or increase the fertility of large game animals and thereby ensure a plentiful supply of food. These suggestions are based on depictions in many of the paintings of wounded, trapped, pregnant, or mating animals. Others have suggested that they symbolize male and female forces in nature. Researchers have also speculated that some of the symbols in these paintings may represent **entoptic** images associated with altered states of consciousness such as trances (Lewis-Williams and Dowson 1988).

Later Upper Palaeolithic people were also famous for their figurines made in various shapes and sizes. Since the discovery of the first figurine in the 1860s at the site of Laugerie-Basse in the Dordogne region of France, approximately 200 have been found to date, most of them in Central Europe and Russia from archaeological sites dating between 11,000 and 35,000 years ago. Made of stone, bone, ivory, or clay, and in some cases bearing the marks of the stone tools used to produce them, they range in size from about 5 to 25 cm and exhibit considerable stylistic variation. Some are unadorned although others depict engravings that appear to represent clothing or jewelry. The majority of figurines depict the female form or anatomy, while others lack anatomical detail. Research has focused largely on the female representations with exaggerated sexual characteristics (Figure 12.15). Commonly referred to as Venus figurines, their significance has been debated for decades, with interpretations ranging from fertility figures to self-portraits to symbols of female power and status to Upper Paleolithic pornography (McDermott 1996; Rice 1981). In all likelihood, however, these specimens had multiple functions, and the long-standing assumption that they were made by men for men has been challenged (Nelson 1990). A variety of animal figurines have also been recovered from Upper Paleolithic sites.

Burials associated with later Upper Paleolithic peoples were more elaborate than those of Neandertals and early modern humans, and a diversity of burial practices with respect to the position and treatment of the body (e.g., cremation and the use of red ochre) and the inclusion of grave goods with the body, have been documented. The most remarkable example comes from the 24,000-year-old site of Sungir in Russia, where archaeologists have uncovered the remains of three skeletons, including two children whose bodies had been placed head to head in a trench and covered with red ochre and thousands of ivory beads and other artifacts (Formicola and Buzhilova 2004). Randall White's experimental work on such beads indicates that each one would have taken about three hours to produce (White 2007, 299). It is clear from this and other examples that symbolism played an important role in the lives of anatomically modern humans. While the meanings of such symbols remain unknown to us, they may have communicated a variety of information, including social relationships, status, and group identity.

FIGURE 12.15 Venus figurines, such as the famous Venus of Willendorf (left) and the Venus of Hohle Fels (right), varied regionally and likely carried a variety of meanings.

(Left) © Ali Meyer/CORBIS; (Right) Photo: H. Jensen, copyright University of Tübingen

IN SEARCH OF NEW LANDS

Colonization of Australia

The remarkable voyage of modern humans culminated in the occupation of Australia and the Americas. The timing of the initial occupation of Australia has been the subject of controversy, with some archaeologists arguing for an early date of 60,000 years ago (Roberts et al. 1994; Thorne et al. 1999), and others arguing for a more recent date of no more than about 40,000 years ago (O'Connell and Allen 2004). Much of the controversy stems from the limitations of radiocarbon dating. Recall from Chapter 7 that carbon-14 dating cannot be used reliably to date organic materials more than 40,000 to 45,000 years old. In addition, erroneous dates can be obtained if samples are contaminated with carbon from other sources. Concern has also been expressed about the relationship between artifacts found at some of these "early" sites and the deposits with which they were dated.

In recent years, improved sample preparation techniques have alleviated some of the problems with sample contamination, and many of the archaeological sites initially dated decades ago have been re-dated using newly developed techniques such as optically stimulated luminescence (OSL), ultrafiltration accelerator mass spectrometry, and uranium-series dating. Together this evidence points to an initial occupation of Australia sometime between 40,000 and 45,000 years ago (O'Connell and Allen 2004), although dates derived from some sites suggest a somewhat earlier occupation (Turney et al. 2001). Genetic evidence suggests an occupation of the continent 40,000 to 50,000 years ago (Hudjashov et al. 2007; van Holst Pellekaan et al. 2006), and possibly two separate colonization events (van Holst Pellekaan 2013). The oldest human remains recovered from Australia so far consist of a 40,000-year-old skeleton and a cremation burial excavated from the site of Lake Mungo (Bowler et al. 2003). So modern humans appear to have reached Australia as early as they reached Europe!

To appreciate the significance of these dates, it is important to recognize that Australia has been separated from southeast Asia for millions of years by a significant stretch of water, so colonization would have required the use of some form of watercraft and the ability to

CHAPTER 12 The Emergence of Anatomically Modern Humans

navigate (O'Connell and Allen 1998, 133, 143). This technological innovation would also have been required to colonize the Pacific Islands of Melanesia, Micronesia, and Polynesia; however, most of these islands were occupied only within the last 3,500 years or so.

Coming to the Americas

The occupation of North and South America has also been the subject of considerable debate, much of it focusing on the date of arrival of the first migrants, the number of migrations, and location of their entry routes. In the 1920s, clues to the arrival of the first occupants of North America came in the form of a technology known as fluted projectile points[3] (Figure 12.16) found in association with the remains of extinct bison at the site of Folsom, New Mexico. Several years later, another type of fluted point was found in association with mammoth bones at a site near Clovis, New Mexico. Subsequent dating of these sites revealed that the Clovis people—**Paleo-Indians**, as we now call them—were present in North America by 13,000 years ago. In the decades that followed, however, additional archaeological sites have provided compelling evidence for an even earlier "pre-Clovis" occupation dating to at least 15,000 years ago. These sites include Meadowcroft Rockshelter in Pennsylvania (Figure 12.17), which is thought to have been occupied by about 14,000 years ago (Adovasio et al. 1998). Other possible candidates include Cactus Hill in Virginia, dated between 15,000 and 18,000 years ago (Wagner and McAvoy 2004);

Paleo-Indians

the name given to the first occupants of North and South America

FIGURE 12.16 Paleo-Indians used fluted projectile points to hunt large game animals. The fluting is clearly visible on both sides of this point.

Royal Alberta Museum, Archaeology

---

3. Archaeologists have suggested that the removal of a flake from the face of a projectile point to create a groove or "flute" may have been done to facilitate hafting of a point onto a piece of wood.

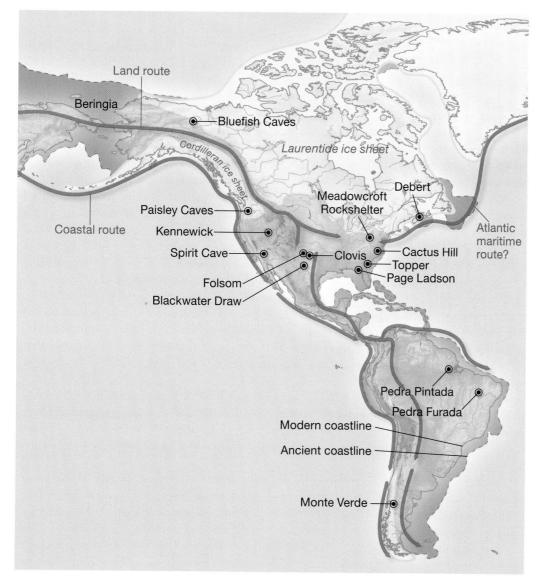

FIGURE 12.17 Several possible entry routes into North America have been proposed. Of these, an ice-free corridor between the Cordilleran and Laurentide ice sheets, and a western coastal route are supported by both archaeological and genetic evidence.

the Topper site in South Carolina, dated between 15,000 and 16,000 years ago (Goodyear 2005); Page-Ladson in Florida, dated to just over 14,000 BP (Dunbar and Hemmings 2004); Paisley Caves in Oregon, which has yielded 14,000-year-old human coprolites (Gilbert et al. 2008); the Manis site in the state of Washington, at which a mastodon bone projectile point dating to 13,800 years ago was uncovered (Waters et al. 2011b); and the Friedkin site in Texas, from which what is claimed to be a pre-Clovis stone tool industry known as the Buttermilk Creek complex, dated to between 15,500 and 13,200 years ago, has been identified (Waters et al. 2011a).[4] Possible pre-Clovis sites have also been uncovered in South America. Among the most widely accepted is Monte Verde in south-central Chile, which has been dated to nearly 15,000 years ago (Dillehay 2000).

Where did these individuals come from, and how did they get to North and South America? Archaeological, morphological, and genetic evidence indicate that the ancestors

---

4. The claim for a Pre-Clovis stone tool industry at this site has been refuted based on the argument that the associated sediments could not be precisely dated, some of the artifacts may have shifted to a different stratigraphic level, and the tools do not differ significantly from known Clovis assemblages (Morrow et al. 2012).

of the Clovis people came from Northeast Asia, and a number of early sites, including the Yana Rhinoceros Horn site, dating to 30,000 years ago (Pitulko et al. 2004), have been found in Siberia. From here these migrants crossed into North America via a land bridge that would have been exposed periodically during the last glacial period, when sea levels were low.[5] Known as the Bering Land Bridge, or **Beringia**, it would have been a migration route not only for humans but also for herds of large game animals on which these humans depended for food. Hints of the early occupation of eastern Beringia come from the site of Swan Point in Alaska, which has yielded 14,000-year-old stone tools, and the site of Bluefish Caves in Yukon, from which tools dating to nearly 25,000 years ago have been recovered (Cinq-Mars and Morlan 1999). Once in North America, Paleo-Indians moved southward, reaching South America within a relatively short time.

Archaeologists have long believed that the earliest migrants to the Americas passed through an "ice-free corridor" between the Laurentian and Cordilleran ice sheets, which covered North America during the last glacial period (Figure 12.17)[6], and there is genetic evidence for the use of this route by at least some migrants (Kashani et al. 2012; Perego et al. 2009). An alternative route along the Pacific coast (Figure 12.17), which would have been open to humans by 15,000 years ago, is also gaining increasing support based on the discovery of a number of early coastal sites (Goebel, Waters, and O'Rourke 2008). Such a route implies the use of boats, as would have been required for the occupation of California's Channel Islands some 12,200 years ago (Erlandson et al. 2011). Unfortunately, one of the major challenges to identifying this particular route is the fact that sites that may once have been located on ancient coastlines are now submerged under hundreds of metres of water.

In 2004, archaeologists Dennis Stanford and Bruce Bradley proposed a third entry route known as the Atlantic maritime route (Stanford and Bradley 2004). Based on similarities in stone tool technologies between southern Europe and eastern North America, this hypothesis, known as the Solutrean hypothesis, has now been dismissed based on genetic evidence (Kashani et al. 2012).

Based on the low level of genetic diversity seen in modern Native Americans, researchers have argued that the founding population of the New World was small, numbering perhaps only 1,000 to 2,000 individuals (Mulligan et al. 2008). Our knowledge of the biology of some of the early occupants of North and South America comes from only a small number of skeletons, all of them anatomically modern humans. These include the postcranial skeleton of a male found at the site of Gore Creek in Kamloops, British Columbia, and dating to 8,250 BP (Cybulski et al. 1981), some 8,000- to 9,000-year-old teeth found at the site of Namu on the BC coast (Carlson and Dalla Bona 1996), an 8,900-year-old cranium found at Browns Valley, Minnesota (Myster and O'Connell, 1997), 10,000-year-old remains from Warm Mineral Springs in Florida (Clausen et al. 1975), and a partial skeleton recovered from the 10,300-year-old site of On Your Knees Cave in Alaska (Kemp et al. 2007). Mitochondrial DNA extracted from a tooth found at this last site indicates that migration into the Americas did not occur until sometime after 15,000 years ago.

The most significant find in recent years is the nearly complete skeleton of a middle-aged male discovered in 1996 on the banks of the Columbia River near the town of Kennewick in Washington. Commonly referred to as Kennewick Man (Figure 12.18), this 9,300-year-old skeleton gained considerable attention because of its lack of resemblance to modern First Nations. In fact, initial assessments highlighted its Caucasian features such as its long, narrow skull (Chatters 2001), and much discussion has ensued over its relationship to modern indigenous populations. Subsequent analyses have revealed similarities between Kennewick

---

5. First Nations peoples today have their own stories about how they came to occupy North and South America.

6. This corridor, which extended from Yukon through Alberta and southern Saskatchewan, was created when the two ice sheets began to retreat after about 14,000 years ago.

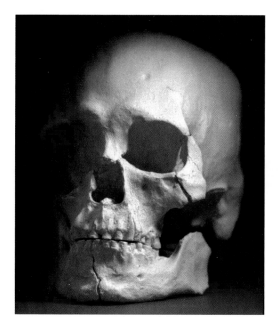 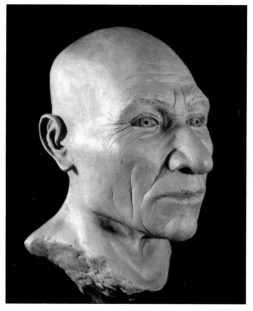

FIGURE 12.18 Kennewick Man's skull (left). A plaster cast of Kennewick Man's skull was used to make this facial reconstruction (right).

(Left) © AP Photo/Elaine Thompson; (Right) © Emmanuel Laurent/Eurelios/Science Photo Library

Man and populations from Polynesia and southern Asia (Powell and Rose 1999), and studies of other early modern skeletons from North America have revealed morphological features not seen in modern indigenous populations. Thus there are no grounds to reject Kennewick as being ancestral to modern First Nations.[7]

The recent sequencing of the draft genome of a 24,000-year-old child from Siberia has revealed genetic similarities to both modern First Nations people and modern Europeans, suggesting that a good portion of the genome of the first inhabitants of North and South America was derived from western Europe (Raghavan et al. 2013). This could occur if a group of western Europeans, moving eastward some 25,000 years ago, came into contact and interbred with people from central Siberia.

Another contentious issue concerning the occupation of the Americas is the number of migrations that occurred. In the 1980s, Greenberg and colleagues (1986) argued for three separate migrations based on linguistic, dental, and genetic evidence, the first of them giving rise to Amerindian populations, the second one to the Inuit and Aleut, and the third one to Na-Dene–speaking groups of northwestern North America and parts of the American Southwest. Genetic analyses of Native American populations have revealed that their mtDNA belongs to five founding **haplogroups** (A, B, C, D, and X) (Figure 12.19; Schurr 2004), and two Y chromosome haplogroups (C and Q), the same ones shared by northeastern Asians. These analyses also point to an initial migration into North America between 20,000 and 15,000 years ago, thus supporting a pre-Clovis occupation, and to multiple migrations (Schurr 2004).

Further indication that colonization of the New World occurred in multiple waves comes from a more recent comprehensive survey of genetic diversity in 52 Native American populations, 17 Siberian populations, and 57 other populations (Reich et al. 2012). This

haplogroups

groups of similar haplotypes that share a common ancestor; haplotypes are groups of genes that are inherited together

---

7. This skeleton has been the focus of a major legal battle between First Nations groups demanding repatriation under the Native American Grave Protection and Repatriation Act (NAGPRA) on the basis of affiliation, and biological anthropologists wanting to study these remains. The legal battle was effectively settled in 2004 allowing scientific study of the remains, which are stored at the Burke Museum at the University of Washington.

study revealed that Native Americans are descended from at least three waves of migration, with the majority descending from a single ancestral population dubbed "First Americans," Eskimo-Aleuts deriving from a second wave, and Na-Dene speakers from a third wave. Furthermore, the study revealed evidence of extensive admixture between the first and subsequent waves of migrants (Reich et al. 2012).

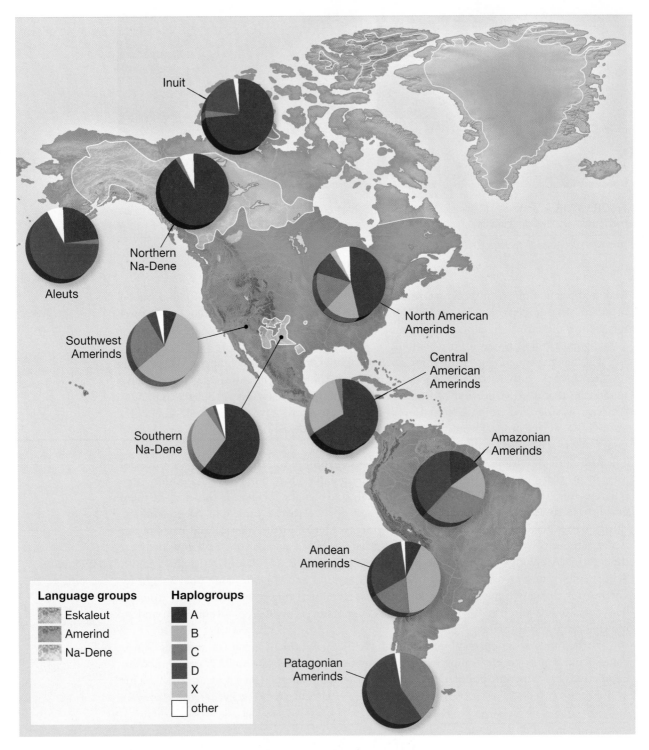

FIGURE 12.19 Map showing the distribution of Native American mtDNA haplogroups.

Theodore Schurr, (2000). Mitochondrial DNA and the peopling of the New World, *American Scientist* Vol. 88: 246. Reprinted with permission

LEARNING KEYS

KEY IDEAS

- The earliest anatomically modern humans possessed a higher, more rounded cranium; an average cranial capacity of about 1,500 cc; a more vertically oriented forehead with relatively small browridges; a smaller and flatter face; a well-developed chin; and smaller teeth compared to archaic hominins.

- Early modern humans had a more lightly built postcranial skeleton with straighter, less robust limb bones than earlier hominins, and their body proportions most closely resembled those of modern-day populations living in Africa.

- The recent out-of-Africa model proposes that modern humans evolved from earlier archaic populations in Africa sometime between 150,000 and 200,000 years ago, then spread to Europe and Asia, replacing pre-existing archaic populations in these regions with little or no interbreeding.

- The assimilation model proposes that modern humans first evolved in Africa and spread from there to other parts of the Old World, where they interbred with local archaic populations, genetically swamping them.

- The multiregional evolution model proposes that archaic humans evolved into modern *Homo sapiens* in several regions of the Old World, with extensive gene flow between regions maintaining these populations as a single species.

- The earliest anatomically modern human fossils, securely dated to 160,000 years ago, have been found in Africa, indicating that modern humans emerged there.

- Modern humans likely dispersed from Africa sometime after 60,000 years ago and expanded into Europe and Asia, reaching central and western Europe after 45,000 years ago, and China, southeastern Asia, and Australia by 40,000 years ago.

- Mitochondrial and Y chromosome DNA data indicate that modern humans appeared first in Africa.

- Neandertal genome data indicate the presence of Neandertal genes in modern humans, pointing to local (regional) contributions to later human evolution outside of Africa.

- Modern human behaviour appears to have emerged in Africa during the Middle Stone Age period, but aspects of behavioural modernity were also evident in Neandertals.

- The earliest anatomically modern humans made and used stone blades, some of which were used to make composite tools, tools from bone and antler, including needles and harpoons, and items of art and personal adornment.

- Early modern humans relied on a broad subsistence base that included terrestrial herbivores, marine resources, and plants.

- Later Stone Age (LSA) and Upper Paleolithic (UP) peoples made a greater number and variety of blade tools using more sophisticated flaking techniques, as well as elaborately fashioned tools of bone, antler, and ivory.

- LSA and UP peoples relied on a broad spectrum of resources that included fish and waterfowl, and they utilized more complex hunting strategies and specialized hunting equipment.

- LSA and UP peoples also produced remarkable works of art, including cave paintings and figurines, and conducted more elaborate burials than their predecessors.

- Archaeological evidence points to an initial occupation of Australia occurring sometime between 40,000 and 45,000 years ago.

- Occupation of North and South America appears to have occurred by 15,000 years.

- The earliest occupants of the Americas were big-game hunters who migrated from northeastern Siberia into North America via the Bering Land Bridge.

- Once in North America, they the earliest occupants of the Americas spread southward by one of two routes: through an interior ice-free corridor between the Laurentian and Cordilleran ice sheets that covered the continent during the last glacial period, and/or along the Pacific coast.

KEY TERMS

population bottleneck (p. 282)

behavioural modernity (p. 283)

Middle Stone Age (p. 283)

blade tools (p. 283)

microliths (p. 283)

composite tools (p. 283)

Later Stone Age (p. 284)

Paleo-Indians (p. 288)

haplogroups (p. 291)

KEY QUESTIONS TO ASK MYSELF

1. Why is it that anatomically modern humans are phenotypically diverse yet genetically quite homogenous?

2. Why do many people tend to think that only modern humans were capable of complex behaviours and spoken language?

3. If modern humans colonized the Americas as recently as 15,000 years ago, why don't we find more archaeological evidence of their early existence on these continents?

KEY CRITICAL THINKING QUESTIONS

1. What reasons might explain a lack of agreement, for some regions of the Old World, between the fossil, archaeological, and genetic evidence for the origins, timing, and migration routes of modern humans?

2. How are changes in anatomy linked to changes in culture in Middle and Late Pleistocene hominins? Is there a correlation between the two?

3. We often use the term "ritual" to describe human behaviours for which the significance is unclear to us. What does this term imply? Are there other terms that might be more appropriate?

KEY THINGS TO DO NEXT

CourseMate Visit **CourseMate** at www.nelson.com/humanvoyage2e to build your comprehension, practise your critical thinking skills, review core concepts, and explore other resources at your disposal.

13 Contemplating Modern Human Diversity

> *Human diversity makes tolerance more than a virtue;*
> *it makes it a requirement for survival.*
>
> Rene Dubos (1901–1982)

OVERVIEW

One of the most divisive and harmful enterprises undertaken in the name of human biology has been the characterization and explanation of geographic variation within humankind. Beginning with the concept of race,[1] and continuing to supposedly less baggage-laden notions such as "ethnicity" or "ancestry," interpretations of phenotypic (and later genotypic) variation within and between populations have historically diminished human social and political landscapes. At the same time, scientific debates regarding human classification and its meaning have enriched our appreciation for the biocultural diversity of our species and its adaptive histories. Many fields of study in human biology have entered an era of comparative objectivity with respect to human difference; but others—including Western biomedicine—continue to struggle to integrate a nonracial/ethnic model of human population variation into their research domains.

KEY CONCEPTS

Race, typology, cline, polytypism, polymorphism, heritability, biomedicine, intelligence, eugenics

KEY LEARNING OBJECTIVES

At the end of this chapter, you will be able to

LO1   Describe the historical roots of the race concept in human biology

LO2   Explain the essential features of clinal variation

LO3   List six fallacies of the race concept as applied to human populations

LO4   Contrast polytypism and polymorphism

LO5   Critique race-based models for variation in intelligence

LO6   Develop an argument against the pursuit of racialized medicine

---

1. The term "race" in the context of human biological variation has, in the latter half of the 20th century, become extremely problematic. Here we use the term to reflect its (erroneous) historical referent as a discrete population of humans whose members share particular morphological features to the exclusion of other such populations.

PROLOGUE: WE ARE ALL HUMAN

In previous chapters we explored the nature and importance of "differences." We discussed, for example, how different evolutionary mechanisms produce variation within and between populations (Chapters 3 and 4) and how different behavioural, ecological, and reproductive strategies are employed by male and female primates, or by one species of primate in competition with another (Chapters 5 and 6). We also looked at how paleoanthropologists identify different kinds of fossil hominins and remnants of their behaviour (Chapters 9 through 11). As we introduce this text's final section examining modern population biology, we want to emphasize one overarching reality—while modern humans are wonderfully diverse both biologically and culturally, we remain nonetheless a single species. In many ways our similarities transcend our differences, and this is certainly true of our biology, owing to the comparatively slow pace of biological evolution and our relatively recent origin as *Homo sapiens*. So it is a sad and unfortunate historical fact that it has been the latter—an emphasis on differences, both biological and cultural—that has defined human social relations throughout recent history.

Human variation is as fascinating as it is complex; no other organism has adapted to such a wide variety of habitats, aided by an artful melding of biology, culture, and technology. In the following chapters we explore and exemplify some of the myriad ways in which our capacity for adaptation and adaptability has become manifest within our species as a whole, within individual geographically circumscribed populations, and within distinct ethnic and cultural entities. As we will learn, many of these biological features set us apart and distinguish us as members of a particular instance of humankind—they are bone fide differences. But it is our ability as a species to acquire, develop, and reveal these differences while remaining at the same time alike in our fundamental biology that is something not to lose sight of—at the end of the day, it is what makes us all human.

In this chapter, we delve into two central themes: (1) How do we understand past and present approaches to characterizing human diversity, in particular as they embrace or critique the concept of "**race**"? (2) How do we interpret methods that shape our understanding of genotype, phenotype, and identity, including the especially problematic topic of the heritability of intelligence?

RACE, PLACE, AND FACE

Humans in all places and in all times classify the natural world—a process evident in all narrative traditions studied to date, written or oral. Classification is a necessary act of ordering information into groups of objects that do us good or bring us harm, of thinking about time, space, community, identity, and "self and other." It is a necessary part of understanding the past and predicting the future. Such classifications, founded on experience and tradition and used in everyday life, constitute **folk taxonomies**. Although similarities exist between folk taxonomies and scientific classifications, what sets the latter apart is the degree to which they are codified, rule-bound, hierarchically complex, and—in biology—evolutionary. Scientific classifications develop complexity as a consequence of variation in the natural world (see Chapter 4). Humans exhibit a high degree of biological variation (as we explore in the following chapters). How then, should we approach a biological classification of humanity?

It is next to impossible to frame a discussion of human population variation without referring to geography—a fact apparent since the first modern classification of people into discrete categories was proposed by Linnaeus (Marks 2007; see also Chapter 2). The important question is how geography arbitrates human diversity: Does biology adhere to boundaries in the same fashion as national identity? In the 18th and 19th centuries, it was logical and not at all unreasonable for European natural historians and anthropologists to divvy up humanity according to where European explorers first encountered other groups: notions of the meaning

race
in general biology, a category often considered synonymous with "subspecies," into which individuals can be placed based on distinctive physiological, morphological, and/or ecological features; it is now generally held that the complexity of human biobehavioural variation cannot be usefully understood in terms of race

folk taxonomies
informal albeit consensual classifications of the world used by ordinary people in everyday life

or mechanism behind population variation were still poorly developed within natural history (the forerunner of modern biological science).

These early thinkers all belonged to one or another nationality defined by distinct political borders; they identified with discrete spaces and lived during a time of European geopolitical expansion—a project of colonization aimed at mapping, dividing, and exploitation. Furthermore, global travel at the time was accomplished by ship. Such long-distance travel offered at best a snapshot of apparently major differences between human populations living in far-removed places such as Africa, Asia, the East Indies, Australia, and the Americas, with relatively little appreciation for the small-scale variation occurring across intervening regions. And the differences noted were invariably those easily observed: the size and shape of bodies, the colour of skin, and features of face and hair (Figure 13.1). Differences regarding temperament, moral character, or intelligence were little more than fabricated constructions—what European "geopolitics" needed other peoples to be in comparison to themselves, as justification for European expansion.

Such essentialist and typological approaches to subdividing human biological diversity continued well into the 20th century (Table 13.1): humankind was divided into a variety of discrete races, and the transition from one to the next consisted of stepping across a geographic line rather than shifting through geographic space. Indeed, in the 1860s Alfred Russel Wallace, who had proposed along with Darwin that species evolved by means of natural selection, famously contributed to this typology by identifying Malays and

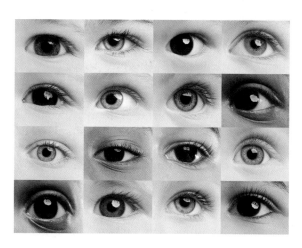

FIGURE 13.1 Humans vary in many dimensions, as noted here with regard to the eye. Note differences in shape, colour, and contour.

Richard Newstead/Lifesize/Getty Images

TABLE 13.1 Human typology in the 18th and 20th centuries. The expansion in number of categories reflects increasing awareness of diversity but adherence to the concept of discreteness.

Linnaeus, 1758, *Systema Naturae*, 10th ed.	Blumenbach, 1795, *Decas prima[-sexta] collectionis ...*	Stanley Garn, 1971, *Human Races* 3rd ed.
Varieties	**Varieties**	**Major geographic races**
American	American	American
European	Caucasian	European, North African, and Middle Eastern
Asian	Mongolian	Asiatic
		Indian
African	Ethiopian	African (sub-Saharan)
	Malay	Melasian
		Micronesian
		Polynesian
		Australian

Papuans as distinct races during one of his sojourns in the Malay Archipelago (Vetter 2006). The major change in the 200 years following the publication of the 10th edition of Linnaeus' *Systema Naturae* (see Chapter 2) lay not so much in whether races were real biological entities, but rather in how many distinct pieces of the human pie existed and how they should be defined. Mid-20th-century biological anthropologists such as Stanley Garn had devised a system for packaging humanity into a nested series of geographic races, local races, and microraces, characterized by ever finer degrees of presumed breeding isolation and more and more commonly held characteristics.[2]

As biological anthropologist Rachel Caspari (2003) has noted, all of these entities—from race to microrace—were viewed as closed systems with restricted gene flow, creating high degrees of similarity within geographic zones, however large or small one wanted to define them—for example, "micro-geography" or "local geography." This line of reasoning falls apart because human populations are not, in fact, reproductively closed systems (as we discuss later in this chapter). Nonetheless, a reasonable question to ask is whether such supposedly distinct and isolated groups could trace their beginnings to one or several points of origin. This question was especially problematic for some scholars in the 18th and 19th centuries who were trying to reconcile the Biblical story of a single human creation with the agenda of European expansion and colonization—an agenda that included the subjugation, displacement, and enslavement of indigenous peoples. Those scholars, now referred to as **monogenists**, clung to the idea that humanity was created but once and that the different populations encountered by European colonizers reflected degeneration from that original form following expulsion from Eden. Exposure to different climates as human populations dispersed over the landscape was argued to be the mechanism behind the formation of different varieties of people. A problem with this view, however, was time. According to Biblical accounts, the world was only 6,000 or so years old. On the other hand, a contrasting view known as **polygenesis** held that races were created as *separate* biological species, a perspective that allowed polygenists to rationalize both the superiority of the European race with its dominant culture, as well as the relatively brief Old Testament history of humankind.

If People Are Not Packages, Then Why Are Asians from Asia, Africans from Africa ...?

Whether you are shopping at Toronto's St. Lawrence Market, riding the C Train in Calgary, attending the Solstice Festival in Yellowknife, waiting to board a flight at Vancouver's International Airport, or strolling rue Sainte-Catherine in Montréal, you will invariably see people who look more like one another than any of them look like you. We say this making no presumptions about your own ancestry because, as a student of biological anthropology, it matters not whether you are an Aboriginal Canadian, a fifth-generation Québécois, or are newly arrived from Beijing, Beirut, or Botswana. The diversity around us is a fact of our multicultural, pluralistic, multiethnic society, born of a long history of immigration.[3] Someone else's complexion may be differently pigmented than yours, their bodies and faces differently proportioned, their hair a different form—kinky and black rather than straight and blond. Perhaps your eyes are notable for their **epicanthic fold**,

monogenists

18th- and 19th-century scholars who believed that all human populations ("races") could be traced to a single origin (mono + genesis), specifically related to the Judeo–Christian account of human origins; the diversity of human races was ascribed to exposure to different climates following humanity's fall from grace as related in the Old Testament

polygenesis

in contrast to monogenesis, polygenesis maintains that different human races were created as separate species; note that both monogenesis and polygenesis assign primacy to European peoples

epicanthic fold

a fold of skin of the upper eyelid adjacent to the bridge of the nose covering the medial canthus (corner) of the eye, commonly present in peoples of central and eastern Asian ancestry

---

2. In his 1961 text *Human Races*, Garn identified 9 geographic races corresponding to peoples inhabiting major continental landmasses (e.g., Europe) or extended island groups (e.g., Polynesia), and up to 30 local or microraces divisible within these larger zones (e.g., northwestern Europeans). The degree of "likeness" decreases as one moves from microraces to geographic races.

3. Canadian history in this regard is not so enviable. It has been marked by several less than stellar moments, including the levying of a prohibitive and escalating "head tax" (i.e., a fee each prospective Chinese migrant had to pay) from the late 19th to the mid-20th century; the refusal in 1914 to allow more than 350 East Indian migrants, arriving aboard the Japanese freighter *Komagata Maru*, to land in Vancouver in order to thwart the so-called "brown invasion"; and in 1939, the refusal of sanctuary to German Jewish refugees aboard the *SS St. Louis*, who were forced to return to Europe prior to the outbreak of World War II.

perhaps not (Figure 13.2a). The point we make is simply this: there *are* demonstrable differences, both phenotypic and genotypic, between people who can trace their ancestry to one place as opposed to another.

Such differences reflect the fact that for much of human history, people have by necessity chosen mates living close by (and to this extent, Stanley Garn's reasoning holds some water). As a result, a variant for a particular trait that developed in neighbouring populations would understandably occur in much higher frequencies within those groups than in more distantly removed populations. Thus the epicanthic fold is most common among peoples from East and Central Asia, and while the frequency of ginger hair is about 4% among Europeans generally, it reaches as high as 13% in Scotland. Consequently, humans are to some degree what we call a **polytypic** species, meaning that there are broad geographic patterns (clusters) to some aspects of our biology, just as there are similar geographic patterns characterizing languages and social and cultural traditions.

This reasoning also accounts for the fact that, as molecular studies indicate, the greatest amount of genetic diversity occurs *within* populations rather than between them. That is to say, at the population level, humans are also a highly **polymorphic** species. **Local breeding populations** accumulate mutations (polymorphisms) at particular genetic loci at rates that are independent of changes occurring at these same loci in other groups; thus, group A might have a lot of genetic variation for a trait, while group B might have comparatively little. A good example is eye colour. Europeans display a greater range of lighter iris pigmentation than is found in non-European populations (Sturm and Frukadis 2004; Figure 13.2b), a result of having more polymorphic melanin pigment coding alleles (gene variants, as you learned in Chapter 3), including the genes *OCA2* on chromosome 15 and *MC1R* on chromosome 16 (the latter also contributes to the frequency of ginger hair, freckles, and sensitivity to ultraviolet radiation). Population size, physical and/or cultural isolation, and history can also help modify the polymorphic structure of different populations. Recall for example the migration to New France of Louis XIV's *filles du roy* and their contribution to the higher occurrence of Leber hereditary optic neuropathy among modern Québécois (see Chapter 4).

polytypic

"many types"; refers to the existence of geographic variation within species

polymorphic

refers to the existence of alternative forms of a trait (e.g., eye colour in humans is polymorphic)

local breeding populations

groups of individuals within geographically dispersed species who find mates in a local region rather than from farther afield

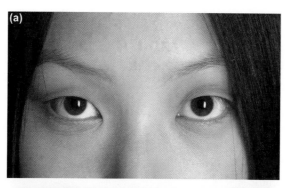
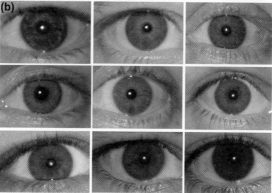

What about Spaces between "Races"?

Whether we wish to consider three races, five races, or even 30 or so "microraces," the problem will always lie in the necessity of drawing lines. Two immediate difficulties arise. First, where should these lines be drawn? Second—and surely the more important question—*who gets to draw the lines?* We will address this concern later in this chapter with particular regard to the

FIGURE 13.2 The upper and lower eyelids in some human populations, notably Central and East Asians, overlap at the medial canthus, producing an "epicanthic fold," a morphological feature distinguishing these groups from non-Asian populations (a). European peoples are more polymorphic for iris colour than non-Europeans (b).

(Top) © visual7/iStockphoto.com; (Bottom) Reprinted from *Trends in Genetics* 20 (8), Richard A. Sturm and Tony N. Frudakis, "Eye color: Portals into pigmentation genes and ancestry," copyright 2004, with permission from Elsevier Ltd.

question of intelligence and aptitude. Suffice to say for now that in recent human history, "line drawing" has always been a matter of economic, political, and military clout and has invariably produced tragic consequences (see Chapters 15 and 16).

But "race" as a concept, an entity, a category, is nothing if not a boundary, and divisive by definition. From what you have already learned regarding the ways in which biological variation is produced and transmitted, does this notion make sense to you at all? You may wish to refer back to Chapters 3 and 4. Ask yourself this rather simple question: Where does one variety end and another begin (Marks 2010)? Our hope at this point is that your answer is that, for most human variation, there is neither an ending nor a beginning, but rather a matter of "more or less." More or less melanin production, more or less blood type A, more or less sickle cell anaemia—these and other human polymorphisms are discussed in detail in Chapter 14.

The existence of gradual shifts in trait prevalence through geographic space is captured by the concept of **cline** (Box 13.1). A cline is literally a depiction of the frequency with which a character appears in one population compared to its occurrence in a neighbouring group (Figure 13.3). Unlike the concept of race, divisions marking changes in clinal frequency are transient, reflecting sources of population data (i.e., where and how observations have been taken); they are not preconceived notions of "this race lives here, and that race lives there."

cline

a continuous gradient observed in geographical space over which the frequency of expression of a character changes across contiguous populations

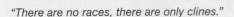

BOX 13.1

**RETROSPECTION: The Cline Appears ...
from Frank Livingstone (1962)**

"There are no races, there are only clines."

The aphorism with which Livingstone concludes this paragraph has achieved the status of doctrine within biological anthropology. The publication of his article in *Current Anthropology* coincided with that of Carleton S. Coon's *On the Origin of Races* (Coon 1962), a book heavily criticized for its explicitly typological approach to human population variation and its racist undertones.[4] Livingstone's article contributed to a growing movement away from "typological [toward] population thinking" in human biology—a movement led by scientists such as Ashley Montague in the 1940s and Joseph Birdsell, Sherwood Washburn, and C. Loring Brace (among others) through the 1950s and 1960s. After World War II ended in 1945—in particular, after a momentous meeting at the Cold Spring Harbour Institute for Quantitative Biology in 1951 concerning the "Origin and Evolution of Man"—the idea that human populations could be catalogued into neat and tidy "discrete packages" increasingly fell out of favour within anthropology.

Population genetic concepts such as selection, adaptation, genetic drift, gene flow, and founder effect have been shown to account for subtle shifts over geographic space in the frequency of phenotypic and genotypic characters—for example, skin pigmentation, blood groups, and immune system proteins, among many others. In a now classic example of research merging history and culture with biology, Livingstone himself demonstrated that the pattern of sickle cell anemia followed a cline from high to low frequency coincident with the degree of endemism of *Falciparum* malaria in Africa and the transition to more settled, farming lifeways (Livingstone 1958; see Chapter 3).

It is also important to note that the race concept, which had been used to classify *and* explain human biological variation for more than 200 years, was encountering resistance just as the Civil Rights Movement was gaining momentum in the United States. Nonetheless, its fall from favour in biological anthropology was a long and hard one (Cartmill 1998). One subfield in particular—forensic anthropology—persists in identifying race as a determinable feature in human skeletal remains (e.g., Byers 2007; see Chapter 15), and fields such as medicine and psychology continue to wrestle with race as a legitimate construction of heritable human biological variation (e.g., Smedley and Smedley 2005).

4. Coon maintained that there were five distinct races of humankind, which could be identified also in the fossil record as distinct subspecies of *Homo erectus*. He further proposed that the evolution of intellect—as epitomized by civilization—did not proceed uniformly but was achieved first by "Caucasians" and last and only recently by the "Congoids" and "Capoids" of Africa (the former represented by peoples of Central Africa and the latter by those of the Southern Cape, e.g., Khoi San).

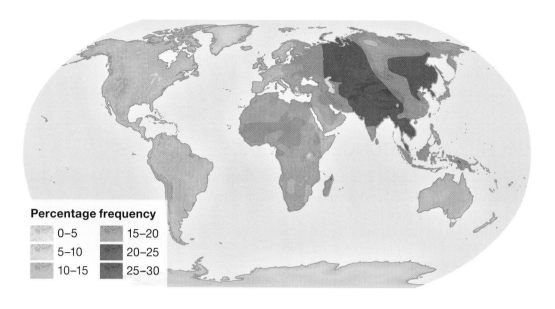

Percentage frequency

- 0–5
- 5–10
- 10–15
- 15–20
- 20–25
- 25–30

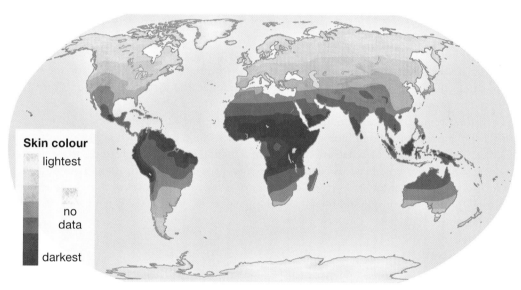

Skin colour

lightest

no data

darkest

FIGURE 13.3 Clines are continuous gradients of phenotypic or genotypic expression through space, as seen here for blood type B (top) and skin pigmentation (bottom).

The reality of clinal variation reveals the error inherent in assuming that human populations have behaved as reproductively closed systems. Even though historically most of our ancestors found mates close to home, people and genes did flow through and over all divides—geographic, cultural, linguistic, and so forth—and adaptation to local circumstances followed. A fascinating example of clinal variation and adaptation is the existence of a latitudinal cline for differential susceptibility to hypertension (high blood pressure), a known leading cause of many cardiovascular diseases, including stroke and renal failure (Young et al. 2005). Young and colleagues argue that the greater likelihood of becoming hypertensive among African Americans today is in part genetic, reflecting an adaptation in their early African hominin ancestors some 150,000 years ago for water and salt **avidity**. Such an adaptation would compensate for excessive losses of these nutrients through sweating as a response to heat stress. Water loss during the heat of the day also translates into reduced blood volume, and one measure to maintain blood pressure and to ensure that organs receive

avidity

having a physiological craving for a particular thing

CHAPTER 13 Contemplating Modern Human Diversity

sufficient blood-borne nutrition is to develop a greater ability for the heart muscle to contract and for arteries to maintain tone (known as vascular reactivity). Using data provided by the Human Genome Diversity Project, Young and colleagues showed that several genetic variants (single nucleotide polymorphisms, or SNPs) associated with high blood pressure occur with declining frequency with increasing latitude, consistent with data showing that temperate populations have reduced cardiac reactivity and a lower craving for salt.

SIX FALLACIES CONCERNING RACE

As we suggest in Box 13.1, race has continued to appear as an organizing and explanatory variable within biological anthropology and related fields. Studies may be structured as a comparison among "white," "black," "Asian," and so on, and any differences found attributed to membership in one or the other specified group. Matt Cartmill's (1998) survey of its usage in articles on human variation published over three decades in the *American Journal of Physical Anthropology* saw considerable fluctuation year by year but little change on average, with about equal proportions (about 33% of papers published) appearing in 1965 and in 1996. The suggestion that the concept of race had been progressively falling out of favour within the discipline over this period (Lieberman, Kirk, and Littlefield 2003) may not be warranted (Cartmill and Brown 2003). And while those who study human variation may couch their analyses within a population framework, that alone does not guarantee against the presence of an underlying typological perspective (Caspari 2003). Practitioners in the field must remain aware that while certain polymorphic or polytypic features may be characteristic for a given population, they do not define it—a premise reinforced in the various "Statements on Race" adopted by professional bodies.

In their text surveying human biological variation, Mielke and colleagues (2006) noted the lack of agreement among biological anthropologists (and others such as psychologists and medical researchers) as to what a definition of a biological race might look like—indeed, there is some doubt whether it is even possible to contrive such a definition. They suggested that this lack of consensus arises from a number of erroneous premises as to which factors or features constitute and supposedly validate the concept of "race." We restate these premises here in terms of fallacies.

Fallacy 1: Human Populations Are Homogenous

A homogenous population is one in which differences are minimal or non-existent, and clearly this is not so for any human population. There are numerous physical and physiological differences within and between different human populations (the subject of Chapter 14). In a broad survey of published literature, Leonard and Katzmarzyk (2010) argued that, on a global level, measures of body size and shape hold specific relationships with climatic variables such as temperature, as well as nutritional influences such as energy intake. For example, it is commonly found that tall, linear bodies occur in hot, arid climates and short, stockier bodies predominate in colder regions—a pattern of selection to the challenges of thermoregulation that appears to have considerable antiquity in human evolution (Ruff 2002; see also the Meet the Anthropologist link in Chapter 11 on the CourseMate site). Founder effect and genetic drift also act to diminish homogeneity (and enhance heterogeneity) among human groups. For example, in the ABO blood system, type O occurs at a high frequency in both living and ancient Native Americans, consistent with a founder effect (Halverson and Bolnick 2008), whereas type B is virtually nonexistent in the Americas but occurs in 15 to 25% of people living in eastern Asia (the putative region of origin for Native American peoples).

Fallacy 2: Polygenic Traits Can Be Measured Accurately

As you learned in Chapter 3, polygenic traits are influenced by a number of genes and result in phenotypes that vary continuously rather than in the discrete, "present/absent" fashion typical of Mendelian characters. Both your height and your eye colour, for example, are influenced by several genes, although the exact number is unknown. The heritability for height is estimated to be approximately 0.80. In other words, about 80% of the population variance for stature reflects underlying genetic variance in the population, with the balance of differences in stature attributed to environmental factors such as nutrition and health (discussed in more detail later in this chapter). Sanna and colleagues (2008) have identified a variant of a gene known as *HMGA2* that has an additive effect on body height of 0.44 cm on average for those with one copy of the gene, and almost a full 1.0 cm when this variant is present for both alleles. Clearly, this is a very precise and presumably accurate measure.[5] Unlike most polygenic traits, a person's stature *can* be measured with a great deal of confidence. But what about other continuously varying characters, such as skin or hair colour, or polygenic systems such as the **human leukocyte antigens**, or variably expressive disease conditions such as systemic lupus erythematosus? In fact, most human variation is polygenic and not at all easily quantified. Simply put, most human features that have long been at the core of human racial classifications—such as skin colour—are too complex to measure accurately, even with fairly sophisticated instrumentation.[6] Similarly, the phenotypic expression of polygenic, continuous traits invariably involves some contribution from the environment, either directly through agents such as diet or disease, or via epigenetic mechanisms during development (as discussed in Chapter 4).

human leukocyte antigens (HLAs)

HLAs are the chief component of the major histocompatibility complex and regulate the human immune response

Fallacy 3: Continuously Varying Traits Can Be Marked by Discrete Boundaries

Given that measuring polygenic trait expression accurately is problematic, it is doubtful that we can trace reliable geographic boundaries that would set one character state apart from another. However, the problem behind this fallacy is as much philosophical as it is practical: a continuously varying trait has no meaningful boundaries. This is true even for reliably measured characters such as stature. We challenge you to draw a line in Figure 13.4 separating someone who is "short" and someone who is "medium-short." Such boundaries will always be arbitrary, and more often than not reflect some form of bias. In the case of clines, however, lines demarcating the frequency of expression for a character reflect empirical data. They are analogous to lines joining places of equal mean atmospheric temperature (isotherms) or lines of equal elevation on a map (contours)—all are transient and changeable. In the case of clines, migration and mutation alter genotypic and phenotypic frequencies, whereas global warming shifts isotherms and continental drift, erosion, and uplift modify contours. When, how, and where we take measurements are important considerations whenever we characterize human variation. In our example of height, it is more informative to depict the geographic distribution of population means for stature than it is to say that "Britons are taller than Basques."

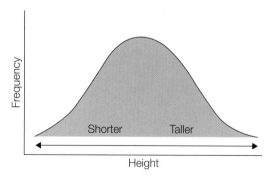

FIGURE 13.4 Continuous traits such as stature that are determined by the action of a number of genes as well as environmental influences do not lend themselves to simple descriptions. A person is not *short* so much as they are *shorter than* someone who is taller, and they will be taller than someone who is even shorter.

5. In measurement, *precision* and *accuracy* are not the same. *Precision* refers to whether our measurements provide a consistent answer, whether they are accurate or not. *Accuracy* refers to the degree to which a measurement represents the true value.
6. Recent developments in 3D imaging and computation models such as the bidirectional reflectance distribution function (BDRF; Weyrich et al. 2008) appear to offer highly quantifiable resolution of variation in human skin pigmentation, although the technology is currently too cumbersome for large, population-based surveys.

Fallacy 4: Traits Used in Racial Classification Are Linked

The racial argument that people can be classified into discrete entities rests on the premise that somatic (body) features typically credited to a particular group always occur together as phenotypic clusters to the exclusion of members of a different group. This can easily be shown to be false, since it implies a uniform geographic distribution for each racial character—that is, clines for each so-called racial character should be concordant. But as the two clines shown in Figure 13.3 attest, individual traits develop their own patterns of variation in space as a result of their own particular histories of gene flow, drift, selection, and so on. The suggestion that human variation consists of homogenous packages of linked traits corresponding with the biological notion of "subspecies" is clearly false (Keita et al. 2004). Indeed, the action of independent assortment during meiosis, as discussed in Chapter 3, prohibits traits being inherited as packages, although in some instances linkage can occur when alleles for different traits occur on the same chromosome. However, since most human variation is polygenic, involving alleles distributed over a number of different chromosomes, linkage of phenotypes is uncommon.

Fallacy 5: A Specific Number of Traits Can Define a Race

Can "race" be quantified? Is one feature, such as ginger hair or an epicanthic fold, sufficient to assign each of us to a given "race"? Perhaps three features are necessary. If you have dark skin, kinky hair, and the *HbS* allele for sickle cell disease, clearly you are African. Or are you? Perhaps your parents are of Middle Eastern ancestry, or possibly even Asian, as all three of these features occur in Africa, Asia, and the Middle East, albeit with variable degrees of expression. The fact that they may collectively be more frequent in Africa does not resolve the question; you might be African or you might not.

In fact, for the same reasons given with regard to Fallacy 4, you would be completely frustrated if you tried to list a series of biological traits that could *unambiguously* assign a given individual to a specific population of origin (Figure 13.5). Even in cases of rare genetic disorders that have very high population affinity, the issue can be far from clear. Tay-Sachs disease is a case in point. Although it occurs with a very high frequency among Ashkenazi Jews (roughly 1 person in 30 carries a copy of the recessive allele), a variant of the allele can be found at similar frequencies in a few other populations, including French Canadians from the

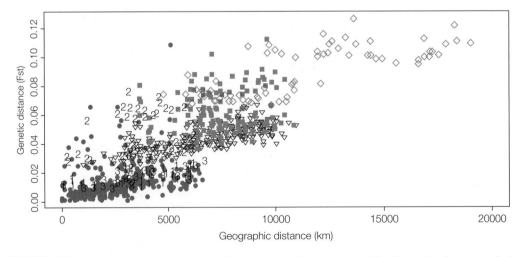

FIGURE 13.5 Genetic distance increases with geographic distance, supporting the notion that an analysis based on sufficient polymorphic variation can discriminate among different clusters of human populations. However, note that the changes are linear, indicating that the clusters themselves vary in a clinal fashion through geographic space.

From N.A. Rosenberg, S. Mahajan, S. Ramachandran, et al. 2005. Clines, clusters, and the effect of study design on the inference of human population structure. *PLoS Genetics* 1:e70; Figure 6.

Bas-Saint-Laurent-Gaspésie region of Québec, and among small populations of Cajuns and Pennsylvania Dutch. In all of these instances, founder effect and culturally mediated genetic isolation are effective agents underlying the high frequency of this fatal condition in these populations. So, while having a disease such as Tay-Sachs might lead us to identify someone to a few populations, it does not necessarily pinpoint a specific group of origin.

Fallacy 6: Between-Group Genetic Diversity Distinguishes Geographic Races

How much genetic difference actually matters? In the case of genetically determined diseases such as Tay-Sachs, very small differences can have a huge impact on the lives of individuals, who may either express the disease or carry the allele for its expression. But does the occurrence of such a marker in a population readily distinguish it from some other population? Clearly not, as noted above. Fallacy 6 derives from an oft-cited classic study of genetic polymorphism within and between human populations, published by Harvard geneticist Richard Lewontin (1972). Lewontin argued that upward of 85% of the genetic diversity in *Homo sapiens* occurs among individuals within populations, leaving relatively little genetic variation capable of distinguishing one group from another.[7] Although his statistical analysis has been criticized (Edwards 2003), his fundamental conclusion has been substantiated by other studies examining the genetic structure of human populations. For example, Bamshad and colleagues (2004), using more powerful **multilocus analysis** statistical methods and data for more than 400 genetic loci, showed that "pairs of individuals from different populations are often more similar than pairs from the same population" (Witherspoon et al. 2007, 351). So a randomly selected European will be classified as European as opposed to Asian only 62% of the time (meaning that she would be classified as Asian approximately 38% of the time).

> **multilocus analysis**
> a method for characterizing genetic diversity at multiple sites, or loci, within the genome

However, a number of recent studies have shown that, as the number of polymorphic loci included in a study increases, the likelihood of being able to discriminate among major geographical populations also increases (e.g., Rosenberg et al. 2005). What this suggests is that some human variation exists as both clines as we noted earlier, and as clusters. Importantly, as Rosenberg and colleagues' study shows, the clusters themselves form clines over large geographic distances (Figure 13.5). There are two profound implications to these findings. First, any classification of humankind based on only a handful of characters (genotypic or phenotypic) is meaningless, even though this has been the practice both historically and in contemporary fields such as psychology and medicine. Second, genetic analyses can provide important insight into historical patterns of human population migration and interbreeding. Thus, studies of mtDNA and Y chromosomal variation have dramatically altered our view of major population expansions, as seen, for example, in the recent argument for a single versus multiple migration model for the peopling of the Americas from an Asian site of origin (Achilli et al. 2013).

DIFFERENCE ABUSED AND USED

Although modern genetic analyses lend credibility to the proposition that if enough genes are used, geographically distinct populations become identifiable, there is still no evidence that individuals from these various populations can be arranged on a scale of "better–worse," "higher–lower," or "greater–lesser." Yet the history of how the biological concept of race has been employed in the social, economic, and political arenas has emphasized just those dimensions. We close this chapter examining how "race" has been abused in Western political economic discourse, emphasizing the rise of the Eugenics Movement in North America in the early 20th century and the debate over race and intelligence (which continues to this day).

---

7. In his 1972 study, Lewontin analyzed 17 polymorphic loci from populations distributed over 7 major geographical "races," including Caucasian, African, Mongoloid, South Asian Aborigines, Amerinds, Oceanians, and Australian Aborigines.

We also look at how race continues to be used, ostensibly with good intentions, in Western biomedicine—although here as well it remains a thorny issue.

"The Great Problem of Civilization ..."

In January 1913, Theodore Roosevelt wrote to Charles Davenport: "The great problem of civilization is to secure a relative increase of the valuable as compared with the less valuable or noxious elements in the population." At the time, Roosevelt was a recent past president of the United States (serving from 1901–1909) and still a person of great political authority; Davenport was the leading American figure in the growing field of genetics, director of the prestigious Cold Spring Harbor Laboratory, and founder of the Eugenics Record Office (Marks 2008). Roosevelt's admonition was written in support of Davenport's call for a state-sponsored program of eugenics, which he championed in his influential 1911 book *Heredity in Relation to Eugenics*. This text marked the formal marriage of the philosophical core of the Eugenics Movement (as advocated by Charles Darwin's first cousin Sir Francis Galton in the late 19th century) with the recently rediscovered principles of Mendelian genetics. The essential goal of eugenicists was to improve the racial quality of society, in the hope of removing any possible threat to the existing dominant position of Western European-derived upper classes.

The early 20th century was an era of unprecedented migration to North America. During Roosevelt's presidency, almost 9 million immigrants began new lives in the United States, most arriving from eastern and southern Europe, Russia, and from the lower classes of western Europe. Around the same time, Asian immigrants were arriving on the Pacific coast. The influx of these peoples, most of them poor, disenfranchised, uneducated, and Catholic (in eastern North America), raised alarm among the established western European and Protestant American aristocracy. Although the numbers were smaller, a similar pattern existed in Canada, with a 20th-century record of over 400,000 migrants arriving in 1913 alone (CCR 2009).

In both Canada and the United States, the initial response was to enact legislation of various kinds to restrict the numbers of new arrivals from "undesirable" countries of origin. For example, Canada's Immigration Act of 1910 allowed for prohibition against anyone "belonging to any race deemed unsuited to the climate or requirements of Canada, or of immigrants of any specified class, occupation or character." Other acts or amendments invoked "continuous journey" clauses and "head taxes" (see footnote 3; Figure 13.6). However, restricting immigration would not remove the threat embodied by the hundreds of thousands who had already arrived; further measures would need to be introduced.

The more sinister response of the eugenicists' program was to develop policies regulating the reproduction of those members of society deemed a threat to the status quo. Charles Davenport himself advocated that young people of the appropriate (i.e., upper) classes be persuaded "to fall in love intelligently," by which he meant to choose mates of similar class and creed (Marks 1995). But a more effective limitation was to impose programs of forced nontherapeutic sterilization targeting those deemed unfit by virtue of "**feeble-mindedness**." Although phenotypically ambiguous, feeble-mindedness was made out to be genetic in origin, supposedly following a Mendelian pattern of inheritance. Clearly, in the eugenicists' view, controlling birth was the most effective intervention to keep society from degenerating as a result of the overzealous reproductive capacity of the immigrant classes.

Advocates such as the notable feminist Margaret Sanger would later promote a different form of "**negative eugenics**" by arguing that contraception should be made widely accessible to the lower classes.[8] Similarly in Canada, Emily Murphy—a champion in the movement to have women recognized as persons under the British North America Act—believed that

feeble-mindedness
an artificial construct that suggested that defects of personality, intellect, ethnicity, or behaviour were inborn, and so could be selected against by policies restricting reproduction; sterilization was often the method of choice

negative eugenics
programs or policies designed to prevent successful reproduction in targeted groups (via conception or sterilization)

---

8. Sanger founded the American Birth Control League in 1921 to advocate for women's reproductive rights; the ABCL was renamed in 1942 as Planned Parenthood of America. While widely recognized as a strong feminist and activist, Sanger's eugenics philosophy, as reflected in her argument that "birth control must lead ultimately to a cleaner race" (Sanger 1922, 12) has tarnished her reputation.

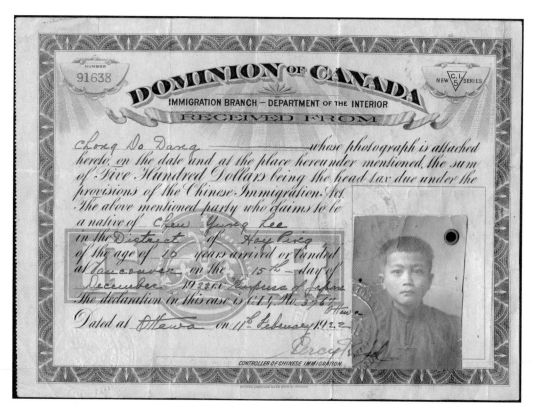

FIGURE 13.6 Under the "head tax" provision of Canada's immigration laws, enacted in 1885, Chinese immigrants were required to pay an entry fee of $50, an amount raised to $500 in 1903. The federal government issued an official apology to the Chinese Canadian community on June 22, 2006.

a program of negative eugenics was a solution to the problem of overpopulation, especially among the lower classes. Possibly the foremost proponent of eugenics in Canada was Dr. Helen MacMurchy, appointed in 1915 as Ontario's "inspector of the feeble-minded." While campaigning on the one hand for a reduction in maternal and infant death rates, work for which she was recognized by being named a Commander of the British Empire, MacMurchy also argued for sterilization as a means to prevent the production of "degenerate babies." It was in Alberta and British Columbia that these measures were embraced most strongly. For example, the Alberta Sexual Sterilization Act of 1928 created a Eugenics Board that over the next 43 years approved more than 98% of cases heard. Of these individuals, almost 3,000 were subjected to forced sterilization. Most of these people were from minority groups and most were women; all had been identified as feeble-minded or otherwise deviant.

Eugenics-based sterilization programs were instituted in many countries, including social democratic states such as Sweden. Most such programs, though, fell into decline after World War II, when it was realized how relentlessly the Nazi regime had implemented American eugenic politics. In this light, it is sobering to note that legislated non-therapeutic sterilization of the "feeble-minded" continued in Alberta until 1972 and in British Columbia until 1973.[9]

Programs promoting negative eugenics stand in contrast to earlier **positive eugenic** approaches advocating for "marrying well" and extolling the virtues of reproduction within higher social classes. In recent years, with advances in reproductive technologies, the latter have reappeared and not without controversy in a form termed "liberal eugenics"— see Box 13.2.

positive eugenics
programs or policies advocating reproduction among the favoured sectors of society, typically those of the dominant social and economic classes

---

9. Leilani Muir, involuntarily sterilized in 1959, successfully sued the Alberta government in 1996 and was awarded almost $1 million for damages and legal costs. Since then more than 850 additional victims of wrongful sterilization have brought legal action against the Alberta government. Most of these cases have been settled out of court with awards totalling $142 million.

BOX 13.2

FOCUS ON ... LIBERAL EUGENICS: POSSIBLE, PROBABLE, DESIRABLE?

But with the Paradice method, there would be ninety-nine percent accuracy. Whole populations could be created that would have pre-selected characteristics. Beauty, of course; that would be in high demand. And docility: several world leaders had expressed interest in that. Paradice had already developed a UV-resistant skin, a built-in insect repellant, an unprecedented ability to digest unrefined plant material. As for immunity from microbes, what had until now been done with drugs would soon be innate.

This passage, from Margaret Atwood's 2003 apocalyptic novel *Oryx and Crake*, captures the "con" side of the debate vis-à-vis genetic engineering applied to human reproductive choice. The idea carried within this excerpt—that we can fabricate "designer babies" at will—is but a stone's throw from early 20th-century arguments that humanity would best be served by "breeding out unsavoury kinds," identified by colour or creed—hence the mid-20th-century Nazi pogroms against, for example, Jewish and Romani peoples throughout Europe. Today the mention of "eugenics" leaves a sour taste in the mouth; the notion of "true breeding" bears a nasty history. In recent years, however, new technologies have reopened that Pandora's box to the possibility that parents can indeed intentionally design future generations.

These methods, known by the labels "liberal eugenics" or "reprogenetics," trace their origin to the development of oral contraceptives and in vitro methods of fertilization, notably with Gregory Pincus's success in 1934 at combining rabbit egg and sperm in the inverted crystal of his watch glass and implanting the subsequent embryo into a surrogate rabbit mother (Andrews 2008).[10] Over the intervening seven decades, research has greatly extended the options available to prospective parents—including fully fertile couples—to manipulate and control their reproductive choices. As an extension of assisted reproductive technology, reprogenetics permits couples to either ensure or prevent particular genes appearing in offspring.

As molecular biologist Lee Silver (2000) has noted, humans have always practised a form of reprogenetics: mating is hardly ever random in human populations, and mate choices are often made to bring phenotypic traits together (positive assortative mating) or to keep them apart (negative assortative mating). Selecting appropriate egg or sperm donors, and decisions to abort an abnormal fetus based on the results of genetic screening tests such as amniocentesis, also constitute forms of reprogenetics. But in an era of genome sequencing and germline engineering, the choices are as biologically remarkable as they are ethically complex. Genes can potentially be modified, deleted, or added in, in a nonrandom manner, to ensure a healthy, happy, long-lived, and successful baby.

But is this something we should be pursuing? Silver (1998) holds that reprogenetics simply offers one more tool for parents to provide advantages to their future offspring; there is little difference between providing good genes and providing a good environment, such as high-quality nutrition and a first-class education. On the other hand, bioethicists such as McGill University medical anthropologist Margaret Lock (2002) argue that reprogenetics, because of the high costs involved, extends much further than individual choices (of parents) and individual outcomes (of babies); indeed, it represents a new form of biocapitalism that is likely to exacerbate both social and biological/genetic inequities. In the case of germline engineering (a form of positive eugenics that has the sole aim of genetically enhancing babies), Lock asks a fundamental question: Who gets to decide which genes are "good" and which are "bad"? Clearly, this is an issue with many questions: societal, political, ethical, and spiritual. The answers must come from a wider field than simply those who devise the technology.

Race as Advantage

When a program of eugenics advocates sterilizing individuals on grounds of "race" or ethnicity, it is based on the belief that some peoples are innately superior to others—that is, endowed with genes that provide biological advantages. Given that geographically distant human populations have somewhat unique histories of selection and adaptation, we should not be surprised that biologically meaningful differences occur in some areas of human endeavour—for example, in certain domains of athleticism. But the arena in which the most effort has been exhausted arguing for the existence of inborn differences (ranking from greater to lesser) is that of "intelligence." While it is true that individuals vary with

---

10. Louise Joy Brown, the first human in vitro baby, was born July 25, 1978, in England to Lesley and John Brown, whose attempts at natural conception had proved futile owing to Lesley's blocked fallopian tubes. In 2006, Louise gave birth to her own son, conceived without the need of in vitro technology.

regard to different measures of aptitude—just as they do for traits such as stature, hair colour, disease risk, and so on—there is no credible evidence that populations can be hierarchically ordered along any measure of intellectual or cognitive capacity. Why, then, does the debate continue? There are at least three prominent reasons: the first relates to what intelligence *is;* the second, to the historical rootedness of racist essentialism (as we saw earlier); and the third, to the personal motives (i.e., the politics and philosophies) of a handful of individuals who assert that "average intelligence" is reflected in the classic tripartite classification of race—Caucasian, Negroid, Asian—and that these differences are the result of natural selection and adaptation.

Defining and Measuring Intelligence

The question "what is intelligence" has vexed scholars across disciplines. Is it "innate ability," as Galton supposed? Is it "competence in problem solving," as many educational psychologists have maintained? More than 100 years ago the English psychometrician Charles Spearman proposed a quantity known as "g" (standing for "general intelligence factor"), which could be derived from an individual's performance on specific intelligence tests[11] and from performances grouped over a larger number of cognitive tasks. The modern version of "g" is called the Full Scale Intelligence Quotient (FSIQ), a composite score of accomplishment over 11 tests of verbal and cognitive performance abilities. Measures of FSIQ have been variously shown to be positively correlated with educational outcomes, health outcomes (e.g., sickness and death), occupational success, physical attributes such as body asymmetry (Prokosch, Yeo, and Miller 2005), brain volume, and cortical grey matter thickness (Narr et al. 2007). However, test outcomes have also been shown to vary across the life span and to be influenced by numerous social and economic determinants. For example, a recent study among Canadian schoolchildren aged 6 to 16 years found that "demographic" variables alone (age, sex, parental education, region of country, ethnicity) accounted for 18% of the variance in predicting FSIQ scores (Scheonberg, Lange, and Saklofske 2007). Even with a full battery of additional tests, only 70% of the variance in FSIQ could be accounted for, leaving one to wonder whether other, nonspecified social and economic factors might explain any of the remaining 30% of variance in "intelligence." Consider also that Scheonberg and colleagues' characterization of ethnicity included only Caucasian, Asian, Aboriginal and "other"—hardly a reflection of the diversity one finds in many Canadian school classrooms!

Do Populations Differ in Intelligence?

At the root of the question of innate differences in intelligence conferring advantages to some populations over others[12] is the degree to which intelligence is inherited—that is, genetically determined. Given that defining "intelligence" is such a nebulous exercise, you might well wonder how this issue can be approached. Researchers have relied mainly on family and **monozygotic (MZ)** twin studies to investigate the genetic contribution to intelligence. Especially useful are studies of MZ twins reared together (having the same genome and similar environment) versus MZ twins raised apart (same genome, different environment). Such studies report correlation coefficients for intelligence test results ranging from 0.20 to 0.87; other degrees of biological relationship tend to report lower correlations for test results. However, as Molnar (2006) points out, it is erroneous to equate correlation with genetic causation. At issue is the concept of heritability (symbolized as H^2), which is often assumed—in error—to be a measure of genetic determination. For example, a heritability of 0.87 for stature (Visscher et al. 2007) does *not* mean that 87% of an individual's stature is determined by genes. Rather, in its broadest sense, this estimate of heritability means that

monozygotic (MZ)
twins derived from a single zygote; commonly called "identical twins," they result from splitting of the fertilized egg very early in pregnancy (at the blastocyst stage), and so possess the same genome

---

11. The history of intelligence testing—IQ tests—is also one fraught with controversy; see S.J. Gould (1996) for a thorough discussion.

12. Historically, this ranking has placed Caucasians on top, followed by Asians and Africans. In the late 1980s and early 1990s, this was turned around in a series of controversial publications to switch the order to one of Asian–Caucasian–African. Lieberman (2001) provides an interesting political–economic analysis of this transformation.

additive effect

in quantitative genetics,
refers to a genetic
contribution to a trait
that either increases or
decreases (if the effect
has a "negative value") the
degree of expression

87% of the phenotypic variance for height *in a population* can be attributed to underlying genetic variance within that population, suggesting that 13% can be attributed to nongenetic (environmental) variance. In fact, height is a complex polygenic trait, with genes on at least 6 chromosomes (3, 4, 8, 15, 17, and 18) having **additive effects** (Visscher et al. 2007), which explains in part why heritability for height can be so high, yet variability in trait expression so broad. Heritability is calculated as $H^2 = Vg/(Vg + Ve)$. So, in simple terms, heritability is the proportion of genetic variance (Vg) in a population relative to the total variance for a trait from all sources, environmental (Ve) *and* genetic.

Heritability estimates will be high for populations with high degrees of genetic variance, as well as for populations reared in environments with little environmental variance (e.g., mould in an agar medium under controlled conditions). Similarly, if Vg is low or Ve very high, heritability estimates will be low. It is also important to understand that H^2 is an estimate of heritability for a trait in a given population at a given time—*it is not a constant!* This is easily comprehended if we realize that environments are also not constant; thus, Ve is always changing. As Moore (2006, 349) has stated, "the amount of variation that can be accounted for by one factor always depends on the amount of variation in the other factor." In other words, the contribution of genetic variance is not independent of the contribution of environmental variance. For this reason alone, it should be anticipated that different human populations will have different heritability estimates for all traits, including intelligence, and that such differences say nothing about the innate character of the trait in question.

ONE INTELLIGENCE OR SEVERAL INTELLIGENCES?

A final consideration regarding intelligence is how many kinds there may be. Although psychologists measure general or full-scale intelligence in terms of concepts such as fluid intelligence (reasoning and problem solving) or crystallized intelligence (acquired knowledge and experiential learning), others—notably animal behaviourists and paleoanthropologists—speak of ecological intelligence, social intelligence, or technical intelligence. These "intelligences" imply specific aptitudes hypothesized to have been essential adaptations for group living and foraging, including the use of tools, in complex habitats. Remembering the location of food sources in patchy or seasonal environments, your position relative to other group members in a hierarchically ranked society, and where to build nests and how to use reeds for termite fishing, can be vital in terms of survival and reproduction, and each capacity will have significant selective pressures attached to it.

These capacities have been linked to the evolution of brain size among primates. Features such as social learning and innovation are essential components of behavioural flexibility (see Chapter 6). For example, Reader and LaLand (2002) surveyed the literature on primate behaviour, social intelligence, and brain size and found strong positive correlations with measures of behavioural flexibility and "executive" brain volume (i.e., the size of the brain regions involved in processes of learning, planning, rule acquisition, and abstract thinking). Herrmann and colleagues (2007) have proposed a model of **cultural intelligence** unique to hominins, as shown by their tests carried out with chimpanzees, orangutans, and human toddlers. They found that 2.5-year-old human children were equally adept at solving problems in the physical world, but more savvy in dealing with social problems than either of the great apes (Figure 13.7).

The point we make here is that different cognitive capacities and abilities (skills) are necessary for survival and confer distinct but not necessarily mutually exclusive selective advantages. Some individuals may have exceptional abilities for learning, innovation, and problem solving, others for tool use, still others for spatial mapping, planning, and ecological memory. Humans in particular may have evolved special talents applied to the multifaceted world of a long-lived, socially complex, culture-bearing hominin. These variations may create differences among individuals, but not among different populations composed of such individuals.

cultural intelligence

the capacity of humans
to acquire early in
life complex skills for
negotiating social
situations

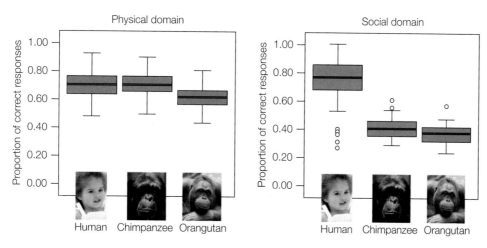

FIGURE 13.7 Human children and apes have similar capacities in dealing with the physical world (left), but humans have exceptional skills with respect to social situations (right).

From E. Herrmann, et al. (2007). Humans have evolved specialized skills of social cognition: the cultural intelligence hypothesis. *Science* 317: 1362. Reprinted with permission AAAS. Photos: Monkey Business Images/Shutterstock.com (child); Devid Camerlynck/Shutterstock.com (chimpanzee); Olga OSA/Shutterstock.com (orangutan)

RACE AND BIOMEDICINE

In June 2005 the U.S. Food and Drug Administration (FDA) approved a drug known as BiDil to treat congestive heart failure, the first ever therapeutic measure carrying a race-specific label. The target population was African Americans. The immediate response inside and outside the medical community was by and large critical. Some suggested that it was scientifically unreasonable to render such approvals based on race rather than **pathophysiology** (Bloche 2004); others saw it as an attempt to avoid the cost of lengthy clinical trials and to "exploit race" to gain market advantage (Sankar and Kahn 2005). A 2007 article in the popular magazine *Scientific American* referred to it as "Race in a Bottle," noting that drugmakers were using questionable scientific research to reach unsound conclusions (Kahn 2007). The response of the FDA was to point out that its decision was founded not on the results of one clinical trial in which only black subjects were enrolled, but on three such investigations, two of which included self-identified black *and* white participants (Temple and Stockbridge 2007). In each case, BiDil was shown to have a marked benefit for health improvement and quality of life in the black sample studied; indeed, the black-only trial was terminated early after initial results showed a 43% to 63% reduction in mortality for those participants adding BiDil to a standard therapy. Moreover, as we noted earlier in this chapter, African Americans are especially prone to hypertension and heart disease, so the need for such an intervention was already well established.

The controversy around BiDil ranged from biologists and medical geneticists pointing out that there is a sound evolutionary rationale for designing "race-specific" therapies, to social scientists and politicians raising spectres of racialized medicine and the entrenchment of already damaging negative stereotypes (Carlson 2005). As a case study, BiDil provides a classic example of the struggle that biomedicine has had for many years in attempting to cope with population diversity and the interplay of biology, economics, and culture (Hardimon 2013). People of African origin may well have a genetic predisposition to heart disease, but it is as important to ask what degree diet, poverty, education, access to health care, and other lifestyle factors come into play. As a further example, African American adults and adolescents are much more likely to be diagnosed with AIDS than either white or Hispanic Americans (nine times and three times more likely, respectively); however, these disparities are founded almost exclusively in nonbiological causes (Kraut-Becher et al. 2008).

pathophysiology
a disturbance of normal body function as a result of disease, genetic disorder, or impaired development

placebo

a medical intervention (drug or procedure) that has no demonstrable therapeutic effect, often used in clinical trials

In modern biomedicine, the gold standard for assessing population disease risk is the randomized clinical trial, in which defined groups (populations) are evaluated for outcomes under different treatments. Subjects are randomly assigned to a treatment group receiving a new therapy under investigation or to a control group, which is administered either an experimental/proven treatment or a **placebo**. But how are such populations to be defined, and how is relative risk to be assigned? Subject groups are often identified according to known health outcomes: if there is a higher prevalence of heart disease among African Americans, it would seem reasonable to compare samples of black, white, Hispanic, and so on. Indeed, as Jackson (2008) notes, more than 113,000 scientific articles had been published and reported by the indexing service PubMed (as of March 2007) using the classic Linnaean racial classification system.

But if the predisposition is genetically based, how do we control for population admixture, and what impact might *that* have on disease susceptibility? Yaeger and colleagues (2008) compared more than 100 genome markers for ancestry in 50 self-identified African Americans and 40 Nigerians and found that while the latter had about 4% European admixture, the African American sample had 15% European ancestry—a statistically significant difference. Indeed, in the United States, the Agency for Health Care Policy and Research recommends screening *all* infants for the presence of sickle cell disease—generally considered a condition affecting primarily African Americans—since it is generally not possible to determine an infant's ancestry "by appearance, name or self-report" (Ashley-Koch et al. 2000, 844).

If the use of self-identified race or ethnicity is problematic in clinical medical research, what are the alternatives? Ng and colleagues (2008) have proposed that with increasing availability and reduced cost of obtaining full genome sequencing of patients, medicine should move away from a race-based model of pharmacological investigation and therapeutics toward one based on individual genetic variation. They argue that the design of personalized medicines would mark an endpoint to the often tragic (albeit relatively rare) adverse event, in which a prescribed drug or treatment causes harm and sometimes death instead of providing relief. However, they also note (Ng et al. 2009) that variation in methods used by different "direct-to-consumer" genetic screening companies can lead to dissimilarities in calculated risk of disease, which would have potentially disastrous consequences for treatment.

LEARNING KEYS

KEY IDEAS

- The race concept states that humankind can be divided into discrete populations sharing clusters of features that distinguish members of one race from another.

- Biological variation across geographic space can be described in terms of continuous gradations of frequencies known as clines.

- Clines are established by historical processes such as local breeding and population migration.

- The race concept can be shown to suffer from several fallacies of logic and therefore should not be used to explain or interpret human differences.

- Human populations are not homogenous; individual traits vary greatly in frequency from one group to the next in widely different patterns.

- Most human variation is regulated by many genes, making measurement a difficult task.

- Drawing dividing lines for continuously varying traits (such as height) is arbitrary.

- Most human traits are not linked and vary independently from one population to the next, so there are no discrete "racial clusters" of human variation.

- There is no set number of traits that can define any particular human population as belonging to a given race.

- Humans are a polymorphic species, meaning that more human variation occurs within populations than between them.

- In the early 20th century, proponents of eugenics attempted to prevent people considered undesirable— that is, not members of their own "race," religion, or social/political class—from reproducing.

- In Canada, eugenics policies were enacted by way of restrictive immigration policies and through practices such as forced sterilization; the latter continued into the latter half of the 20th century, particularly in Alberta and British Columbia.

- One of the most insidious applications of the race concept ranked human populations in terms of innate intelligence, even though the notion of what constitutes intelligence—let alone how it might be measured—is highly debatable.

- Biomedicine remains an area in which researchers continue to struggle with how to characterize variation in the occurrence of disease and disease risk.

KEY TERMS

race (p. 298)

polytypic (p. 301)

polymorphic (p. 301)

cline (p. 302)

cultural intelligence (p. 312)

KEY QUESTIONS TO ASK MYSELF

1. My best friend's family came from a different part of the world than my own, but I don't think of him as being from a different race. Why is that?

2. I'm not sure I understand the idea of liberal eugenics. Who's going to benefit from these kinds of technologies after all?

3. Some scientists really think that they can say that one group of people is more intelligent than another by measuring the size of their heads. What does the size of my head have to do with how smart I am?

KEY CRITICAL THINKING QUESTIONS

1. Is intelligence measurable? If so, should we measure it?

2. Under what circumstances do you think the concept of race might be used legitimately in a discussion of human population variation?

KEY THINGS TO DO NEXT

CourseMate Visit **CourseMate** at www.nelson.com/humanvoyage2e to build your comprehension, practise your critical thinking skills, review core concepts, and explore other resources at your disposal.

We do not grow absolutely, chronologically. We grow sometimes in one dimension, and not in another, unevenly. We grow partially. We are relative. We are mature in one realm, childish in another. The past, present, and future mingle and pull us backward, forward, or fix us in the present. We are made up of layers, cells, constellations.

Anaïs Nin (1903–1977)

OVERVIEW

In Part III of this book, we took you on a journey from our earliest ancestors to the appearance of anatomically modern humans. As you have seen, this transition was characterized by profound anatomical and behavioural changes that are evident in the fossil and archaeological record. Human populations today are a product of that evolutionary journey, and the morphological and genetic diversity we see today reflects long-term natural selection and other evolutionary mechanisms. In the first half of this chapter, we explore the ways in which humans have adapted to their environments, particularly those characterized by extreme conditions. We also examine emerging and re-emerging infectious diseases, nutritional anthropology, and the human life cycle. In the second half of the chapter, we examine how past populations are studied through analyses of their skeletal remains, highlighting the variety of data that such remains can provide.

KEY CONCEPTS

Biocultural perspective, biomedical anthropology, epidemiology, epidemiologic transition, emerging infectious diseases, human adaptability, nutritional anthropology, human life course, bioarchaeology, paleopathology, paleonutrition

KEY LEARNING OBJECTIVES

At the end of this chapter, you will be able to

LO1   Identify the factors contributing to the emergence and re-emergence of infectious diseases today

LO2   Explain how biological anthropologists can contribute to the study of the human life course

LO3   Apply a biocultural approach to understanding undereating and overeating

LO4   Compare and contrast the ways in which humans have adapted physiologically to their environments

PROLOGUE: "THREE OF THESE THINGS BELONG TOGETHER ..."

Those of us who grew up with *Sesame Street* remember the song *Three of These Things Belong Together*, written by Joe Raposo and Jeff Moss in 1970, a bit before most of you were born! It accompanied a game in which several similar objects were shown, one of which was somehow unlike the rest. The message was about the nature and meaning of difference: How do we know when things belong together? In this chapter we explore the wonderful world of modern human variation and celebrate difference for what it means, as testimony to human adaptation throughout history *and* as a living record of human population dynamics, including recent migration and marriage.

The dimensions along which human populations vary are as diverse as the variation itself. They range from disease experience and resistance, to patterns of growth and development, to aging, to the biology of lifestyle choices. One of the questions we have to ask when we are confronted with population variation is this: To what degree do variations reflect fundamental genetic differences acquired over many generations, as opposed to merely reflecting our ability to produce adapted phenotypes over the course of a lifetime of exposure to a particular environment? This dichotomy underlies the distinction between *adaptation* and *adaptability*, the latter referring to an intrinsic biological plasticity, or capacity to respond to specific environmental cues in an appropriate fashion. A fascinating aspect of our biology that we explore in this chapter is that different human populations have followed different routes—in some cases genetic and in others plastic—to accommodate similar environmental challenges.

One aspect of modern population biology that demands our attention is that of ethics. Whether we are studying the skeletal remains of the ancestors of contemporary First Nations peoples or taking buccal swabs for DNA analysis from people around the world, we need to remember that what we learn has as much (or more) importance and impact for the future of those studied as it does for the future of "science." If nothing else, recognizing and respecting the truth in this should make one thing patently clear: all of us belong together.

BIOLOGY OF CONTEMPORARY POPULATIONS

In Chapter 1 we introduced you to the biocultural approach, which recognizes that biology and culture are interrelated. Much of the research being done today by biological anthropologists is guided by this perspective (see, for example, *Medical Anthropology: A Biocultural Approach* by Andrea Wiley and John Allen [2008]). It is also evident in the interdisciplinary nature of our field. For example, the integration of biological and medical anthropology has led to the emergence of **biomedical anthropology.** Similarly, the integration of anthropology and **epidemiology**, exemplified by the volume *Anthropology and Epidemiology: Interdisciplinary Approach to the Study of Health and Disease* (eds. James, Stall, and Gifford 2002), has resulted in numerous studies of the cultural and behavioural factors underlying the spread of infectious disease. Central to this perspective has been the realization over the past several decades that a good deal of human phenotypic variation arises as a consequence of each individual's capacity to respond differentially to challenges posed by life's circumstances—a process known as adaptability. Humans are malleable in the face of varying environmental conditions (and environments are themselves diverse, ranging from the environment of the uterus to that of the International Space Station). One example of a plastic response familiar to us all is that

biomedical anthropology

the study of health from a biocultural and epidemiological perspective

epidemiology

the study of the distribution and determinants of disease

our bodies accommodate seasonal changes in temperature and exposure to UV-B radiation. Adaptability differs from our general understanding of biological adaptation in that our responses are not (typically) passed on to future generations in a fashion akin to Lamarckian inheritance (see Chapter 2); nonetheless, as we will see in this chapter and the following ones, adaptability is essential to our capacity as a species to survive, reproduce, and expand into previously unexplored habitats.

INFECTIOUS DISEASES

Emerging and Re-emerging Infectious Diseases

You are probably all familiar with the Black Death, the outbreak of bubonic plague that struck Europe in the 14th century, killing an estimated one-third of the population. Over the centuries that followed, plague and other infectious diseases such as tuberculosis, smallpox, influenza, and cholera were leading causes of death, and many anthropological studies have focused on the biological and social impact of these diseases on human populations (see, for example, Burke 2011; Padiak 2008; Sattenspiel and Herring 1998, 2003; Sawchuk and Burke 1998, 2003).

In the early 1970s, epidemiologist Abdel R. Omran formulated what he called the **epidemiologic transition model** to explain changing patterns of health and disease over time. Integrating epidemiological and demographic data, he identified three stages: (1) the "age of pestilence and famine," characterized by high death rates from **epidemics**, famines, and war; (2) the "age of receding pandemics," marked by a decline in infectious diseases and famine resulting from improved nutrition and living conditions; and (3) the "age of degenerative and man-made diseases," characterized by an increase in chronic diseases and a reduction in infectious diseases (Omran 1971). One of the implications of Omran's model is that infectious diseases are a thing of the past. Nothing could be further from the truth, however, and today more than one-quarter of all annual deaths worldwide are estimated to be directly related to infectious diseases (Morens et al. 2004; Figure 14.1). We have thus entered

epidemiologic transition model

developed by epidemiologist Abdel Omran to explain changing patterns of health and disease over time

epidemics

outbreaks of disease exceeding the normal level of occurrence

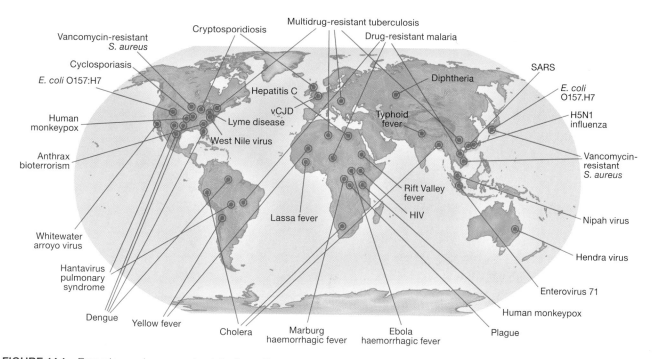

FIGURE 14.1 Emerging and re-emerging infectious diseases pose a significant health threat today. While many of these diseases are appearing in North America, this might simply reflect greater identification and reporting on this continent than elsewhere.

F.S. Fauci. (2001). Infectious diseases: Considerations for the 21st century. *Clinical Infectious Diseases* 32: 675–685. Reprinted with permission of Oxford University Press.

CHAPTER 14 Biology of Contemporary and Past Populations

what Barrett and colleagues (1998) have described as the third epidemiologic transition: the age of emerging and re-emerging infectious diseases.[1] Since 1973 alone, more than 30 new **pathogens** have been identified, and South Asia, Central America, and tropical Africa have been highlighted as potential "hotspots" for emerging infectious diseases (Jones et al. 2008). These are defined as diseases that (1) are new to humans, (2) have been identified only recently in humans, or (3) existed previously but have reappeared after a period of decline (Lederberg et al. 1992). At the root of these diseases are human behaviours that have created ideal conditions for their outbreak and spread.

Among the most frequently identified factors underlying the emergence and re-emergence of infectious diseases are ecological changes associated with agriculture, mining, logging, and deforestation (Figure 14.2). Slash-and-burn agriculture, for example, creates standing pools of water that provide ideal breeding grounds for mosquitoes that carry malaria. The digging of irrigation ditches has facilitated the spread of schistosomiasis, and deforestation and logging have brought humans into contact with pathogenic microorganisms to which they have never been exposed before, resulting in the transmission of **zoonotic diseases** to humans. HIV, for example, is closely related to SIV, the simian immunodeficiency virus that is carried by chimpanzees as well as by an Old World monkey called the sooty mangabey. This virus is believed to have jumped from these primates to humans through hunting, butchering, and consumption of bush meat, a practice that is widespread among poorer households in parts of Central and West Africa. The hunting of primates for bush meat also appears to have caused the emergence of a new type of retrovirus, HTLV (human T-cell lymphotropic virus), among hunters in Cameroon as a result of their exposure to a related simian virus through cuts and bites on the skin (Wolfe et al. 2005).

Climate change and global warming have also contributed to the increased incidence of infectious diseases such as malaria, which kills 2 to 3 million people worldwide each year. As a result of rising temperatures, we are now seeing cases of malaria at higher latitudes and higher altitudes than before.[2] The mosquito that transmits dengue fever has also expanded its range as a result of global warming, from tropical regions where it is endemic to more temperate zones.

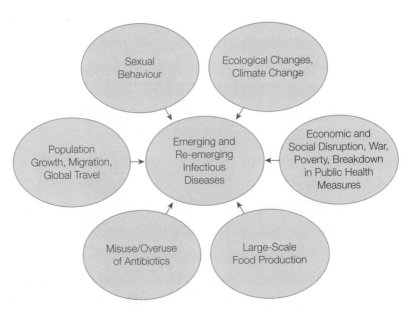

FIGURE 14.2 A variety of anthropogenic factors have contributed to the emergence and re-emergence of infectious diseases.

1. According to Barrett and colleagues (1998), the first epidemiologic transition was characterized by an increase in infectious diseases associated with the Neolithic Revolution, and the second transition was marked by a shift from infectious to chronic diseases associated with industrialization.

2. Most cases of malaria documented in Canada each year are brought into the country from geographic areas where the disease is endemic.

FIGURE 14.3 Lack of access to safe drinking water and inadequate sanitation in impoverished regions of the world contribute to cholera epidemics.

© Karim Kadim/AP Photo

In addition to ecological disruption and climate change, economic and social disruption, poverty, poor sanitation (Figure 14.3), sexual behaviour, and the increased movement of people (e.g., air travel, migration from rural to urban areas, flight from war) have resulted in the spread of infectious diseases. Airline travel means that pathogenic microorganisms can now be transported from one side of the globe to the other within a matter of hours. A perfect example is the 2003 outbreak of SARS (severe acute respiratory syndrome) in Toronto, which was ultimately traced to an individual who had boarded a plane in Hong Kong. Some of you may remember the fear and panic associated with that outbreak. To put this into perspective, however, keep in mind that nearly 800 individuals worldwide succumbed to SARS compared to an average of 4,000 who die of seasonal influenza *each year* in Canada alone.

Travel to exotic locations also places tourists at risk of contracting diseases to which they have never been exposed. In urban areas of Indonesia, for instance, macaques trained to perform tricks for human audiences have been found to carry several retroviruses that are capable of infecting humans via scratches or bites (Engel et al. 2002; Schillaci et al. 2005, 2006). Tourist sites that are frequented by monkeys are another potential source of disease. Analyses of blood samples taken from macaques who reside in the "monkey temple" in Bali, for example, have revealed antibodies to the herpes virus, raising the possibility of its transmission to humans (Engel et al. 2002).

Large-scale food production has also come at a cost to our health. The mad cow disease scare in Britain in the 1990s highlighted the consequences of feeding cattle with meat from sheep that were infected with scrapie, a degenerative disease that affects sheep and goats. Consumption of meat thereby contaminated resulted in the transmission of mad cow disease (bovine spongiform encephalopathy, or BSE) to humans.[3] Closer to home, outbreaks of

---

3. Humans who consume BSE-infected meat develop a similar neurodegenerative disease known as new variant Creutzfeldt-Jakob disease.

E. coli infection resulting from the ingestion of contaminated water, cheese, hamburger meat, and ready-to-eat salads have been reported in Canada and elsewhere in North America. In the town of Walkerton, Ontario, for example, contamination of the town's water supply by runoff from local farms was identified as the source of an *E. coli* outbreak in May 2000, which sickened about 2,500 individuals, killing seven.[4] The 2008 outbreak of another bacterial infection, listeriosis, was linked to contaminated meat-slicing machines at a well-known food processing plant in Ontario.[5]

Changes in the pathogenic organisms themselves are also leading to the emergence and re-emergence of infectious diseases. Like humans, disease-causing microorganisms evolve, and increased virulence can result from the exchange of genes with other organisms. Harmful strains of *Streptococcus*—once the cause of scarlet fever—have been linked to necrotizing fasciitis (flesh-eating disease) and toxic shock syndrome.[6] One of the major roadblocks to preventing and treating AIDS is that HIV constantly mutates. Similarly, the influenza virus changes its appearance from year to year, necessitating the development of a new vaccine annually to target the strains that could potentially strike. While most outbreaks of influenza are caused by type B and type C viruses, it is type A that has been responsible for the flu pandemics that have occurred in human history. What makes type A so dangerous is its ability to change dramatically by combining with a flu virus from another organism. Pigs, for instance, can become infected with both human and avian influenza type A viruses, and the mixing of these two viruses in pigs can give rise to deadlier strains that can be transmitted to humans and passed from person to person. It was this mixing of flu strains that gave rise to the 1918 flu pandemic that killed 40 to 50 million people worldwide. In Canada alone, the pandemic claimed 30,000 to 50,000 lives (Herring 2000); small northern communities lacking stored food supplies and medicines were especially hard hit (Herring 1994a, b). In contrast, the 2009 flu pandemic involved a new strain of H1N1 influenza that was made up of genes from human, swine, and avian flu viruses; however, it lacked the genes that made the 1918 strain so lethal.

The other major challenge facing public health officials today is the emergence of antibiotic-resistant strains of bacteria. Factors that have contributed to this trend are the overuse of antibiotics (e.g., taking them for viral infections for which they do no good), the failure by patients to take the full course of their medication, and the practice of putting antibiotics in animal feed in order to prevent infections among livestock. Tuberculosis (Box 14.1) has re-emerged as a leading killer, due in part to the rise of drug-resistant strains of the bacterium responsible for the disease, and to HIV/AIDS, with which an estimated 35 million people worldwide are now living. (Individuals with HIV are more susceptible to tuberculosis; infection with HIV can also lead to reactivation of latent tuberculosis.) Other notable examples of antibiotic-resistant bacteria include *Neisseria gonorrhoeae*, methicillin-resistant *Staphylococcus aureus* (MRSA), vancomycin-resistant *Staphylococcus aureus* (VRSA), and *C. difficile*.

THE HUMAN LIFE COURSE

As we discussed in Chapter 5, in comparison to nonhuman primates, humans have slower growth, a longer period of maturation and dependency, a longer life span, and—in the case of females—a longer postmenopausal stage. As you will recall from Chapter 10, there has been much debate about the rate of growth in earlier *Homo* species such as *Homo erectus/ergaster*. Patterns of growth in modern humans have also been the focus of numerous studies (e.g., Bogin 1999; Hoppa and Fitzgerald 1999).

---

4. Millions of *E. coli* bacteria are present in our intestines and help maintain a healthy digestive system. The O157:H7 strain normally found in the intestines of cattle and other livestock, however, can cause serious illness and death in humans.

5. In this particular case, infection with *Listeria* bacteria in deli meats resulted in more than 50 cases of illness and a number of deaths.

6. Outbreaks of this syndrome in the 1980s were linked to the use of superabsorbent tampons.

BOX 14.1	PROFILE ... Tuberculosis and the Sanatorium in Canada

© Mike Latschislaw

As a biological anthropologist, I am interested in evolutionary, historic, and ongoing relationships between humans and infectious diseases. Infectious diseases have the power to shape and transform human populations, both biologically and culturally. Historically, in Canada, tuberculosis was an endemic disease, always present and well-known to individuals, families, and communities. In 1882, Robert Koch, a German microbiologist and physician, determined that tuberculosis was caused by a bacterium, *Mycobacterium tuberculosis*, and firmly challenged the ongoing debate that tuberculosis was a hereditary disease. Tuberculosis tended to cluster in families not because it was inherited, but because there was regular transmission of the bacterium within the confines of family homes. The results of mass screening surveys for tuberculosis infection suggested that transmission was such a regular phenomenon, both in and outside of family homes, that most Canadians were likely to be infected at some point in childhood or adolescence.

Among those infected before effective drug therapies were introduced in the 1940s, the infection was lifelong and the possibility of developing active tuberculosis disease always lingered. Within the body, tuberculosis bacteria remained alive and viable in macrophages, phagocytic cells of the human immune system that typically play a role in clearing infection from the body. Before drug therapies were developed, medicine focused on reducing the risk of active tuberculosis disease through resistance building, or encouraging good immune function through means such as rest and nutrition.

As modern scientific medicine expanded, drawing on insights from microbiology, anatomy, and pathology, new approaches to treating tuberculosis would emerge.

In Canada, tuberculosis sanatoria, specialized hospitals for tuberculosis treatment, materialized within the rise of scientific medicine. The first Canadian tuberculosis sanatorium, the Muskoka Cottage Sanatorium, opened near Gravenhurst, Ontario, in 1897, followed by the Muskoka Free Hospital for Consumptives in 1902. These may have been Canada's earliest sanatoria, but tuberculosis sanatoria would soon appear across the country. Under the developing scientific paradigm, even the most long-standing of medical treatments, such as bed rest, were medicalized and new approaches to place tuberculous lungs at rest to encourage healing, including tuberculosis-related surgeries like artificial pneumothorax (lung compression through the insertion of gas into the pleural cavity) and thoracoplasty (lung compression through the surgical removal of selected ribs), were developed. As a biological anthropologist, my interests lay in these relationships between bodies and microbes, the transitions experienced in the rise of scientific medicine, and the social and medical experiences of patients who were admitted to sanatoria suffering from a chronic infection that could never truly be cured.

The role of the tuberculosis sanatorium, both as a medical and a cultural phenomenon, would change over time. Equipped with new, effective drug treatments by the 1940s, the sanatorium would be redefined as a place of isolation and cure, before disappearing altogether as a medical phenomenon in Canada with the retreat of endemic tuberculosis. Today, however, mere decades after tuberculosis sanatoria closed in Canada, the disease has re-emerged in the minds of Canadians because of bacterial adaptations and resistance to previously effective drug treatments.

Source: Written by Dr. Stacie Burke, Associate Professor, Associate Department Head, Anthropology, University of Manitoba

The Early Years: Breastfeeding, Weaning, and Child Growth

Biological anthropologists have brought their unique biocultural perspective to the study of infant feeding practices in contemporary populations. Considerable variation exists in breastfeeding and **weaning** practices, with some infants being breastfed for only a short period of time, if at all, and others for several years. Factors underlying this variation include cultural beliefs about weaning, the availability of supplementary foods, a woman's reproductive status, and her role in the labour force. University of Calgary biocultural anthropologist Warren Wilson and colleagues have examined weaning practices of the Makushi Amerindians of central Guyana in order to investigate the relationship between the length of exclusive breastfeeding and infant and child mortality (Wilson et al. 2006; see Chapter 16, Box 16.2). This study was motivated by the controversy surrounding the World Health Organization's recommendation for exclusive breastfeeding during the first six months of life owing to the immunological benefits of breast milk. In contrast to their

weaning

the process by which infants gradually shift from a diet of breast milk to one consisting of other foods hypothesis that exclusive breastfeeding (EBF) for less than six months compromises the health of infants and children, Wilson and colleagues found no relationship between the length of EBF and infant and child mortality. They suggest several possible explanations for this finding, and conclude that international recommendations for exclusive breastfeeding up to six months of age must consider local cultural and environmental factors. Tina Moffat's (2001) study of growth and **morbidity** indices in partially and exclusively breastfed infants from birth to seven months in Kathmandu, Nepal, also revealed no differences between the two groups, suggesting that a more relaxed recommendation of four to six months of EBF instead of the rigid recommendation of EBF for the first six months of life may be more bioculturally appropriate.

On a broader scale, Dan Sellen's (2007, 2010) research on lactation biology and variation in breastfeeding and weaning practices also has public health implications. Humans are the only mammals to use complementary feeding, meaning that we routinely provide infants with complementary foods following a period of exclusive breastfeeding. Unfortunately, infant and child feeding practices are suboptimal in many parts of the world, resulting in high rates of illness and death. Identifying the social and cultural reasons for the failure to adopt current international recommendations for infant and child feeding is therefore crucial if we are to reduce morbidity and mortality rates in this age group.

Considerable research has been devoted to child growth. Taking a biocultural perspective, human biologists have examined the growth of children living in a variety of different environments and have identified multiple factors underlying variation in growth patterns. Moffat's (2003) study of child growth in peri-urban Nepal, for instance, linked stunted growth—defined as low height for age—to parasitic infections associated with poor sanitation and contaminated drinking water. Similarly, a study by Warren Wilson and colleagues (Wilson et al. 2011) attributed growth faltering among a group of Amazonian Indians to infectious disease and political marginalization, among other factors (see Chapter 16, Box 16.2). Closer to home, Rob Hoppa and Todd Garlie's (1998) analysis of child growth in 19th- to 20th-century Toronto revealed a **secular trend** toward increased height for age in more recent children—a trend common in industrialized countries over the past two centuries. Major contributing factors include a decline in infectious diseases and improvements in nutrition, hygiene, sanitation, and medical care.

The Anthropology of Aging

At the other end of the human life cycle is old age. In developed countries, 20% of the population is over the age of 60, and this percentage is expected to increase to over 30% by 2030 (Kinsella and Velkoff 2001). Developing countries have increasingly aging populations, home to over half the world's senior citizens (individuals 65 years of age and older) (ibid.). The anthropological study of **senescence** has attracted considerable attention in recent years as our population becomes increasingly older (Crews 1993). Taking a biocultural approach, biological anthropologists have examined a variety of aspects of aging, including changes in life expectancy over the course of our evolutionary history, skeletal and reproductive aging, and the development of chronic diseases (Ice 2005). A variety of factors affect the rate of aging, including diet, physical activity, smoking, hormones, and genetics. Considerable individual and population variation exists, and some populations—such as the residents of the Japanese island of Okinawa—are known for being long-lived.[7] You may recall from Chapter 11 that old age for Neandertals was about 40 years, if they were lucky enough to live that long. Medical advances in recent decades have allowed us to extend our life span, and people in industrialized countries are now living longer than ever (see Figure 14.4). In Canada the life expectancy is currently 82.7 years for women and 78 years for men. It is considerably lower in countries where access to a healthy diet and medical care is lacking, however, and despite hopes of reaching the maximum human life span of 120 years (Ruiz-Torres and Beier 2005), few people ever come close to this age.

---

7. This particular population has been identified as having the longest life span in the world. As of 2004, approximately 1,800 individuals out of a total population of 1.35 million on Okinawa were over the age of 100 (Wiley and Allen 2009).

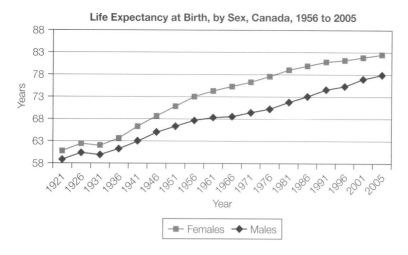

FIGURE 14.4 The life expectancy of Canadians continues to increase.

Statistics Canada, "Life expectancy at birth, by sex, Canada, 1956–2005," from http://www.statcan.gc.ca/pub/82-229-x/2009001/demo/lif-eng.htm

As we get older, our bodies begin to break down. We become shorter as our vertebral column compresses, and many of us become heavier as our metabolic rate slows down. So why do we age in the first place? Hypotheses proposed to explain aging have focused on both physiological and evolutionary mechanisms. The former include the damaging effects of mutations and **free radicals** on the somatic (i.e., body) cells, as well as wear and tear on the joints and other tissues (Ricklefs and Finch 1995). With respect to evolutionary explanations, two theories predominate: the **antagonistic pleiotropy theory** (Williams 1957) and the **disposable soma theory** (Kirkwood and Holliday 1979). In Chapter 3 we introduced you to the concept of pleiotropy, a phenomenon whereby a gene controls for more than one phenotypic trait. According to the antagonistic pleiotropy theory of aging, selection for a gene that benefits an organism early in life by enhancing fertility is harmful later on (Williams 1957). Alternatively, the disposable soma theory is based on the argument that since energy is required for both reproduction and the maintenance of the body, organisms balance these needs by directing more of their energy to reproduction and less to maintaining the body's cells (Kirkwood and Holliday 1979). The end result in both cases is aging and ultimately death.

NUTRITIONAL ANTHROPOLOGY

Undernutrition

If we look at *Canada's Food Guide*, a healthy diet consists of a balance of four different food groups: protein, dairy, fruits and vegetables, and grains. Yet some populations have traditionally subsisted on a diet that would not be considered "balanced" by North American standards. The Inuit are a case in point. Their traditional diet consisted primarily of protein and fat, with very little plant food and no dairy products, yet they were able to derive all of the nutrients they need from these foods. Clearly, then, what matters is not so much the types of foods you eat but what nutrients they contain.

An estimated 2 billion people worldwide suffer from nutritional deficiencies, including protein malnutrition and deficiencies of vitamins A, B_1, B_3, C, and D, as well as iron, iodine, and folic acid (see Table 14.1). Many of these deficiencies are the direct result of a lack of access to foods containing these nutrients, either because people cannot afford to buy them or because they are simply unavailable. In other cases, an overreliance on a narrow range of food items means that some populations lack key nutrients in their diet. Populations that rely heavily on cereals, for instance, are prone to protein, iron, and vitamin B deficiencies. In the

free radicals

unstable molecules that react with other molecules, causing damage to the body's cells

antagonistic pleiotropy theory

the theory that aging is the result of a gene that benefits an organism early in life by enhancing fertility but that is detrimental later on

disposable soma theory

the theory that organisms balance their energy needs by directing more of their energy to reproduction and less to maintaining the body

TABLE 14.1 Common Nutritional Deficiencies Seen Today

Nutrient	Sources	Disease/Condition	Symptoms	Individuals at Risk
Protein	Meat, eggs, dairy	Kwashiorkor	Swollen abdomen, loss of muscle mass, changes in skin pigmentation	Mainly young children; a high prevalence in sub-Saharan Africa
Vitamin A	Carrots, sweet potatoes, squash, liver	Vitamin A deficiency	Blindness, weakened immune system, impaired embryonic development, increased risk of maternal mortality	Young children; a high prevalence in Southeast Asia
Vitamin B$_1$ (thiamine)	Brown rice, beans, peas	Beriberi	Fatigue, weight loss, cardiovascular, gastrointestinal, and neurological symptoms	Individuals who rely heavily on refined rice; common in parts of Asia
Vitamin B$_3$ (niacin)	Red meat, fish, dairy products, almonds, leafy green vegetables	Pellagra	Diarrhea, dermatitis, dementia	Individuals who rely heavily on corn and other niacin-deficient foods; common in parts of Africa and Asia
Vitamin D	Sunlight, egg yolks, cod liver oil	Rickets (infants and children); osteomalacia (adults)	Skeletal deformities, loss of bone mass	Infants and children, especially dark-skinned individuals living in northern climates or individuals confined to the indoors
Iron	Meat, fish, poultry, broccoli	Iron deficiency anemia	Fatigue, irritability, pale skin, mental impairment	Pregnant women and children
Iodine	Seafood, seaweed, iodized salt	Iodine deficiency	Goiter in adolescents and adults, impaired fetal development	People living in areas with iodine-poor soil and water; common in parts of Africa
Folic Acid	Leafy green vegetables, chickpeas, lentils, fruits	Folic acid deficiency	Birth defects; heart disease in adults	Pregnant women

past, scurvy resulting from a deficiency in vitamin C—a nutrient required for the synthesis of collagen in bones and other connective tissues—was common among sailors who spent long periods of time at sea with no fresh fruits and vegetables. Food processing also plays a role in the availability of nutrients. Some food processing methods can destroy nutrients or prevent their absorption by the intestine. The refining of rice, for instance, removes vitamin B$_1$, thereby increasing the risk of vitamin B$_1$ deficiency, or **beriberi**, among populations that rely heavily on this food item.

To prevent nutritional deficiencies from occurring, some of the foods we eat today have been fortified. For example, vitamins A and D are added to milk, vitamin C to fruit drinks,

beriberi

a disease caused by a deficiency of vitamin B$_1$ resulting in a number of neurological, cardiovascular, and physiological ailments iodine to salt, iron to cereal grains, calcium to orange juice, and folic acid to flour. Scientists at the University of Toronto have come up with a way of fortifying salt with iron in an attempt to treat and prevent iron deficiency anemia, one of the most common health problems in the world today. When iron is combined with iodine, the reaction that occurs results in evaporation of the iodine, so the challenge facing this research team, led by L.L. Diosady, professor of Food Engineering at the University of Toronto, was to add iron in such a way that the iodine would remain stable and both elements would be easily absorbed by the digestive system. After 10 years of experimenting, they developed a technique known as microencapsulation, which involves coating iodine with an agent consisting of a water-soluble starch (Diosady and Venkatesh Mannar 2000; Romita et al. 2011). This new double-fortified salt has already been distributed to parts of India and Africa, and further testing is currently under way.

If left untreated, nutritional deficiencies can have a profound effect on the health of an individual. Poor nutrition among females, for example, can result in low birth weight babies, which in turn can increase the risk of infant mortality. Protein-calorie malnutrition and vitamin deficiencies during childhood can impair cognitive ability and result in growth stunting, skeletal abnormalities, reduced adult stature, and reduced work capacity in adulthood. The synergistic relationship between malnutrition and infectious diseases also means that malnourished individuals are more susceptible to infectious diseases. You might be surprised to learn that nutritional deficiencies exist today not only in developing countries but also in industrialized nations. A study by the Canadian Paediatric Society revealed 104 confirmed cases of rickets in Canadian children between 2002 and 2004, the majority of them individuals living in the North and infants with darker skin who were breastfed without receiving supplemental vitamin D (Ward et al. 2007). Dan Sellen, Canada Research Chair in Human Ecology and Public Health Nutrition at the University of Toronto, Tina Moffat, and Warren Wilson are currently investigating the vitamin D status among immigrants to Canada with the goal of identifying the risk factors underlying vitamin D deficiency in this community, and assessing the knowledge and adoption by new Canadians of current recommendations to supplement breastfed infants with this vitamin (see Chapter 15).

Nutritional Excess: Overnutrition and Obesity

The past few decades have witnessed a dramatic increase in the number of people who are overweight or obese. Anthropometric data typically used to assess obesity and body fatness include height, weight, waist circumference, and skinfold thicknesses. The standard measure of obesity is the **body mass index (BMI)**, calculated as body weight (kg)/height(m)^2. In Canada and elsewhere, BMI values are grouped into four categories: (1) underweight (BMI < 18.5 kg/m^2); (2) normal weight (BMI ranging from 18.5 to 24.9 kg/m^2); (3) overweight (BMI ranging from 25 to 29.9 kg/m^2); and (4) obese (BMI > 30 kg/m^2). Over 300 million adults worldwide are estimated to have a BMI greater than 30, and an additional 700 million are considered to be overweight (Ulijaszek and Lofink 2006). Regions with the highest rates of obesity include the United States, much of Europe and the Middle East, parts of Latin America, South Africa, and the South Pacific. In Canada, a national survey conducted in 2004 revealed that 23.1% of adults were obese. Rates are even higher for First Nations and Inuit peoples and for long-term immigrants. Scientists studying the health effects of immigration to North America, for example, have found that new Canadians, while less likely to be overweight or obese than non-immigrants when they first arrive in the country, show higher rates of overweight and obesity after a decade or so than recently arrived immigrants, due to factors such as the transition to a less healthy diet and a decline in activity levels (Tremblay et al. 2005). This phenomenon is part of the **healthy immigrant effect**. Other factors contributing to rising rates of obesity include the availability of ready-to-eat prepackaged foods, larger portion sizes (i.e., "supersizing"), increased snacking, aggressive marketing of cheap, high-calorie/high-fat foods, dining out, high degrees of economic inequality, and low levels of physical activity. As obesity is a major risk factor for chronic diseases such as diabetes and cardiovascular disease, reducing the incidence of this condition has become a major public health priority.

body mass index (BMI)
a measure of body fatness, calculated as body weight (kg)/height(m)^2

healthy immigrant effect
a pattern in which the initially positive health status of new immigrants declines following immigration as they adopt less healthy lifestyles in their new country of residence

Biological anthropologists have contributed a great deal to our knowledge of the distribution and determinants of obesity, and their biocultural perspective is reflected in numerous studies of this condition (Ulijaszek and Lofink 2006). Kue Young's (1996) investigation of obesity among the Inuit of the central Arctic, for example, linked high rates of obesity to low levels of education, low socioeconomic status, and high levels of acculturation. Cultural perceptions of body image also play a role, with some cultures such as those of the South Pacific viewing a larger body size as a symbol of health, fertility, high status, and beauty.

A particularly worrying trend is the increase in the prevalence of overweight and obese children. From 1978 to 2004, the prevalence of overweight and obesity in Canadian children aged 2 to 17 jumped from 17% to 27% for boys and from 15% to 25% for girls (Shields 2006) (Figure 14.5). Given the rising rates of obesity among children, this age group has become the focus of an increasing number of studies in recent years. One of the authors of this textbook, Richard Lazenby and his colleagues, for instance, examined obesity in children from four different elementary schools in Prince George, British Columbia, located in neighbourhoods of differing socioeconomic status (Lazenby et al. 2007). They found a trend toward increasing rates of overweight and obesity in all four schools compared to national standards, with the trend most pronounced in the school with the lowest socioeconomic status.

Similarly, Tina Moffat's and Tracey Galloway's studies of growth and food consumption patterns in elementary schoolchildren in Hamilton, Ontario, revealed high rates of overweight and obesity in children of lower socioeconomic status (Moffat and Galloway 2007; Moffat et al. 2005). Furthermore, the majority of children they surveyed did not consume the recommended daily servings of fruits and vegetables, or grain or milk products (Moffat and Galloway 2008) (visit the CourseMate site for a discussion of Moffat and Galloway's biocultural research on child growth and nutrition). More recently, Galloway and colleagues (Galloway et al. 2010) documented an increase in overweight prevalence among Inuit children compared to previous studies, as well as evidence for a continued decline in the age of onset of obesity.

What Exactly Are We Putting into Our Bodies?

The increased prevalence of overweight and obese children has also led to increased scrutiny of the types of foods sold in schools. How many times have you had a craving for a slice of pizza or a juicy burger while sitting in the library or in class? Before you head off to the cafeteria, consider this: by eating just one of these items you run the risk of exceeding your

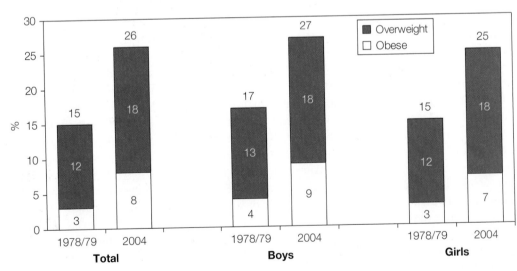

FIGURE 14.5 The prevalence of overweight and obesity in Canadian children aged 2 to 17 years has increased significantly from 1978/79 to 2004.

Statistics Canada, *Measured Obesity: Overweight Canadian children and adolescents, 2004* (Nutrition: Findings from the Canadian community Health Survey), 82-620-M, Issue 2005001, July 6, 2006.

total daily recommended intake of fat and/or calories. Yet many public and high schools, colleges, and universities continue to sell foods that are high in fat. An anthropologist investigating one such school in eastern Kentucky found that the decision to sell unhealthy snack foods was driven by underfunding of the school and the need to fund extracurricular activities and programs in order to enrich the educational experience of the children (Crooks 2003). The end result, not surprisingly, was that children at this particular school exhibited higher rates of overweight than the general population (ibid.).

Nutritional Adaptation

As we discussed above, many of us today have access to a seemingly limitless supply of food. Obesity was virtually nonexistent until about 10,000 years ago (Brown and Krick 2001, cited in Ulijaszek and Lofink 2006). Our earlier ancestors lived a very different existence, characterized by a reliance on wild animal and plant foods. According to S. Boyd Eaton, a physician and medical anthropologist, we are genetically programmed to consume a diet very different from the one that most North Americans consume today (Eaton and Konner 1985). Significant differences between the Paleolithic and modern Western diet include a higher intake of cereals, dairy products, refined sugars, vegetable oils, saturated fat, and salt in the latter (Cordain et al. 2005). As a consequence, we are now experiencing many diet-related chronic diseases that would have been absent in the past. Among affluent nations today, these "diseases of civilization" are the leading cause of morbidity and mortality.

Diabetes and the Thrifty Genotype

One manifestation of the disjunction between the diet to which we have genetically adapted and the diet we consume today is the rising rate of diabetes, a chronic disease characterized by high blood sugar. There are two main forms of diabetes: type 1, also known as juvenile diabetes, and type 2, also referred to as non-insulin dependent diabetes mellitus (NIDDM).[8] In individuals with type 1 diabetes, the pancreas stops producing insulin, the hormone that allows for the absorption of glucose from the blood into the cells. This leads to blood sugar levels that are higher than normal. Type 2, in contrast, is characterized by **insulin resistance**, i.e., the failure of tissues to react to the insulin produced by the pancreas. Consequences of both types of the disease include organ damage, blindness, amputation and, if untreated, ultimately death.

Global rates of diabetes have skyrocketed in recent decades, and more than 180 million people are estimated to have either type 1 or type II diabetes. It is becoming more and more prevalent worldwide and is also occurring at younger ages.[9] The major contributors are obesity and decreased physical activity; other risk factors include low socioeconomic status, a high level of acculturation, high unemployment rates, and a lack of education. As with obesity, rates of diabetes are significantly higher among Aboriginal populations than non-Aboriginal ones. The Pima Indians of Arizona, for example, currently have the world's highest rate of type 2 diabetes. Rates of diabetes in Canada are also markedly higher among First Nations populations compared to the general population (Figure 14.6).

Considerable debate has focused on the contribution of genetic versus environmental factors to the development of diabetes. The idea that diabetes has a genetic basis was first articulated by the geneticist James Neel in his classic 1962 paper *Diabetes mellitus: A "thrifty" genotype rendered detrimental by "progress"?* In that paper, Neel postulated that Indigenous populations possessed a genotype that allowed them to store excess carbohydrates as fat in times of plenty and to draw from those stores when food was scarce. While this genotype would have been advantageous in the past when periodic food shortages were common, in times when food was plentiful (as it is today), the genotype would promote the continuous storage of fat reserves, leading to obesity and ultimately to diabetes.

insulin resistance
the failure of body cells to respond to insulin in order to regulate plasma glucose, resulting in elevated levels of both insulin (hyperinsulemia) and glucose (hyperglycemia)

---

8. A third form, gestational diabetes, is a temporary condition characterized by the body's inability to use insulin during pregnancy.

9. In the past, type 2 diabetes was seen mainly in older adults but is now being diagnosed in children as young as eight (Dean et al. 1998).

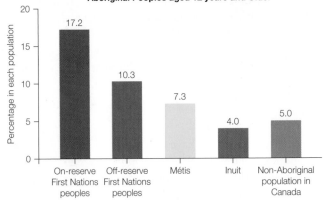

The Prevalence of Self-reported Diabetes among Aboriginal Peoples aged 12 years and Older

Notes: Diabetes prevalence includes type 1 and type 2. Gestational diabetes is also included for Inuit. The percentages in the exhibit are based on information from different data sources covering time periods ranging from 2006 to the 2009–10 fiscal year. Because different data sources are used, different ages are captured: aged 18+ for First Nations on-reserve; aged 15+ for Inuit; and aged 12+ for First Nations off-reserve, Métis, and the non-Aboriginal population.

FIGURE 14.6   First Nations populations have higher rates of diabetes than the general Canadian population. Rates are particularly high among those living on reserves.

Public Health Agency of Canada, *Diabetes in Canada: Facts and figures from a public health perspective.* Ottawa, 2011.

cytokines

proteins produced by white blood cells in response to the presence of pathogens; they interact with cells of the immune system and stimulate them to respond to the infection

Critics of this hypothesis point out that famines severe enough to cause substantial mortality are uncommon and that when they do strike, they target primarily the very young and the very old (i.e., nonreproductive members of society). Furthermore, deaths during periods of famine tend to result from disease rather than starvation, and rates of obesity do not increase between famines (Speakman 2006). Finally, these "thrifty genes" have yet to be discovered (ibid.). Higher frequencies of certain **cytokines** have been found to characterize Canadian First Nations populations compared to Caucasians, but these may be linked to selective pressures associated with parasitic and fungal infections present in the environment to which First Nations have adapted (Larcombe et al. 2005).

It is clear today that diabetes results from a complex interaction between genetic and environmental factors. Efforts to identify these factors are exemplified by a number of interdisciplinary projects in Canada and elsewhere. At the University of Toronto Mississauga, Esteban Parra is searching for genes that he believes increase the susceptibility of Mexican Americans to type 2 diabetes. Using a technique called "admixture mapping," which involves looking at the proportions of genes derived from different populations (e.g., Native American versus European), Parra and his colleagues have estimated the proportion of Native American admixture in a sample of individuals from Mexico City to be 65%, which suggests that Mexican Americans are at high risk for this disease (Martinez-Marignac et al. 2007).

Closer to home, a number of community-based projects have been set up to investigate the high rate of diabetes in First Nations communities in Canada. One example is the Sandy Lake Health and Diabetes Project (SLHDP), initiated in 1991 in the Sioux Lookout region of northwestern Ontario. The objectives of this project are to determine the prevalence of diabetes at Sandy Lake, identify the risk factors involved, and develop a strategy to prevent the disease (see Kakekagumick et al. [2013] for a review of this project). Researchers from the University of Western Ontario and Mount Sinai Hospital in Toronto have already identified a genetic variant among residents of this community who have type 2 diabetes (Hegele et al. 1999).[10] Similar community-based initiatives to prevent diabetes have been established elsewhere in Ontario as well as in other provinces.

Lactose Intolerance

A survey of your class would probably reveal that some of you are lactose intolerant or lactase deficient, meaning that you possess a variant of the lactase gene that results in the inability of your body to produce lactase, the enzyme required to digest lactose, the sugar found in milk. As a result, when you drink a glass of milk or consume other dairy products such as ice cream, you experience gastrointestinal discomfort, diarrhoea, bloating, and gas. For most individuals, lactose intolerance develops naturally after the age of about two years, when the body begins to produce less lactase.[11] Some individuals, however, retain the ability to digest lactose throughout life. In fact, the incidence of lactose intolerance varies greatly worldwide, from less than 5% in Swedish populations to nearly 100% in many Asian populations (Figure 14.7).

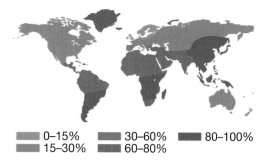

0–15%   30–60%   80–100%
15–30%   60–80%

FIGURE 14.7 The prevalence of lactose intolerance is highest among populations that have no history of dairy farming.

Michael Zechmann, "Worldwide prevalence of lactose intolerance in recent populations," from Food Intolerance Network, www.food-intolerance-network.com

We all know the benefits of drinking milk: it helps build strong bones and teeth. Why, then, do some populations possess the ability to digest dairy products while others do not? The key lies in the cultural history of certain populations. More specifically, populations who possess this ability have a long history of cattle domestication and dairy farming. These include northern and central Europeans and African pastoralists (herders). Lactose intolerance is, in fact, the norm for most populations around the world, and this condition was present in our early ancestors, who would have had no source of milk after weaning. Under such circumstances, natural selection would have favoured an end to the production of lactase after weaning, possibly to allow the body to save energy (Weiss 2004).

With the domestication of cattle some 5,000 to 10,000 years ago, however, the persistence of lactase after early childhood would have been advantageous in allowing for digestion of nutrient-rich milk. Thus natural selection would have favoured a mutation allowing for the continued production of lactase, either to allow individuals to take advantage of the nutrients in milk, or possibly to facilitate increased absorption of calcium in more northern latitudes where levels of ultraviolet radiation are lower and the production of vitamin D, required for the uptake of calcium in the body, is reduced. Being able to drink milk would also have been advantageous to those populations living in hot, arid environments where water is scarce (ibid.). The extraction of DNA from one Mesolithic and eight early Neolithic skeletons from Europe points to a recent origin for this mutation and provides support for the argument that dairy farming was the catalyst for the rapid evolution of lactose tolerance (Burger et al. 2007). Furthermore, analyses of DNA taken from modern East Africans have revealed several mutations that differ from the one found in northern Europeans, indicating that the ability to digest lactose arose independently in the two regions (Tishkoff et al. 2007).[12]

---

10. This variant of the hepatic nuclear factor 1–alpha gene, known as the S319 allele, was found to be significantly more common in residents with diabetes than in those without.

11. Congenital lactose intolerance, a much rarer condition, is characterized by the inability to digest lactose at birth. The prevalence of self-reported lactose intolerance in Canada is 16% according to a recent survey (Barr 2013).

12. This is an excellent example of convergent evolution.

CHAPTER 14 Biology of Contemporary and Past Populations

HUMAN ADAPTABILITY

The Adaptive Significance of Skin Colour

The largest organ in the human body is the skin. Would you believe it covers more than two square metres! The colour of your skin is directly related to the amount of melanin it produces.[13] Formed in cells called **melanocytes**, melanin production is controlled by an enzyme called **tyrosinase**. If the gene for this enzyme is defective, the end result is **albinism**, a condition in which no melanin is produced. Scientists have yet to identify the genes that underlie skin colour, although a number of candidate genes, including the *MC1R* gene (see Chapter 11), have been suggested (Norton et al. 2007).

The evolution of skin colour variation has been the focus of numerous studies, and a variety of biological, cultural, and environmental factors have been implicated. When we look at the global distribution of skin colour (Figure 14.8), we notice a close correlation between skin colour and latitude. Specifically, populations living at higher latitudes have lighter skin than those living closer to the equator.[14]

A number of hypotheses have been proposed to explain the adaptive significance of light-coloured skin. The most widely accepted hypothesis is that light skin was selected for in areas of lower ultraviolet radiation in order to allow for the adequate synthesis of vitamin D, which is crucial for bone growth and development. This explanation—commonly referred to as the vitamin D hypothesis—has gained widespread acceptance (but see Robins 2009), and today dark-skinned populations living in northern Europe and the northeastern United States suffer from higher rates of rickets and osteomalacia than light-skinned populations living in the same areas.[15]

melanocytes
cells that produce melanin

tyrosinase
the enzyme that controls the production of melanin

albinism
a condition characterized by a complete lack of melanin

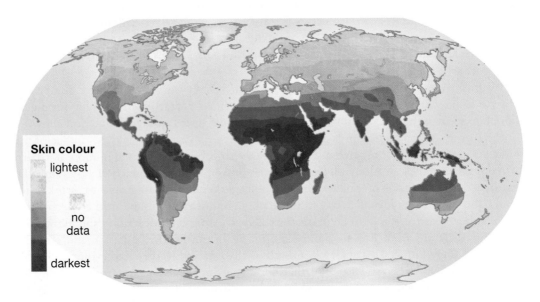

FIGURE 14.8 The geographic distribution of skin colour corresponds closely with latitude. Note, however, that this pattern is stronger in the southern hemisphere than in the northern hemisphere and is more pronounced in Africa than in South America.

Reproduced with permission of Annual Reviews, Inc. *Annual Review of Anthropology* by N.G. Jablonski. Copyright 2004 by Annual Reviews, http://www.annualreviews.org

---

13. Skin colour has traditionally been measured by reflectometry, a technique that measures the amount of light reflected off the skin. Light-coloured skin reflects more light and dark-coloured skin, less light.

14. This relationship was first described by Italian geographer Renato Basutti, who plotted the distribution on a map but extrapolated for those regions for which he had no data.

15. Light-skinned individuals can also suffer from rickets if they spend most of their time indoors or are fully covered with clothing when they are outdoors.

There are, however, exceptions to the pattern of light skin in northern latitudes. The Inuit, for instance, have darker skin than we would expect, given the latitude at which they live. One explanation for this deviation from the normal pattern lies in the high vitamin D content of fish and marine mammals, foods that make up their traditional diet. As well, the Inuit are relatively recent newcomers to the Arctic, having migrated to North America only about 5,000 years ago. A recent migration also explains why populations of Bantu-speakers living in South Africa have darker skin than other populations in this region. Indeed, sub-Saharan African populations exhibit a great deal of variation in skin colour, in part reflecting their migratory history and the length of time these populations have lived in their new homeland (Relethford 2000). The same explanation holds true for Indigenous populations of South America, whose lighter skin compared to populations living at similar latitudes elsewhere in the world likely reflects their more recent arrival on that continent (Jablonski and Chaplin 2000).

Hemispheric differences in skin colour are also apparent. Specifically, a greater proportion of people with dark skin are found in the southern hemisphere, where ultraviolet radiation is greater than in the northern hemisphere (Relethford 1997). Finally, sex differences in skin colour have been noted, with females generally having lighter coloured skin than males. While sexual selection has been invoked to explain this phenomenon (Darwin 1871; Frost 1994; Aoki 2002)—namely, that males prefer females with lighter skin—this observation may also reflect females' greater need for calcium—in part regulated by vitamin D—during pregnancy and lactation (Jablonski and Chaplin 2000).

What about the adaptive significance of dark skin? One of the most common explanations is that dark skin was selected for in areas of high UV radiation in order to protect the skin from cancer. One criticism of this argument is that skin cancer does not typically strike individuals until their post-reproductive years and would therefore have had no effect on their reproductive fitness. Thus there would be little selective pressure for darker skin. More recently, an alternative explanation has been proposed based on the observation that exposure to intense sunlight can substantially reduce folate levels in light-skinned individuals. Folate is a B vitamin that is essential for the development of the brain and spinal cord in the embryo. It is also important in spermatogenesis. In pregnant women, low levels of folate can result in neural-tube defects such as spina bifida. This is why women planning to become pregnant are advised to take folic acid supplements (folic acid is the synthetic form of folate). Because high levels of ultraviolet radiation can break down folate, dark skin was selected for, according to this argument, in order to protect the body's supply of folate and thereby increase the survival chances of a woman's offspring (Jablonski and Chaplin 2002).

What, then, was the skin colour of our earliest ancestors? According to anthropologist Nina Jablonski, early hominins probably had fair skin like chimpanzees. Moving from the forest to the savannah, however, meant greater exposure to the sun and a greater need for a more efficient cooling system. A subsequent reduction in body hair and an increase in the number of sweat glands, which were more widely distributed across the body, would have allowed early hominins to dissipate body heat.[16] Recall from Chapter 10 that *Homo erectus* had long legs, suggesting that this hominin walked longer distances and thus would have required a more efficient cooling mechanism. At the same time, natural selection would have begun to favour darker skin in order to protect hominins from the damaging effects of high levels of ultraviolet radiation in tropical Africa. Early members of the genus *Homo* would therefore have had dark skin (ibid.). As they moved farther from the equator, however, selection for lighter coloured skin would have occurred in order to allow them to produce sufficient quantities of vitamin D.

Living at High Altitude

Living in a high-altitude environment poses a number of challenges, including cold temperatures, low humidity, wind, and reduced food resources. The most significant challenge, however, is hypoxia—that is, lack of oxygen. The higher you go, the fewer the number of

---

16. The loss of body hair is thought to have occurred by about 1.2 Ma (Rogers et al. 2004).

CHAPTER 14 Biology of Contemporary and Past Populations

oxygen molecules are found per unit volume of air. At the peak of Mount Everest, for example, the lungs get only 25% of the oxygen available at sea level. The physiological responses to this condition include increased ventilation (i.e., breathing) and heart rate as the body attempts to obtain more oxygen and carry it to the tissues. Individuals born and raised at low elevation who move to high altitude later in life may experience the onset of acute mountain sickness, which is characterized by headaches, dizziness, and nausea. If you have ever travelled to a high altitude, you may have experienced some of these symptoms. Prolonged stays at high altitude can lead to pulmonary and cerebral edema—the accumulation of fluid in the lungs and brain respectively, both of which can be fatal. While native lowlanders can avoid these problems through gradual **acclimatization**,[17] a number of populations are well adapted to high-altitude environments (defined as elevations above 2,500 m) and can function very well in such settings. For example, the Tibetans of the Himalayas and the Quechua and Aymara of the Andes exhibit physiological characteristics that differ from those of native lowlanders. These include greater lung volume, greater blood flow to the tissues, and a higher number of red blood cells.

Various hypotheses have been proposed to explain how these populations have adapted to their environments. The **developmental adaptation hypothesis**, put forward by human biologist Roberto Frisancho (1969, 1977), proposes that the physiological characteristics displayed by high-altitude natives are acquired during growth and development. Specifically, metabolic energy is preferentially directed toward the body's oxygen transport system at the expense of the musculoskeletal system. The end result is earlier maturation, smaller adult stature, and lower birth weight babies.

Physiological differences among high-altitude populations suggest that genetic factors may also be involved and that high-altitude adaptation may be a product of natural selection. Compared to Andeans, for instance, Tibetans have higher ventilation levels, lower concentrations of hemoglobin, lower levels of oxygen in their arterial blood, greater blood flow, and a higher density of capillaries, which are the tiny vessels that supply blood to the tissues (Beall 2007; Figure 14.9). Similarly, high-altitude Ethiopian populations seem to have adapted

acclimatization

physiological changes that occur in response to changes in the environment

developmental adaptation hypothesis

the hypothesis that the physiological characteristics exhibited by high-altitude populations arise during growth and development

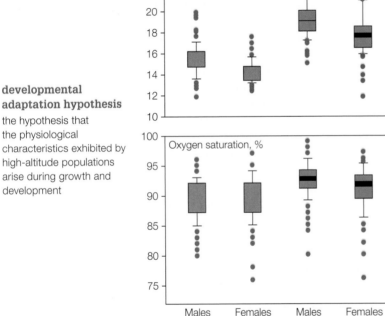

FIGURE 14.9 Physiological differences are apparent among high-altitude populations. These include differences in resting ventilation, hemoglobin concentration, and oxygen saturation.

Beall, C.M. 2007. "Two routes to functional adaptation: Tibetan and Andean high-altitude natives," *Proceedings of the National Academy of Sciences* 104 (1): 8655–8660. Copyright 2007 National Academy of Sciences, USA.

17. Mountain climbers attempting to scale Mount Everest typically undertake a series of short ascents followed by descents in preparation for their final climb to the top.

physiologically to their environments differently than Andeans and Tibetans (Beall et al. 2002). The search for factors underlying these differences has focused largely on genes. While a number of candidate genes have been identified, the specific genetic loci have yet to be identified.

Other factors have been implicated in the variation seen among populations living at high elevations. For instance, differences between the Andean Aymara and Quechua in the physical growth of children have been linked to differences in microclimates and consequently food availability and nutritional status of these children (deMeer et al. 1993).

Adaptation to Temperature Extremes

Before we look at the specific ways in which humans adapt to temperature stress, it is important to understand how the body maintains its internal temperature, a process we call thermoregulation. Our normal body temperature is 37°C, but it can fluctuate by up to one degree depending on time of day and activity level. Greater temperatures can occur as a result of illness, unusually high activity, or exposure to extreme heat. Conversely, lower temperatures can result from exposure to extreme cold. The maintenance of a stable internal environment, or **homeostasis**, requires a balance between heat gain and heat loss. This requires a variety of physiological (i.e., involuntary) and behavioural (i.e., voluntary) mechanisms.

homeostasis
the maintenance within the body of a stable environment

Heat Stress

As you learned in Chapter 12, modern humans evolved in Africa, and our greater tolerance to heat stress than cold stress reflects, to a large extent, this evolutionary history. All human populations, regardless of where they live, have the ability to respond to heat stress both biologically and behaviourally. Those of you who have travelled to southern climates know that people living in these regions tend to dress in light clothes, live in houses that are built to absorb heat and keep it away from sleeping quarters, and schedule their activities to avoid the hottest part of the day (thus, the siesta). The dangers of overheating include muscle cramps due to salt depletion, heat exhaustion due to loss of fluids, and heat stroke, which can be life threatening. Every year many lives are lost to heat stroke during the summer months.

We respond biologically to heat stress in two ways: **vasodilation** and sweating. Vasodilation is characterized by the expansion of peripheral blood vessels, which allows for increased blood flow to the skin surface and, consequently, the loss of body heat. Sweating, the primary cooling mechanism, involves the sweat glands, of which we have more than a million in our bodies.[18] An increase in temperature signals the activation of these glands, and perspiration begins to form on the skin surface. The convective evaporation of this perspiration cools the body.[19]

vasodilation
expansion of the peripheral blood vessels, resulting in increased blood flow to the skin surface, with subsequent transfer of body heat to the environment

Factors influencing responses to, and tolerance of, heat stress include sex, age, the amount of body fat, and the level of physical fitness and overall health (Hanna and Brown 1983). Women, for example, tend to sweat less than men (you have probably heard the expression "men sweat and women glow"). Also, the very young and the very old are less tolerant of heat than young and middle-aged adults because of reduced thermoregulatory capacity; individuals with greater amounts of body fat have a harder time coping with heat than those with less body fat; and fitter and healthier individuals are better able to endure heat than individuals with poor physical fitness and pre-existing health problems. Body size and shape also influence one's ability to cope with heat stress. In general, people living in warmer climates tend to have lower body mass than those living in colder climates (Bergmann's Rule), and people living in warmer climates tend to have longer appendages than those living in colder climates (Allen's Rule). It must be noted, however, that this is only a very general rule and that other factors, including diet and health, can affect body size and shape (see Box 14.2).

---

18. Humans have two types of sweat glands: apocrine and eccrine. It is the latter that produce the watery secretions that help cool the body.

19. While sweating is an adaptive mechanism in allowing for heat loss, it can also be maladaptive if the water and electrolytes such as sodium and magnesium lost from the body are not replaced.

BOX 14.2 PROFILE ... Size Matters: Shape Variation of Small-Bodied Humans

Courtesy of Dr. Helen Kurki

Humans vary significantly in body size (e.g., stature and body mass) and body shape, (e.g., body breadth and relative limb lengths). Short stature and low body mass are characteristics of some populations, and these are believed to represent adaptations to local conditions such as climate, food availability, and adult mortality. Body shape is also thought to reflect adaptation to climate in that in cold climates, humans tend to be larger and broader bodied with relatively shorter arms and legs compared with humans from warmer climates (so-called ecogeographic patterning, or Bergmann's and Allen's rules).

I have been studying an archaeologically known population of small-bodied foragers from the Later Stone Age (LSA) of southern Africa along with several colleagues, and was particularly interested in understanding adaptations to small body size. This population is best known from archaeological sites from the coastal regions of South Africa, and is represented by hundreds of well-preserved skeletons, dating back to 10,000 years ago. They are often considered a good representation of a hot climate-adapted population due to their very narrow bodies and low body mass, and because

they are from Africa. However, the climate in the coastal regions of South Africa is not tropical, but more similar to the Mediterranean, with cool, wet winters.

My colleagues Jaime Ginter (Sheridan College), Jay Stock (University of Cambridge), and Susan Pfeiffer (University of Toronto) and I were interested to know whether body shape of the LSA foragers actually did conform to ecogeographic expectations in light of their small body size. Using skeletal samples of the three small-bodied populations (the LSA foragers, Andaman Islanders, and Ituri rainforest foragers), we compared several aspects of body proportionality to skeletal samples representing larger-bodied populations from different climatic regions. We used latitude as a proxy for climate—low latitudes are generally hot climates, and high latitudes are cold. Coastal South Africa, and North Africa are mid-latitude regions. None of the samples from high-latitude, cold climates would be classified as small-bodied.

Our results demonstrated that the three small-bodied populations varied significantly in body shape. In relative limb lengths, the LSA foragers were similar to the sample from North Africa, who are also from a mid-latitude region, but are taller, broader, and heavier. However, the very narrow bodies of the LSA were more similar to populations from low-latitude, warm climate East and West Africa. The Andaman Islanders were also very narrow bodied, although with relatively long limbs as expected for their low-latitude environments. The third small-bodied population, the Ituri foragers, displayed relatively long limbs as expected, but were broader bodied despite their low-latitude location.

We concluded that outside of climatic extremes, body shape might be influenced by factors in addition to climate, such as life history. Further, there may be different ways in which small-bodied populations meet thermoregulatory pressures relative to each other and to larger-bodied (i.e., taller, broader, or heavier) populations. Climatic adaptations may therefore be less important to determining body size and proportionality than is often assumed.

Source: Written by Dr. Helen Kurki, Assistant Professor and Undergraduate Advisor, Department of Anthropology, University of Victoria.

Individuals who are fully acclimatized to hot environments respond differently to heat stress than non-acclimated individuals. For example, if you were to compare the !Kung San of the Kalahari desert with Canadians born and raised in southern Ontario, you would find that for the latter, initial exposure to heat results in high vasodilation, an increased heart rate as the body attempts to pump more blood to the skin, excessive sweating, and inefficient evaporation. With continued exposure to heat stress, however, the sweat rate decreases and evaporation of sweat becomes more efficient. Interesting variation has been observed among populations living in hot, dry regions such as desert environments and those living in hot, humid regions such as tropical rainforests. The former environments are typically character-ized by high solar radiation, high daytime temperatures, cool night-time temperatures, and relatively low humidity. In contrast, the latter are characterized by less extreme temperature differences between night and day, and high humidity. Populations living in both types of environment respond to heat stress through vasodilation and sweating, but the latter is much less effective in hot, humid regions, where evaporation rates are low.

Cold Stress

Humans are not as well adapted biologically to cold stress as they are to heat stress, so we must rely to a greater extent on cultural adaptations to cope with cold temperatures. Human populations today inhabit a variety of cold environments, some of them characterized by extremely low temperatures (e.g., the Arctic), and others by more moderate temperatures (e.g., high-altitude, subarctic, and desert environments). In addition, populations living in such environments often have to contend with other challenges, including a lack of food resources, as well as high humidity and high winds, which exacerbate the cold.

We respond biologically to cold stress by conserving and generating body heat. The main mechanism of heat conservation is **vasoconstriction**—that is, the narrowing of the peripheral blood vessels to reduce blood flow to the skin and thereby reduce heat loss at the skin's surface. In addition, blood flow is shifted to deeper vessels in the body in order to reduce heat exchange between the core and the shell of the body. At the same time, in a process known as counter-current blood flow, heat is exchanged between veins returning cool blood from the arms and legs, and arteries moving warm blood to the shell, thereby minimizing heat loss from the core. Heat production is facilitated by actively moving around and by involuntary shivering of the muscles, a process that increases the metabolic rate and thus releases energy in the form of heat.

As in the case of heat stress, a variety of factors influence one's response to cold stress, including body size and shape, amount of body fat, age, sex, and level of physical fitness. Infants and older adults as well as individuals in poor physical health are at greater risk of cold injury. Furthermore, women are more susceptible to cold stress than men because they are less able to generate heat through shivering or exercise and they experience a faster rate of cooling in their extremities. The consumption of alcohol can also accelerate heat loss by prompting vasodilation.

Interesting physiological differences in cold response have been observed between populations living in extreme cold environments and those living in more moderate environments. For example, individuals habitually exposed to extreme cold stress (e.g., Inuit) experience not only vasoconstriction but also alternating cycles of vasodilation of the blood vessels, most notably in the hands. Known as the **Lewis hunting phenomenon**, this reaction serves to protect the fingers from frostbite that could occur from prolonged constriction of the peripheral blood vessels. This mechanism has been observed in North Atlantic fishermen who work with their bare hands in extremely cold temperatures.

INVESTIGATING THE BIOLOGY OF PAST POPULATIONS

We have spent a great deal of this chapter talking about contemporary populations. What about populations that lived hundreds or thousands of years ago? What kinds of information can we draw from the mummified (see opening photo) or skeletonized remains of these individuals? In Chapter 1 we introduced you to the terms "skeletal biology" and "osteology," which is the study of human skeletal remains. This is an immensely popular subfield of biological anthropology, and many graduate students choose to pursue this area of research, some devoting their attention to modern human remains from legal contexts (which is the domain of forensic anthropology; see Chapter 15), and others focusing on the study of human remains from archaeological contexts, a subfield known as **bioarchaeology**.

The breadth and scope of bioarchaeology is reflected in the diversity of research topics pursued by graduate students, faculty, and other researchers. These include (1) the health and diet of past populations; (2) behaviour, lifestyle, and occupation; and (3) geographic origins and migration patterns. Since its origins in the early 20th century, this subfield has

vasoconstriction
the narrowing of the peripheral blood vessels to reduce blood flow to the skin and thereby reduce heat loss at the skin's surface

Lewis hunting phenomenon
a physiological reaction characterized by alternating cycles of vasoconstriction and vasodilation

bioarchaeology
the study of human remains from archaeological contexts

seen a dramatic shift in focus, from descriptive studies of individual specimens to studies of populations. Canadian bioarchaeologists have been involved in field projects all over the world, including Italy, Egypt, Portugal, Bulgaria (Figure 14.10), South Africa, Siberia, Poland (Figure 14.11), Antigua, Mexico, and Peru. Closer to home, samples of 18th- and 19th-century human remains have also been the focus of bioarchaeological study. Among these are the remains of more than 500 individuals excavated from the St. Thomas' Anglican Church cemetery in Belleville, Ontario (Saunders, DeVito, and Katzenberg 1997; Saunders, Hoppa, and Southern 1993), the remains of individuals massacred at Fort William Henry (Liston and Baker 1996), and the frozen and skeletonized remains of crew members of the last expedition of Sir John Franklin to the Canadian Arctic (Beattie and Geiger 2004; Keenleyside, Bertulli, and Fricke 1997).

Health and Disease

It is rarely possible to determine the cause of death of an individual from his or her skeleton, and acute diseases such as measles and influenza do not affect bone. So when we talk about skeletal lesions, we are referring to those caused by chronic conditions, and it is these lesions that can provide us with clues to the health status of past populations. Reconstructing the health of populations that lived long ago from their skeletal remains is no easy task, however. Hindering the analysis of disease in bone is the fact that some diseases affect bone in only a small percentage of cases, individuals may die before bone lesions develop, and different disease-causing microorganisms may produce similar bone lesions, making them difficult to diagnose. Incomplete and fragmentary skeletal remains also pose a challenge to reconstructing the health of past populations. For instance, evidence of disease may not be preserved, and in some cases it may even make bone more susceptible to decay. Also, small sample sizes reduce the likelihood of finding evidence of disease.

FIGURE 14.10 Anne Keenleyside examines a partially excavated skeleton interred in a necropolis associated with the ancient Greek colony of Apollonia Pontica on the Black Sea coast of Bulgaria.

Courtesy of Anne Keenleyside

FIGURE 14.11 Bioarchaeologist Amy Scott carefully excavates a skeleton from a cemetery in Drawsko, Poland, while participating in a mortuary archaeology field school run by the Slavia Foundation.

Courtesy of Amy Scott

The calculation of sex- and age-specific prevalence rates of disease may be hindered by the inability to accurately determine the sex and estimate the age at death of an individual from his or her skeleton, especially if it is incomplete or poorly preserved. Another confounding factor is that skeletal samples may not represent the living population from which they are derived. Skeletal samples are, after all, samples of individuals who failed to survive. As such, they may reflect the less healthy segment of the population, and consequently they may display more lesions than the healthy group. Paradoxically, skeletons with lesions may represent the *healthier* segment of the population, whose stronger immune systems enabled them to fight off infectious agents long enough for lesions to develop on their bones (Wood et al. 1992).

Despite the limitations outlined above, a wide range of ailments suffered during life may be recorded in an individual's bones and teeth, and these indicators of stress can provide valuable information on health, diet, and nutritional status, as well as individual behavioural patterns. For example, we know from studies of skeletal remains that nutritional deficiencies were common in the past. Porous lesions on the cranial vault and on the roof of the eye socket (see Chapter 1, Figure 1.7) have been linked to several forms of anemia, including childhood episodes of iron deficiency resulting from a low dietary intake, poor intestinal absorption, and/or excess loss of iron due to parasitic and other infections. These lesions may also result from other nutritional deficiencies such as scurvy (vitamin C deficiency) and rickets (vitamin D deficiency), as well as tumours and eye infections. Also, nutritional stress and/or infectious diseases experienced during childhood can disrupt the growth of the skeleton, leading to defects that are visible on X-rays of immature long bones.

Traumatic injuries such as fractures are often observed in archaeological samples. These injuries can provide valuable insights into the lifeways of past societies. The location and nature of fractures, for instance, can tell us something about the circumstances in which they were sustained. Unhealed fractures to the skull and facial bones are sometimes a sign of violent interactions, whereas well-healed fractures to the ribs, clavicles, long bones, and hands

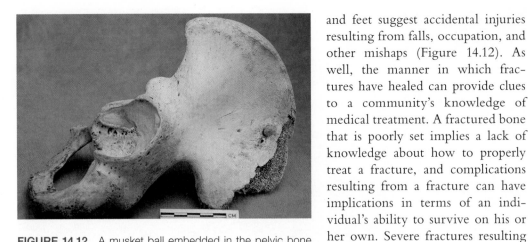

FIGURE 14.12 A musket ball embedded in the pelvic bone of this individual suggests that he was the victim of a violent encounter.

Courtesy of Anne Keenleyside

and feet suggest accidental injuries resulting from falls, occupation, and other mishaps (Figure 14.12). As well, the manner in which fractures have healed can provide clues to a community's knowledge of medical treatment. A fractured bone that is poorly set implies a lack of knowledge about how to properly treat a fracture, and complications resulting from a fracture can have implications in terms of an individual's ability to survive on his or her own. Severe fractures resulting in a loss of mobility, for instance, may have necessitated the care of an individual by other members of his or her group. Similarly, individuals with congenital abnormalities such as cleft palate or clubfoot may have required assistance, although we must be cautious in drawing conclusions about the quality of life of these individuals and the manner in which they were treated (Dettwyler 1991).

A variety of infectious diseases can leave their mark on skeletal remains. Some of these diseases are nonspecific, meaning that they can be caused by a variety of different microorganisms, many of them bacteria. The lesions resulting from these infections typically take the form of a buildup of new bone on the external, or **periosteal** surface of affected elements, or lesions extending into the marrow cavity, a condition known as **osteomyelitis** (Figure 14.13). They can occur as a result of localized infection, such as an overlying skin ulcer, or from an infection that has spread through the bloodstream from another location in the body, or from a wound. Besides nonspecific infections, there are a host of specific infectious diseases such as tuberculosis, leprosy, and venereal syphilis (Figure 14.14) that can cause alterations to the skeleton.

Paleohistology, the microscopic study of bones and teeth, can provide clues to the health of individuals who lived long ago. Scanning electron and light microscopy have enabled researchers to evaluate the etiology of periosteal new bone formation (Weston 2009) and cribra orbitalia (Wapler et al. 2004), to investigate osteoporosis (Agarwal and Stout 2003), syphilis (von Hunnius et al. 2006), and sinus infections (Merrett and Pfeiffer 2000), and to identify episodes of physiological stress in teeth (Fitzgerald et al. 2006). The detection in

periosteal
relating to the periosteum, the connective tissue membrane that covers the outer (periosteal) surface of a bone

osteomyelitis
an infection of the marrow cavity of bone

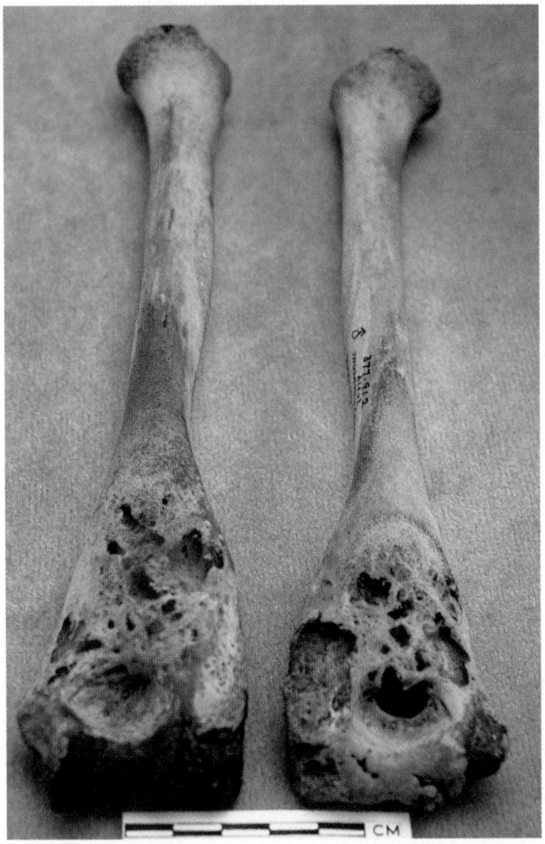

paleohistology
the microscopic study of ancient tissues

FIGURE 14.13 Infection that involves the marrow cavity is referred to as osteomyelitis. It is a chronic condition that can last for months or years if untreated.

Courtesy of Anne Keenleyside

archaeological remains of the DNA of pathogenic microorganisms has enabled the diagnosis of infectious diseases such as tuberculosis, leprosy, and bubonic plague. The analysis of certain elements in bones and teeth has the potential to tell us something about health and diet (Dolphin and Goodman 2009; Dolphin, Goodman, and Amarasiriwardena 2005; Dolphin, Naftel, and Nelson 2013). Finally, delayed skeletal growth, as reflected in long bones of diminished size, points to poor nutritional status and compromised health (Hoppa and Fitzgerald 1999).

Paleonutrition

The study of ancient diets, or **paleonutrition**, is an important component of bioarchaeology, and human tissues can provide a variety of information on the foods eaten long ago. The study of teeth, for example, can provide clues to the type and nature of foods consumed and the level of oral hygiene in past populations. Teeth can also reveal evidence of nutritional and disease stress, as well as nondietary functions (e.g., use of the teeth as tools). The level of tooth decay is an important indicator of diet, in that cavities are associated with the consumption of refined carbohydrates, especially sugars. High rates of tooth decay can lead to the loss of teeth prior to death, due either to the complete destruction of the teeth or to the intentional extraction of teeth to alleviate pain. Tooth decay, trauma, and/or heavy wear can also lead to exposure of the pulp cavity of the tooth, allowing bacteria to infiltrate the crown and root, causing inflammation and the formation of an abscess (Figure 14.15). In the days

before antibiotics, abscesses could result in blood poisoning leading to death, as the bacteria spread through an affected individual's body. Nutritional stress and/or infectious diseases can also disrupt the process of tooth enamel formation, resulting in the appearance of permanent defects on the anterior surface of the teeth (see Chapter 11, Figure 11.16). Because teeth are not physiologically altered as a normal process of aging, these defects provide a permanent record of episodes of stress in early childhood. High levels of tooth wear can result from a diet of uncooked and unrefined food items (such as coarse cereal grains), the consumption of poorly washed foods, and the consumption of foods ground with grinding stones that inadvertently introduce particles of grit into the diet.

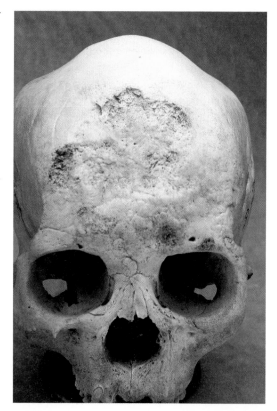

FIGURE 14.14 The bacteria that cause venereal syphilis target the cranial vault, the facial region, and the anterior surfaces of the tibiae.

Courtesy of Anne Keenleyside

paleonutrition
the study of diet in past populations

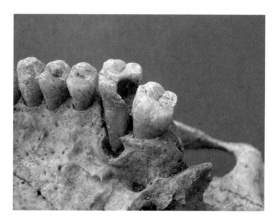

FIGURE 14.15 Exposure of the pulp cavity as a result of tooth decay, tooth trauma, or heavy wear allows bacteria to infiltrate the cavity and root, leading to an abscess.

Courtesy of Anne Keenleyside

The chemical analysis of bones, teeth, and other tissues can also provide valuable insight into the diet of past societies. As you learned in Chapters 1 and 10, stable carbon and nitrogen isotope analysis of collagen, the protein found in bone, yields direct evidence of the foods that were consumed. For example, it can tell us something about the types of plant foods eaten and the proportion of marine versus terrestrial foods in the diet. In southern Ontario, for instance, it has been used to detect the introduction of maize agriculture and to investigate changes in diet over time (Katzenberg et al. 1995). This technique has been applied to hair, nail, and soft tissues to investigate seasonal differences in diet (Webb et al. 2013; White et al. 1999; Williams and Katzenberg 2012). It has also been a useful tool for investigating the timing and duration of breastfeeding in past populations (Bourbou et al. 2013; Dupras, Schwarcz, and Fairgrieve 2001; Herring, Saunders, and Katzenberg 1998; Kwok and Keenleyside 2014; Prowse et al. 2008; Waters-Rist et al. 2011; Williams, White, and Longstaffe 2005). This application is based on the fact that breastfeeding infants have $\delta^{15}N$ values that are higher than those of their mothers. Once weaning begins, however, these values begin to decline to adult levels.

Coprolite research, founded by the late Eric Callen, a professor of plant pathology at McGill University (Bryant and Dean 2006), can also yield clues to ancient human diets. Studies of preserved feces can reveal evidence of **phytoliths**, which are silica particles found in plants that can be used to identify particular plant foods consumed, and pollen grains, which may tell us something about the time of year foods were eaten. Researchers have successfully extracted plant and animal DNA from coprolite samples (Poinar et al. 2001) and have even detected human myoglobin, a protein found in muscle tissue. Its presence has been interpreted as evidence of cannibalism (Marlar et al. 2000). In addition, coprolites may contain the remains of parasites that afflicted individuals during their life. Evidence of intestinal parasites has also been detected in shell midden sediments (Bathurst 2005).

Activity Patterns

Skeletal stress indicators and the biomechanical properties of bones can provide a glimpse into the activity patterns of past populations. Osteoarthritis, or degenerative joint disease, for instance, is one of the most common conditions observed in skeletal remains, and its prevalence and distribution can tell us something about habitual activities and workloads. Nancy Lovell and her graduate students linked osteoarthritis and other markers of occupational stress in skeletons excavated from two 19th-century trading post cemeteries in Alberta to activities associated with the fur trade, including paddling, rowing, carrying, and lifting (Lai and Lovell 1992; Lovell and Dublenko 1999). Lovell (1994) also attributed vertebral arthritis in a skeletal sample from the urban Bronze Age site of Harappa in Pakistan to physical stress associated with carrying heavy loads on top of the head—a practice still seen in many parts of Africa, Asia, and Central and South America. In a more recent study, Angela Lieverse and colleagues (Lieverse et al. 2007) found the distribution of osteoarthritis to vary among foragers living in Siberia's Cis-Baikal region, pointing to changes in mobility and activity patterns over time.

Entheseal changes, bony changes at the sites of attachment of muscles, ligaments and tendons to bone, have also been used to reconstruct past activities and habitual behaviours. The use of these features to infer activity is based on the fact that bone responds to mechanical loading or strain, or lack thereof. High activity levels that place increased strain on sites of attachment of muscles and ligaments, for example, stimulate the formation of new bone, while low activity levels result in a loss of bone. Bioarchaeologist Angela Lieverse and colleagues have explored upper and lower limb entheseal changes among five skeletal samples of Middle Holocene Siberian foragers and have found evidence of varied activity patterns within and between samples (Lieverse et al. 2009, 2013). Their upper limb data also suggest the use of watercraft (Lieverse et al. 2009). The relationship between the degree and type of activity and entheseal changes is by no means straightforward, however, as the latter are also associated with age at death, sex, and body size.

Mechanical loading or strain is also reflected in the geometric properties of long bones (e.g., strength, shape, asymmetry), and as such, can also shed light on the habitual behaviours of individuals who lived long ago. Stock and Pfeiffer (2001, 2004), for example, linked

coprolite
preserved feces

phytoliths
silica particles found in plants; variation in their size and shape allows scientists to identify the particular species from which they derive

entheseal
relating to entheses: sites of attachment of muscles, ligaments, and tendons to bone

variability in the robusticity of long bones to the differing subsistence practices of two groups of South African foragers.

Finally, evidence of habitual activities may also be recorded in teeth. For instance, dental modification in the form of grooves on the occlusal surfaces of teeth from Holocene period hunter–fisher–gatherers may have resulted from the processing of fibres to make implements related to fishing (Waters-Rist et al. 2010). Interproximal grooving seen in a sample of 19th-century Australian Aboriginal remains may be related to the stripping of animal sinews between the posterior teeth (Brown and Molnar 1990), while grooves observed on the occlusal surfaces of the incisors of five females from an archaeological site in northern Anatolia are hypothesized to have resulted from the passage of yarn between the front teeth (Erdal 2008).

Residential Histories

Stable isotope analysis of bones and teeth can be used to determine the geographic origins and movement of individuals who lived in the past. Stable oxygen isotope analysis is based on the fact that the ratio of the stable isotopes of oxygen (O^{16} and O^{18}) in drinking water is recorded in the mineral component of an individual's bones and in her or his tooth enamel. Because the teeth form very early in life, they record the geographic location (i.e., source of the drinking water) of an individual during early childhood. In contrast, bones, which undergo constant remodelling throughout life, record the isotopic signature of drinking water consumed *later* in life. These signatures must be interpreted with caution, however, since they may be altered by diagenesis, or postmortem changes, especially to bone tissue. Similar oxygen isotopic signatures in the bones and teeth of an individual thus indicate that an individual spent most of his or her life in one place. In contrast, differing values tell us that an individual was born in one place but moved to another later in life (Figure 14.16).

Similarly, the ratio of the stable isotopes of strontium (Sr^{87} and Sr^{86}), which can be detected in an individual's dental tissues, points to the geographic location in which he or she once lived—specifically, the underlying geology of the area as reflected in the food and drink that person consumed. Because diagenesis can significantly alter strontium isotopic signatures in bone, this technique can be used only on teeth. Christine White, a Canada Research Chair at the University of Western Ontario, has utilized both oxygen and strontium isotopes to investigate geographic origins and migration in Mesoamerica (White et al. 1998, 2007). Bioarchaeologists Tracy Prowse, Tosha Dupras, and Anne Keenleyside have also used oxygen isotope analysis to identify immigrants in Roman Italy (Prowse et al. 2008), Roman Egypt (Dupras and Schwarcz 2001), and an ancient Greek colony (Keenleyside et al. 2011), respectively. Mobility has also been inferred from stable carbon and nitrogen isotope analysis of hair samples from pre-contact burials in Peru (White et al. 2009).

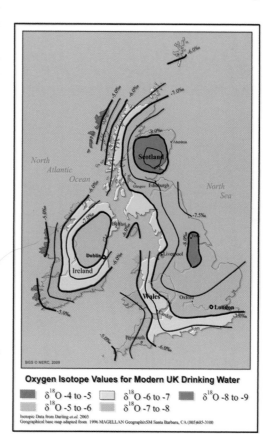

Oxygen Isotope Values for Modern UK Drinking Water

FIGURE 14.16 Stable oxygen isotope analysis of bones and teeth is based on the fact that the ratio of O^{16} and O^{18} in local meteoric precipitation and thus in drinking water varies geographically, as seen in this map of oxygen isotope values for the United Kingdom. Thus, measuring oxygen isotopic signatures in skeletal and dental tissues can provide clues to the regions where an individual was born and died.

THE ETHICS OF STUDYING HUMAN REMAINS

The collection and study of human remains has engendered a long history of controversy and debate. In 1990 the U.S. Congress passed the Native American Graves Protection and Repatriation Act (NAGPRA), which laid out in detail the process by which Native remains found on federally recognized tribal lands or in federally funded institutions must be handled. Specifically, the act requires federal museums and institutions to conduct an inventory of their collections of Native American skeletal remains and associated objects, and return them to culturally affiliated tribes upon request. Canada has no comparable federal legislation; the manner in which Aboriginal human remains are dealt with is determined by various

BOX 14.3 PROFILE ... The China Lake and Big Bar Lake Burials

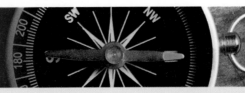

Courtesy of the Canadian Museum of Civilization

In October 2002, I approached the Canoe Creek Indian Band of British Columbia to obtain their consent to carry out mitochondrial DNA analysis on two ancient skeletons from the nearby archaeological site of China Lake. This wasn't something new to me as I had been working with Native American or First Nations bands in either the United States or Canada since 1965. In the case of Canoe Creek, I received an overwhelmingly enthusiastic response as I explained to the community at a town meeting my request and its purpose. About 50 people from Canoe Creek and three neighbouring communities came to this meeting. I hardly expected 10, much less that many, but it quickly became obvious that there was much interest in the ancestral past and in what I might bring to bear on that knowledge through the study of human

remains. Twenty years previously, two male skeletons had been accidentally unearthed during road building. They had been radiocarbon dated to 5,000 years, they were developmentally about the same age at death, their skeletal morphology was strikingly similar and unique compared with other Plateau skeletal remains I had studied, and the bodies had been buried next to each other. Were they brothers or even twins? DNA testing might hold the answer.

After I presented my case and listened to contributions from the audience, I was treated to a tour of the Fraser Plateau, an area of British Columbia that I had not previously visited. We relocated the China Lake site thanks to the knowledge of elders and field photographs lent to me by Simon Fraser University, whose archaeologists had recovered the remains. My hosts also took me to other suspected ancient burial grounds. At nearby Big Bar Lake, we identified human remains eroding from the top of a knoll within a broad area of lithic debris and pithouse depressions marking an ancient habitation site.

Over the winter, I prepared and submitted a formal request for the China Lake analysis in a letter to the Chief and Council. We also put our heads together to figure out what to do about the exposed human remains at Big Bar Lake. The knoll was on the path of a road leading to a provincial park and thus accessible to many tourists. The community decision was to protect those remains by removing them for reburial in a more secure context but only with rigorous scientific method and utmost respect for the deceased.

An archaeological excavation and anthropological study of the remains began in 2003 as a community-based project attended by Canoe Creek band members and those from the nearby High Bar First Nation, which shared territorial jurisdiction. Comprehensive study and publication of all of the remains culminated in ceremonial reburials at China Lake in 2006 and Big Bar Lake in 2008. The success of the project signified the importance of cooperation and collaboration with the descendants of those who walked this earth before us.

Source: Courtesy Dr. Jerome Cybulski, Research Associate, Canadian Museum of History, Gatineau, Quebec, and Adjunct Research Professor, University of Western Ontario, London, Ontario.

institutes, municipalities, provinces, and territories individually. The University of Toronto, for example, recently signed a Memorandum of Understanding with the Huron-Wendat Nation allowing for the repatriation of human skeletal remains and artifacts excavated during the last century from sites that were home to ancestors of the Huron-Wendat.

Canadian bioarchaeologists have a history of positive collaboration with First Nations, and their calls for a cooperative and collaborative relationship with First Nations have been voiced in a series of conference papers and reports (Canadian Museum of Civilization 1992; Cybulski 1976, 2007; Cybulski, Ossenberg, and Wade 1979). A number of collaborative projects exemplify this close working relationship. These include excavations of the Greenville burial ground (Cybulski 1992) and the China Lake and Big Bar Lake burials (Cybulski et al. 2007; Malhi et al. 2007; see Box 14.3), analyses of Cree remains from northern Manitoba (Brownlee and Syms 1999), the excavation and analysis of the Moatfield ossuary in Ontario (Williamson and Pfeiffer 2003), the genetic sequencing of ancient and modern individuals from the Lucy Islands and Prince Rupert region of British Columbia (Cui et al. 2013), and the analysis of Kwäday Dän Ts'ínchi,[20] an individual whose partially preserved body was found eroding from a British Columbia glacier in 1999 (Beattie et al. 2000; Corr et al. 2008; Dickson et al. 2004).

---

20. This name, given to the remains of this individual by the Champagne and Aishihik First Nations community, means "Long ago person found." In 2008, scientists announced that they had found 17 living relatives of Kwäday Dän Ts'ínchi through DNA analysis of members of the Champagne and Aishihik communities.

LEARNING KEYS

KEY IDEAS

- Factors contributing to the emergence and re-emergence of infectious diseases include ecological, social, and economic changes, and changes in pathogenic microorganisms.

- Biological anthropologists who study the human life course examine infant feeding practices, child growth, and aging, among other things.

- Reliance on a diet insufficient in quantity and quality can result in malnutrition and a variety of vitamin and mineral deficiencies that can lead to low birth weights, impaired cognitive ability, growth stunting, reduced adult stature, and increased susceptibility to infectious diseases.

- Overeating can lead to overweight and obesity, a major risk factor for diabetes, cardiovascular disease, and other chronic conditions.

- Populations living in conditions of high ultraviolet radiation, low levels of oxygen, or extreme temperatures have adapted physiologically in a number of ways.

- Humans living closer to the equator have darker skin that protects them from the harmful effects of UV radiation; those living farther from the equator have lighter coloured skin that allows for the synthesis of adequate amounts of vitamin D.

- Populations native to high altitudes exhibit greater lung volume, greater blood flow to the tissues, and a higher number of red blood cells compared to those living at lower elevations.

- Humans living under conditions of extreme heat respond physiologically through vasodilation and sweating, whereas those living under conditions of extreme cold respond through vasoconstriction and shivering.

- Analyses of human skeletal remains can reveal information about the type and prevalence of diseases that afflicted individuals in the past, the kinds of foods they ate, their activity patterns, and their residential histories.

KEY TERMS

biomedical anthropology (p. 318)

epidemiology (p. 318)

epidemiologic transition model (p. 319)

zoonotic diseases (p. 320)

healthy immigrant effect (p. 327)

acclimatization (p. 334)

developmental adaptation hypothesis (p. 334)

homeostasis (p. 335)

bioarchaeology (p. 337)

paleonutrition (p. 341)

KEY QUESTIONS TO ASK MYSELF

1. If I eat too much junk food, will I get sick?

2. I'm thinking of teaching English as a second language in Southeast Asia next year. Should I be worried about my health while I'm there?

3. What might a future bioarchaeologist learn about me from my skeleton?

KEY CRITICAL THINKING QUESTIONS

1. To what extent do you think the study of archaeological human remains can inform us about the health of modern-day populations?

2. Who would be more challenged in terms of day-to-day functioning—you arriving in La Paz, Bolivia, for a one-week vacation (elevation 3,660 m) or a resident of La Paz taking classes at Dalhousie University in Halifax (elevation 0–145 m)?

KEY THINGS TO DO NEXT

CourseMate Visit **CourseMate** at www.nelson.com/humanvoyage2e to build your comprehension, practise your critical thinking skills, review core concepts, and explore other resources at your disposal.

15 Biological Anthropology as Applied Science

> *The purpose of anthropology is to make the world safe for human differences.*
>
> Ruth Benedict (1887–1948)

OVERVIEW

As do all sciences, anthropology aims to reveal fundamental aspects of its subject matter—in this case, humankind. So we ask some very basic questions. Where did we come from? Why do we look the way we do? How did culture and technology develop? How have we come to dominate—and in many cases transform—the planet's varied environments and ecosystems? The answers to these questions reveal a complex history of social and ecological interactions, many of which have become strained over time. Consequently, humanity today faces a diverse array of problems, and many anthropologists are now applying this basic knowledge of who we are and what we are about toward finding solutions to these issues. This chapter explores a few of the ways in which the field of applied anthropology seeks to address difficulties arising from the inequities of human social, cultural, and technological relations.

KEY CONCEPTS

Applied anthropology, medical anthropology, community-based research, public anthropology, evolutionary medicine, anthropometrics, ergonomics, forensic anthropology

KEY LEARNING OBJECTIVES

At the end of this chapter, you will be able to

LO1 Describe the ways in which biological anthropologists apply anthropological perspectives and methods in developing solutions to human problems

LO2 Explain how anthropometry is used to design work areas and products that optimize human performance

LO3 Apply the concept of Darwinian evolution to the study of infectious diseases and reproductive health

LO4 Differentiate community-based research with indigenous communities from "traditional" methods of research used by biological anthropologists

PROLOGUE: REAL WORLDS, REAL PROBLEMS

In previous chapters, we emphasized the ways in which anthropology generates new understandings of ourselves as a biologically and culturally diverse global species. Much of this knowledge has been gained through basic research—that is, by testing hypotheses about our place in nature, how we evolved, and why we differ from one place or time to the next. We develop or modify theories to account for these phenomena. This knowledge swirls round and round in the world of academia—it is peer reviewed and published, it is discussed and debated at conferences and in classrooms, and it justifies new grants for yet more new research. But the academic world is only a small fragment of the world at large, and over the past few decades an increasing number of anthropologists have been turning their attention away from creating more and more "new" knowledge in favour of putting the knowledge that we already possess to good use in the wider world. This is the purview of an "emerging" subfield known as applied anthropology.[1] The objectives of applied anthropology encompass "the integration of anthropological perspectives and methods in solving human problems throughout the world; to advocate for fair and just public policy based upon sound research; to promote public recognition of anthropology as a profession; and to support the continuing professionalization of the field" (Society for Applied Anthropology 2009). There are numerous domains within which this mission is made manifest, from health and medicine to human rights, environmental issues, and local, national, and international development policy, to name but a few.

More often than not, the problems addressed by applied anthropologists are **anthropogenic** in origin. They are the outcomes of the actions and interactions of individuals and societies with one another, with the environment in which they live, and with technology. In these final two chapters, we examine a few areas in which anthropological knowledge has been, or could be, usefully brought to bear on problems both practical and distressing. In this chapter we examine four such areas: medical anthropology, evolutionary medicine, ergonomics, and forensic anthropology.

anthropogenic

literally, "of human origin," as an outcome of human actions or deliberate manufacture (e.g., urban crowding, pollution)

MEDICAL ANTHROPOLOGY

In Chapter 1 we introduced you to the field of medical anthropology, which is the study of health, illness, and healing from a cross-cultural perspective. Medical anthropologists are often employed by international organizations such as the World Health Organization, international development agencies such as the Canadian International Development Agency (CIDA), public health departments, and nongovernmental organizations (NGOs) to help design and implement health policies and treatment strategies. Medical anthropologists also undertake basic research to identify the scope of problems that may arise as societies change through mechanisms such as migration and refugee resettlement (Box 15.1). Such basic research can then be applied to develop appropriate interventions to address such issues. As

---

1. Some authors (e.g., Rylko-Bauer, Singer, and Van Willigen 2006; Scheper-Hughes and Bourgois 2004; Weiss 2006) have noted that anthropology, be it ethnological or biological, has a long and fairly dark history as an applied science. One example is anthropology's role in constructing racial divides supporting colonial expansion, xenophobic immigration policies, and genocide (e.g., 1930s German eugenicist anthropology and the rise of National Socialism under Adolph Hitler).

FIGURE 15.1 University of Victoria medical anthropologist Eric Roth and his colleagues have conducted extensive research in the community of Kibera, Nairobi, Kenya, to understand the local social dynamics contributing to the HIV/AIDS epidemic in sub-Saharan Africa. With a population of over half a million people, Kibera is Africa's second-largest slum.

© Crispin Hughes/Panos Pictures

anthropologists with expertise in ethnographic research, they may also contribute to the development of disease control campaigns by collecting data on cultural beliefs, attitudes, and behaviours of at-risk individuals. Here the purpose is to design culturally appropriate and meaningful treatment regimes that are more likely to be adopted by the group in question. For example, University of Victoria anthropologist Eric Roth and his colleagues have examined perceptions of HIV/AIDS risk in northern Kenya (Ngugi et al. 2012; Roth et al. 2009; Figure 15.1) to understand the relationship between sexual behaviour and HIV transmission with the goal of assessing the effectiveness of public health measures such as education programs in combating the spread of HIV.

Another good example of applied medical anthropology is the cholera control campaign that was implemented in northeastern Brazil in 1993 (Nations and Monte 1996). Attempts by public health officials to control the outbreak and spread of this disease in two urban slums were met with resistance in the form of denying the existence of the disease, downplaying its virulence, making a joke of it, and refusing treatment. Interviews conducted by anthropologists revealed the true meaning behind these reactions. As they discovered, the word for cholera in Portuguese is used not only to refer to the disease but also to rabies. So, for the residents of these slums,

Vitamin D has recently received much attention as a nutrient essential to health maintenance and disease prevention. Vitamin D is synthesized in the body through exposure of skin to ultraviolet radiation (UVR), but is also found in some foods. An essential part of bone growth and remodelling, vitamin D is now also known to be vital to the functioning of the immune system, and may play a major role in disease prevention (see Chapter 14 for a discussion of the role of vitamin D in the evolution of human skin pigmentation).

Human breast milk is low in vitamin D if the mother herself is deficient (Hollis and Wagner 2004). In the late 20th century, cases of rickets still occurred in higher-income, northern-latitude countries like Canada (Ward et al. 2007). Health Canada (2012) recommends that all exclusively breastfed infants be given daily oral doses of 400 IU of vitamin D.

As biological anthropologists working in the area of applied human biology, we wondered about vitamin D deficiency among newcomers to Canada, many of whom come from countries closer to the equator with more sun exposure, may have darker skin pigmentation and clothing customs that reduce UVR exposure, and may experience food insecurity or food customs that decrease the consumption of vitamin D-rich foods such as fatty fish and fortified milk. Our research team, consisting of the three authors of this article and three student research assistants (Sophia Amarra, Laura Anderson, and Sarah Chadwick), conducted research with both Canadian-born and immigrant mothers of children aged newborn to three years in Calgary, Hamilton, and Toronto. We wanted to learn about these mothers' knowledge and practice of infant vitamin D supplementation (Moffat et al. in press).

We interviewed 64 new Canadians and 30 Canadian-born mothers. We found that immigrant mothers in Hamilton and Toronto were as knowledgeable as Canadian-born mothers about the Health Canada recommendation, and although their daily infant supplementation practice was not perfect, they maintained it quite well (Figure 15.2). Many of the mothers, however, reported inconsistent guidance on infant

supplementation by their health care providers. The main source of their information came from public health prenatal classes.

Mothers in Calgary were classified as government-assisted refugees, which means that they were resettled in Canada due to extremely difficult circumstances in their home countries, such as Sudan. In contrast to the immigrant mothers in Ontario, these refugee mothers were less likely to supplement their exclusively breastfed infants and did not know much about vitamin D. In addition, some of the Sudanese mothers expressed concern about supplementing their children with vitamins before the age of three. They explained: "You give them vitamins, that means they're very sick, not like normal people who can support themselves and prevent themselves from the sickness."

FIGURE 15.2 New Canadian mothers have different understandings of the benefits of breastfeeding and supplementation, shaped by experiences in their home countries.

© Jose Luis Pelaez, Inc./Blend Images/Corbis

Two applied lessons were learned from this research that may inform future public health policy and practice: (1) Caregivers of all backgrounds require clear and consistent messaging from health professionals about infant vitamin D supplementation, and (2) immigrants are a diverse group; refugee mothers, many of whom have multiple and competing health and economic issues, require more educational and practical support to increase knowledge and practice of infant vitamin D supplementation.

Source: Written by Dr. Tina Moffat, McMaster University; Dr. Daniel Sellen, University of Toronto, and Dr. Warren Wilson, University of Calgary.

---

cholera was seen as a conspiracy against the poor, who believed themselves to be equated by the wealthy to rabid stray dogs that had to be exterminated. An effective cholera control campaign therefore required addressing harmful metaphors that stigmatized the poor.

Vaccination programs designed to eradicate diseases such as polio have also become the focus of numerous studies by medical anthropologists. Of all of the major programs launched in the 20th century to eliminate infectious diseases, only one, the World Health Organization's Smallpox Eradication Programme, has been successful, and public health officials continue to wage war on other diseases that kill large numbers of people each year. Wiping out these diseases has proven to be no easy task, however, and reasons for the failure of such programs are complex. In the case of polio, for instance, the failure of an immunization program designed to eliminate this disease in northern Nigeria has been linked to fears that the vaccines had been intentionally contaminated by Western governments with HIV and anti-fertility agents in a plot to reduce Muslim populations worldwide (Yahya 2007). Fears of sterilization also surrounded the 1990 anti-tetanus campaign in Cameroon, leading to a reduction in the number of women vaccinated against tetanus, as well as increased mistrust of public health workers (Feldman-Savelsberg et al. 2000). These and other cases highlight the crucial need for understanding local beliefs and concerns when developing public health campaigns. In the case of Nigeria, for example, polio was not a health priority for local communities for whom basic medicines were beyond the reach of most people (Yahya 2007). Similarly, in Pakistan where many other diseases pose a much greater health risk, the eradication of polio is a low priority for the general population (Closser 2012).

Medical anthropologists have also played an important role in identifying the social factors associated with resistance to blood donation. Many people routinely donate blood to the Canadian Blood Services for use in life-saving operations. As you may know, some cultural and religious groups refuse to donate blood or receive blood transfusion on the basis of certain beliefs. Objections to donating blood may, however, pose considerable problems for people who have rare blood types or genetic blood disorders and require blood for transfusions. This situation exists in places such as France that have large immigrant populations from Africa. For one such community, originating from the Comoros Islands off the coast of Mozambique and now living in Marseille, blood is closely linked to family identity, and blood donations traditionally occur only between close relatives. As a result, there is great reluctance to donate blood to nonrelated individuals with whom sharing blood would create an "unnatural tie." To address this issue, anthropologist Dominique Grassineau and colleagues interviewed members of the Comorian community to develop a recruitment message that would address the concerns of the community (Grassineau et al. 2007). This involved identifying the barriers to blood donation, using cultural mediators to facilitate communication between the community and the blood bank and to deal with cultural misunderstandings, and recruiting political and religious leaders to spread the message.

Community-Based Research: Fostering Respectful Collaboration

Historically, doing scientific research involved a particular relationship between an observer (the "scientist") and the observed (the "subject"). As we have seen throughout this textbook, subjects of research in biological anthropology can span many domains: living and past populations, fossils, primates, biological and social systems, diseases, morphology, behaviour, and so on. For the most part, the research process begins with the researcher developing a question, finding appropriate subjects, collecting data, conducting analyses, and publishing results (you might want to refer back to the discussion on the nature of science in Chapter 4). Seldom has the subject of research (a bone, a primate society, a human population) been an active participant in that process. In the latter half of the 20th century a new model of research began to emerge in which researchers actively engaged with communities to develop research questions and methods that would both advance general knowledge and provide tangible benefits to the "researched community." This new approach to discovery has come to be known as community-based research (CBR). Two essential features of CBR are *capacity-building* (enhancing the ability of communities to further their own goals) and *advocacy* (knowledge directed toward achieving positive change); thus it is easy to appreciate the very real connection of CBR to applied anthropology and the related field of public anthropology. Here we exemplify this model with respect to research with Canada's Indigenous peoples, although CBR may involve any identifiable community, from street-involved youth to migrant farmworkers to incarcerated women and so on.

CBR and Indigenous Peoples

In a commentary on Indigenous health disparities, anthropologist Naomi Adelson (2005) was critical of the many programs and resources that are targeted to health issues at the level of the *individual*, when research evidence repeatedly demonstrates direct and indirect associations between health outcomes and their social, cultural, economic, and political contexts. Biological anthropologists produce knowledge of these contextual influences, referred to collectively as the **social determinants of health**, but there has clearly been a disconnect between this knowledge and its application to the development of programs and allocation of resources intended to improve health outcomes. When Ron Ignace, George Speck, and Renee Taylor were asked to reflect on the usefulness of anthropology to peoples and communities, Speck, an anthropologist himself, responded (Ignace, Speck, and Taylor 1993, 183): "Of what use can it [anthropology] be? I tend to see things from the point of view of intervention to make life better." His co-author Taylor added, "I don't think there's an end to what could be done, it's whether or not anthropology as a science and anthropologists as a people are going to have the courage to say we have a responsibility here, using our tools, to give something back to the communities, or carrying on, as many anthropologists do, enhancing their reputation, anthropologist qua anthropologist. Last week the Kwakiutl, this week off to look at the land tenure system in Australia. *Adios amigo*" (Ignace, Speck, and Taylor 1993,189). CBR brings with it the potential of addressing the sentiments expressed here as well as our disciplinary concern at the limited success with which anthropological knowledge, or scientific knowledge generally, has had a positive impact on the well-being of Indigenous peoples and communities of Canada (Figure 15.3). There are two important research focuses of relevance to biological anthropology that have emerged from the applied health literature: (1) action on the social determinants of health and (2) advancing the process of self-determination and control over information and decision making for Indigenous peoples and communities.[2]

Biological anthropologists have, in recent years, been actively engaged in research that addresses one or both of these opportunities—located in a community-based research approach and following the newly developed ethical guidelines described previously. The nutrition

FIGURE 15.3 A painting by indigenous artist Gary Natomagan, commissioned for a community-based research project on HIV/AIDS and hepatitis C, showing his interpretation of his community participating in an open and inclusive discussion on the issue.

Gary Natomagan

2. Contributed by Dr. Sylvia Abonyi, Department of Community Health and Epidemiology, University of Saskatchewan; excerpted from S. Abonyi, 2013. *Biological Anthropology and the Indigenous Peoples of Canada*. Toronto. Nelson Education

studies conducted through the Centre for Indigenous Nutrition and Environment (CINE) are a good, long-standing example of this kind of engagement and impact. Addressing one of the previously identified demographic gaps in research on Aboriginal child health, for example, anthropologists Dr. Tracey Galloway and Dr. T. Kue Young, with CINE colleague Dr. Grace Egeland, analyzed child growth and nutrition data from the 2007–08 International Polar Year Inuit Health Survey (Galloway et al 2010). The survey was developed as a collaborative project in partnership with Inuit organizations, communities, and regional and territorial health departments across northern Canada. The survey team collected data in questionnaires that covered household crowding and food security; nutrition, food sources, and eating habits; mental health and community wellness; and medical histories. Clinical data were also collected on heart health, blood glucose and diabetes risk, infection exposures, bone health (women older than 40), nutrient status, and exposure to environmental contaminants. More than 30 communities participated. Individual-level results were returned to each adult and child participant, and reports were produced for each community summarizing the health of its residents, as well as at the regional level for the jurisdictions that were part of the collaboration.

Galloway and colleagues' analysis of the child survey data (2010) showed an overall high prevalence of overweight (50.8%), with significantly more boys than girls in the overweight range. Analysis of associations with dietary factors failed to reveal any statistically significant relationships, however, Galloway and colleagues (2010) cite other dietary analyses from the survey data that found a high prevalence of consumption of energy-dense foods and beverages, as well as socioeconomic factors such as a high degree of food insecurity and a high prevalence of poverty. They note that these factors have been associated with obesity in other studies, suggesting that the growth patterns observed in the boys in particular may, without intervention, lead to increases in obesity-related illnesses for young Inuit men. At the time of publication, discussions on these findings were under way with community members and territorial leaders, including follow-up plans for qualitative health promotion-oriented research (Galloway et al 2010).

Biological anthropologists are actively working with Indigenous communities and peoples elsewhere in Canada as well. Dr. Marion Maar has worked for many years on Manitoulin Island in Ontario, collaborating on research projects that include a focus on Aboriginal research ethics (Maar et al 2007), diabetes care and prevention (Maar et al 2011), and mental health services (Maar et al 2009). Dr. Sharon Bruce has worked with national-level survey data and at the community level to understand the prevalence and determinants of diabetes among the Métis (Bruce et al 2003) and First Nations (Bruce and Young 2003). Dr. Linda Larcombe and colleagues (2011) have focused on the determinants of tuberculosis in Manitoba First Nations. Her research successfully combines disciplinary scope in biological anthropology (bringing together genetics, evolution, and environment) with a community-based research approach.

EVOLUTIONARY MEDICINE

In 1991, evolutionary biologists George Williams and Randolph Nesse published an influential article entitled "The Dawn of Darwinian Medicine," in which they applied Darwin's theory of evolution by natural selection to medicine (Williams and Nesse 1991). Since that time, the field of Darwinian medicine—or **evolutionary medicine**, as it is more commonly known—has become an increasingly important area of applied biological anthropology (see Trevathan 2007), and is gaining greater acceptance within the domain of modern medical practice (Fuller 2011).[3] The premise of evolutionary medicine is that pathogens and our resistance to them have co-evolved. That is, we have adapted to the challenges of disease, and disease-causing agents have in turn adapted to our responses to them.

evolutionary medicine
the application of Darwinian evolutionary theory to medicine

---

3. While this field gained particular attention in the 1990s, anthropologists and other researchers have been doing research in this area for decades (Trevathan 2007).

As we noted in Chapter 4, natural selection has maintained ("balanced") certain alleles in some populations because of the advantage they provide to individuals who are heterozygous for those alleles and who are living in environments where particular diseases are endemic. Taking an evolutionary approach to the study of infectious diseases allows us to understand the ways in which populations have adapted to particular pathogens. It also enables us to determine why some strains of pathogenic microorganisms have much lower virulence than others. In recent decades, for instance, a less virulent strain of cholera known as the El Tor strain has arisen in many parts of the world. Unlike its more dangerous predecessor, this strain has the ability to infect many more people by virtue of the fact that it is not virulent enough to kill its host. The survival of infected individuals therefore ensures that the bacteria continue to be transmitted to new hosts. So in this case, low virulence is beneficial to both pathogen and its human host.

The application of evolutionary theory to infectious disease has also resulted in a shift in our way of thinking about the human body's response to pathogens (Nesse 2007). Our bodies possess a number of defence mechanisms that protect us from disease-causing microorganisms. These include physical barriers such as the skin; chemical barriers such as tears, mucous, and stomach acid; and mechanisms of expulsion such as vomiting and diarrhea that rid the body of harmful organisms that may have been ingested. While we are all familiar with some of the more unpleasant symptoms of illness, we may never have considered the possibility that they may, in fact, have some adaptive significance. Similarly, coughing allows pathogens to be expelled. Fever also serves an adaptive function by creating an environment of elevated temperature that is inhospitable to invading bacteria or viruses, thus helping the body fight infection (Kluger 1978; Kluger et al. 1996). Even withholding iron to the point where an individual becomes anemic may deprive a pathogen of an element required for growth and development (Stuart-Macadam 1992). So, in a society that promotes pill-popping every time we are feeling unwell, it is wise to consider the consequences of taking medication the next time you feel sick. It may simply prolong your illness or, worse yet, increase the likelihood of developing a secondary infection.

The concept of evolutionary medicine has also been applied to reproductive health. For example, Margie Profet (1993) has hypothesized that menstruation is an adaptive trait that evolved to protect females from pathogens carried on sperm. Because ovulation is concealed in humans (but see Chapter 6 for an alternative view on this question), sexual activity takes place throughout the year, potentially increasing the risk of sexually transmitted diseases. By shedding the lining of the uterus each month, females thereby rid themselves of organisms that might cause infection. Her hypothesis has been met with a great deal of criticism, however, and a number of competing hypotheses have been proposed. Some researchers have argued, for example, that menstruation may have evolved because it is more energy-efficient for the body to shed the uterine lining than to permanently maintain it (Strassman 1999). Others have suggested that it evolved to eliminate defective embryos (Clarke 1994), and still others have suggested that menstruation has no adaptive significance at all but was simply a consequence of evolutionary changes to the uterus (Finn 1998).

Whatever the case may be, it is interesting that women today experience far more menstrual cycles than they did in the past. Modern American women have as many as 450 monthly cycles in their lifetime compared to only 160 in women living in foraging societies, who spend more of their time pregnant or lactating (Eaton et al. 1994). In this respect, the current pattern of menstruation seen in North American women can be seen as abnormal. Earlier onset and a greater number of menstrual cycles in modern women may, in fact, be contributing to the high rates of breast and reproductive cancers that we see today (Eaton and Eaton 1999).[4] This has important implications for the pharmaceutical industry, and efforts are currently under way to develop birth control methods that reduce the number of monthly cycles (Trevathan 2007).

---

4. Menarche is now occurring in girls as young as nine in many industrialized countries and is linked to increased caloric intake.

Morning sickness has also been hypothesized to have evolved for a specific purpose—namely, to protect the embryo from toxins that the mother may have inadvertently ingested early in pregnancy when the developing fetus is most vulnerable to these harmful substances (Flaxman and Sherman 2000; Profet 1992). Thus medications to combat nausea may do more harm than good, a lesson learned at great human cost and suffering with the introduction of the drug thalidomide in the 1950s and 1960s (Figure 15.4).[5] Similarly, an aversion to certain foods such as spicy and smoked foods, strong-smelling meats, and bitter vegetables, all of which may contain substances that could potentially harm the fetus, may be adaptive in preventing the mother from consuming such foods. The study of food aversions is a good example of the biocultural perspective used by anthropologists, as not only do we consider the biological implications of avoiding certain foods during pregnancy, but we also consider the significance of cultural taboos imposed on many women during pregnancy (Patil and Young 2012).

In recognizing the important roles that evolutionary processes play in human health, anthropologists have made valuable contributions to evolutionary medicine, and the insights that their research has provided have the potential to make a significant impact on public health (Trevathan 2007). It is important to remember, however, that natural selection "maximizes the reproductive success of genes," not health (Nesse and Williams 1998, 92). It is therefore up to us to follow a healthy lifestyle as best we can.

FIGURE 15.4 A bronze statue by German sculptor Bonifatius Stirnberg stands in the city of Stolberg, Germany, where the drug thalidomide was first produced by the pharmaceutical firm Grunenthal.

© Jens Schlueter/dapd/AP Photo

5. Women who took thalidomide in the late 1950s and early 1960s to alleviate pregnancy symptoms such as morning sickness gave birth to infants with severe birth defects, including shortened or missing limbs. Approximately 10,000 children were born with such defects in over 50 countries worldwide, although primarily in Germany, Great Britain, Canada, Australia, and Japan. When the link between the drug and birth defects was finally established in 1961 it was withdrawn almost immediately in all countries except Canada, which continued to distribute thalidomide for a further three months. Not until 2012 was an apology issued by the pharmaceutical company Grunenthal.

ANTHROPOMETRY AND ERGONOMICS

Anthropometry is the measurement of the human body. This practice has a long and at times controversial history. First used in the 19th century to identify criminals based on their physical characteristics,[6] it was later used to distinguish between "races" and to promote eugenics policies such as the restriction of immigration based on the presumed inferiority of certain populations (Gould 1996; see Chapter 13). Today, however, anthropometric studies are conducted for very different reasons. As we noted in the previous chapter, human biologists often measure living populations to study growth and development, assess health and diet, and examine population differences in body size and proportions. From a more practical perspective, anthropometry has become an important component of ergonomics, which is the science of designing work areas and products that optimize human performance and provide the best "fit." Anthropometric data were, in fact, widely collected during World War II and were used to improve the flying efficiency of Air Force personnel through the design of optimal cockpit size and seat configuration, and the manufacture of well-fitted uniforms and helmets.

ergonomics

the application of anthropological methods and analysis in the design of functional and efficient clothing and work environments, with the intent of maximizing comfort and safety

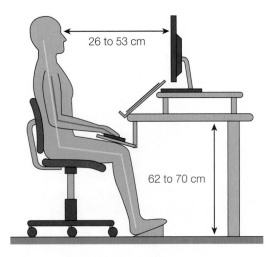

FIGURE 15.5 Designing an ergonomic workspace involves considering body proportions and the range of movements of different parts of the body.

Just as we spend one-third of our life sleeping, we spend at least one-third of our life in the workplace. The purpose of **ergonomics** is to ensure that our working and living environments are safe and comfortable and that they allow us to perform our daily tasks at our optimal level. Office jobs, for example, may require us to sit in front of a computer for seven or eight hours a day. It is therefore essential that we be comfortable and safe from injuries or ailments that could be debilitating (Figure 15.5). Those of you who have suffered from repetitive strain injuries like carpal tunnel syndrome or chronic neck problems from sitting in front of a computer day and night writing papers and checking e-mail or Facebook will know exactly what we mean. Similarly, the side-mounted desktop chairs many of you sit in to listen to your lectures have been designed based on anthropometric data taken from undergraduate students to maximize your comfort level and facilitate learning (Thariq et al. 2010).

Outside the workplace, anthropometry is also used to design appropriately sized clothing and footwear for a number of applications, including athletics and the military (see Box 15.2), as well as car and airplane seats and leg room, and crash test dummies to improve car safety. The design of user-friendly cellphones also relies on measurements, most notably hand length, hand breadth, thumb length, and thumb circumference (Jain and Pathmanathan 2012).

It is important to keep in mind that while human stature has increased over time (remember our discussion of secular trends in Chapter 14), so too have other body dimensions, especially those related to the current obesity epidemic. As a result, these anthropometric changes have necessitated changes in the design of office furniture and other structures (Gordon and Bradtmiller 2012).

human factors engineers

specialists who study the relationship between humans and the products they interact with on a daily basis

tariff

the determination of each size of an item needed to fit a specific user population

---

6. The method was developed by French criminologist Alphonse Bertillon.

BOX 15.2

PROFILE ... Applied Anthropometry in the Military

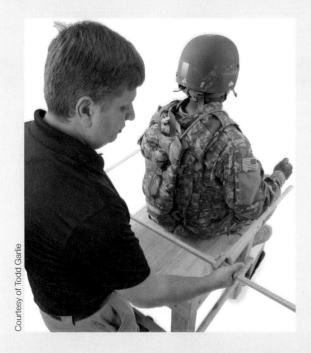

Courtesy of Todd Garlie

I obtained my Ph.D. in physical anthropology from McMaster University in Hamilton, Ontario, in 2000, investigating changes in stature and body mass of Canadian children during the last half of the 20th century. I completed an SSHRC Post-Doctoral Fellowship in 2002 at the University of Winnipeg in Manitoba, focusing on human osteology and skeletal repatriation. In 2003, I joined the Natick Soldier Research, Development and Engineering Center (NSRDEC) as a civilian biological research anthropologist with the U.S. Army. I am a member of the Ergonomics Team, a group of physical anthropologists, **human factors engineers**, and biomechanical researchers who fall under the Human Systems Integration and Sciences Division of the Warfighter Directorate.

My role as a physical anthropologist at NSRDEC is to conduct human-centric research (basic and applied) to support the development and testing of military clothing and individual equipment (CIE) to include such items as helmets, chemical protective garments, blast protective garments, and any other item that is requested in order to provide soldiers with the best-fitting CIE for improved performance, safety, and comfort. In this role, I provide subject-matter expertise on characterizing size and shape variation of soldiers to support design and development of such new and improved CIE and/or workstations.

One of my projects involved leading the collection of unclothed and clothed anthropometry for a Special Forces unit to aid in the development of a side gunner's seat. Due to space restrictions, body size dimensions were critical for understanding the occupant's envelope in the design of this seat. Other ongoing projects include the evaluation of toxicological agent protective (TAP) gloves and the evaluation and development of tariffs for a cold-weather clothing system. In the first project, chemical personnel tasked with the destruction of chemical agents were having issues with the fit of their gloves. To evaluate these fit issues, a field evaluation was undertaken to obtain a series of hand measurements and fit assessments of different glove types and sizes. The goal is to try to discern issues of fit surrounding their current gloves and to provide recommendations for fixing such issues. In the second project, I have been tasked with evaluating sizing dimensions for a newly obtained cold-weather clothing system to determine whether there are any fit issues and to provide **tariff** estimates to the customer.

My most recent work has focused on characterizing the size and shape of soldiers while wearing CIE, known as encumbered anthropometry (Garlie and Choi 2013; Mitchell et al. 2014). We currently have an excellent understanding of the size and shape of minimally clad soldiers (see Gordon et al. 1989, 2012), which is necessary for CIE design and development. However, soldiers do not conduct their missions in this manner (see Figure 15.6) and it is important to understand size and shape variation while wearing CIE. These encumbered dimensions are critical for the development of soldier-centric workstations to improve soldier performance, comfort, and safety. In addition, I am a reviewer for the Human Subjects Research Determination (HSRD) committee and the Human Use Review Committee (HURC), the local Institutional Review Boards (IRBs) for the protection of research volunteers, as well as an ongoing manuscript and thesis reviewer.

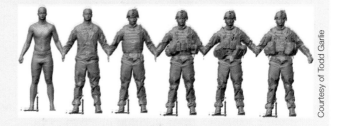

Courtesy of Todd Garlie

FIGURE 15.6 Unencumbered vs. encumbered soldiers

Source: Written by Todd Garlie, Biological Research Anthropologist, Ergonomics Team, Warfighter Directorate, Natick Soldier Research, Development and Engineering Center (NSRDEC), US Army Research, Development and Engineering Command (RDECOM), Natick, MA.

FORENSIC ANTHROPOLOGY

The arena for applied biological anthropology with the highest public profile is undoubtedly that of forensic science, as witnessed by the popularity in recent years of television programs such as *CSI* and *Bones*, and crime novels such as the Temperance Brennan series written by Dr. Kathy Reichs, a practising forensic anthropologist. Because forensic anthropologists are deeply familiar with normal population variation in skeletal and dental tissues, they are able to assist government agencies (municipal, provincial, and national police forces, as well as coroners and medical examiners) in identifying and interpreting remains of individuals that would otherwise be unidentifiable as a result of decomposition, taphonomic factors (e.g., animal scavenging), and **perimortem** and **postmortem** trauma (Dupras et al. 2006). Cremation, in which bodies are partially or completely burned[7] is another context in which the expertise of a trained human osteologist may help identify the victim and provide evidence for criminal proceedings (Mayne Correia and Beattie 2002; Fairgrieve 2007; Figure 15.7). It is important to note that in Canada, forensic anthropology does not exist as a career per se (see Box 15.3). Instead it is practised by biological anthropologists and archaeologists as an adjunct to their normal responsibilities as teachers and researchers employed in universities, colleges, and museums. Nonetheless, most are members of professional forensic science associations, such as the Canadian Forensic Science Society or the American Academy of Forensic Sciences.

perimortem
occurring at or around the time of death

postmortem
occurring after death

From Field to Lab

Crime scene investigators are highly trained in assessing and "processing" (i.e., locating, recording, and collecting) evidence germane to reconstructing the circumstances around a suspicious death; few, however, are familiar with human skeletal anatomy, especially in cases

FIGURE 15.7 Cremations are complex scenes requiring both archaeological (for recovery) and bioanthropological (for identification) expertise. Here, one of the authors (Lazenby) examines cremains of a homicide victim prior to recovery.

Courtesy of Richard Lazenby

---

7. The term "cremains," abbreviated from "cremated remains," is often applied to such occurrences.

BOX 15.3

PROFILE ... Can I Have a Career Doing Forensic Anthropology?

Dr. Tanya Peckmann excavates a mock crime scene with graduate student Ciara Logar.

Forensic anthropology is an area of applied anthropology and falls within the subfield of biological anthropology. Forensic anthropologists apply the methods used by biological anthropologists to forensic cases. Forensic science is the application of scientific knowledge to legal matters. Forensic scientists provide impartial scientific evidence for use in courts of law to support the prosecution or defence in criminal and civil investigations.

In Canada, most forensic anthropologists have a Ph.D. degree and work full-time in universities, teaching biological anthropology courses and conducting research. They may also be employed by the Department of National Defence, assisting with the identification of unknown Canadian military persons or as a consultant for coroner and medical examiner offices. We just don't have enough crime in Canada to keep a forensic anthropologist employed full-time in the medico–legal system (which is a good thing!). Forensic anthropologists also offer assistance to human rights organizations in situations of mass disaster or war casualties. However, these are usually contract jobs for a few months and not full-time employment.

I am a professor at Saint Mary's University in Halifax and the Coordinator for the Forensic Sciences program. I received my Ph.D. from the University of Cape Town Medical School in the Department of Human Biology. I teach courses in human osteology and anatomy, human variation, and forensic anthropology. Through my research I have worked with Canadian Mi'kmaq peoples to collect facial tissue depth data for use in 3D facial reconstructions. I also consult for the Nova Scotia Medical Examiner Service as a forensic anthropologist. Whenever individuals are found who are skeletonized or in the advanced stages of decomposition, my team and I are called to assist with the excavation, examination, and identification of the deceased.

During the excavation process, we use the principles of archaeology to systematically and methodologically remove the body. Through the forensic examination, we create a biological profile of the individual, which includes the determination of sex, age, ancestry, stature, time since death, and the evaluation of trauma and pathologies seen on bones. This information will hopefully allow us to positively identify this individual.

My forensic anthropology team is composed of me and my graduate students—they are all students enrolled in the M.Sc. Applied Science program at Saint Mary's University. The students receive hands-on experience with the excavation and analysis of human remains from forensic cases. Forensic science is multidisciplinary so we work with local law enforcement at the scene to determine the approach that will allow us all to collect the most amount of evidence to solve the case.

But there are other careers where you can use your forensic anthropology training and not specifically hold the title of "forensic anthropologist": forensic identification assistant (FIA, RCMP), forensic identification officer (RCMP), morgue technician, forensic lab technician, physician, dentist, forensic photographer, chiropractor, X-ray technician, EMT, museum curator. With these careers you can use your human osteology and critical thinking skills gained while working toward your degree, while also allowing you to be involved with forensic-like cases, e.g., homicides or patients involved in car accidents.

Source: Courtesy Dr. Tanya Peckmann, Department of Anthropology, Coordinator Forensic Sciences Program, Saint Mary's University, Halifax, Nova Scotia

where bodies are fragmented, scavenged, traumatized, or burned. Sub–adult or fetal remains offer their own complexities, as individual bones and teeth are much smaller in size and incompletely formed and have unfused epiphyses that may easily be lost or overlooked. So the presence of a forensic anthropologist/archaeologist at the site where remains are discovered can contribute immensely to the completeness of the recovery of the skeletal remains and thus to the quality of the information that can be gleaned from them.

Two excellent examples of such cooperative efforts are the investigation of the World Trade Center tragedy following the 9/11 attack (Budimlija et al. 2003) and the systematic

FIGURE 15.8 The anthropological excavation of the 6-hectare Pickton crime scene was a unique event in Canadian criminal history, involving the coordinated efforts of more than 100 anthropology and archaeology students and many more police investigators.

Courtesy of S/Sgt. Wayne Clary

search for the remains of more than 60 women who had disappeared from Vancouver's notorious Downtown Eastside between 1978 and 2001. The latter search involved the laborious excavation of almost half-a-million cubic metres of soil from convicted serial killer Robert Pickton's 6-hectare farm in Port Coquitlam, British Columbia (Figure 15.8). At any given time over the course of the two-and-a-half-year project, more than 100 anthropology and archaeology students from universities and colleges across Canada assisted police investigators in the search for the remains of these women, under the direction of University of Toronto forensic anthropologist Dr. Tracy Rogers and one of the authors of this text (Richard Lazenby).[8]

When remains are recovered and brought back to the lab for analysis, several tasks must be carried out by the forensic anthropologist. First, the bones must be cleaned and catalogued. This is necessary in order to observe any details of normal or abnormal morphology, as well as to determine whether more than a single individual is represented. For example, the occurrence of the same portions of two left femora (thigh bones) clearly indicates the presence of at least two separate individuals. In more complex situations, mass graves may be intentionally disturbed in the weeks or months following their initial formation in order to disguise their existence or mask the identities of the perpetrators, and the skeletons interred therein may become **commingled**, presenting the anthropologist with the difficult task of sorting out one individual from another in order to complete an analysis and eventually repatriate the remains to surviving family members (Figure 15.9).

commingled

in burial contexts, the situation in which more than one individual is present in the same grave, making it difficult to distinguish which skeletal elements belong to which individual

8. Robert Pickton was charged in the deaths of 26 of these women, and was convicted of second-degree murder in late 2007 on the first 6 counts brought forward; he is currently serving a sentence of life in prison.

FIGURE 15.9 Following a complete forensic anthropological analysis, remains of victims of genocide are repatriated to their families in Guatemala.

Courtesy of Fundación de Antropología Forense de Guatemala/Guatemalan Forensic Anthropology Foundation

Once the remains have been cleaned and sorted, the process of identifying the individual begins. This is a multistage endeavour, which begins with deriving the **biological profile** of the remains (including age, sex, body size, and ancestry), followed by searching for any uniquely individualizing features (such as dental or osteopathic restorations, healed fractures, or developmental anomalies; see Figure 15.10) and determining how long the person may have been deceased.[9]

Evaluation of the biological profile is aided by the fact that the human skeleton varies in predictable ways as an individual grows from infancy to adulthood, as well as by the presence of well-studied patterns of sexual dimorphism—particularly with regard to the cranium and pelvis (Albanese, Eklics and Tuck, 2008; Williams and Rogers 2006). In addition, a wide variety of methods have been developed to calculate a person's body size (usually stature) from various intact or even fragmented bones, owing to the fact that the size of an individual bone is proportionate to that of the body overall.

biological profile

in forensic anthropology, the fundamental biological characteristics of a person, including age, sex, body size, and ancestry

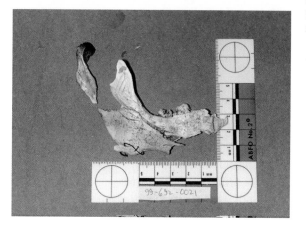

FIGURE 15.10 The presence of a unique surgically implanted wire following a jaw fracture confirmed the identity of a homicide victim, even after the body had been consumed by an intentionally set fire.

Courtesy of Richard Lazenby

9. This period is known as the "postmortem interval" or, alternatively, as "elapsed time since death."

CHAPTER 15 Biological Anthropology as Applied Science

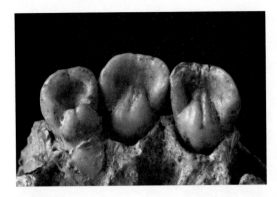

FIGURE 15.11 Forensic anthropologists rely on traits that occur at higher frequencies in some populations versus others. Shovel-shaped upper incisors as seen here suggest affinity with Asian populations.

© IRA BLOCK/National Geographic Stock

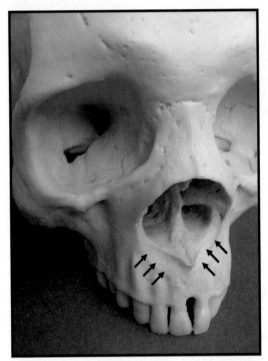

FIGURE 15.12 Nasal guttering, seen here, is another feature suggestive of ancestry; in this case, African.

Courtesy of Anne Keenleyside

tool marks

with regard to the skeleton, these are marks left on the surface of bone that may be linked through a process of replication in the lab to a suspect instrument (e.g., knife, axe, saw)

trier of fact

in law, the person or persons who decide which facts are to be accepted as evidence; in a jury trial, the trier of fact is the jury; in a bench trial in which no jury is present, the trier of fact is the judge

The most challenging component of the biological profile is that of ancestry.[10] As discussed in Chapter 13, assigning any single individual to a particular population of origin (i.e., "race") based on his or her physical features is highly problematic. At the same time, this aspect of someone's identity may be significant to a criminal investigation, as different ethnic groups (as determined, for example, by national censuses) are disproportionately represented among victims of crime. Over half of the missing women from Vancouver's Downtown Eastside, for example, were of Aboriginal descent, although First Nations people in British Columbia comprise only 4.77% of the provincial population (Statistics Canada 2006). Ascertaining ancestry from skeletal remains, therefore, is often a necessary step toward reaching a conclusion as to identity. Using logic similar to analyzing clines for biological traits such as skin pigmentation or the HbS allele, forensic anthropologists diagnose ancestry based on features present in the skeleton that occur at higher frequencies among some populations than others. An attribute of the upper central incisors known as "incisor shovelling" (Figure 15.11) is more prevalent among peoples of Asian ancestry than, for example, among European-derived peoples; similarly, "nasal guttering" (Figure 15.12) is more common among individuals of African origin (Byers 2007).

The assessment and interpretation of perimortem and postmortem traumatic events that impart traces on bone comprise another significant piece of what the modern forensic anthropologist is asked to do. While it remains the purview of the coroner or medical examiner to formally determine the manner and cause of death,[11] these conclusions are often supported by evidence present in the physical (i.e., skeletal) remains. Perimortem trauma is, as the name suggests, most closely tied to actions around the time of death. In a criminal proceeding, evidence of penetrating wounds, fractures from blunt force impacts, or **tool marks** may support or refute other lines of evidence (such as witness statements) and help the **trier of fact** reach an informed conclusion as to guilt or innocence. After death, and prior to discovery, bones may also be modified by various elements in the environment—animal scavenging, water, sun, and wind can all change the appearance of bones and teeth, although these are usually easily distinguished from trauma occurring at the time of death (Figure 15.13; Byers 2007).

10. While many forensic anthropologists are using the term "ancestry" to connote a person's genetic heritage or population of origin, some still adhere to the more problematic, albeit historically entrenched, notion of "race" (see Byers 2007).

11. "Manner of death" refers to the circumstance in which death occurred, such as accident, homicide, or suicide, whereas cause of death refers to the specific agent responsible, e.g., gunshot, fall, or asphyxiation.

A New Forensic Anthropology?

As we noted in Chapter 1, more than 60 years ago, Sherwood Washburn (1951) proclaimed the arrival of a "new" physical anthropology, one that embraced the concepts of adaptation and evolutionary biology. Dennis Dirkmaat and colleagues from the Department of Applied Forensic Sciences at Mercyhurst College (2008) borrowed a page from Washburn's thesis, announcing that a "new forensic anthropology" has materialized from a series of significant developments over the past 20 years. These advances have transformed the role of the forensic anthropologist from a bone specialist who does little more than identify bones and provide a biological profile, to one of forensic archaeologist, taphonomist, osteologist, trauma analyst, and "expert witness." Dirkmaat and colleagues asked: "Does conventional physical anthropology training fully qualify an individual—if you can stomach the smell—as a forensic practitioner, or has forensic anthropology acquired a level of specialization and sophistication requiring special training?" (ibid., 34). A positive answer to the second of these questions would suggest, as these authors argued, that in requiring its own basic research and professional development, forensic anthropology has shifted from an applied branch of biological anthropology to a fully fledged scientific discipline in its own right.

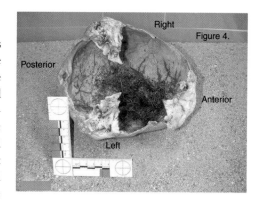

FIGURE 15.13 Animal scavenging leaves distinctive gnaw marks on bone. In this case, the entire lower and facial portions of a skull have been destroyed by animals in their quest for nutrition (i.e., the brain).

Courtesy of Richard Lazenby

While Dirkmaat and colleagues (2008) discussed six major developments underlying this "paradigm shift" (see Chapter 2 for a discussion of this concept), two have been particularly transformative. First, there is the revolutionizing role of DNA as an investigative and **evidentiary** tool; second, there is the establishment of standards in Canadian and U.S. courts for determining the admissibility of expert testimony. Our DNA, mitochondrial or nuclear, is without question the most uniquely identifying feature of our biology, and by virtue of reproduction, our particular version of it can be linked to those with whom we are most closely related: parents and siblings. Since the mid-1980s, techniques for collecting, **amplifying**, sequencing, and comparing DNA profiles have progressed to the point where the probability of a correct match between an unknown sample and an **exemplar** approaches 100%, and multiple comparisons can be made simultaneously. From the standpoint of identification of unknown remains, be they single and intact individuals or multiple, fragmented, and commingled, DNA analysis is much more efficient than the traditional biological profile described previously, although it is entirely dependent on being able to connect the unknown individual with a sample of known missing persons. While the Pickton investigation referred to earlier employed large numbers of anthropologists and archaeologists, their primary function was to locate skeletal remains—all of the personal identifications were achieved via DNA analysis, and the role of the forensic anthropologists at trial was relatively minor. This of course was made possible by the fact that there was a fairly small pool of missing individuals believed to have been associated with the Pickton site, which meant that the necessary exemplar DNA was readily obtained from relatives.

Does this mean that the traditional role of the anthropologist in identifying found remains through the analysis of "dry bones" will be usurped by test tubes and gene sequencers in sterile laboratories? Certainly not in the near future; DNA analysis is still relatively costly, and forensic labs are overwhelmed with work. Furthermore, in the case of fragmented and commingled remains involving multiple individuals (mass disasters and mass graves come to mind), the anthropologist remains an essential element in sorting and reconstructing bodies. The World Trade Center disaster is a case in point (Figure 15.14). Budimlija and colleagues (2003), for example, note an instance in which DNA recovered from muscle mass from two isolated human fragments was matched to one individual; however, the bony portions to which the muscle was attached were duplicates from the right pelvis. When DNA was extracted from the bone

evidentiary
anything that constitutes evidence or that has the quality of evidence, as a substantiation of fact, related to a court proceeding

amplifying
a step in DNA analysis in which small quantities of DNA collected by investigators are multiplied to provide sufficient material for the subsequent steps of identifying the nucleotide sequence and comparing it with known sequences stored in databases or obtained from putative relatives

exemplar
a sample of DNA obtained from a known individual to be used in comparison with an unknown sample for purposes of matching and identification

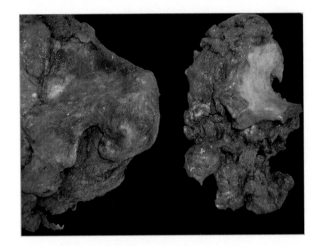

FIGURE 15.14 As we learned from the World Trade Center experience (right), DNA may not always provide conclusive results as to identification. In the left image, two portions of right pelvis thought to belong to one individual were later shown to contain the DNA of two people: one profile from bone and the other from soft tissue.

(Left) Reprinted by permission of The Croatian Medical Journal. Image courtesy of Zoran Budimlijo; (Right) © AFP/Getty Images

DNA methylation

a chemical modification of DNA that adds methyl group compounds to certain base pairs (adenine and cytosine) during cell division and differentiation and that may be inherited

fragments, two different profiles emerged, the original one found in the earlier soft tissue analysis and a new one from the bone analysis. The investigators concluded that the force of the event was so intense that soft tissue from one person had actually become fused to the skeletal remains of someone else! Perhaps somewhat disturbingly, in a recent paper, Frumkin et al. (2009) have shown that it is possible to create fake DNA that can be made to match anyone's profile. Current techniques used by police forces worldwide do not have the ability to distinguish real from fake DNA, although in the same paper, these authors demonstrate a new assay method that is able to tell one from the other based on the degree of **DNA methylation**.

Not all of the work performed by a forensic anthropologist is necessarily related to criminal cases. Skeletal remains believed to be human may prove to be nonhuman in origin, or if human may sometimes derive from unmarked archaeological gravesites. Others may be recent but represent remains of individuals who died as a result of misfortune rather than foul play. While coroners and medical examiners have an interest in resolving these occurrences, the legal community (police and Crown persecutors) generally does not. On occasion, however, the forensic anthropologist works closely with these authorities to assist in solving deaths resulting from homicide. In such cases, a forensic anthropologist may be required to appear in court as an "expert witness"[12] and to assist the trier of fact in understanding complex evidence requiring particular kinds of knowledge not commonly held by the public.

Since the 1990s, two cases, one in the United States and the other in Canada, have redefined the relationship between the expert's opinion and the courts. Known as the *Daubert* (U.S.) and *Mohan* (Canada) rulings, they specifically require that all experts (not just forensic anthropologists) ground their expertise in methods that are "testable, replicable, reliable, and scientifically valid" (Dirkmaat et al. 2008, 35). These rulings have had a profound impact on forensic anthropology; in particular, they have resulted in a serious undertaking on the part of the forensic anthropological community to show that its methods are, in fact, as scientifically

12. The status of "expert" is determined by the court through a process of *qualification*, based on credentials (academic training, experience, professional status) possessed by the witness.

robust as practitioners assert them to be (Steadman, Adams, and Konigsberg 2006). Thus, for example, we see studies published in peer-reviewed journals testing existing methods or developing new methods so that experts can be more precise in their explanations as to how certain conclusions were reached.

University of Toronto forensic anthropologist Tracy Rogers and her students have recently been "proofing" methods based on cranial morphology with the express purpose of identifying which particular features are best able to distinguish male from female (e.g., Williams and Rogers 2006; see also Albanese, Eklics, and Tuck 2008) and to establish positive identification based on cranial suture patterns (Rogers and Allard 2004). It is precisely this kind of research activity that suggested to Dirkmaat and colleagues (2008) that forensic anthropology, in developing its own literature and basic science, has shifted from an applied branch of biological anthropology to become its own bone fide discipline.

LEARNING KEYS

KEY IDEAS

- Medical anthropology is the study of health, illness, and healing from a cross-cultural perspective.

- Applied medical anthropology involves collecting ethnographic data on cultural beliefs, attitudes, and behaviours in order to design and implement health policies and treatment strategies that are culturally appropriate.

- Community-based research is a method of research collaboration in which the subject community has an active voice in developing and directing the research process, often of direct benefit to the community.

- Evolutionary (or Darwinian) medicine is an interdisciplinary field that involves applying the principles of evolutionary theory to medicine.

- Key areas of research in this field are nutrition, disease epidemiology, and reproductive health.

- Anthropologists have made valuable contributions to all three areas through their studies of the health impact of changing diets, chronic and infectious diseases, and population variation in reproductive patterns and outcomes.

- Ergonomics is the science of designing work areas and products that optimize human performance and ensure that our working and living environments are safe and comfortable.

- Anthropometry, the measurement of the human body, provides the data used to design optimal workspaces, clothing and footwear, and car and airplane seats.

- Forensic anthropologists apply methods of skeletal analysis to identify unknown human remains within a medico–legal framework.

KEY TERMS

social determinants of health (p. 354)

evolutionary medicine (p. 355)

ergonomics (p. 358)

KEY QUESTIONS TO ASK MYSELF

1. I've heard rumours that the mumps vaccine can cause autism in children. Is that true? Should I have my children vaccinated?

2. Why can I have a career as a forensic anthropologist in the United States but not in Canada?

3. Why is it that when I try on clothes in other countries they don't fit me as well as those in Canada?

4. Should I run to the doctor every time I get sick, or let nature take its course?

KEY CRITICAL THINKING QUESTIONS

1. Are television programs such as *CSI* and *Bones* beneficial in terms of public awareness and understanding of the field of forensic science and forensic anthropology? In what ways might they be misleading?

2. Until recently, anthropometric data used in the aircraft, automotive, and clothing industries have come almost entirely from military samples. What are the problems with using such samples?

KEY THINGS TO DO NEXT

CourseMate Visit **CourseMate** at www.nelson.com/humanvoyage2e to build your comprehension, practise your critical thinking skills, review core concepts, and explore other resources at your disposal.

16 Human Legacies, Human Prospects

© Lucian Coman/Shutterstock.com

> *As human beings, we are endowed with freedom of choice, and we cannot shuffle off our responsibility upon the shoulders of God or nature. We must shoulder it ourselves. It is our responsibility.*
>
> Arnold J. Toynbee (1889–1975)

OVERVIEW

A Human Voyage comes to an end with this chapter—but not with respect to your own lives. That voyage will go on, and will take each of you to distant corners of the world. For some that may mean a few hundred kilometres, for others many thousands. Regardless, you will be touched by events and actions far removed from your personal (or virtual) space. You will be challenged by diverse inequities—social, economic, historical, and structural—and we hope that what you have learned here will be a kind benefit to you along the way. Some of these challenges are explored in this chapter. Your generation will be required to address major issues over the next few decades: a burgeoning population rapidly depleting nonrenewable resources, consumption-driven environmental degradation, and the growing divide between rich and poor households in your own neighbourhood and nation, and between rich and poor nations within the global community. But the history of human biocultural evolution has always been one of surmounting various challenges, and that will also continue.

KEY CONCEPTS

Population growth, demography, Malthusian dilemma, population momentum, political economy, natural capital, poverty, genetic load, positive selection

KEY LEARNING OBJECTIVES

At the end of this chapter, you will be able to

LO1 Describe the relationship between the concepts of natural capital and ecological footprint

LO2 Explain the four phases of the demographic transition in terms of fertility and mortality

LO3 Identify 10 "inescapable realities" of historical trends in population growth

LO4 Diagram the relationship of population growth and carrying capacity

LO5 Evaluate the impact of food insecurity within and between populations

LO6 Construct a reasonable argument for ongoing human evolution

PROLOGUE: PAST, PRESENT, FUTURE

Turn back to the first page of this text and you will see that we introduced the opening chapter of *A Human Voyage* with a quotation from the British historian Arnold Toynbee, as we do in this closing chapter. Toynbee suggested that the current state of humankind ("civilization") was not something that could—by any measure—be viewed as an endpoint or a destination. We hope that, having completed your reading of this book, you will agree with us (and with Toynbee) that there is no harbour waiting for humankind. As we have illustrated in the intervening chapters, *Homo sapiens* in the 21st century is simply at one particular moment on a long, historically contingent, and fascinating journey. Our understanding of that enterprise is much clearer today than it was when Charles Darwin correctly pointed toward Africa as the birthplace of our species in *The Descent of Man* (1871).

Today, technological innovation occurs at a jarring, mind-numbing pace, perhaps most especially in the realm of information technologies. They shape our world physically, biologically, politically, and economically in innumerable ways (Figure 16.1). They blur cultural boundaries, and it is far from clear whether humankind is improved or burdened (or both!) by these developments. Thus, we should appreciate that our understanding of humanity in 2171 will be ... well, will be what? A reasonable question to ask is just that: What will that understanding of ourselves look like at the tricentennial of *The Descent of Man*? What kind of world will that knowledge be situated within? Will people still be interested in who we are as a species, where we came from, where we are going? Will your grandchildren be attending a college or a university and reading a textbook such as this? Will textbooks or books of any sort still exist?

We have seen that as a species, humans share very close affinities—genetic, physiological, and functional—with many other organisms. Some of these, chimpanzees for example, are very closely related to us—so near in fact that some scholars have argued for their inclusion in the genus *Homo* (or humans within the genus *Pan*). Other animals, such as rodents and honeybees, are more distantly related. But in all cases, the biological relationships are

FIGURE 16.1 Modern technology now has a global reach. It is no longer a question of adopting technology, but of finding ways to cope with its imposition in all aspects of our lives.

significant, demonstrable, and persistent. We are both mouse and chimpanzee (and mice are both chimp and human, and so on).

This brings us to Toynbee's second quote. There are two ideas central to it and to this closing chapter: human choice and human responsibility. You might think these to be strange concepts for a text, and a course, in biological anthropology. But in fact they extend from the point just made in the previous paragraph: while there is something certainly special about humans as a species, we are simply that—one species among so many more, and all of them our relatives. Let us ask what makes us special. As Toynbee would have it, it is the power of our choice and the breadth of our responsibility that follows from that power. As biological anthropologists, we (and you) are more aware than many others of the ways in which humans are integral to, and yet have become disenfranchised from, the biological world that nurtured us for so many millennia. Who better, then, to speak with some authority on matters of choice and responsibility? In this chapter we focus on several pressing engagements awaiting human action: population growth, the biologies of inequity, and the future of human evolution. There are so many more—too many more—from which we could have chosen. There is a common thread to our selection, however, and it is the same thread that has brought us from Toynbee first to Toynbee last: generation and variation.

POPULATION GROWTH

In the September 2008 issue of *National Geographic* magazine, journalist Charles Mann noted that a mere 11% of the world's land surface is devoted to growing food for over 6 billion people, and only 3% of that land can be characterized as being inherently fertile soil (the balance requiring technological interventions, such as irrigation and chemical fertilization). Moreover, in the most comprehensive study to date on the state of the world's marine fishery, Worm and colleagues (2006) note that without immediate remediation, global food fish stocks will be depleted beyond recovery by 2048 (Figure 16.2), although trends toward recovery in several marine ecosystems provide some hope for future sustainability (Worm et al. 2009). At the same time as land and ocean productivity is dwindling, the creation of waste increases annually, including a new form of toxic waste unique to the end of the 20th century—namely, e-waste (Wong et al. 2007; Figure 16.3).[1] In Canada, nonhazardous solid waste production reached 755 kilograms per person as of 2008, in spite of intensified programs for reuse and recycling (Statistics Canada 2012). The common threads to these realities are the twinned economic forces of production and consumption, both of which can be tied to one overwhelming demographic factor: population growth. However, as we explore in this chapter, the challenge is not limited to the total number of individuals on the planet; it also encompasses the inequitable distribution of people with respect to necessary resources, including space, wealth, and security (Ehrlich et al. 2012). Such inequities have significant ramifications for human biology, impacting growth and development, health, fertility, and mortality.

Measuring Population Growth

Demographers speak of population growth as either negative (more deaths than births) or positive (more births than deaths), although these are crude measures; more precise estimates would also consider changes due to immigration or emigration. Population growth also varies over time with changing patterns of fertility and mortality associated with sociocultural development, resulting in a phenomenon known as the **demographic transition** (Figure 16.4). Such changes might come about through advancements in technology reducing the risk of dying at a given age, through improvements in nutrition, hygiene, and health care extending

demographers

researchers who study population dynamics, including measures such as fertility, mortality, migration, survivorship, and life expectancy

demographic transition

the change in a population's age and sex structure with changing birth and death rates. Declines in mortality are typically followed by declines in fertility, shifting a population from an expansion phase to one of stability or contraction

---

1. The term "e-waste" refers to the disposal of obsolete electronic equipment of all varieties, including cathode-tube televisions and computers, computer monitors, printers, scanners, and keyboards. These components contain a toxic mix of heavy metals, PCBs, furans, and dioxins known to be harmful to human health. Recycling of reusable components has become a major industry for developing nations with lax environmental and worker safety standards.

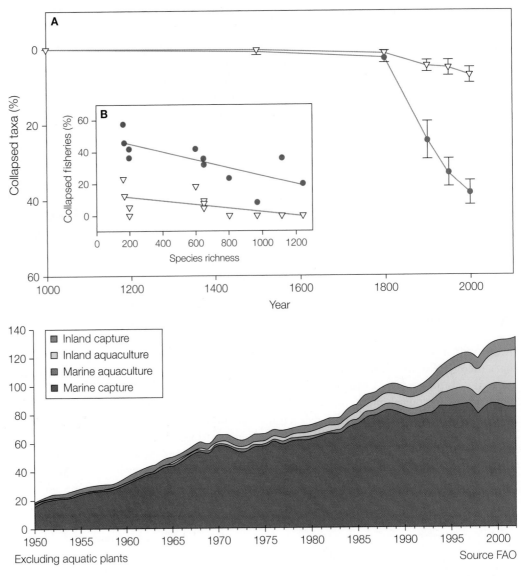

FIGURE 16.2 The number of fish taxa that have collapsed (closed circles) or become extinct (open triangles) has increased dramatically over the past 200 years (top). The total capture in the marine fishery has increased over 400% in the last 50 years alone (bottom).

(Top) Food and Agriculture Organization of the United Nations (2005). *Review of the State of World Marine Fishery Resources*, FAO Technical Paper 457, Figure A1.1; http://www.fao.org/docrep/009/y5852e/y5852e00.htm. Reprinted by permission; (Bottom) From B. Worm, et al. (2006). Impacts of biodiversity loss on ocean ecosystem services. *Science* 314: 787–790. Reprinted with permission from AAAS.

replacement rate fertility

the rate of fertility required to replace a parental generation and to account for differences in local mortality rates

life spans, or through shifts in cultural attitudes with respect to birth control, abortion, or family size, thereby reducing fertility.[2] A measure of the pace at which a population is expanding or shrinking is **replacement rate fertility**. On a global scale, this measure is approximately 2.33— one child each to account for the parents and one-third of a child to make up for variations in sex ratio at birth[3] and early adult mortality. However, there is considerable variation by country

2. Many other factors influence the demographic structure of a population, including political or civil strife, famine, itinerant labour migration, and disease outbreaks that preferentially affect certain age/sex groups. Lifestyle choices such as smoking, alcohol consumption, and lack of exercise, long known to reduce longevity, have also been correlated with reduced reproductive output (Homan, Davies, and Norman 2007).

3. Sex ratio is calculated as the number of males to females at given periods over the life cycle (e.g., conception, birth, at puberty, and post-reproductive). In humans, the birth sex ratio (also known as the secondary sex ratio) is approximately 105 males per 100 females, although this can be affected by cultural practices such as selective abortion and infanticide. For most countries, the post-reproductive sex ratio favours females due to differences in longevity.

in fertility rates (Table 16.1). For example, in 2013, Canada had an annual population growth rate of 0.77% and a **total fertility rate** (TFR) of 1.59, while Niger's growth rate was 3.32% with a TFR of 7.03. The fact that Canada's 2013 TFR was below replacement level indicates that future growth in the Canadian population will need to rely heavily on immigration.

There is also considerable variation within national boundaries. For example, traditional Anabaptist religious sects such as Hutterites, Mennonites, and Amish are well known for having TFRs of 10.0 or higher (Hurd 2006)—a rate supported by high levels of both economic and **social capital** within these populations. There is some indication of recent declines in fertility among these groups; TFR for Canadian Hutterite colonies in Alberta dropped from 9.99 in the 1950s to 8.80 by the mid-1980s (Nonoka, Miura, and Peter 1994), primarily through a decline in the number of children borne by women over age 35.

The other side of the population growth coin is mortality, and as we saw with birth rates, there is considerable variation among nations with respect to death rates (Figure 16.5). Here again, the causes of death are diverse and are not equitably distributed across or within national boundaries. To illustrate, consider that the infant mortality rate (per 1,000 live births) in 2013 for Canada overall was 4.78, while in Nunavut it was 26.30 (2011 data), and that suicide among males in Nunavut was nine times the national average. Such

FIGURE 16.3 The disposal or recycling of nonbiodegradable electronic components is a new phenomenon associated with the "information age." Many of these components contain toxic waste harmful to human health.

© Andrew McConnell/Alamy

total fertility rate
the average number of children born per woman if all women in the country concerned lived to the end of their childbearing years and bore children according to the age-specific pattern for the region or group

social capital
the resources available to a person or group deriving from their connection to social networks

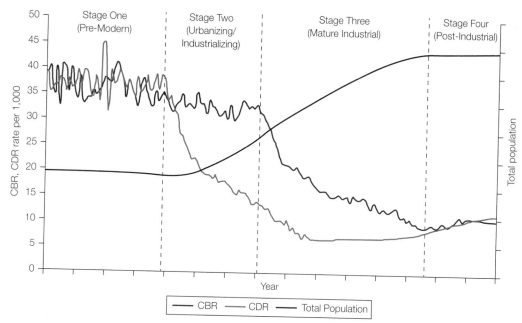

FIGURE 16.4 The demographic transition is marked by several stages associated with social transformation. An initial decline in rates of death (CDR) is followed by reductions in birth rate (CBR). Overall, population tends to increase.

University of Wisconsin, http://www.uwmc.uwc.edu/geography/demotrans/demtran.htm

TABLE 16.1 Total fertility rate (TFR) and infant mortality (IM, deaths per 1,000 live births) for selected countries, ranked in order as per TFR. The correlation of the ranks for these two measures in this table is 0.85; that is, countries with high TFR also have high IM, although some exceptions do occur (e.g., Israel).

Country	TFR	Rank	IM	Rank
Niger	7.03	1	87.98	7
Afghanistan	5.54	8	119.41	1
Rwanda	4.71	26	61.03	24
Kenya	3.76	43	42.18	51
Guatemala	3.08	54	24.32	78
Israel	2.65	76	4.03	199
United States	2.06	121	5.90	174
United Kingdom	1.90	140	4.50	189
Sweden	1.67	173	2.73	220
CANADA	1.59	180	4.78	182
China	1.55	184	15.20	110
Germany	1.42	200	3.48	210
Singapore	0.79	224	2.59	221

CIA *World Fact Book*, 2013

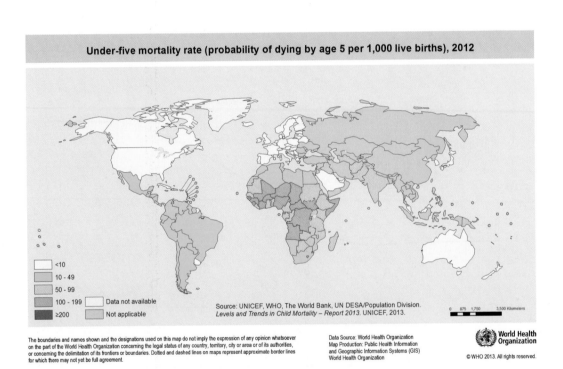

Under-five mortality rate (probability of dying by age 5 per 1,000 live births), 2012

<10
10 - 49
50 - 99
100 - 199   Data not available
≥200   Not applicable

Source: UNICEF, WHO, The World Bank, UN DESA/Population Division.
Levels and Trends in Child Mortality – Report 2013. UNICEF, 2013.

0   875   1,750   3,500 Kilometers

FIGURE 16.5 Infant mortality rate varies globally, mainly due to intrinsic factors regarding nutrition, maternal health care, and endemic disease risk.

disparities in rate and manner of death point to profound inequities in access to health care, in cultural dissonance, and to myriad other cultural and socioeconomic factors.

Future Tense?

As this sentence was being written (11:30 a.m., October 19, 2013), the world's population was 7,186,865,055. In 1950, the figure was approximately 2.5 billion. It is estimated that 10 millennia ago, as settled life and agriculture were getting under way, world population was about 1 million (Michael 1993). In other words, between c. 8000 BCE and 1950, global population increased on average by about 700,000 people per year, but in the past six decades by almost 73 million per year. Clearly, the change in the rate of growth has not been this abrupt; nonetheless, it has been dramatic over the past 200 years (Figure 16.6). Two questions are raised: How did this happen? And what are the implications going forward in the 21st century?

It is far easier to answer the first of these queries. Aside from opening the door to the nuclear age and the Cold War, the end of World War II led into two decades of economic prosperity in the developed world; to important advances in medical knowledge, including antibiotic drugs; and to significant developments in agricultural science—the "Green Revolution"—which resulted in unprecedented levels of production of staple crops as new, higher yielding varieties of rice, wheat, and maize were developed (Conway and Toenniessen 1999).[4] The demographic impacts were several, including the Baby Boom in Europe, North America, Australia, and parts of Asia, the provision of sufficient calories in developing states to sustain high levels of population growth, and a reduction in levels of mortality worldwide through the application and distribution of health care advances (principally through agencies of the United Nations). Consequently, more babies were born (typically to younger women), and fewer people died in any given year. In Canada, the Baby Boom resulted in an additional 1.5 million births between 1940 and 1965 (among whom are included the authors of this text!).

A Neo-Malthusian Dilemma?

The implications of the recent historic trend in population growth are profound. Although the annual rate of population increase is slowing down on a global scale (it is almost half today what it was in the early 1960s: around 1.2% versus 2.2%), the decline is not evenly distributed across the board and remains beyond

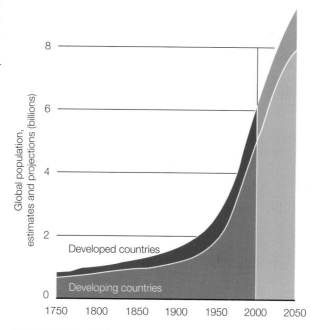

FIGURE 16.6 Global population growth rate has increased dramatically since the end of World War II. The vast majority of this increase occurred in developing countries.

UNEP/GRID-Arendal, Trends in population, developed and developing countries, 1750–2050 (estimates and projections). Cartographer: Hugo Ahlenius, Nordpil. UNEP/GRID-Arendal Maps and Graphics Library, http://maps.grida.no/go/graphic/trends-in-population-developed-and-developing-countries-1750-2050-estimates-and-projections (Accessed 7 November 2009).

---

4. As a result of current population pressures in developing states, biological and social scientists alike are calling for greater efforts in producing a second Green Revolution, via biotechnology, to provide crops that will provide even greater yields, besides being resistant to drought, pests, and pesticides (Wollenweber, Porter, and Lübberstedt 2005).

replacement levels in regions of the world that can least support rapidly growing populations. The ominous consequences of unsustainable growth were first pointed out more than 200 years ago by Thomas Robert Malthus (1766–1834), an English political economist whose now famous 1798 essay on population not only established the foundations of modern demography but also influenced a number of his peers and intellectual successors (see Box 16.1). Since the 1960s, social demographers (most famously the Stanford ecologist Paul Ehrlich; see Ehrlich et al 2012) have revived Malthusian prognostications for significant declines in human well-being as a result of overpopulation and its implication for depletion of **natural capital**—the resources required for sustaining human populations (Williams 2008).

natural capital

the organic and inorganic resources contained in the earth's lands and waters, providing for the goods we produce and consume

While dire warnings of impending demographic calamity, famine, and population decline have not been received without criticism (Lomborg 2001), there is cause to reconsider the implications of global human expansion and local inequities in population growth. In this regard, in a series of articles published in the *American Journal of Physical Anthropology*, J. Kenneth Smail (2002, 2003a,

BOX 16.1

RETROSPECTION: Thomas Robert Malthus—An Essay on the Principle of Population (1798)

The power of population is so superior to the power of the earth to produce subsistence for man, that premature death must in some shape or other visit the human race. The vices of mankind are active and able ministers of depopulation. They are the precursors in the great army of destruction, and often finish the dreadful work themselves. But should they fail in this war of extermination, sickly seasons, epidemics, pestilence, and plague advance in terrific array, and sweep off their thousands and tens of thousands. Should success be still incomplete, gigantic inevitable famine stalks in the rear, and with one mighty blow, levels the population with the food of the world.

T.R. Malthus's small *Essay*, originally published anonymously and reprinted through six editions, owes as much to his training as a mathematician and political economist as it does to his philosophical conversations with his father and his vocation as curate of Okewood Chapel in Surrey, England, whose parishioners were illiterate and extremely poor (Avery 2005). Combining his lived and learned experience, Malthus reasoned that all animal populations, including human, were capable of multiplying exponentially. For us, this means doubling every 25 years, quadrupling every 50, and so on; left unchecked, in theory an initial population of 100 sexually mature persons would become 1,600 after four generations! Clearly, positive checks on population growth must exist that increase mortality, as Malthus dramatically evokes in the above passage. In later editions (in response to critics), he included several "negative" checks on population growth aimed at controlling fertility. These included birth control, late marriage, and "Moral Restraint" outside of marriage.

Malthus's influence extended into numerous spheres, from politics, to theology, sociology, natural history, and beyond. National censuses were established in the United Kingdom in 1801, and birth control programs were created in the latter part of the century based on Malthusian ideas. Charles Darwin and Alfred Russel Wallace drew heavily on Malthus's analysis

of the limits by which human populations might be "improved" in formulating their principle of natural selection. Malthus's central premise was that the capacity of human population to reproduce, as noted above, exceeded that of agricultural production to sustain it. His ideas were also incorporated into 20th-century ecological modelling of the relationship between population increase and **carrying capacity** (Figure 16.7): growth rate should slow as population size approaches the limit of the environment to support it. Failure to do so results in "overshoot," which in turn leads to a reduction in carrying capacity from previous levels. While the degree to which carrying capacity is suppressed may be mitigated by further advances in technology (e.g., genetically engineered high-yield crops that are both drought- and pest-resistant), an emerging consensus suggests that such innovations will have less and less impact in the future as the natural fertility of soils and available arable land is depleted (Ramankutty, Foley, and Olejniczak 2008). Both outcomes were predicted by Malthus two centuries ago.

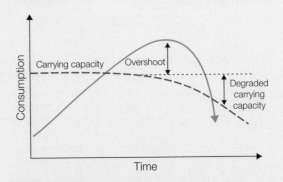

FIGURE 16.7 Populations are able to grow in size to an upper limit determined by local ecological factors; typically, this limit is set by the least available essential resource.

b) argued that the world does not have the resources to support its current population, let alone one numbering over 9 billion, as projected for 2050.[5] It is worth examining Smail's argument for a number of reasons. First, global population has increased by over 700 million people since his 2002 publication. Second, Smail concludes that significant remedial action must be enacted urgently in order to ameliorate an impending and chaotic reduction in world population over the next 150 years. Finally, Smail specifically exhorts biological anthropologists to become active voices in developing recommendations relevant to such action—we are, after all, consummate describers and explainers of the history of human reproduction!

Smail (2002) outlines his position as a series of 10 "inescapable realties" (Table 16.2), 5 of which are demographic and 5 economic/ecological. The essential message is not difficult to comprehend: the bulk of future population growth will occur disproportionately in sub-Saharan Africa, India, and Asia, all centres of massive **population momentum**, while the largest per capita consumption of goods, services, and nonrenewable resources (e.g., oil, minerals, arable land, and potable water) will continue to occur in developed countries (Europe, North America, Japan, and Australia, with China rapidly joining their ranks with alarming environmental impact). Indeed, at some 6.5 hectares, Canada's per capita **ecological footprint** is the eighth-largest in the world (WWF [World Wide Fund for Nature] 2012), over half related to carbon emissions.[6] This is not an enviable position!

carrying capacity

the population size of a given organism that a habitat could comfortably sustain given available resources, denoted by the symbol K; K fluctuates with variation in resources, and for human populations these include not only space, food, and water but also variables such as sanitation, health care, and social capital

population momentum

the reproductive potential of those yet to reproduce; typically measured as the proportion of a population under 18 years of age. Expanding populations with broad-based demographic pyramids have considerable population momentum

ecological footprint

a measure of the ecological impact of human behaviour and activity, measured in the amount of land and seascape required, per person, to produce resources consumed and to absorb waste produced

zero population growth (ZPG)

arises when the balance of birth and death, and the sum of net migration (immigration and emigration), is zero; ZPG denotes a stationary population that neither increases nor declines

TABLE 16.2 Ten Inescapable Realities Regarding Human Population Growth

1.	In spite of geopolitical events causing major reductions in human population (world wars, disease pandemics), global population increased fourfold during the 20th century—15% in the final decade alone.
2.	Population momentum is such that it would take two to three generations of **zero population growth** implemented immediately and globally just to stabilize numbers.
3.	Growth is not just fertility, but also declining mortality; life expectancy will increase in future years, especially in developing states.
4.	There are no historical precedents to guide us; population growth is analogous to a malignant cancer capable of permanently destabilizing planetary ecology.
5.	The time frame for remedial action lies within the life span of those already born.
6.	Long-term sustainable carrying capacity is finite (consider space and potable water); technological "fixes" are incremental, not revolutionary.
7.	We have likely exceeded the planet's optimal carrying capacity (vis-à-vis long-term adaptive balance with ecosystem, resources, and one another).
8.	Only about 20% of the current population has an adequate standard of living; almost 5 billion live in conditions of mild deprivation to severe deficiency.
9.	By the year 2100, the ecological footprint of humanity on planetary ecosystems, already demonstrably unsustainable, is expected to quadruple. This estimate takes into account future improvements in energy conservation and resource-use efficiencies through technological advancements.
10.	Remedial action to reduce population size must also account for unknowns, requiring a redundancy in planning that, at a minimum, accommodates biodiversity and wilderness conservation, and the possibility of loss of ecosystem resilience.

Source: Based on Smail, J. K. 2002. Remembering Malthus—a preliminary argument for a significant reduction in global human numbers. *American Journal of Physical Anthropology* 118: 292–297.

5. Current projections, Malthus notwithstanding, are that the human population will stabilize around this figure by mid-century.

6. As you might expect, our use of resources—comprising food, housing, mobility, goods, and services—is not equitably distributed among Canadian households. The wealthiest 10% of Canadians have an ecological footprint 66% larger than the national average.

While on the surface this analysis smacks of pessimism, the question needs to be asked: Can the world afford for Smail (and others in the neo-Malthusian camp) to be wrong? Even if only half-right, it buys little more than a modest reprieve from impending population collapse—perhaps a century or so. Smail argues that what is needed now is a multilateral program of guided social engineering. At first glimpse, guided social engineering looks like a euphemism for a new eugenics initiative. However, Smail's (2003b) intention is for all nations to make a coordinated effort to achieve a global subreplacement fertility rate of around 1.5 to 1.8, starting immediately and lasting until at least the 22nd century. Unlike eugenics policies implemented in the 20th century that encouraged reproduction in some sectors of society and that discouraged (or eliminated) it in other select groups (see Chapter 13), guided social engineering with respect to fertility in Smail's sense targets all of humanity, across class, ethnicity, religion, and nationality. And here lies the role for sciences such as biological anthropology, which articulates both the biological and the cultural diversity of humankind, and which can undertake the kind of research necessary to support and develop such measures and policies. Such advocacy is explored further in the following section.

BIOLOGIES OF EXCESS AND NEGLECT

In 1998, biological anthropologists Alan Goodman and Thomas Leatherman published an edited volume of essays entitled *Building a New Biocultural Synthesis: Political–Economic Perspectives on Human Biology.*[7] The intent of the book was to illustrate "how sociocultural and political–economic processes affect human biologies, and then how compromised biologies further threaten the social fabric" (Goodman and Leatherman 1998, 5). In *A Human Voyage* we have explicitly noted that biology cannot be comprehended without regard to culture; for example, farming in Africa predisposes people to increased incidence of malaria by providing breeding grounds for mosquitoes, and chewing coca leaves facilitates work at high altitude in South American Quechua Indians, increasing stamina and heart rate (see Box 16.2). However, Goodman and Leatherman ask a more compelling question: How does human biology respond when challenged by a transformed and transformative global network of intertwined relationships of power, influence, and wealth? Economic structures such as the World Bank and the International Monetary Fund, multinational corporations such as Coca-Cola and China Minmetals, commodity cartels such as OPEC, and trade agreements such as the North American Free Trade Agreement (NAFTA) and the recently announced Canada–Europe Trade Agreement (CETA, 2013, with implementation anticipated by 2015), are not benign with respect to the lives of people, who have no option but to live and work in the communities and countries exposed to their influence. Modernizing forces of economic development, with international movement of labour, raw material, and capital, impact not only developing states but developed ones as well. The rapid growth of the *maquiladoras* in Mexico, coincident with manufacturing job losses, especially in the United States, has taken advantage of a considerably cheaper workforce and has been linked to NAFTA's implementation in 1994. Job loss equates with loss of income, inevitably leading to lower standards of living, poorer nutrition, and compromised health.

Internal state politics and policies aimed at attracting foreign investment and capital can lead to the displacement of entire civilian populations (Figure 16.9) and increased disparity among classes. For example, Leatherman and Goodman (2005) reviewed the impact of ecotourism and **archaeotourism** in Central America—specifically, Mexico's Yucatan Peninsula and its indigenous Mayan population. They noted, for example, that Cancun—today one of the most popular destinations for tourists, with a human population of about 500,000 and a hotel room "population" of over 25,000 (Figure 16.10)—was only 35 years ago a small fishing village with a population of 426. Such rapid development affects many aspects of life: Indigenous people shift from subsistence to wage labour as waiters, groundskeepers, and chambermaids; cultural

archaeotourism

a form of tourism in which the attraction consists of archaeological sites, typically megalithic locations (e.g., cities, pyramids)

---

7. The essays were mostly derived from a conference sponsored by the Wenner-Gren Foundation, held in Mexico in 1992.

BOX 16.2

PROFILE ... Explaining Variation in Growth among the Makushi

Courtesy of Warren Wilson

For the past decade, the Makushi Amerindians of Guyana's rainforests and savannas have undergone a rapid cultural transformation, largely the result of a national park established in 1996 in the traditional Makushi homelands (Figure 16.8). I started working with the Makushi in 2000 to assess the impact of this park on their children's health. To that end we collected data for weight, height, and percentage body fat, measures of dietary intake, and interview data. To assess the impact of chronic undernutrition or infectious disease among the Makushi, the anthropometric data were compared to international growth standards for healthy children created by the World Health Organization (WHO). In 2000–01 we found that overall, the girls were doing better than the boys. Compared to the girls, the boys were significantly more likely to be quite short for their age. How might we then explain the variation in growth between boys and girls?

Part of the answer may come from work by William Greulich, who was working in Guam just after World War II and

noticed the same phenomenon—females fared better during the privations of war than did males. Greulich hypothesized that females are physiologically more resistant to environmental insults such as chronic malnutrition. But why would this be the case? In 1973, William Stini proposed that in order for a sexually reproducing species to survive, females must produce offspring. The condition of pregnancy and lactation is extremely demanding physiologically, so Stini concluded that females should be more resistant to deprivation in order to meet the challenges of reproduction. This idea seemed to go a long way toward explaining the pattern we observed among Makushi boys and girls. Makushi boys and girls grow up in a difficult environment, where there is often not enough to eat and infectious disease is prevalent.

Recall, however, that as human population biologists, we are encouraged to consider both biology *and* cultural variables. I was reminded of this by my collaborator on this project, Janette Bulkan, a cultural anthropologist who has worked for years among the Makushi. Janette suggested that we may be missing another explanation. In Makushi households, daughters are favoured over sons. One reason for this is that traditional marriage practices dictate that a new husband will move into the house with his wife and her parents. For one year, he is on a type of probation and must contribute to the economic well-being of his parents-in-law's household. If he passes this probationary period, he is accepted into the household and is allowed to remain as the husband. Hence, daughters are valued as they attract this source of labour and economic support. Another reason is that the bulk of the food consumed by the Makushi comes from a root crop known as manioc, the cultivation and laborious processing of which is the responsibility of females. Since many Makushi households remain subsistence-based, healthy, robust girls would retain their high status. The presence of this bias toward females led us to ask whether parents were allocating more resources to daughters than to sons. Our dietary intake data revealed that, indeed, females had a superior diet relative to males—significantly so in the 13- to 19-year-old age group.

Our research among the Makushi provides a classic example of what human biologists have come to appreciate worldwide—the most rewarding interpretations result from applying a biocultural perspective to the study of human variation.

Courtesy of Warren Wilson

FIGURE 16.8 A Makushi family

Source: Written by Dr. Warren Wilson, Associate Professor, Department of Archaeology, University of Calgary

FIGURE 16.9 International interests often usurp local rights, displacing landowners and fomenting dissent. Here, Mayan people of the community of Comitancillo, San Marcos, Guatemala, were protesting in May 2008 against the Canadian mining company Goldcorp and its Guatemalan subsidiary Montana Exploradora.

Courtesy of Catherine Nolin

coca-colonialism

refers to the ability of multinational companies to usurp local traditions and lifeways, effectively replacing local customs with Western surrogates

empty-calorie foods

in nutritional science, empty-calorie foods offer no nutrition other than energy (calories); the vast majority of "junk foods" fall into this category

height-for-age

a measure of achieved growth in height, standardized for age; a person suffering significant growth deficits for their age compared to normal standards is considered stunted

weight-for-height

a measure of body mass standardized for a given height; high weight-for-height values indicate overweight/obesity

artifacts and foodways are commoditized, becoming souvenirs and "ethnic cuisine"; rural populations are depleted as people move to these new centres seeking opportunity; and water and nutritional quality decline as these resources are saved for resort guests.

Leatherman and Goodman (2005) describe the situation in the Mexican Yucatan as **coca-colonialism**, referring specifically to the transformative power of **empty-calorie foods**. The undernourishment resulting in low **height-for-age** and **weight-for-height** measures that are characteristic of predevelopment populations has been replaced by chronic obesity among adults; for example, they found that among the Mayan people of the Yucatan, 40% of men and 64% of women were obese by North American clinical standards. This is not to say that such economic development is negative in all respects, and many Maya have an improved quality of life. But it has not been universal, and especially lacking is the ability of Indigenous peoples to have a

FIGURE 16.10 Only a generation has passed since Cancun was converted from a small fishing village into a world tourist destination, transforming local lives, culture, and biologies.

© Mike Liu/Shutterstock.com

voice in the direction of future development. As Leatherman and Goodman remark (2005, 844), local Maya "are primarily seen as sources of cheap labor and ethnic backdrop at tourist sites."

The point we make here is that a "new" biocultural synthesis views the "cultural" component in its broadest sense as influenced by global and invariably inequitable forces of change and transformation, with concomitant impact on the biologies of those less able to insulate themselves from their impact. In the following sections we illustrate this with particular regard to the biology of children.

Children and Canaries

In the 19th and early 20th centuries, it was common practice for English and American coal miners to take caged canaries into the mines to act as sentinels, warning the miners of the presence

FIGURE 16.11 Sensitive species act as early warning systems to adverse environments. In human populations the same function is served by children, whose growth and development can be impaired by lack of adequate resources (such as food and clean water) or exposure to disease.

© Trinity Mirror/Mirrorpix/Alamy

of noxious gases such as methane or carbon monoxide (Figure 16.11). Being more sensitive to such environmental hazards, the birds would succumb before the miners suffered adverse effects, thereby allowing the men to escape to the surface. In modern population biology, children are de facto canaries (Pelto 2008). There are good reasons for asserting this metaphor: infants and children have less robust **adaptive immune systems** and are continually enmeshed in the shifting sands of growth and development. From conception through adolescence, there is a huge demand for resources—physical, nutritional, and psychosocial—which must be satisfied so that the child can meet standards of normal growth (Moffat and Galloway 2007). The major constraint on providing for child growth is poverty, which, as we saw with demographic measures such as fertility, is not equitably distributed around the globe. For example, 51.3% of Bolivia's population were living below that country's poverty line in 2009, while in Belarus, the comparable value was 5.4% (World Bank Development Indicators 2013). In Canada, the estimate of people living at low income for 2012 for the country as a whole was about 12% according to the Market Basket Measure,[8] although this varied considerably province by province.

The impact of inequality in household wealth is well established, with **food insecurity** and undernutrition as significant corollaries. Hong and colleagues (2006), for example, found that children living in the poorest 20% of Bangladeshi households were more than twice as likely to suffer growth stunting as those from the top 20%, after adjusting for numerous social and economic determinants (the World Bank estimates that 31% of *all* Bangladeshis live below the national poverty line; 2010 data). The UN Food and Agriculture Organization (FAO 2013) estimates that 12% of humanity lacks food security at least part of the time, leading to undernourishment, with the vast majority living in sub-Saharan Africa and southern Asia (an estimated 518 million people).

Researchers from the Université de Montréal (Ehounoux et al. 2009) studying families enrolled in the Québec Longitudinal Study of Child Development found that four-year-old children living in households that had experienced two episodes of not being able to purchase

adaptive immune systems

a component of the immune response targets specific pathogens and requires prior exposure to establish an "immunological memory"; a short-term adaptive immune response is transferred to the newborn across the placenta and via breast milk, although it is less effective in resisting infection than that developed by an individual through his or her own exposure to invading organisms

food insecurity

the real or anticipated lack of safe, nutritious foods that would normally be available at all times and in socially acceptable ways

---

8. The Market Basket Measure (MBM) was developed by Human Resources Development Canada to track changes in low-income distribution across the country. The MBM is based on affordability of a standardized set of goods and services, including housing, transportation, food, and clothing. It is not intended as a measure of poverty per se.

basic needs were significantly growth-delayed. In related studies, these researchers found negative impacts on other health indicators, such as frequency of asthma attacks or "perceived poor health" as rated by the mother (Nikiéma et al. 2012). On the other side of the coin is the apparent paradox of childhood obesity: a study of elementary schoolchildren found that a higher proportion of children in poorer households were overweight or obese (Lazenby et al. 2007; see Chapter 14).

This paradox is resolved when we recognize that the issue remains one of food insecurity: lower income households tend to purchase less expensive, calorically dense but nutritionally deficient foods. Impairments other than physical growth have also been documented, in both developed and developing nations, particularly with regard to cognition and behavioural outcomes (Morris 2008). Significantly, those aspects of neurological development most impacted by material deprivation appear to be areas associated with language and memory (Farah et al. 2006), predisposing children to learning impairment and mental health disorders. Larson (2007) observes that as many as 100,000 children in Canada are born into poverty each year, with a higher likelihood of being preterm, low birth weight babies suffering delayed cognitive development, which ultimately contributes to poor educational outcomes. Again, as we have seen before, these impacts are not equitably distributed across the country (Figure 16.12). While such effects manifest themselves in infancy and childhood, they are also recognized as major contributors to negative health experience in older adults. Low birth weight, for example, is a significant risk factor for coronary heart disease, hypertension, and type II diabetes in middle-aged and older adults through a mechanism known as fetal programming (Barker 2013; see Box 4.1).

What do such studies tell us, and why should a field such as biological anthropology be interested? Clearly, it is important to understand that living in a First World country such as Canada, with a stable government, a complex and well-funded medical system, a "social safety net," and a high per capita GDP, guarantees neither good quality of life nor physical and psychological well-being. The WHO (1946) defined health as "a state of complete physical, mental and social well-being and not merely the absence of disease or infirmity." Many people you know—indeed, perhaps some of your classmates or even yourself—may not satisfy this definition. And it does not take a rocket scientist (as the

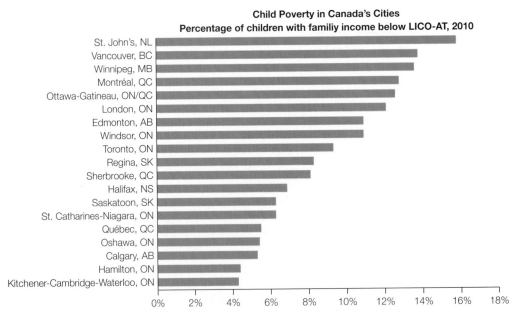

FIGURE 16.12 Child poverty, measured as low income cut-off-after taxes (LICO-AT), varies widely across the country and even within provinces, pointing to the importance of local factors such as employment levels.

Statistics Canada, Cansim table 202-0802.

saying goes) to appreciate that most people living in politically tenuous, economically disadvantaged, and geographically marginal countries of the world fall far short. One need only consider the rate of desertification in Africa (Figure 16.13), a continent already ravaged by political strife and a massive burden of disease. Over 30% of nondesert land in continental Africa is vulnerable to being transformed into a desert landscape through increased aridification; 8% of this area—some 1 million km^2—is considered at very high risk for becoming unsustainable for agricultural use, directly impacting more than 200 million people who already live "on the edge" (Reich et al. 2001).

Here we would remind you of Goodman and Leatherman's (1998) call for an integration of political–economic variables into the analysis of human biology. As biological anthropologists, we are fundamentally interested in human variation and variability in time and space and in the genetic, epigenetic, and environmental mechanisms responsible (see Chapter 4). Through the latter half of the 20th century, and going forward into the 21st century, it has become increasingly

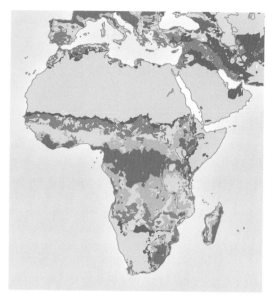

Vulnerability
- Low
- Moderate
- High
- Very High

Other Regions
- Dry
- Cold
- Humid/Not Vulnerable
- Ice/Glacier

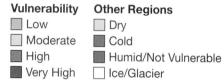

FIGURE 16.13 Desertification threatens significant portions of arable land in sub-Saharan Africa and the Near East.

USDA, http://soils.usda.gov/use/worldsoils/papers/desertification-africa.html

evident that the epigenetic and environmental components of human variation are being shaped by forces far beyond the economic and ecological boundaries of households and local communities; we are now shaped also by events and decisions made by governments, multinational corporations, international finance, and sectarian ideologies. Such inputs are not new to human history, but they have never before attained such a far-reaching and sinister authority to undermine the ability of individuals to provide for and control their basic well-being. Such variation, its sources and its impact on current and future generations, is inherently the subject matter of our discipline. And this of course generates the following question: What lies in wait for the evolutionary future of humankind?

THE END OF HUMAN EVOLUTION?

Having taught university-level courses in biological anthropology for a combined total of almost 40 years, we can say that there is one question that is invariably asked by students: Are humans still evolving? It is a reasonable question, but one that needs to be qualified: because evolution is not predictive, we cannot say what changes may occur as generations pass. But we can look back retrospectively and speak of recent developments. By all accounts, humans seem to be the pinnacle of evolutionary progress, the dominant species on the planet, conquerors of the highest mountains and the deepest ocean trenches, interstellar explorers mapping the origin of the universe, having played golf on the moon. We are so surrounded, embedded, and insulated from nature by our culture and our technology, how could something as base as natural selection possibly fabricate significant advances over what has previously been fashioned? To some degree, we feel we should leave you to ponder this question beyond the confines of this course and this textbook, as it implores you to always ask: Are humans so perfect? But we feel obligated to remind you that "perfection" will always be a moving target—evolution will always be playing catch-up.[9] There is always room for improvement and humans are as eligible as nematodes in that regard!

Blondes Had More Fun?

In the fall of 2002, a number of news agencies, including the Canadian Press and the BBC, reported that scientists in Germany were predicting that natural blondes would become "extinct" at some point in the next 200 years, owing to the fact that men found women with dyed blonde hair more attractive. The story turned out to be a prank, but as journalist Michael Balter (2005) noted, the fact that the story garnered so much attention reveals the public's fascination with the possibility of ongoing human evolution. In Darwinian terms, this hoax would have us believe that mate choice is entirely based on hair colour and that chemically enhanced blondes are more fit than natural blondes, whom they out-perform in the competition for males.[10] It is equally difficult to imagine non-Darwinian mechanisms such as genetic drift randomly eliminating blondes. A number of biologically valid questions could be posed with respect to such phenomena, however, including these: How are technological advances impeding or promoting the action of natural selection in human populations? What are the biological ramifications of technologically mediated reduction in selection pressure? What evidence is there for ongoing or recent Darwinian evolution within *Homo sapiens*?

Esotropia

Exotropia

Hypertropia

Hypertropia

FIGURE 16.14 Strabismus involves a misalignment of the eyes due a failure of the extraocular muscles to coordinate the gaze, resulting in loss of depth perception.

Technology, Genetic Load, and Adaptation

As noted above, technology surrounds us, particularly those of us living in developed post-industrial states with well-funded public and private research sectors (but see Figure 16.1). The intervention of technology into human biology is perhaps most apparent in terms of biomedicine. Thousands of people with congenital or acquired disabilities, both mild and severe, are now able to lead reasonably (if not completely) normal productive *and* reproductive lives.

From an evolutionary perspective, however, the issue is how technology interferes with the role of selection in eliminating less fit phenotypes. For example, individuals with reduced visual acuity resulting from conditions such as congenital strabismus (Figure 16.14), with its attendant loss of binocular vision and depth perception, would likely have had reduced Darwinian fitness in hunting–gathering societies (or for that matter, in automotive societies!). The several common forms of this polygenic trait,

---

9. This reality is captured by evolutionary biologist Leigh Van Valen's (1973) invocation of the Red Queen Hypothesis for evolutionary change, named after Lewis Carroll's character in *Through the Looking Glass*, who exclaimed: "It takes all the running you can do, to keep in the same place." Metaphorically, evolution is always "one step behind" the selective challenges imposed by a changing habitat.

10. The absurdity of the hoax should have been apparent to anyone remotely familiar with evolutionary theory, given that dyed blonde hair could not be passed on to future generations unless one ascribed to Lamarckian notions of the inheritance of acquired characteristics! In fact, this hoax has been resurrected many times, most recently in an *MSN News* report in August 2013 (http://news.msn.com/rumors/rumor-natural-blondes-will-be-extinct-in-200-years). The humour inherent in the proposition was not lost on the American satirist Stephen Colbert (*The Colbert Report*, March 6, 2006), who promoted establishing a eugenics program of selective breeding to "save blondes"!

with a heritability of 73% to 82% based on monozygotic twin studies, are more prevalent in European-derived populations than in African or Asian groups (around 5% vs. < 1%, respectively; see Engle 2007). However, early detection and the use of corrective lenses (or in some cases, surgery) lessen any negative consequences of strabismus.

In a similar fashion, the adoption of softer diets and the use of technology to preprocess foods (cooking, cutlery) has removed any selective disadvantages associated with reduced mandible and maxillary size, dental crowding, or malocclusion (Varrela 2006). The result of these kinds of nonbiological interventions is that those genetic variants responsible for previously less fit phenotypes are not removed through the normal course of selection, which increases the **genetic load** borne by the population as a result of a higher proportion of deleterious alleles carried by individuals.

Evidence for Recent Human Evolution

An alternative approach to showing how technology alleviates selective disadvantage and increases genetic load is to consider the impact of selection when such interventions are absent. This of course is how we understand the operation of Darwinian evolution—adaptation via natural selection. There are effectively two approaches by which we can identify recent evolutionary change. The first is by generating hypotheses linking a specific phenotype to a putative selective agent that itself can be historically dated. The relationship of the sickle cell phenotype with malaria and the latter's association with settled agriculture (as recounted in Chapter 14) is the paradigmatic example. But others have become known in recent years with the advent of genomic mapping as an investigative tool. For example, Perry and colleagues (2007; Luca et al. 2010) tested the hypothesis that populations living in regions of high starch consumption would benefit from higher levels of salivary amylase, the enzyme that breaks down complex starches. Starches form a significant portion of the diet in agricultural societies. They found that high starch-consuming populations had significantly greater **copy number variation** for the gene *AMY1,* which codes for salivary amylase, compared to those whose diets contained little in the way of starches (Figure 16.15). Genomic analysis shows that this adaptation can be located historically within the past 10,000 years, and becomes a marker for recent human evolution. Perry and colleagues suggest that selection has favoured greater levels of salivary amylase[11] to protect against the possibility of "fitness-reducing intestinal disease," which is more prevalent among agriculturalists. Additionally, amylase breaks down starches in the oral cavity, enhancing energy absorption during bouts of diarrheal disease (a condition also more prevalent in settled societies). This is important because diarrheal diseases lead to rapid loss of hydration and important macro- and micronutrients, including calories.

Recently, population geneticists at the University of Chicago and their colleagues have argued that humans have undergone recent positive selection for two genes associated with brain size, one called *microcephalin* (Evans et al. 2005) and the other by the more cumbersome name *abnormal spindle-like microcephaly-associated protein (ASPM)* (Mekel-Bobrov et al. 2005). Mutations in these genes have been linked to primary microcephaly (Figure 16.16), a condition of significantly reduced brain size (approximately 400 cm^3 versus a normal range of 1,200 to 1,600 cm^3) but otherwise normal neuroarchitecture. A human variant of *microcephalin* is estimated to have appeared around 37,000 years ago and *ASPM* only 5,800 years ago. In a sample of 1,184 individuals from diverse ancestral backgrounds, they found that one version of the *microcephalin* gene occurred at significantly higher levels for human populations outside of sub-Saharan Africa (allele frequency around 80%), supporting the hypothesis that it arose after the divergence of anatomically modern humans. Moreover, the young date estimated for the appearance of this variant of *microcephalin* in humans (about 37,000 years ago) is associated with the appearance of anatomically modern *Homo sapiens* in Europe,[12] as well as

genetic load
formally, the average deviation of an individual from the best possible phenotype determined by the relative proportion of deleterious alleles he or she carries; because genetic load varies from 0 (maximum fitness) to 1.0 (minimum fitness), it can also be taken as a measure of the probability that an individual will die before reproducing

copy number variation
inter-individual variations in the number of copies of a gene present in the genome; classic Mendelian genetics suggests that we should possess two copies for each gene, one inherited from each parent. Recent studies suggest, however, that individuals can have more than two copies, through processes such as duplication and recombination

---

11. The alternative hypothesis would be to propose selection for lower levels of amylase in non–starch-eating populations; this is seen as less likely, since high levels of amylase pose no selective disadvantage.

12. Some authors (e.g., Evans et al. 2006) have suggested that the *microcephalin* gene was contributed by Neandertals into the modern human genome. However, the recently published draft sequence for Neandertals (Green et al. 2010) did not identify the haplogroup for this gene, nor did a genome analysis of the Monti Lessini Neandertal dated to 50,000 BCE (Lari et al. 2010).

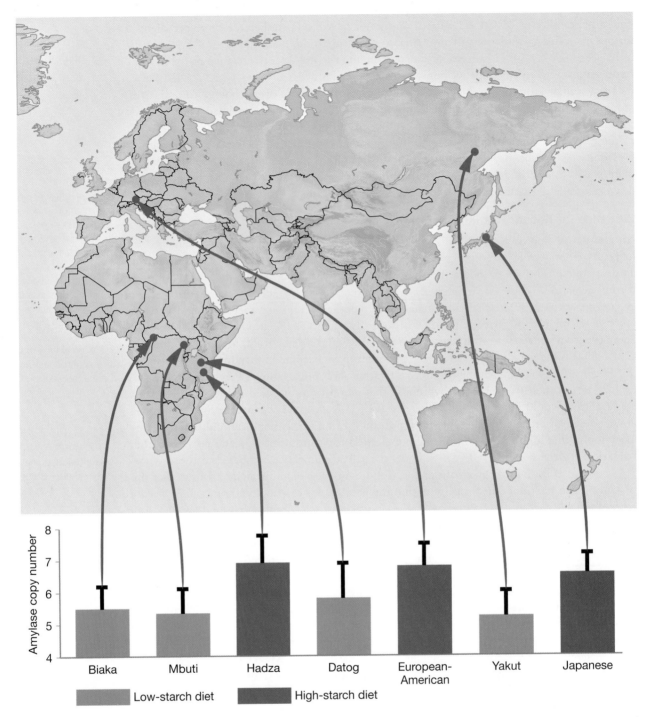

FIGURE 16.15 The cultural shift to increased starch in the human diet promoted an evolutionary adaptation for increased frequency of the *AMY1* gene in those populations and enhanced production of salivary amylase.

Evolutionary adaptations to dietary changes. *Annual Review of Nutrition* 30: 291–314. Reproduced with permission of Annual Review of Nutrition, Vol. 30 by Annual Reviews, http://www.annualreviews.org

the development and elaboration of symbolic traditions (e.g., art). The even younger *ASPM* gene variant is also argued to be due to strong positive selection for its role in regulating neural stem cell proliferation (Mekel-Bobrov et al. 2005). Again, in a survey of subjects representing diverse ancestries, they found one variant, haplotype 63, to occur at particularly high values among Europeans and people of Middle Eastern extraction (allele frequency around 40%) and at very low levels among other human populations.

The very young age estimated for *ASPM* and its geographic distribution suggests it may be associated with major cultural developments in the circum-Mediterranean region over the past 5,000 to 10,000 years—notably domestication, development of writing, and the rise of cities. However, it must be remembered that the historical associations attached to the appearance of these variants of *microcephalin* and *ASPM* are merely correlative, and not necessarily causal.

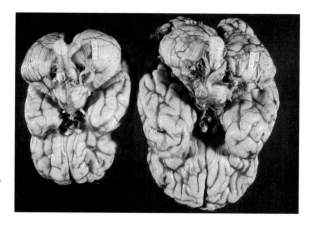

FIGURE 16.16 Mutation in the *ASPM* or *microcephalin* genes leads to primary microcephaly, as seen in this image of a microcephalic 13-year-old female (left) versus a normal 11-year-old (right).

© Martin M. Rotker/Photo Researchers, Inc.

The suggestion that selection has acted on genes regulating brain size in recent human history that correlate with specific transformative events in human behaviour leads one to wonder whether these genes are in any way associated with cognition. Timpson and colleagues (2007) explored this question in a sample of 9,000 children, correlating the occurrence of the *microcephalin* and *ASPM* variants with a range of phenotypic measures, including anthropometry, physiology, and cognitive functioning (including general IQ, working memory, and verbal and motor skills). No significant associations were found, suggesting that some other selective advantage must have accrued to those individuals having the variants for these two genes. Timpson and colleagues (2007) note that both of these genetic variants occur in adult and fetal tissues and that both have functional roles beyond contributing to neurological development; thus, positive selection may have acted on those extraneural effects, possibly related to immune function or spermatogenesis. Interestingly, in a separate study, the University of Chicago team also found no association of the *ASPM* and *microcephalin* genotypes with standardized measures of general intelligence (Mekel-Bobrov et al. 2007).

The story of *ASPM* and *microcephalin* does not end here. Ali and Meier (2008), for example, have shown positive selection of *ASPM* and cerebral cortex size across nine primate lineages, but not with whole-brain size. Université Laval anthropologist Peter Frost (2011) has hypothesized that the 5,800-year-old *ASPM* variant may have been associated with the advent of alphabetical writing, and that individuals with such latent ability would occupy highly valued roles in society as scribes and secretaries. He also argues that the earlier studies discounting cognitive associations with *ASPM* may not have been sufficiently robust (adequate in scope or duration) to capture the high-level cognitive functioning underlying early alphabetical writing, which lacked punctuation and necessitated real-time recording of oral commentary—both features placing high demands on short-term memory and motor skills.

It is also informative to consider that not all genetic variants for which positive selection can be demonstrated may have been selected for by agents with which they are currently associated. For example, in the 1990s it was discovered that a mutation in the gene producing a protein known as chemokine (C–C motif) receptor 5 (*CCR5*) conferred resistance to HIV in individuals who had two copies of the mutation. This mutation, termed *CCR5Δ32*, is found in high frequency in peoples of northern European descent. However, in spite of the obviously high selective advantage conferred by *CCR5Δ32* in this scenario, exposure to HIV played no role in the origin of this allele. We can say this because HIV has a relatively short epidemiological history[13] and the origin of *CCR5Δ32* has been estimated at around 700 years ago based on molecular genetic studies. Selective forces such as the bubonic plague

---

13. HIV is derived from simian immunodeficiency virus (SIV) via cross-species transfer from nonhuman primates, which still act as a reservoir for several ancestral strains of HIV (Van Heuverswyn and Peeters 2007).

or smallpox have been proposed, as both were major diseases in the 13th and 14th centuries in Europe, but these hypotheses have not been confirmed by laboratory studies (Mecsas et al. 2005). Recent studies have also questioned proposed relationships of the *CCR5Δ32* mutation with other immune system-related diseases such as multiple sclerosis, asthma and type 2 diabetes (Ghorban et al. 2013). Thus, the pattern of its higher frequency in peoples from northern Europe awaits explanation.

So we return to the question posed earlier: Are we at the end of human evolution? The evidence for recent positive selection at a number of loci across the human genome associated with features such as skin pigmentation, immune response, and metabolic diseases (Barreiro et al. 2008), as well as the examples discussed above, would suggest not. But the answer may be much simpler than the one obtained through genomic analyses. As University of Calgary primatologist Mary Pavelka succinctly remarked (quoted in Balter 2005, 234): "The question, 'Are humans still evolving?' should be rephrased as 'Do all people have the same number of children?' The answer is that we do not make equal contributions to the next generation, and thus we are still evolving."

LEARNING KEYS

KEY IDEAS

- Humankind faces many challenges in the coming years, as we adapt to new habitats that are fundamentally of our own making.

- The demographic transition charts the pattern of human population growth in changing rates of mortality and fertility associated with technological and social evolution.

- Some authors have used the metaphor of cancer to describe the impact of human population on our planetary "host."

- Global patterns of production and consumption point to significant inequities in the burden of population growth, with the developed post-industrial world having excessively large ecological footprints as measures of per capita consumption.

- Inequities in the distribution of wealth and power, labelled by some as "coca-colonialism," result in significant health and nutritional deficiencies among peoples in developing states, most typically reflected in child growth and development.

- Food insecurity, which challenges physical and cognitive development, is common among the poorer segments of all human societies, including those within advanced First World states with very high measures of economic well-being, including Canada.

- Social, economic, and political inequity impacts many aspects of human biology, and thus presents the discipline of biological anthropology with both the opportunity and the responsibility of identifying and understanding these relationships as well as promoting avenues for addressing the barriers.

- Technological achievement may isolate humankind from many selective challenges, thus increasing genetic load through survivorship of individuals with mild physical handicaps (such as poorer sight, hearing or mobility).

- Technological advances may also create opportunities for continued human biological evolution, as they create new selective environments favouring novel genetic mutations.

- Individuals do not contribute equally to succeeding generations; in this sense, humankind continues to evolve.

KEY TERMS

demographers (p. 371)

demographic transition (p. 371)

social capital (p. 373)

natural capital (p. 376)

carrying capacity (p. 377)

ecological footprint (p. 377)

coca-colonialism (p. 380)

food insecurity (p. 381)

genetic load (p. 385)

KEY QUESTIONS TO ASK MYSELF

1. The prospect of population growth seems really scary. Does this mean I shouldn't have any kids?

2. Ghandi once said, "Be the change you want to see in the world." Can I really make a difference?

3. Why do many science fiction depictions of humans in the future emphasize excessively large brains?

KEY CRITICAL THINKING QUESTIONS

1. Can you imagine a situation in which humans cease to evolve?

2. To what degree should biological anthropologists advocate for social and/or political economic change? What particular issues in Canada might qualify for such an agenda?

KEY THINGS TO DO NEXT

CourseMate Visit **CourseMate** at www.nelson.com/humanvoyage2e to build your comprehension, practise your critical thinking skills, review core concepts, and explore other resources at your disposal.

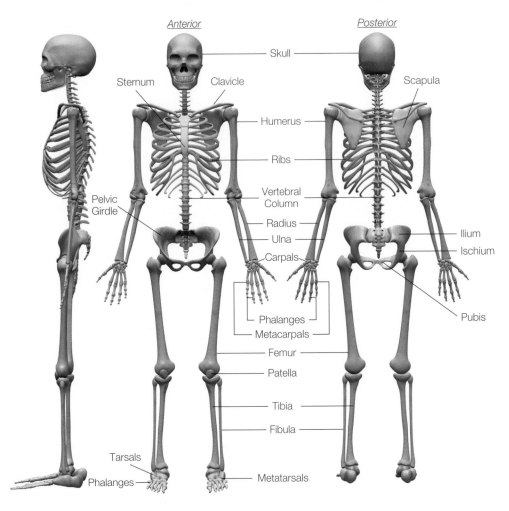

FIGURE A.1 The Human Skeletal System

© 3drenderings/Shutterstock

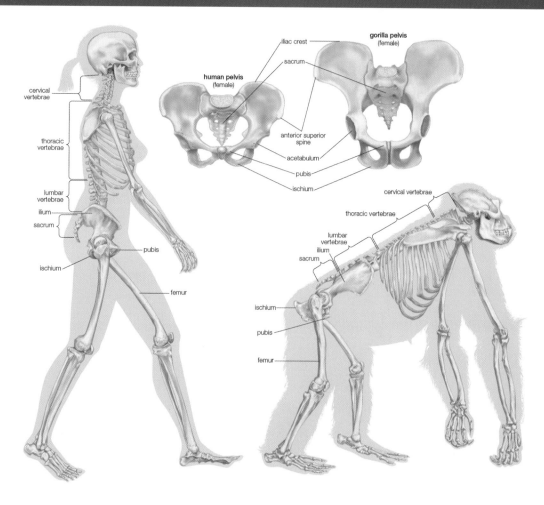

FIGURE A.2   Human Skeleton and Pelvis Compared to those of a Gorilla

© Universal Image Group/Getty Images

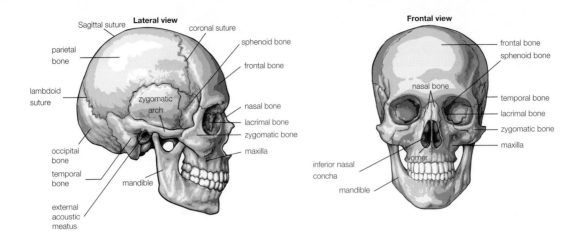

Lateral view

Sagittal suture

coronal suture

parietal bone

sphenoid bone

frontal bone

lambdoid suture

zygomatic arch

nasal bone

lacrimal bone

zygomatic bone

maxilla

occipital bone

temporal bone

mandible

external acoustic meatus

Frontal view

frontal bone

sphenoid bone

nasal bone

temporal bone

lacrimal bone

zygomatic bone

maxilla

inferior nasal concha

vomer

mandible

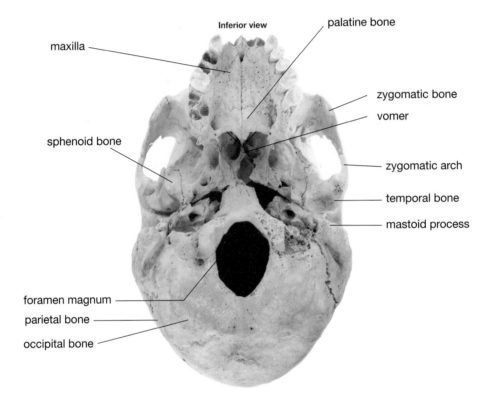

Inferior view

palatine bone

maxilla

zygomatic bone

vomer

sphenoid bone

zygomatic arch

temporal bone

mastoid process

foramen magnum

parietal bone

occipital bone

FIGURE A.3 Human Skull: Lateral, Frontal, and Inferior Views.

(Top) © Oguz Ara/Shutterstock; (Bottom) © iStock/Thinkstock

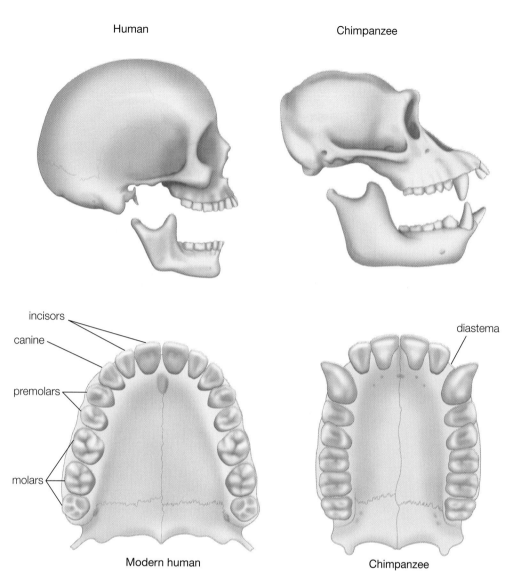

Human

Chimpanzee

incisors

canine

premolars

molars

diastema

Modern human

Chimpanzee

FIGURE A.4 Human and Chimpanzee Dentition

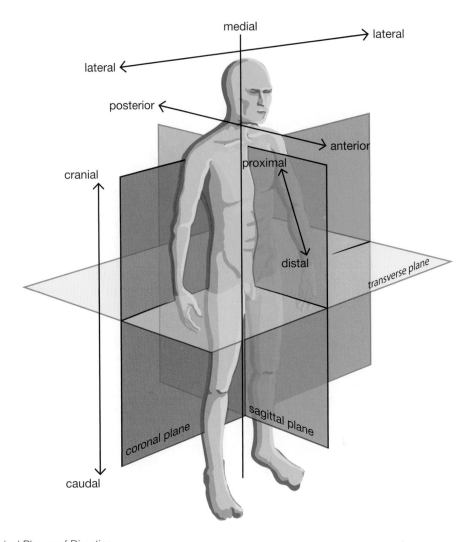

FIGURE A.5 Anatomical Planes of Direction

Appendix B: The Hardy-Weinberg Equilibrium Principle

In Chapter 4, we introduced the concept of the Hardy-Weinberg (H-W) Equilibrium, a theorem within population genetics stipulating conditions under which the frequency of a given allele does not change (i.e., evolution is not occurring). These conditions (see Table 4.1) include an infinitely large population size, random mating, and the absence of mutation, natural selection, and migration (i.e., gene flow). If one or more of these conditions is not met, allele frequencies in the population will change and indicate that (micro) evolution is occurring, as far as that gene is concerned.

The mathematical formulation of H-W Equilibrium allows us to predict allele frequencies from one generation to the next, after each mating. We begin with the understanding that no matter how many alleles exist for a given gene, the sum of their frequencies in a population must add up to 1, accounting for 100% of variation for that gene. This is most easily illustrated for the case of a single gene, two-allele system (but can be calculated for more complex scenarios).

A familiar example would be the gene for seed colour in Gregor Mendel's pea plants: yellow (Y) and green (y), with the yellow allele dominant over green (as explained in Chapter 3). Using a Punnett square (Figure B.1), we can specify the following genotypes: YY, Yy, and yy from a heterozygote (Yy with Yy) mating (both parents carry one copy of each allele). The relative proportions of these three genotypes in our population of pea plants are determined by the mathematical formula $p^2 + 2pq + q^2 = 1$, with p denoting the frequency of the dominant Y allele, and q the frequency of the recessive y allele.[1] Let's say that 60% of all alleles for seed colour are Y, giving a frequency of 0.6; y must therefore be 0.4 (40%), since in this example it is the only other form of the gene, and the total must equal 1. The genotype frequencies would thus be $0.6^2 + 2(0.6)(0.4) + 0.4^2$, or 0.36 YY, 0.48 Yy, and 0.16 yy, and according to the H-W Equilibrium theorem, would remain as such as long as the conditions noted above remained true. When you are thinking about H-W Equilibrium, remember that in this example, each genotype consists of two alleles.

♀ \ ♂	Allele Y = p = 0.6	Allele y = q = 0.4
Allele Y = p = 0.6	Genotype YY = p^2= 0.36	Genotype Yy = pq = 0.24
Allele y = q = 0.4	Genotype Yy = pq = 0.24	Genotype yy = q^2= 0.16

FIGURE B.1 Hypothetical allele and genotype frequencies for the example of seed colour in Mendel's peas.

However, as we observed in Chapter 4, it is unlikely that all of the H-W conditions are met, and indeed one of the applications of the H-W model is to show that a population is not in equilibrium. This is achieved by comparing observed and expected genotype frequencies given estimates for allele frequencies. Let's explore a recent example. Paganotti and colleagues (2012) studied the distribution of a variant allele of a gene called *CYP2C8*2* in three geographically isolated African populations: Senegal, Uganda, and Madagascar (Figure B.2).

This genetic variant reduces the effectiveness of drugs used to control malarial infection; individuals with this form of the gene suffer from greater parasite loads, and thus greater morbidity. While there are other variants of the *CYP2C8* gene, we will treat this example as a two-allele system and ignore the question of dominance (thus, all of our alleles use capital letters). The normal (called wild-type) allele is designated A, and the *CYP2C8*2* variant is labelled T. The frequency of the T allele is known to vary among populations (Table B.1), and for our example we can calculate the frequency of A as simply 1 – T.

Given these allele frequencies, we can calculate the *expected* proportions of the three genotypes AA, AT, and TT using the formula $p^2 + 2pq + q^2 = 1$ (Table B.2, top). However, when the researchers determined the actual genotypes from blood samples, the results were somewhat different (Table B.2, bottom).

1. If we were talking about a trait having three alleles, we would label the relative proportions as p, q, and r, and the formula would be expanded as $p^2 + 2pq + q^2 + 2pr + r^2 + 2qr = 1$. Note again that all proportions still sum to 1. It is also important to understand that it is the frequency of alleles that matters in this calculation, not the actual number of individuals in the population. Our garden might have 10 pea plants, or 200; the frequency of alleles must still sum to 1!

FIGURE B.2 Map of Africa showing location of study sites sampled by Paganotti et al. (2012).

TABLE B.1 Allele Frequency

Population	T (measured)	A (1 – T)
Senegal	0.222	0.778
Uganda	0.105	0.895
Madagascar	0.150	0.850

Statistically, Uganda and Madagascar were effectively in H-W Equilibrium (the frequencies were not significantly different); however, Senegal was not, having a greater than expected proportion of the AT

TABLE B.2 Expected and Actual Frequencies of the Three Genotypes AA, AT, and TT

Expected Genotype Frequencies (from H-W Formula)			
	AA	AT	TT
Senegal	0.605	0.345	0.049
Uganda	0.801	0.188	0.011
Madagascar	0.723	0.255	0.023

Observed Genotype Frequencies (from Blood Samples)			
	AA	AT	TT
Senegal	0.557	0.443	0
Uganda	0.797	0.199	0.004
Madagascar	0.739	0.222	0.039

genotype (0.443 vs. 0.345). The authors note that this outcome could be a result of having a small sample of individuals from Senegal, but it might also derive from evolutionary forces such as nonrandom mating or migration from neighbouring countries—the allele frequency of the T variant is known to be higher in western Africa than in eastern Africa.

Selected Bibliography

This selected bibliography, with the exception of a few of the most important "classic" works, cites only recent (2004+) sources consulted in the writing of this text. The full bibliography is on the text's CourseMate site (accessible through NELSONbrain.com).

Abzhanov, A, Protas, M, Grant, BR, et al. 2004. *Bmp4* and morphological variation of beaks in Darwin's finches. *Science* 305: 1462–1465.

Achilli, A, Perego, UA, Lancioni, H, et al. 2013. Reconciling migration models to the Americas with the variation of North American native mitogenomes. *Proceedings of the National Academy of Sciences* 110: 14308–14313.

Adelson, N. 2005. The embodiment of inequity. Health disparities in Aboriginal Canada. *Canadian Journal of Public Health* 96(2): S45–S61.

Agarwal, SC, and Stout, SD. 2003. *Bone Loss and Osteoporosis: An Anthropological Perspective*. Berlin: Springer.

Agoramoothy, G. 2012. Primate conservation research crucial for Asia. *Journal of Primatology* http://dx.doi.org/10.4172/jpmt.1000e103

Albanese, J, Eklics, G, and Tuck, A. 2008. A metric method for sex determination using the proximal femur and fragmentary hipbone. *Journal of Forensic Sciences* 53: 1283–1288.

Alemseged, A. 2013. *Australopithecus* in Ethiopia. In KE Reed, JG Fleagle, and RF Leakey, eds., *The Paleobiology of Australopithecus*. 2013. Springer Dordrecht. 63–71.

Alemseged, Z, Spoor, F, Kimbel, WH, et al. 2006. A juvenile early hominin skeleton from Dikka, Ethiopia. *Nature* 443: 296–301.

Ali, F, and Meier, R. 2008. Positive selection in ASPM is correlated with cerebral cortex evolution across primates but not with whole-brain size. *Molecular Biology and Evolution* 25: 2247–2250.

Amaral, LA. 2008. Mechanical analysis of infant carrying in hominoids. *Naturwissenschaften* 95: 281–292.

Anderson, DP, Nordheim, EV, and Boesch, C. 2006. Environmental factors influencing the seasonality of estrus in chimpanzees. *Primates* 47: 43–50.

Andrews, L. 2008. Book review: Reprogenetics: Law, Policy and Ethical Issues. *New England Journal of Medicine* 358: 204–205.

Andrews, P. 2007. The biogeography of hominid evolution. *Journal of Biogeography* 34: 381–382.

Anestis, SF. 2010. Hormones and social behavior in primates. *Evolutionary Anthropology* 19: 66–78.

Anholt, RRH, and Mackay, TFC. 2012. Genetics of aggression. *Annual Review of Genetics* 46: 145–164.

Antón, SC. 2012. Early *Homo*: Who, when, and where. *Current Anthropology* 53(6): S278–S298.

Antón, SC, Spoor, F, Fellmann, C, and Swisher CC III. 2007. Defining *Homo erectus*: Size considered. In W Henke and I Tattersall, eds., *Handbook of Paleoanthropology*. Berlin: Springer. 1655–1693.

Anway, MD, Cupp, AS, Uzumcu, M, et al. 2005. Epigenetic transgenerational actions of endocrine disruptors and male fertility. *Science* 308: 1466–1469.

Argue, D, Donlon, D, Groves, C, et al. 2006. *Homo floresiensis*: Microcephalic, pygmoid, *Australopithecus*, or *Homo*? *Journal of Human Evolution* 51: 360–374.

Austin, C, Smith, TM, Bradman, A, et al. 2013. Barium distributions in teeth reveal early-life dietary transitions in primates. *Nature* 498: 216–219.

Avery, J. 2005. Malthus' Essay on the Principle of Population. http://www.learndev.org/dl/MalthusEssay-Avery.pdf. Accessed January 17, 2009.

Bajpai, S, Kay, RF, Williams, BA, et al. 2008. The oldest Asian record of Anthropoidea. Proceedings of the National Academy of Sciences 105(32): 11093–11098.

Balter, M. 2005. Are humans still evolving? *Science* 309: 234–237.

Bamshad, M, Wooding, S, Salisbury, BA, et al. 2004. Deconstructing the relationship between genetics and race. *Nature Reviews Genetics* 8: 598–609.

Barker, DJ. 2012. The developmental origins of chronic disease. In NS Landale et al., eds., *Families and Child Health. National Symposium on Family Issues*. 3–11.

Barker, G, Barton, H, Bird, M, et al. 2007. The "human revolution" in lowland tropical Southeast Asia: The antiquity and behaviour of anatomically modern humans at Niah Cave (Sarawak, Borneo). *Journal of Human Evolution* 52: 243–261.

Barr, SI. 2013. Perceived lactose intolerance in adult Canadians: A national survey. Applied Physiology, Nutrition, and Metabolism 38: 830–835.

Barreiro, LB, Guillaume, L, Quach, H, et al. 2008. Natural selection has driven population differentiation in modern humans. Nature Genetics 40: 340–345.

Bartel, DP. 2004. MicroRNAs: Genomics, biogenesis, mechanism, and function. Cell 116: 281–297. Bartel, DP. 2009. MicroRNAs: Target recognition and regulatory functions. Cell 136: 215–233.

Baruch, S, Kaufman, DJ, and Hudson, K. 2008. Genetic testing of embryos: Practices and perspectives of US IVF Clinics. Fertility and Sterility 89: 1053–1058.

Bar-Yosef Mayer, DE, Vandermeersch, B, Bar-Yosef, O. 2009. Shells and ochre in Middle Paleolithic Qafzeh Cave, Israel: Indications for modern behavior. *Journal of Human Evolution* 56: 307–314.

Bastiaens, M, ter Huurne, J, Gruis, N, et al. 2001. The melanocortin-1-receptor gene is the major freckle gene. *Human Molecular Genetics* 10: 1701–1708.

Bathurst, RR 2005. Archaeological evidence of intestinal parasites from coastal shell middens. *Journal of Archaeological Science* 321: 115–123.

Beall, CM. 2006. Andean, Tibetan, and Ethiopian patterns of adaptation to high-altitude hypoxia. *Integrative and Comparative Biology* 46:18–24.

Beall, CM. 2007. Two routes to functional adaptation: Tibetan and Andean high-altitude natives. *Proceedings of the National Academy of Sciences* 104(1): 8655–8660.

Beard, KC. 2004. *The Hunt for the Dawn Monkey: Unearthing the Origins of Monkeys, Apes, and Humans.* Berkeley: University of California Press. Beard, KC, Marivaux, L, Tun, ST, et al. 2007. New Sivaladapid primates from the Eocene Pondaung Formation of Myanmar and the anthropoid status of Amphipithecidae. *Bulletin of the Carnegie Museum of Natural History* 39: 67–76.

Beattie, O, and Geiger, J. 2004. *Frozen in Time.* Vancouver: Douglas and McIntyre.

Beattie, O, Apland, B, Blake, EW, et al. 2000. The Kwäday Dän Ts'ínchi discovery from a glacier in British Columbia. *Canadian Journal of Archaeology* 24: 129–147.

Beauval, C, Maureille, B, Lacrampe-Cuyaubere, F, et al. 2005. A late Neandertal femur from Les Rochers-de-Villeneuve, France. *Proceedings of the National Academy of Sciences* 102: 7085–7090.

Becquet, C, Patterson, N, Stone, AC, et al. 2007. Genetic structure of chimpanzee populations. *Public Library of Science. Genetics* 3: e66.

Begun, DR. 1992. Miocene fossil hominids and the chimp–human clade. *Science* 257: 1929–1933.

Begun, DR. 2002. European Hominoids. In W Hartwig, ed., *The Primate Fossil Record.* Cambridge: Cambridge University Press. 339–368.

Begun, DR. 2004a. The three "Cs" of behavioral reconstruction in fossil primates. *Journal of Human Evolution* 46: 497–505.

Begun, DR. 2004b. The earliest hominins—Is less more? *Science* 303: 1478–1480.

Begun, DR. 2004c. Knuckle-walking and the origin of human bipedalism. In DJ Meldrum and CE Hilton, eds., *From Biped to Strider: The Emergence of Modern Human Walking, Running, and Resource Transport.* New York: Kluwer Academic. 9–34.

Begun, DR. 2005. *Sivapithecus* is east and *Dryopithecus* is west, and never the twain shall meet. *Anthropological Science* 113: 53–64.

Begun, DR. 2007a. Fossil record of Miocene hominoids. In W Henke and I Tattersall, eds., *Handbook of Palaeoanthropology.* Berlin: Springer. 921–977.

Begun, DR. 2007b. How to identify (as opposed to define) a homoplasy: Examples from fossil and living great apes. *Journal of Human Evolution* 52: 559–572.

Begun, DR. 2010a. Catarrhine cousins: The origin and evolution of monkeys and apes of the Old World. In CS Larsen, ed., *A Companion to Biological Anthropology.* Chichester: Wiley-Blackwell. 295–313.

Begun, DR. 2010b. Miocene hominids and the origins of the African apes and humans. *Annual Review of Anthropology* 39: 67–84.

Begun, DR. 2013. The past, present and future of paleoanthropology. In D Begun, ed., *A Companion to Paleoanthropology.* Oxford: Blackwell Publishing. 10.1002/9781118332344.ch1.

Begun, DR, ed. 2013. *A Companion to Paleoanthropology.* Oxford: Blackwell Publishing.

Begun, DR, and Kivell, TL. 2011. Knuckle-walking in *Sivapithecus*? The combined effects of homology and homoplasy with possible implications for pongine dispersals. *Journal of Human Evolution* 60: 158–170.

Begun, DR, Nargolwalla, MC, and Kordos, L. 2012. European Miocene hominids and the origin of the African ape and human clade. *Evolutionary Anthropology* 21: 10–21.

Begun, DR, Richmond, BG, and Strait, DS. 2007. Comment on "Origin of human bipedalism as an adaptation for locomotion on flexible branches." *Science* 318: 1066d–1067d.

Behie, AM, and Pavelka, MSM. 2005. The short-term effects of a hurricane on the diet and activity of black howlers (*Alouatta pigra*) in Monkey River, Belize. *Folia Primatologica* 761: 1–9.

Behrensmeyer, A, and Reed, K. 2013. Reconstructing the habitats of *Australopithecus*: Paleoenvironments, site taphonomy and faunas. In KE Reed, JG Fleagle, and RF Leakey, eds., *The Paleobiology of Australopithecus.* 2013. Springer Dordrecht. 41–60.

Benazzi, S, Douka, K, Fornai, C, et al. 2011. Early dispersal of modern humans in Europe and implications for Neanderthal behaviour. *Nature* 479: 525–528.

Bennett, MR, Harris, JWK, Richmond, BG, et al. 2009. Early hominin foot morphology based on 1.5-million-year-old footprints from Ileret, Kenya. *Science* 323: 1197–1201.

Berge, C, Penin, X, and Pellé, É. 2006. New interpretation of Laetoli footprints using an experimental approach and Procrustes analysis: Preliminary results. *Comptes Rendus Palevolution* 5: 561–569.

Berger, L. 2013. The mosaic nature of *Australopithecus sediba.* *Science* 340: 163–165.

Bergman, TJ, Phillips-Conroy, JE and Jolly, CJ. 2008. Behavioral variation and reproductive success of male baboons (Papio anubis x Papio hamadryas) in a hybrid social group. *American Journal of Primatology* 70: 136–147.

Bermejo, M, Rodríguez-Teijeiro, JD, Illera, G, et al. 2006. Ebola outbreak killed 5000 gorillas. *Science* 314: 1564.

Bermúdez de Castro, JM, Martinón-Torres, M, Carbonell, E, et al. 2004. The Atapuerca sites and their contribution to the knowledge of human evolution in Europe. *Evolutionary Anthropology* 131: 25–41.

Berna, F, Goldberg, P, Horwitz, LK, et al. 2012. Microstratigraphic evidence of in situ fire in the Acheulean strata of Wonderwerk Cave, Northern Cape province, South Africa. *Proceedings of the National Academy of Sciences* 109(2): E1215–E1220.

Bhopal, R. 2007. The beautiful skull and Blumenbach's errors. *British Medical Journal* 335: 1308–1309.

Bienvenu, T, Falk, D, Semendeferi, K, et al. 2013. Virtual reconstruction of the endocast of Sahelanthropus tchadensis. *Abstract of the Paleoanthropology Society Meetings*, Honolulu, April 2–3, 2013.

Black, D. 1931a. Evidences of the use of fire by *Sinanthropus*. *Bulletin of the Geological Society of China* 11: 107.

Black, D. 1931b. On an adolescent skull of Sinanthropus pekinensis in comparison with an adult skull of the same species and with other hominid skulls, recent and fossil. *Palaeontologica Sinica Series D* 7: 1–114.

Bloch, JI, and Silcox, MT. 2006. Cranial anatomy of the Paleocene plesiadapiform *Carpolestes simpsoni* (Mammalia, Primates) using ultra high-resolution X-ray computed tomography, and the relationships of plesiadapiforms to Euprimates. *Journal of Human Evolution* 50(1): 1–35.

Bloch, JI, Silcox, MT, Boyer, DM, et al. 2007. New Paleocene skeletons and the relationship of plesiadapiforms to crown-clade primates. *Proceedings of the National Academy of Sciences* 104(4): 1159–1164.

Bloche, MG. 2004. Race-based therapeutics. *New England Journal of Medicine* 351: 2035–2037.

Blumenbach, JF. 1795 (1820). *Decas prima [-sexta] collectionis suae craniorum diversarum gentium illustrate*. Ottingae : Apud Henricum Dieterich. Reproduction published by Nabu Press (http://nabupress.com), January 25, 2012.

Boback, SM, Cox, CL, Ott , BD, et al. 2007. Cooking and grinding reduces the cost of meat digestion. Comparative Biochemistry and Physiology, Part A 148: 651–656.

Bobe, R, and Behrensmeyer, A. 2004. The expansion of grassland ecosystems in Africa in relation to mammalian evolution and the origin of the genus Homo. Palaeogeography, Palaeoclimatology, Palaeoecology 207: 399–420.

Bocherens, H, Drucker, DG, Billiou, D, et al. 2005. Isotopic evidence for diet and subsistence pattern of the Saint-Césaire I Neanderthal: Review and use of a multi-source mixing model. *Journal of Human Evolution* 49: 71–87.

Bocklandt, S, Horvath, S, Vilain, E, et al. 2006. Extreme skewing of X chromosome inactivation in mothers of homosexual men. *Human Genetics* 118: 691–694.

Boesch, C, Head, J, Robbins, MM. 2009. Complex tool sets for honey extraction among chimpanzees in Loango National Park, Gabon. *Journal of Human Evolution* 56: 560–569.

Bogart, SL, and Pruetz, JD. 2011. Insectivory of savanna chimpanzees (*Pan troglodytes verus*) at Fongoli, Senegal. *American Journal of Physical Anthropology* 145(1): 11–20.

Bokma, F, van den Brink, V, and Stadler, T. 2012. Unexpectedly many extinct hominins. *Evolution* 66: 2969–2974.

Bonduriansky, R. 2012. Rethinking heredity, again. *Trends in Ecology and Evolution* 27: 330–336.

Bos, KI, Schuenemann, VJ, Golding, GB, et al. 2011. A draft genome of *Yersinia pestis* from victims of the Black Death. *Nature* 478: 506–510.

Boswell, R. 2006 (April 6). "Intelligent design" debate evolves into funding fracas. *CanWest News Service*.

Boubli, JP, da Silva, MNF, Amado, MV, et al. 2008. A taxonomic reassessment of *Cacajao melanocephalus* Humboldt (1811), with the description of two new species. *International Journal of Primatology* 29: 723–741.

Bourbou, C, Fuller, BT, Garvie-Lok, SJ, et al. 2013. Nursing mothers and feeding bottles: Reconstructing breastfeeding and weaning patterns in Greek Byzantine populations (6th–15th centuries AD) using carbon and nitrogen stable isotope ratios. *Journal of Archaeological Science* 40: 3903–3913.

Bouzouggar, A, Barton, N, Vanhaeren, M, et al. 2007. 82,000-year-old shell beads from North Africa and implications for the origins of modern human behavior. *Proceedings of the National Academy of Sciences* 104(24): 9964–9969.

Bowler, JM, Johnston, H, Olley, JM, et al. 2003. New ages for human occupation and climatic change at Lake Mungo, Australia. *Nature* 421: 837–840.

Boyd, B. 2006. Getting it all wrong: Bioculture critiques cultural critique. *American Scholar* 75: 18–30.

Bramble, DM, and Lieberman, DE. 2004. Endurance running and the evolution of *Homo*. *Nature* 432: 345–352.

Breuer, T, Ndoundou-Hockemba, M, and Fishlock, V. 2005. First observation of tool use in wild gorillas. *Public Library of Science Biology* 311: e380.

Briggs, AW, Good, JM, Green, RE, et al. 2009. Targeted retrieval and analysis of five Neanderthal mtDNA genomes. *Science* 325: 318–321.

Brown, KS, Marean, CW, Jacobs, Z, et al. 2012. An early and enduring advanced technology originating 71,000 years ago in South Africa. *Nature* 491: 590–594.

Brown, P. 2012. LB1 and LB6 *Homo floresiensis* are not modern human (*Homo sapiens*) cretins. *Journal of Human Evolution* 62: 201–224.

Brown, P, Sutikna, T, Morwood, MJ, et al. 2004. A small-bodied hominin from the Late Pleistocene of Flores, Indonesia. *Nature* 431: 1055–1061.

Browner, WS, Kahn, AJ, Ziv, E, et al. 2004. The genetics of human longevity. *American Journal of Medicine* 117: 851–860.

Brumm, A, Jensen, GM, van den Bergh, GD, Morwood, MJ, Kurniawan, I, Aziz, F, and Storey, M. 2010. Hominins on Flores, Indonesia, by one million years ago. *Nature* 464: 748–753.

Brunet, M, Guy, F, Pilbeam, D, et al. 2005. New material of the earliest hominid from the Upper Miocene of Chad. *Nature* 434: 752–755.

Bryant, VM, and Dean, GW. 2006. Archaeological coprolite science: The legacy of Eric O. Callen (1912–1970). *Palaeogeography, Palaeoclimatology, Palaeoecology* 237: 51–66.

Bunn, JM, Boyer, DM, Lipman, Y, et al. 2011. Comparing Dirichlet Normal Surface Energy of tooth crowns, a new technique of molar shape quantification for dietary inference, with previous methods in isolation and in combination. *American Journal of Physical Anthropology* 145: 247–261.

Burger, J, Kirchner, M, Bramanti, B, et al. 2007. Absence of the lactase-persistence-associated allele in early Neolithic Europeans. *Proceedings of the National Academy of Sciences* 104: 3736–3741.

Burke, SDS. 2011. Tuberculosis: Past and Present. *Reviews in Anthropology* 40.

Byers, SN. 2007. *Introduction to Forensic Anthropology*, 3rd ed. Boston: Allyn and Bacon.

Byrne, JA, Pedersen, D, Clepper, L, et al. 2007. Producing primate embryonic stem cells by somatic cell nuclear transfer. *Nature* 450: 497–502.

Cachel, S. 2006. *Primate and Human Evolution*. Cambridge: Cambridge University Press.

Cahill, AE, Aiello-Lammens, ME, Fiksher-Reid, MC, et al. 2012. How does climate change cause extinction? *Proceedings of the Royal Society B Biological Sciences* published online doi:10.1098/rspb.2012.1890.

Caillaud, D, Levréro, F, Cristescu, R, et al. 2006. Gorilla susceptibility to Ebola virus: the cost of sociality. *Current Biology* 1613: R489–R491.

Caine, NG, Osorio, D, and Mundy, NI. 2010. A foraging advantage for dichromatic marmosets (*Callithrix geoffroyi*) at low light intensity. *Biology Letters* 6: 36–38.Cannon, DS, Baker, TB, Piper, ME, et al. 2005. Associations between phenylthiocarbamide gene polymorphisms and cigarette smoking. *Nicotine and Tobacco Research* 7: 853–858.

Caramelli, D, Lalueza-Fox, C, Condemi, S, et al. 2006. A highly divergent mtDNA sequence in a Neandertal individual from Italy. *Current Biology* 1616: R630–R632.

Carbonell, E, Bermúdez de Castro, JM, Parés, JM, et al. 2008. The first hominin of Europe. *Nature* 452: 465–470.

Carlson, RJ. 2005 (October 11). The case of BiDil: A policy commentary on race and genetics. *Health Affairs*.

Carmody, RN, Weintraub, GS, and Wrangham, RW. 2011. Energetic consequences of thermal and nonthermal food processing. *Proceedings of the National Academy of Sciences* 108: 19199–19203.

Caron, F, d'Errico, F, Del Moral, P, Santos, F, and Zilhão, J. 2011. The reality of Neandertal symbolic behavior at the Grotte du Renne, Arcy-sur-Cure, France. *PLOS ONE* 6(6): e21545.

Carpenter, ML, Buenrostro, JD, Valdiosera, C, et al. 2013. Pulling out the 1%: Whole-genome capture for the targeted enrichment of ancient DNA sequencing libraries. *American Journal of Human Genetics* 93: 1–13.

Cäsar, C, Byrne, RW, Hoppitt, W, et al. 2012. Evidence for semantic communication in titi monkey alarm calls. *Animal Behaviour* 84: 405–411.

CCR. 2009. Canadian Council for Refugees. http://www.ccrweb.ca/history.html. Accessed January 4, 2009.

Cerling, TE, Wynn, JG, Andanje, SA, et al. 2011. Woody cover and hominin environments in the past 6 million years. *Nature* 476: 51–56.

Changizi, MA, Zhang, Q, and Shimojo, S. 2006. Bare skin, blood, and the evolution of primate colour vision. *Biology Letters* 22: 217–221.

Chapais, B. 1995. Alliances as a means of competition in primates: Evolutionary, developmental, and cognitive aspects. *Yearbook of Physical Anthropology* 38: 115–136.

Chapais, B. 2011. The evolutionary history of pair-bonding and parental collaboration. *The Oxford Handbook of Evolutionary Family Psychology.* New York: Oxford University Press. 33–50.

Chapman, CA, and Pavelka, MSM. 2005. Group size in folivorous primates: Ecological constraints and the possible influence of social factors. *Primates* 46: 1–9.

Chapman, CA, and Peres, CA. 2001. Primate conservation in the new millennium: The role of scientists. *Evolutionary Anthropology* 10: 16–33.

Chapman, CA, Balcomb, SR, Gillespie, TR, et al. 2000. Long-term effects of logging on African primate communities: A 28-year comparison from Kibale National Park, Uganda. *Conservation Biology* 141: 207–217.

Chimpanzee Sequencing and Analysis Consortium. 2005. Initial sequence of the chimpanzee genome and comparison with the human genome. *Nature* 437: 69–87.

Chiu, C-h, and Wildman, DE. 2011. Morris Goodman (1925–2010): Founder of the field of molecular anthropology. *Evolutionary Anthropology* 20: 1–2.

Churchill, S. 2008. Bioenergetic perspectives on Neanderthal thermoregulatory and activity budgets. In K Harvati and T Harrison, eds., *Neanderthals Revisited: New Approaches and Perspectives.* Netherlands: Springer. 113–133.

Citizenship and Immigration Canada. 2011. *Canada Facts and Figures, Immigration Overview, Permanent and Temporary Residents 2010.* Minister of Public Works and Government Services Canada.

Clay, Z, and Zuberbühler, K. 2011. The structure of bonobo copulation calls during reproductive and non-reproductive sex. *Ethology* 117: 1158–1169.

Clement, AF, Hillson, SW, and Aiello, LC. 2012. Tooth wear, Neanderthal facial morphology and the anterior dental loading hypothesis. *Journal of Human Evolution* 62(3): 367–376.

Closser, S. 2012. "We can't give up now": Global health optimism and polio eradication in Pakistan. *Medical Anthropology* 31: 385–403.

Cobb, SN. 2008. The facial skeleton of the chimpanzee–human last common ancestor. *Journal of Anatomy* 212: 469–485.

Collins, FS. 2004. What we do and don't know about "race," "ethnicity," genetics, and health at the dawn of the genome era. *Nature Genetics Supplement* 36: S13–S15.

Colquhoun, I. 2006. Predation and cathemerality: Comparing the impact of predators on the activity patterns of lemurids and ceboids. *Folia Primatologica* 77: 143–165.

Conroy, GC. 2005. *Reconstructing Human Origins,* 2nd ed. New York: Norton.

Cordain, L, Eaton, SB, Sebastian, A, et al. 2005. Origins and evolution of the Western diet: Health implications for the 21st century. *American Journal of Clinical Nutrition* 81: 341–354.

Cormack, J. 2000. The scientific influence that Dr. Davidson Black (Bu Dasheng) had on Chinese prehistory. In Conference Proceedings: International Symposium on Paleoanthropology. *Acta Anthropologica Sinica Supplement* 19: 292–298.

Cormack, J. 2003. Davidson Black and his role in Chinese palaeo-anthropology. In C Shen and SG Keates, eds., *Current Research in Chinese Pleistocene Archaeology,* B.A.R. International Series #1179, Oxford. 9–19.

Corr, LT, Richards, MP, Jim, S, et al. 2008. Probing dietary change of the Kwäday Dän Ts'ìnchì individual, an ancient glacier body from British Columbia: I. Complementary use of marine lipid biomarker and carbon isotope signatures as novel indicators of a marine diet. *Journal of Archaeological Science* 35: 2102–2110.

Corsi, P. 2005. Before Darwin: Transformist concepts in European natural history. *Journal of the History of Biology* 38: 67–83.

Crevecoeur, I, Bayle, P, Rougier, H, et al. 2010. The Spy IV child: a newly discovered Neandertal infant. *Journal of Human Evolution* 59(6): 641–656.

Crevecoeur, I, Skinner, MM, Bailey, SE, et al. 2014. First early hominin from Centgreal Africa (Ishango, Democratic Republic of Congo). *PLOS One* 9(1): e84652. doi:10.1371/journal.pone.0084652.

Crews, DE. 2004. *Human Senescence: Evolutionary and Biocultural Perspectives.* Cambridge: Cambridge University Press.

Crompton, R, Pataky, TC, Savage, R, et al. 2012. Human-like external function of the foot, and fully upright gait, confirmed in the 3.66 million year old Laetoli hominin footprints by topographic statistics, experimental footprint-formation and computer simulation. *Journal of the Royal Society Interface* 9: 707–719.

Crompton, RH, Vereecke, E, and Thorpe, S. 2008. Locomotion and posture from the common hominoid ancestor to fully modern humans, with special reference to the last common panin/hominin ancestor. *Journal of Anatomy* 212: 501–543.

Cross, A, and Collard, M. 2011. Estimating surface area in early hominins. *PLOS ONE* 6(1): e16107.

Cross, A, Collard, M, and Nelson, A. 2008. Body segment differences in surface area, skin temperatures, and 3D displacement and the estimation of heat balance during locomotion in hominins. *Public Library of Science ONE* 3: e2464.

Crowley, BE. 2012. Stable isotope techniques and applications for primatologists. *International Journal of Primatology* 33: 673–701.

Cui, Y, Lindo, J, Hughes, CE, et al. 2013. Ancient DNA analysis of Mid-Holocene individuals from the northwest coast of North America reveals different evolutionary paths for mitogenomes. *PLOS ONE* 8(7): e66948.

Currat, M, and Excoffier, L. 2011. Strong reproductive isolation between humans and Neanderthals inferred from observed patterns of introgression. *Proceedings of the National Academy of Sciences* 108(37): 15129–15134.

Cybulski, JS. 1976. Scientific aspects of archaeology in Canada: A physical anthropologist's view. In AG McKay, ed., *Symposium on New Perspectives in Canadian Archaeology*, October 22–23, 1976, Theatre Auditorium, Royal Ontario Museum, Toronto. Ottawa: Royal Society of Canada. 177–184.

Cybulski, JS. 1992. A Greenville burial ground: Human remains and mortuary elements in British Columbia coast prehistory. *Archaeological Survey of Canada*, Mercury Series #146. Hull: Canadian Museum of Civilization.

Cybulski, JS. 2007. *Bioarchaeology, ethics, cooperation, collaboration.* Paper presented at the 35th Annual Meeting of the Canadian Association for Physical Anthropology, Banff, Alberta, November 15–17.

Cybulski, JS, Howes, DE, Haggarty, JC, et al. 1981. An early human skeleton from south-central British Columbia: Dating and bioarchaeological inference. *Canadian Journal of Archaeology* 5: 49.

Cybulski, JS, McMillan, AD, Malhi, RS, et al. 2007. The Big Bar Lake burial: Middle period human remains from the Canadian plateau. *Canadian Journal of Archaeology* 31: 55–79.

Cybulski, JS, Ossenberg, NS, and Wade, WD. 1979. Committee report: Statement of the excavation, treatment, analysis, and disposition of human skeletal remains from archaeological sites in Canada. *Canadian Review of Physical Anthropology* 1: 32–36.

Dausmann, KH, Glos, J, Ganzhorn, JU, et al. 2005. Hibernation in the tropics: Lessons from a primate. *Journal of Comparative Physiology B: Biochemical, Systemic, and Environmental Physiology* 175: 147–155.

Dawodu, B, and Wagner, CL. 2007. Mother–child vitamin D deficiency: An international perspective. *Archives of Diseases of Childhood* 92: 737–740.

Daxinger, L, and Whitelaw, E. 2012. Understanding transgenerational epigenetic inheritance via the gametes in mammals. *Nature Reviews: Genetics* 13: 153–162.

De Boo, HA, and Harding, J. 2006. The developmental origins of adult disease (Barker) hypothesis. *Australian and New Zealand Journal of Obstetrics and Gynaecology* 46: 4–14.

Delezene, LK, Zolnierz, MS, Teaford, MF, et al. 2013. Premolar microwear and tooth use in *Australopithecus afarensis*. *Journal of Human Evolution* http://dx.doi.org/10.1016/j.jhevol.2013.06.001.

Delmore, K, Louis, EE Jr, and Johnson, S. 2010. Morphological characterization of a brown lemur hybgrid zone (*Eulemur rufifrons x E. cinereiceps*). *American Journal of Physical Anthropology* 145: 55–66.

Demeter, F, Shackelford, LL, Bacon, A-M, et al. 2012. Anatomically modern human in Southeast Asia (Laos) by 46 ka. *Proceedings of the National Academy of Sciences* 109(36): 14375–14380.

DeSilva, JM, and Gill, SV. 2013. Brief Communication: A midtarsal (midfoot) break in the human foot. *American Journal of Physical Anthropology* 151: 495–499.

DeSilva. JM, Holt, KG, Churchill, SE, et al. 2013. The lower limb and mechanics of walking in *Australopithecus sediba*. *Science* 340. doi:10.1126/science.1232999.

Dickson, JH, Richards, MP, Hebda, RJ, et al. 2004. Kwäday Dän Ts'ìnchì, the first ancient body of a man from a North American glacier: reconstructing his last days by intestinal and biomolecular analyses. *The Holocene* 14: 481–486.

Dirkmaat, DC, Cabo, LL, Ousley, SD, et al. 2008. New perspectives in forensic anthropology. *Yearbook of Physical Anthropology* 51: 33–52.

Dolphin, AE, and Goodman, AH. 2009. Maternal diets, nutritional status, and zinc in contemporary Mexican infants' teeth: Implications for reconstructing paleodiets. *American Journal of Physical Anthropology* 140(3): 399–409.

Dolphin, AE, Goodman, AH, and Amarasiriwardena, DD. 2005. Variation in elemental intensities among teeth and between pre- and postnatal regions of enamel. *American Journal of Physical Anthropology* 128: 878–888.

Dolphin, AE, Naftel, SJ, Nelson, AJ, et al. 2013. Bromine in teeth and bone as an indicator of marine diet. *Journal of Archaeological Science* 40: 1778–1786.

Dominy, NJ. 2004. Fruits, fingers, and fermentation: The sensory cues available to foraging primates. *Integrative and Comparative Biology* 44: 295–303.

Donoghue, HD, Marcsik, A, Matheson, C, et al. 2005. Co-infection of Mycobacterium tuberculosis and Mycobacterium leprae in human archaeological samples: A possible explanation for the historical decline of leprosy. *Proceedings of the Royal Society of London B* 272: 389–394.

Dunbar, JS, and Hemmings, CA. 2004. Florida Paleoindian points and knives. In BT Lepper and R Bonnichsen, eds., *New Perspectives on the First Americans*. College Station: Texas A&M University Press. 65–72.

Dunbar, RIM. 2012. Bridging the bonding gap: The transition from primates to humans. *Philosophical Transactions of the Royal Society B. Biological Sciences* 367: 1837–1846.

Dupras, T, and Tocheri, M. 2007. Reconstructing infant weaning histories at Roman period Kellis, Egypt, using stable isotope analysis of dentition. *American Journal of Physical Anthropology* 134: 63–74.

Dupras, T.L., and Schwarcz, H.P. 2001. Strangers in a strange land: stable isotope evidence for human migration in the Dakhleh Oasis, Egypt. *Journal of Archaeological Science* 28(11): 1199–1208.

Dupras, T, Schultz, JJ, Wheeler, SA, et al. 2006. *Forensic Recovery of Human Remains: Archaeological Approaches*. Boca Raton: CRC.

Dupras, T, Schwarcz, HP, and Fairgrieve, SI. 2001. Infant feeding and weaning practices in Roman Egypt. *American Journal of Physical Anthropology* 115: 204–212.

Ehounoux, NZ, Zunzunegui, M-V, Séguin, L, et al. 2009. Duration of lack of money for basic needs and growth delay in the Quebec Longitudinal Study of Child Development birth cohort. *Journal of Epidemiology and Community Health* 63: 45–49.

Ehrlich, PR, Kareiva, PM, and Daily, G. 2012. Securing natural capital and expanding equity to rescale civilization. *Nature* 486: 68–73.

Elton, S. 2008. The environmental context of human evolutionary history in Eurasia and Africa. *Journal of Anatomy* 212: 377–393.

Endicott, P, Ho, SYW, Metspalu, M, and Stringer, C. 2009. Evaluating the mitochondrial timescale of human evolution. *Trends in Ecology and Evolution* 24(9): 515–521.

Engle, EC. 2007. Genetic basis of congenital strabismus. *Archives of Ophthalmology* 125: 189–195.

Erdal, YS. 2008. Occlusal grooves in anterior dentition among Kovuklukaya inhabitants (Sinop, northern Anatolia, 10th century AD). *International Journal of Osteoarchaeology* 18: 152–166.

Eriksson, J, Hohmann, G, Boesch, C, et al. 2004. Rivers influence the population genetic structure of bonobos (*Pan paniscus*). *Molecular Ecology* 13: 3425–3435.

Erlandson, JM, Rick, TC, Braje, TJ, et al. 2011. Paleoindian seafaring, maritime technologies, and coastal foraging on California's Channel Islands. *Science* 331: 1181–1185.

Evans, PD, Gilbert, SL, Mekel-Bobrov, N, et al. 2005. *Microcephalin*, a gene regulating brain size, continues to evolve adaptively in humans. *Science* 309: 1717–1720.

Evans, PD, Mekel-Bobrov, N, Vallender, EJ, et al. 2006. Evidence that the adaptive allele of the brain size gene *microcephalin* introgressed into *Homo sapiens* from an archaic *Homo* lineage. *Proceedings of the National Academy of Sciences* 103: 18178–18183.

Faccia, KJ, and Williams, RC. 2007. Schmorl's Nodes: Clinical significance and implications for the bioarchaeological record. *International Journal of Osteoarchaeology* 18: 28–44.

Fagundes, NJR, Kanitz, R, Eckert, R, et al. 2008. Mitochondrial population genomics supports a single pre-Clovis origin with a coastal route for the peopling of the Americas. *American Journal of Human Genetics* 82: 583–592.

Fairgrieve, S. 2007. *Forensic Cremations—Recovery and Analysis*. Boca Raton: CRC.

Falk, D. 2012. Hominin paleoneurology: Where are we now? In MA Hofman and D Falk, eds., *Progress in Brain Research Vol. 195 Evolution of the Primate Brain From Neuron to Behavior*. Amsterdam: Elsevier. 255–272.

Falk, D, Hildebolt, C, Smith, K, et al. 2005. The Brain of LB1, *Homo floresiensis*. *Science* 308: 242–245.

Falk, D, Zollikofer, C, Morimoto, N, et al. 2012. Metopic suture of Taung (*Australopithecus africanus*) and its implication for hominin brain evolution. *Proceedings of the National Academy of Sciences* 109: 8467–8470.

FAO (Food and Agriculture Organization of the United Nations). 2013. *The State of Food Insecurity in the World*.

Farah, MJ, Sherab, DM, Savagea, JH, et al. 2006. Childhood poverty: Specific associations with neurocognitive development. *Brain Research* 1110: 166–174.

Fedigan, LM, and Asquith, PJ, eds. 1991. *The Monkeys of Arashiyama: Thirty-five Years of Research in Japan and the West*. Albany: State University of New York Press.

Fedigan, LM, and Pavelka, MSM. 2001. Is there adaptive value to reproductive termination in Japanese macaques? A test of maternal investment hypotheses. *International Journal of Primatology* 22(2): 109–125.

Fedigan, LM, Carnegie, SD, and Jack, KM. 2008. Predictors of reproductive success in female white-faced capuchins (*Cebus capucinus*). *American Journal of Physical Anthropology* 137: 82–90.

Fedurek, P, and Slocombe, KE. 2011. Primate vocal communication: A useful tool for understanding human speech and language evolution? *Human Biology* 83: 153–173.

Finlayson, C, Pacheco, FG, Rodríguez-Videl, J, et al. 2006. Late survival of Neanderthals at the southernmost extreme of Europe. *Nature* 443: 850–853.

Finlayson, C, Brown, K, Blasco, R, et al. 2012. Birds of a feather: Neanderthal exploitation of raptors and corvids. *PLOS ONE* 7(9): e45927.

Firestone, RB, West, A, Kennett, JP, et al. 2007. Evidence for an extraterrestrial impact 12,900 years ago that contributed to the megafaunal extinctions and the Younger Dryas cooling. *Proceedings of the National Academy of Sciences* 104: 10616–10621.

Fischer, A, Prufer, K, Good, JM, et al. 2011. Bonobos fall within the genomic variation of chimpanzees. *PLOS One* 6: e21605. doi:10.1371/journal.pone.0021605.

Fitzgerald, C, Saunders, S, Bondioli, L, et al. 2006. Health of infants in an Imperial Roman skeletal sample: Perspective from dental microstructure. *American Journal of Physical Anthropology* 1302: 179–189.

Fleagle, JG, and Gilbert, CC. 2006. The biogeography of primate evolution: The role of plate tectonics, climate and chance. In SM Lehman and JG Fleagle, eds., *Primate Biogeography*, New York: Springer. 375–418.

Formicola, V, and Buzhilova, AP. 2004. Double child burial from Sunghir, Russia: Pathology and inferences for Upper Paleolithic funerary practices. *American Journal of Physical Anthropology* 124: 189–198.

Fragaszy, D, Izar, P, Visalberghi, E, et al. 2004. Wild capuchin monkeys (*Cebus libidinosus*) use anvils and stone pounding tools. *American Journal of Primatology* 64: 359–366.

Franzen, JL, Gingerich, PD, Habersetzer, J, et al. 2009. Complete primate skeleton from the middle Eocene of Messel in Germany: Morphology and paleobiology. *PLOS ONE* 4 (e5723): 1–27.

Frayling, TM, Timpson, NJ, Weedon, MN, et al. 2007. A common variant in the FTO gene is associated with body mass index and predisposes to childhood and adult obesity. *Science* 316: 889–894.

Frost, P. 2008. The spread of alphabetical writing may have favored the latest variant of the ASPM gene. *Medical Hypotheses* 70: 17–20.

Frost, P. 2011. Human nature or human natures? *Futures* 43: 740–748.

Frumkin, D, Wassertrom, A, Davidson, A, et al. 2009. Authentication of forensic DNA samples. *Forensic Science International: Genetics* 4(2): 95–103.

Fu, Q, Mittnik, M, Johnson, PLF, et al. 2013. A revised timescale for human evolution based on ancient mitochondrial genomes. *Current Biology* 23: 553–559. http://dx.doi.org/10.1016/j.cub.2013.02.044.

Fu, Q, Meyer, M, Gao, X, et al. 2013. DNA analysis of an early modern human from Tianyuan Cave, China. *Proceedings of the National Academy of Sciences* 110(6): 2223–2227.

Fuller, J. 2011. Darwinian medicine: The past and present state of medicine's unifying science. *University of Toronto Medical Journal* 88: 209–215.

Fürtbauer, I, Heistermann, M, Schülke, O, et al. 2011. Concealed fertility and extended female sexuality in a non-human primate (*Macaca assamensis*). *PLOS ONE* 6: e23105.

Galdikas, B. 1982. Orangutan tool-use at Tan Jung Reserve, Central Indonesian Borneo (Kalimantan Tengah). *Journal of Human Evolution* 11: 19–33.

Galdikas, BMF. 1995. *Reflections of Eden: My Years with the Orangutans of Borneo.* Boston: Little, Brown.

Galdikas, B, and Wood, JW. 1990. Birth spacing patterns in humans and apes. *American Journal of Physical Anthropology* 83: 185–191.

Galloway, T. 2006. Obesity rates among rural Ontario schoolchildren. *Canadian Journal of Public Health* 97: 353–356.

Galloway, T. 2007. Gender differences in growth and nutrition in a sample of rural Canadian schoolchildren. *American Journal of Human Biology* 19: 774–788.

Galloway, T, Kue Young, T, and Egeland, GM. 2010. Emerging obesity among preschool-aged Canadian Inuit children: Results from the Nunavut Inuit Child Health Survey. *International Journal of Circumpolar Health* 69: 151–157.

Galloway, T, Niclasen, BVL, Muckle, G, Young, K, and Egeland, GM. 2012. Growth measures among preschool-age Inuit children living in Canada and Greenland. *Scandinavian Journal of Public Health* (published online October 29, 2012, doi:10.1177/1403494812462495).

Garber, PA, Estrada, A, Bicca-Marques, JC, et al., eds. 2008. *South American Primates: Comparative Perspectives in the Study of Behavior, Ecology, and Conservation.* New York: Springer.

Gardner, JP, Li, S, Srinivasan, SR, et al. 2005. Rise in insulin resistance is associated with escalated telomere attrition. *Circulation* 111: 2171–2177.

Garlie, TN, and Choi, H. 2013. *Characterizing the size of the encumbered soldier.* Natick Soldier Research, Development, and Engineering Center (NSRDEC). Natick, MA. Report. September, 2013.

Garn, SM. 1971. *Human Races,* 3rd ed. Springfield: Charles C. Thomas.

Garrigan, D, Mobasher, Z, Severson, T, et al. 2005. Evidence for archaic Asian ancestry on the human X chromosome. *Molecular Biology and Evolution* 22: 189–192.

Gavrilets, S. 2012. Human origins and the transition from promiscuity to pair-bonding. *Proceedings of the National Academy of Sciences* 109: 9923–9928.

Genton, C, Cristescu, R, Gatti, S, et al. 2012. Recovery potential of a Western Lowland gorilla population following a major ebola outbreak: Results from a ten year study. *PLOS One* 7: e37106.

Ghiselin, M, and Landa, S. 2005. The economics and bioeconomics of folk and scientific classification. *Journal of Bioeconomics* 7: 221–238.

Ghorban, K, Dadmanesh, M, Hassanshabi, G, et al. 2013. Is the CCR5Δ32 mutation associated with immune system-related disease? *Inflammation* 36: 633–642.

Gibbons, A. 2007. Swapping guts for brains. *Science* 316: 1560.

Gibbons, A. 2014. Neandertals and moderns made imperfect mates. *Science* 343: 471–472.

Gibbs, RA, Rogers, J, Katze, MG, et al. 2007. Evolutionary and biomedical insights from the rhesus macaque genome. *Science* 316: 222–234.

Gilbert, MTP, Jenkins, DL, Götherstrom, A, et al. 2008. DNA from pre-Clovis human coprolites in Oregon, North America. *Science* 320: 786–789.

Gilby, IC, Eberly, LE, Pintea, L, et al. 2006. Ecological and social influences on the hunting behavior of wild chimpanzees, *Pan troglodytes schweinfurthii. Animal Behaviour* 72: 169–180.

Gillespie, TR, Chapman, CA, and Greiner, EC. 2005. Effects of logging on gastrointestinal parasite infections and infection risk in African primates. *Journal of Applied Ecology* 42: 699–707.

Gingerich, PD, Franzen, JL, Habersetzer, J, et al. 2010. *Darwinius masillae* is a Haplorhine—Reply to Williams et al. (2010). *Journal of Human Evolution* 59: 574–579.

Goebel, T, Waters, MR, and O'Rourke, DH. 2008. The Late Pleistocene dispersal of modern humans in the Americas. *Science* 319: 1497–1502.

Gomes, CM, and Boesch, C. 2009. Wild chimpanzees exchange meat for sex on a long-term basis. *PLOS ONE* 4: e5116.

Goodall, J. 1986. *The Chimpanzees of Gombe: Patterns of Behavior.* Cambridge, MA: Belknap.

Goodyear, AC. 2005. Evidence of pre-Clovis sites in the eastern United States. In R Bonnichsen, B Lepper, D Standford et al., eds., *Paleoamerican Origins: Beyond Clovis.* College Station: Texas A&M University Press. 103–112.

Gordon, AD. 2013. Sexual size dimorphism in *Australopithecus*: Current understanding and new directions. In KE Reed, JG Fleagle, and RF Leakey, eds., *The Paleobiology of Australopithecus.* 2013. Springer Dordrecht. 195–212.

Gordon, CC, Blackwell, CL, Bradtmiller B, et al. 2012. *Anthropometric survey of U.S. Army personnel (ANSUR II): Methods and summary statistics.* Technical Report. Natick, MA: U.S. Army Natick Research, Development and Engineering Center.

Gordon, CC and Bradtmiller, B. 2012. Anthropometric change: Implications for office ergonomics. *Work* 41: 4606–4611.

Goren-Inbar, N, Alperson, N, Kislev, ME, et al. 2004. Evidence of hominin control of fire at Gesher Benot Ya'aqov, Israel. *Science* 304: 725–727.

Gosman, JH, Stout, SD, and Larsen, CS. 2011. Skeletal biology over the life span: A view from the surfaces. *Yearbook of Physical Anthropology* 54: 86–98.

Gould, L, Sussman, RW, and Sauther, ML. 1999. Natural disasters and primate populations: The effects of a two-year drought on a naturally occurring population of ring-tailed lemurs (*Lemur catta*) in southwestern Madagascar. *International Journal of Primatology* 20: 69–84.

Gould, L, Sussman, RW, and Sauther, ML. 2003. Demographic and life-history patterns in a population of ring-tailed lemurs (*Lemur catta*) at Beza Mahafaly Reserve, Madagascar: A 15-year perspective. *American Journal of Physical Anthropology* 120: 182–194.

Gould, SJ. 1996. *The Mismeasure of Man*, 2nd ed. New York: WW Norton.

Gould, SJ. 1977. *Ontogeny and Phylogeny*. Cambridge: Harvard University Press.

Gould, SJ, and Lewontin, R. 1979. The spandrels of San Marco and the Panglossian paradigm. *Proceedings of the Royal Society of London Series B* 205: 581–598.

Gradstein, FM, and Ogg, JG. 2009. The geological time scale. In SB Hedges and S Kumar, eds., *The Timetree of Life*. Oxford: Oxford University Press. 26–34.

Grammer, K, Fink, B, and Neave, N. 2005. Human pheromones and sexual attraction. *European Journal of Obstetrics and Gynecology and Reproductive Biology* 118: 135–142.

Grant, PR, and Grant, BR. 2011. *How and Why Species Multiply: The Radiation of Darwin's Finches*. Princeton: Princeton University Press.

Grassineau, D, Papa, K, Ducourneau, A, et al. 2007. Improving minority blood donation: Anthropologic approach in a migrant community. *Transfusion* 47: 402–409.

Graves, RR, Lupo, AC, McCarthy, RC, et al. 2010. Just how strapping was KNM-WT 15000? *Journal of Human Evolution* 59: 542–554.

Green, RE, Krause, J, Briggs, AW, et al. 2010. A draft sequence of the Neandertal genome. *Science* 328: 710–722.

Green, RE, Malaspinas, A-S, Krause, J, et al. 2008. A complete Neandertal mitochondrial genome sequence determined by high-throughput sequencing. *Cell* 134: 416–426.

Gregory, TR. 2004. Macroevolution, hierarchy theory, and the C-value enigma. *Paleobiology* 30: 179–202.

Groves, CP. 2007. Species concepts and speciation: Facts and fantasies. In W Henke and I Tattersall, eds., *Handbook of Paleoanthropology*. Berlin: Springer. 1861–1879.

Gruber, T, Clay, Z, and Zuberbühler, K. 2010. A comparison of bonobo and chimpanzee tool use: Evidence for a female bias in the *Pan* lineage. *Animal Behaviour* 80: 1023–1033.

Guatelli-Steinberg, D. 2009. Recent studies of dental development in Neandertals: Implications for Neandertal life histories. *Evolutionary Anthropology* 18: 9–20.

Guatelli-Steinberg, D, Larsen, CS, and Hutchinson, DL. 2004. Prevalence and the duration of linear enamel hypoplasia: A comparative study of Neandertals and Inuit foragers. *Journal of Human Evolution* 47: 65–84.

Guatelli-Steinberg, D, Reid, DJ, Bishop, TA, et al. 2005. Anterior tooth growth periods in Neandertals were comparable to those of modern humans. *Proceedings of the National Academy of Sciences* 102: 14197–14202.

Gumert, MD, and Malaivijitnond, S. 2012. Marine prey processed with stone tools by Burmese long-tailed macaques (*Macaca fascicularis aurea*) in intertidal habitats. *American Journal of Physical Anthropology* 149: 447–457.

Gunnell, GF, and Silcox, MT. 2010. Primate origins: The early Cenozoic fossil record. In CS Larsen, ed., *A Companion to Biological Anthropology*. Chichester: Wiley-Blackwell. 275–294.

Guy, F, Mackaye, H-T, Likius, A, et al. 2008. Sympyseal shape variation in extant and fossil hominoids, and the symphyses of *Australopithecus bahrelghazali*. *Journal of Human Evolution* 55: 37–47.

Haeusler, M, and McHenry, HM. 2007. Evolutionary reversals of limb proportions in early hominids? Evidence from KNM-ER 3735 (*Homo habilis*). *Journal of Human Evolution* 53: 383–405.

Haile-Selassie, Y. 2001. Late Miocene hominids from the Middle Awash, Ethiopia. *Nature* 412: 178–181.

Haile-Selassie, Y, Asfaw, B, and White, TD. 2004. Hominid cranial remains from upper Pleistocene deposits at Aduma, Middle Awash, Ethiopia. *American Journal of Physical Anthropology* 123: 1–10.

Haile-Selassie, Y, Saylor, B, Deino, A, et al. 2010. New hominid fossils from Waranso-Mille (Central Afar, Ethiopia) and taxonomy of early *Australopithecus*. *American Journal of Physical Anthropology* 141: 406–417.

Haile-Selassie, Y, Saylor, B, Deino, A, et al. 2012. A new hominin foot from Ethiopia shows multiple Pliocene bipedal adaptations. *Nature* 483: 565–570.

Haile-Selassie, Y, Suwa, G, and White, TD. 2004. Late Miocene teeth from Middle Awash, Ethiopia, and early hominid dental evolution. *Science* 303: 1503–1505.

Hall, BK, ed. 2007. *Fins and Limbs: Evolution, Development, and Transformation*. Chicago: University of Chicago Press.

Hall, BK. 2012a. Evolutionary developmental biology (evo-devo): Past, present, and future. *Evolution: Education and Outreach* 5: 184–193.

Hall, BK. 2012b. Lamarck, Lamarckism, epigenetics and epigenetic inheritance. *Metascience* 21: 375–378.

Hallgrímsson, B, Lieberman, DE, Liu, W, et al. 2007. Epigenetic interactions and the structure of phenotypic variation in the cranium. *Evolution and Development* 9: 76–91.

Halverson, MS, and Bolnick, DA. 2008. An ancient DNA test of a founder effect in Native American ABO blood group frequencies. *American Journal of Physical Anthropology* 137: 342–347.

Hamilton-Reeves, JM, Rebello, SA, Thomas, W, et al. 2007. Isoflavone-rich soy protein isolate suppresses androgen receptor expression without altering estrogen receptor-ß expression or serum hormonal profiles in men at high risk of prostate cancer. *Journal of Nutrition* 137: 1769–1775.

Harcourt-Smith, WEH. 2007. The origins of bipedal locomotion. In W Henke and I Tattersall, eds., *Handbook of Paleoanthropology*. Berlin: Springer. 1483–1518.

Hardimon, MO. 2013. Race concepts in medicine. *Journal of Medicine & Philosophy* 38: 6–31.

Hardus, ME, Lameira, AR, Zulfa, A, et al. 2012. Behavioral, ecological, and evolutionary aspects of meat-eating by Sumatran orangutans (*Pongo abelii*). *International Journal of Primatology* 33: 287–304.

Hart, JA, Detwiler, KM, Gilbert, CC, et al. 2012. Lesula: A New Species of Cercopithecus Monkey Endemic to the Democratic Republic of Congo and Implications for Conservation of Congo's Central Basin. *PLOS ONE* 7(9): e44271.

Hartl, DL, and Fairbanks, DJ. 2007. Mud sticks: On the alleged falsification of Mendel's data. *Genetics* 175: 975–979.

Haslam, M, Hernandez-Aguilar, A, Ling, V, et al. 2009. Primate archaeology. *Nature* 460:339–344.

Hausdorf, B. 2011. Progress toward a general species concept. *Evolution* 65: 923–931.

Hawks, J. 2012. Longer time scale for human evolution. *Proceedings of the National Academy of Sciences* 109: 15531–15532.

Hayden, B. 2012. Neandertal social structure. *Oxford Journal of Archaeology* 31(1): 1–26.

Health Canada. 2004. *Exclusive Breastfeeding Duration: 2004 Health Canada Recommendation.* www.brandonrha.mb.ca/export/sites/brandonrha/galleries/pdf/Having_a_Baby/Canada_Health _Breastfeeding.pdf.

Health Canada. 2012. *Nutrition for healthy infants: Recommendations from birth to six* months. www.hc-sc.gc.ca/fn-an/nutrition/infant-nourisson/recom/index-eng.php#a6. Retrieved March 7, 2014.

Hemmer, H. 2007. Estimation of basic life history data of fossil hominoids. In W Henke and I Tattersall, eds., *Handbook of Paleoanthropology.* Berlin: Springer. 587–619.

Henke, W, and Tattersall, I, eds. 2007. *Handbook of Paleoanthropology.* Berlin: Springer.

Henn, BM, Cavalli-Sforza, LL, and Feldman, MW. 2012. The great human expansion. *Proceedings of the National Academy of Sciences* 109: 17758–17764.

Henry, AG, Ungar, PS, Passey, BH, et al. 2012. The diet of *Australopithecus sediba. Nature* 487: 990–993.

Henshilwood, C, d'Errico, F, Vanhaeren, M, et al. 2004. Middle Stone Age shell beads from South Africa. *Science* 304(5669): 404.

Hernandez-Aguilar, RA, Moore, J, and Pickering, TR. 2007. Savanna chimpanzees use tools to harvest the underground storage organs of plants. *Proceedings of the National Academy of Sciences* 104: 19210–19213.

Herring, DA. 1994a. "There were young people and old people and babies dying every week": The 1918–1919 influenza pandemic at Norway House. *Ethnohistory* 41: 73–105.

Herring, DA. 1994b. The 1918 influenza epidemic in the central Canadian subarctic. In A Herring and L Chan, eds., *Strength in Diversity: A Reader in Physical Anthropology.* Toronto: Canadian Scholars' Press. 365–384.

Herring, DA. 2000. Mundane diseases can kill: The 1918 influenza pandemic in Canada. *Journal of the Ontario Occupational Health Nurses Association* 19: 6–11.

Herring, DA, and Sattenspiel, L. 2007. Social contexts, syndemics, and infectious disease in northern aboriginal populations. *American Journal of Human Biology* 19: 190–202.

Herring, DA, Saunders, SR, and Katzenberg, MA. 1998. Investigating the weaning process in past populations. *American Journal of Physical Anthropology* 105: 425–439.

Herrmann, E, Call, J, Hernàndez-Lloreda, MV, et al. 2007. Humans have evolved specialized skills of social cognition: The cultural intelligence hypothesis. *Science* 317: 1360–1366.

Hey, J. 2009. The divergence of chimpanzee species and subspecies as revealed in multi-population isolation-with-migration analyses. *Molecular Biology and Evolution*, doi:10.1093/molbev/msp298.

Higham, T, Jacobi, R, Julien, M, et al. 2010. Chronology of the Grotte du Renne (France) and implications for the context of ornaments and human remains within the Châtelperronian. *Proceedings of the National Academy of Sciences* 107(47): 20234–20239.

Higham T, Compton, T, Stringer, C, et al. 2011. The earliest evidence for anatomically modern humans in northwestern Europe. *Nature* 479: 521–524.

Hirata, S, Fuwa, K, Sugama, K, et al. 2011. Mechanism of birth in chimpanzees: Humans are not unique among primates. *Biology Letters* doi:10.1098/rsbl.2011.0214.

Hobolth, A, Christensen, OF, Mailund, T, et al. 2007. Genomic relationships and speciation times of human, chimpanzee, and gorilla inferred from a coalescent hidden Markov model. *Public Library of Science Genetics* 3: e7.

Hodgson, JA, Bergey, CM, Disotell, TR. 2010. Neandertal genome: The ins and outs of African genetic diversity. *Current Biology* 20(12): R517–R519.

Hohmann, G, and Fruth, B. 2008. New records on prey capture and meat eating by bonobos at Lui Kotale, Salonga National Park, Democratic Republic of Congo. *Folia Primatologica* 79: 103–110.

Hollick M. 2006. Resurrection of vitamin D deficiency and rickets. *Journal of Clinical Investigation* 116: 2062–2072.

Holliday, TW. 2003. Species concepts, reticulation, and human evolution. *Current Anthropology* 44: 653–673.

Hollis, BW, and Wagner, CL. 2004. Assessment of dietary vitamin D requirements during pregnancy and lactation. *American Journal of Clinical Nutrition* 79: 717–726.

Holloway, RL. 2012. The issue of brain reorganization in *Australopithecus* and early homininds: Dart had it right. In SR Reynolds and A. Gallagher, eds., *African Genesis: Perspectives on Hominin Evolution.* Cambridge: Cambridge University Press. 163–180.

Holloway, RL, Clarke, RJ, and Tobias, PV. 2004. Posterior lunate sulcus in *Australopithecus africanus*: Was Dart right? *Comptes Rendus Paleoevolution* 3: 287–293.

Holmes, R. 2006. *The Hottentot Venus.* London: Bloomsbury.

Homan, GF, Davies, M, and Norman, R. 2007. The impact of lifestyle factors on reproductive performance in the general population and those undergoing infertility treatment: A review. *Human Reproduction Update* 13: 209–223.

Hong, R, Banta, JE, and Betancourt, JA. 2006. Relationship between household wealth inequality and chronic childhood under-nutrition in Bangladesh. *International Journal for Equity in Health* 5: 15.

Hoppa, RD, and Garlie, TN. 1998. Secular changes in the growth of Toronto children during the last century. *Annals of Human Biology* 25: 553–561.

Huber, SK, and Podos, J. 2006. Beak morphology and song features covary in a population of Darwin's finches (*Geospiza fortis*). *Biological Journal of the Linnean Society* 88: 489–498.

Hudjashov, G, Kivisild, T, Underhill, PA, et al. 2007. Revealing the prehistoric settlement of Australia by Y chromosome and mtDNA analysis. *Proceedings of the National Academy of Sciences* 104: 8726–8730.

Hull, D. 2005. Deconstructing Darwin: Evolutionary theory in context. *Journal of the History of Biology* 38: 137–152.

Hunt, G. 2010. Evolution in fossil lineages: Paleontology and *The Origin of Species*. *The American Naturalist* 176: S61–S76.

Hurd, JP. 2006. The shape of high fertility in a traditional Mennonite population. *Annals of Human Biology* 33: 557–569.

Huxley, TH. 1863. *Man's Place in Nature*. London: Williams and Norgate. Ice, GH. 2005. Biological anthropology and aging. *Journal of Cross-Cultural Gerontology* 20: 87–90.

Ice, GH. 2005. Biological anthropology and aging. *Journal of Cross-Cultural Gerontology* 20: 87–90.

IHGSC. International Human Genome Sequencing Consortium. 2004. Finishing the euchromatic sequence of the human genome. *Nature* 431: 931–45.

Irish, JD, Guatelli-Steinberg, D, Legge, SS, et al. 2013. Dental morphology and the phylogenetic "place" of *Australopithecus sediba*. *Science* 340. doi:10.1126/science.1233062.

Isbell, LA. 2006. Snakes as agents of evolutionary change in primate brains. *Journal of Human Evolution* 51: 1–35.

Isler, K, and van Schaik, C. 2006. Costs of encephalization: The energy trade-off hypothesis tested on birds. *Journal of Human Evolution* 51: 228–243.

Israde-Alcántara, I, Bischoff, JL, Domnique-Vázquez, G, et al. 2012. Evidence from central Mexico supporting the Younger Dryas extraterrestrial impact hypothesis. *Proceedings of the National Academy of Sciences* 109: E738–E747.

Jablonka, E. 2011. Cellular epigenetic inheritance in the twenty-first century. In SB Gissis and E Jablonka, eds., *Transformations of Lamarckism: From Subtle Fluids to Molecular Biology*. Cambridge: MIT Press. 215–226.

Jablonka, E, and Lamb, M. 2005. *Evolution in Four Dimensions—Genetic, Epigenetic, Behavioral, and Symbolic Variation in the History of Life*. Cambridge, MA: MIT.

Jablonka, E, and Lamb, M. 2007. The expanded evolutionary synthesis—A response to Godrey-Smith, Haig, and West-Eberhard. *Biology and Philosophy* 22: 453–472.

Jablonski, NG. 2004. The evolution of human skin and skin color. *Annual Review of Anthropology* 33: 585–623.

Jackson, FLC. 2008. Ancestral links of Chesapeake Bay region African Americans to specific Bight of Bonny (West Africa) microethnic groups and increased frequency of aggressive breast cancer in both regions. *American Journal of Human Biology* 20: 165–173.

Jackson, PW. 2006. *The Search for the Age of the Earth*. Cambridge: Cambridge University Press.

Jacobs, B. 2004. Paleobotanical studies from tropical Africa: Relevance to the evolution of forest, woodland, and savannah biomes. *Philosophical Transactions of the Royal Society London B* 359: 1573–1583.

Jaeger, J-J, Beard, KC, Chaimanee, Y, et al. 2010. Late middle Eocene epoch of Libya yields earliest known radiation of African anthropoids. *Nature* 467: 1095–1098.

Jain, S, and Pathmanathan G. 2012. Importance of anthropometry for designing user-friendly devices: Mobile phones. *Journal of Ergonomics* 2(4): 109–114.

Jeffery, B, Abonyi, S, Labonte, R, et al. 2006. Engaging numbers: Developing health indicators that matter for First Nations and Inuit people. *Journal of Aboriginal Health* (September): 44–52.

Jin, W, Xu, S, Wang, H, et al. 2012. Genome-wide detection of natural selection in African Americans pre- and post-admixture. *Genome Research* 22: 519–527.

Johnson, CR, and McBrearty, S. 2012. Archaeology of middle Pleistocene lacustrine and spring paleoenvironments in the Kapthurin Formation, Kenya. *Journal of Anthropological Archaeology* 31(4): 485–499.

Jones, JH, Wilson, ML, Murray, CM, et al. 2010. Phenotypic quality influences fertility in Gombe chimpanzees. *Journal of Animal Ecology* 79: 1847–1851.

Jones, KE, Patel, NG, Levy, MA, et al. 2008. Global trends in emerging infectious diseases. *Nature* 451: 990–993.

Jungers, WL, Harcourt-Smith, WEH, Wunderlich, RE, et al. 2009. The foot of *Homo floresiensis*. *Nature* 459: 81–84.

Kahn, J. 2007. Race in a Bottle. *Scientific American* 297: 40–45.

Kakekagumick, K, Hayward, MN, Harris, SB, et al. 2013. Sandy Lake health and diabetes project: A community-based intervention targeting type 2 diabetes and its risk factors in a First Nations community. *Frontiers in Endocrinology* 4: 170.

Kappeler, PM, and van Schaik, CP. 2004. Sexual selection in primates: Review and selective preview. In PM Kappeler and CP van Schaik, eds., *Sexual Selection in Primates: New and Comparative Perspectives*. New York: Cambridge University Press. 3–23.

Kareklas, K, Nettle, D, and Smulders, TV. 2013. Water-induced finger wrinkles improve handling of wet objects. *Biology Letters* 9 doi:10.1098/rsbl.2012.0999.

Kashani, BH, Perego, UA, Olivieri, A, et al. 2012. Mitochondrial haplogroup C4c: A rare lineage entering America through the ice-free corridor? *American Journal of Physical Anthropology* 147: 35–39.

Katzenberg, MA, Herring, DA, and Saunders, SR. 1996. Weaning and infant mortality: evaluating the skeletal evidence. *Yearbook of Physical Anthropology* 39: 177–200.

Katzenberg, MA, and Saunders, S, eds. 2008. *Biological Anthropology of the Human Skeleton,* 2nd ed. New York: Wiley.

Katzenberg, MA, Schwarcz, HP, Knyf, M, et al. 1995. Stable isotope evidence for maize horticulture and paleodiet in southern Ontario, Canada. *American Antiquity* 602: 335–350.

Katzmarzyk, PT. 2008. Obesity and physical activity among aboriginal Canadians. *Obesity* 16: 184–190.

Kaur, T, Singh, J, Tong, S, et al. 2008. Descriptive epidemiology of fatal respiratory outbreaks and detection of a human-related metapneumovirus in wild chimpanzees (*Pan troglodytes*) at Mahale Mountains National Park, Western Tanzania. *American Journal of Primatology* 70: 755–765.

Kaurah, P, MacMillan, A, Boyd, N, et al. 2007. Founder and recurrent *CDH1* mutations in families with hereditary diffuse gastric cancer. *JAMA* 297: 2360–2372.

Kay, RF. 2012. Evidence for an Asian origin of stem anthropoids. *Proceedings of the National Academy of Sciences* 109: 10132–10133.

Keeling, R, and Berger, L. 2013. *Potential soft tissue preserved in association with the Australopithecus sediba fossils from Malapa cave site, South Africa.* American Association of Physical Anthropologists meeting, Knoxville (abstract).

Keenleyside, A, Bertulli, M, and Fricke, HC. 1997. The final days of the Franklin expedition: New skeletal evidence. *Arctic* 50(1): 36–46.

Keenleyside, A, and Panayotova, K. 2006. Cribra orbitalia and porotic hyperostosis in a Greek colonial population (5th to 3rd centuries B.C.) from the Black Sea. *International Journal of Osteoarchaeology* 16: 373–384.

Keenleyside, A, Schwarcz, HP, and Panayotova, K. 2011. Oxygen isotopic evidence of residence and migration in a Greek colonial population on the Black Sea. *Journal of Archaeological Science* 38: 2658–2666.

Keita, S, Kittles, R, Royal, C, et al. 2004. Conceptualizing human variation. *Nature Genetics* 36: S17–S20.

Kelly, S, Sprauge, A, and Fell, DB, et al. 2013. Examining Caesarean section rates in Canada using the Robson Classification System. *Journal of Obstetrics and Gynaecology Canada* 35:206–214.

Kemp, BM, Malhi, RS, McDonough, J, et al. 2007. Genetic analysis of early Holocene skeletal remains from Alaska and its implications for the settlement of the Americas. *American Journal of Physical Anthropology* 132: 605–621.

Kemppainen, J, Aalto, S, Fujimoto, T, et al. 2005. High intensity exercise decreases global brain glucose uptake in humans. *Journal of Physiology* 568(1): 323–332.

Kimbel, WH, Lockwood, CA, Ward, CV, et al. 2006. Was *Australopithecus anamensis* ancestral to *A. afarensis*? A case of anagenesis in the hominin fossil record. *Journal of Human Evolution* 51: 134–152.

Kivell, TL, Kibii, JM, Churchill, SE, et al. 2011. *Australopithecus sediba* hand demonstrates mosaic evolution of locomotor and manipulative abilities. *Science* 333: 1411–1417.

Kivell TL, and Schmitt, D. 2009. Independent evolution of knuckle-walking in African apes shows that humans did not evolve from a knuckle-walking ancestor. *Proceedings of the National Academy of Sciences* 106(34): 14241–14246.

Klein, N, Fröhlich, F, and Krief, S. 2008. Geophagy: Soil consumption enhances the bioactivities of plants eaten by chimpanzees. *Naturwissenschaften* 95: 325–331.

Klein, RG. 2008. Out of Africa and the evolution of human behavior. *Evolutionary*

Koda, H, Nishimura, T, Tokuda, IT, et al. 2012. Soprano singing in gibbons. *American Journal of Physical Anthropology* 149(3): 347–355.

Kohn, D, Murrell, G, Parker, J, et al. 2005. What Henslow taught Darwin. *Nature* 436: 643–645.

Köndgen, S, Köhl, H, N'Goran, PK, et al. 2008. Pandemic human viruses cause decline of endangered great apes. *Current Biology* 18: 260–264.

Koné, I, Lambert, JE, Refisch, J, et al. 2008. Primate seed dispersal and its potential role in maintaining useful tree species in the Taï region, Côte-d'Ivoire: Implications for the conservation of forest fragments. *Tropical Conservation Science* 1: 293–306.

Krause, J, Fu, Q, Good, JM, et al. 2010. The complete mitochondrial DNA genome of an unknown hominin from southern Siberia. *Nature* 464: 894–897.

Krause, J, Lalueza-Fox, D, Orlando, L, et al. 2007. The derived *FOXP2* variant of modern humans was shared with Neandertals. *Current Biology* 17: 1908–1912.

Krause, J, Orlando, L, Serre, D, et al. 2007. Neanderthals in central Asia and Siberia. *Nature* 449: 902–904.

Kraut-Becher, J, Eisenberg, M, Voytek, C, et al. 2008. Examining racial disparities in HIV: Lessons from sexually transmitted investigations research. *Journal of Acquired Immune Deficiency Syndromes* 47 (Suppl 1): S20–S27.

Kubo, D, Kono, RT, Kaifu, Y. 2013. Brain size of *Homo floresiensis* and its evolutionary implications. *Proceedings of the Royal Society B* 280: 20130338.

Kurki, HH, Ginter, JK, Stock, JT, et al. 2008. Adult proportionality in small-bodied foragers: A test of ecogeographic expectations. *American Journal of Physical Anthropology* 136: 28–38.

Kurosu, H, Yamamoto, M, Clark, JD, et al. 2005. Suppression of aging in mice by the hormone Klotho. *Science* 309: 1829–1833.

Kuzawa, C. 2005. Fetal origins of developmental plasticity: Are fetal cues reliable predictors of future nutritional environments? *American Journal of Human Biology* 17: 5–21.

Kwa, C. 2011. *Styles of Knowing: A New History of Science from Ancient Times to the Present.* Pittsburgh: University of Pittsburgh Press.

Kwok, C, and Keenleyside, A. 2014. Baby bones, food, and health: Isotopic evidence for infant feeding practices in the Greek colony of Apollonia Pontica (5th–3rd centuries B.C.). In M Richards and A Papathanasiou, eds., *Archaeodiet in the Greek World from Stable Isotope Analysis.* Occasional Weiner Laboratory Series from Hesperia.

Laberge, A-M, Jomphe, M, Houde, L, et al. 2005a. A "fille du Roy" introduced the T14484C Leber Hereditary Optic Neuropathy mutation in French Canadians. *American Journal of Human Genetics* 77: 313–317.

Laberge, A-M, Michaud, J, Richter, A, et al. 2005b. Population history and its impact on medical genetics in Quebec. *Clinical Genetics* 68: 287–301.

Lalueza-Fox, C, Römpler, H, Caramelli, D, et al. 2007. A melano-cortin 1 receptor allele suggests varying pigmentation among Neanderthals. *Science* 318: 1453–1455.

Lalueza-Fox, C, Sampietro, ML, Caramelli, D, et al. 2005. Neandertal evolutionary genetics: Mitochondrial DNA data from the Iberian Peninsula. *Molecular Biology and Evolution* 22: 1077–1081.

Langergraber, KE, Prüfer, K, Rowney, C, et al. 2012. Generation times in wild chimpanzees and gorillas suggest earlier divergence times in great ape and human evolution. *Proceedings of the National Academy of Sciences* 109: 15716–15721.

Larcombe, L, Nickerson, P, Singer, M, Robson, R, Dantouze, J, McKay, L, and Orr, P. 2011. Housing conditions in 2 Canadian First Nations communities. *International Journal of Circumpolar Health* 70(2):141–153.

Larcombe, L, Rempel, JD, Dembinski, I, et al. 2005. Differential cytokine genotype frequencies among Canadian Aboriginal and Caucasian populations. *Genes and Immunity* 6: 140–144.

Lari, M, Rizzi, E, Milani, L, et al. 2010. The microcephalin ancestral allele in a Neanderthal individual. *PLOS ONE* 5(5): e10648. doi:10.1371/journal.pone.0010648.

Larsen, C. (2013). *Essentials of Physical Anthropology*. New York: W.W. Norton.

Larson, CP. 2007. Poverty during pregnancy: Its effects on child health outcomes. *Paediatrics and Child Health* 12: 673–677.

Larson SG, Jungers WL, Tocheri MW, et al. 2009. Descriptions of the upper limb skeleton of *Homo floresiensis*. *Journal of Human Evolution* 57: 555–570.

Lazenby, R, Angus, S, Galloway T, et al. 2007. *Social determinants of childhood overweight and obesity in elementary school children.* 35th Annual Meeting of the Canadian Association for Physical Anthropology, Banff, Alberta.

Lazenby, R, Cooper, DML, Angus, S, et al. 2008a. Articular constraint, handedness, and directional asymmetry in the human second metacarpal. *Journal of Human Evolution* 54: 875–885.

Lazenby, R, Tilgner, R, Hublin, J-J, et al. 2008b. 3D trabecular microarchitecture in SKX 5020, a first metacarpal attributed to *Paranthropus robustus*, compared with *Pan* and *Homo*. Paleoanthropology Society Meetings, Vancouver, Canada.

Leakey, MG, Spoor, F, Dean, MC, et al. 2012. New fossils from Koobi Fora in northern Kenya confirm taxonomic diversity in early *Homo*. *Nature* 488: 201–204.

Leatherman, TL, and Goodman, AH. 2005. Coca-colonization of diets in the Yucatan. *Social Science and Medicine* 61: 843–866.

Lebatard, A-E, Bourels, DL, Duringer, P, et al. 2008. Cosmogenic nuclide dating of *Sahleanthropus tchadensis* and *Australopithecus bahrelghazali*: Mio-Pliocene hominids from Chad. *Proceedings of the National Academy of Sciences* 105: 3226–3231.

Leduc, C, Coonish, J, Haddad, JP, et al. 2006. Plants used by the Cree Nation of Eeyou Istchee (Quebec, Canada) for the treatment of diabetes: A novel approach in quantitative ethnobotany. *Journal of Ethnopharmacology* 105: 55–63.

Lee, AC, Kamalam, A, Adams, SM, et al. 2004. Molecular evidence for absence of Y-linkage of the hairy ears trait. *European Journal of Human Genetics* 12: 1077–1079.

Lehman, SM. 2006. Conservation biology of malagasy strepsirhines: A phylogenetic approach. *American Journal of Physical Anthropology* 130(2): 238–253.

Lehmann, J, Korstjens, AH, and Dunbar, RIM. 2007a. Group size, grooming, and social cohesion in primates. *Animal Behaviour* 74: 1617–1629.

Lehmann, J, Korstjens, AH, and Dunbar, RIM. 2007b. Fission–fusion social systems as a strategy for coping with ecological constraints: A primate case. *Evolutionary Ecology* 21:613–634.

Lehmann, J, Korstjens, TH, and Dunbar, RIM. 2010. Apes in a changing world—The effects of global warming on the behaviour and distribution of African apes. *Journal of Biogeography* 37(12): 2217–2231.

Leonard, W, and Katzmarzyk, P. 2010. Body size and shape: Climatic and nutritional influences on human body morphology. In MH Muehlenbein, ed., *Human Evolutionary Biology*. Cambridge: Cambridge University Press. 157–169.

Leonard, WR, Snodgrass, J-J, and Robertson, M. 2007. Effects of brain evolution on human nutrition and metabolism. *Annual Review of Nutrition* 27: 311–327.

Leonardi, M, Gerbault, P, Thomas, MG, et al. 2012. The evolution of lactase persistence in Europe. A synthesis of archaeological and genetic evidence. *International Dairy Journal* 22: 88–97.

Leroy, EM, et al. 2004. Multiple Ebola virus transmission events and rapid decline of central African wildlife. *Science* 303: 387–390.

Lewis, RJ, and Kappeler, PM. 2005. Seasonality, body condition, and timing of reproduction in *Propithecus verreauxi verreauxi* in the Kirindy Forest. *American Journal of Primatology* 67: 347–364.

Lieberman, DE, Bramble, DM, Raichlen, DA, et al. 2007. The evolution of endurance running and the tyranny of ethnography: A reply to Pickering and Bunn. *Journal of Human Evolution* 53: 434–437.

Lieverse, AR, Weber, AW, Bazaliiskiy, VI, et al. 2007. Osteoarthritis in Siberia's Cis-Baikal: Skeletal indicators of hunter–gatherer adaptation and cultural change. *American Journal of Physical Anthropology* 132(1): 1–16.

Lieverse, AR, Bazaliiskii, VI, Goriunova OI, et al. 2009. Upper limb musculoskeletal stress markers among middle Holocene foragers of Siberia's Cis-Baikal region. *American Journal of Physical Anthropology* 138: 458–472.

Lieverse, AR, Bazaliiskii, VI, Goriunova OI, et al. 2013. Lower limb activity in the Cis-Baikal: Entheseal changes among middle Holocene siberian foragers. *American Journal of Physical Anthropology* 150: 421–432.

Lind, J, Lindenfors, P. 2010. The number of cultural traits is correlated with female group size but not with male group size in chimpanzee communities. *PLOS ONE* 5(3): e9241.

Lindefors, P, Nunn, CL, and Barton, RA. 2007. Primate brain architecture and selection in relation to sex. *BMC Biology* 5: 20.

Linnaeus, C. 1758, 1759. *Systema Naturae,* 10th ed. Holmiae : Impensis Direct. Laurentii Salvii.

Liston, MA, and Baker, BJ. 1996. Reconstructing the massacre at Fort William Henry, New York. *International Journal of Osteoarchaeology* 6: 28–41.

Liu, W, Jin, CZ, Zhang, YQ, et al. 2010. Human remains from Zhirendong, South China, and modern human emergence in East Asia. *Proceedings of the National Academy of Sciences* 107:19201–19206.

Locke, DP, Hillier, LDW, Warren, WC, et al. 2011. Comparative and demographic analysis of orang-utan genomes. *Nature* 469: 529–533.

Lockwood, CA, Kimbel, WH, and Lynch, JM. 2004. Morphometrics and hominoid phylogeny: Support for a chimpanzee–human clade and differentiation among great ape species. *Proceedings of the National Academy of Sciences* 101: 4356–4360.

Lordkipanidze, D, Jashashvili, T, Vekua, A, et al. 2007. Postcranial evidence from early *Homo* from Dmanisi, Georgia. *Nature* 449: 305–310.

Lordkipanidze, D, Ponce de León, M, Margvelashvili, A, et al. 2013. A complete skull from Dmanisi, Georgia, and the evolutionary biology of early *Homo*. *Science* 342: 326–331.

Lovejoy, CO. 2005. The natural history of human gait and posture. Part 1: Spine and pelvis. *Gait and Posture* 21: 95–112.

Lovejoy, CO. 2009. Re-examining human origins in light of *Ardipithecus ramidus*. *Science* 326: 74e1–74e8.

Lovejoy, CO, Suwa, G, Simpson, SW, et al. 2009. The great divides: *Ardipithecus ramidus* reveals the postcrania of our last common ancestors with African apes. *Science* 326: 73.

Lovejoy, CO, Suwa, G, Spurlock, L, et al. 2009. The pelvis and femur of *Ardipithecus ramidus*: The emergence of upright walking. *Science* 236: 71e1–71e6.

Lovell, NC. 1994. Spinal arthritis and physical stress at Bronze Age Harappa. *American Journal of Physical Anthropology* 932: 149–164.

Lovell, NC, and Dublenko, AA. 1999. Further aspects of fur trade life depicted in the skeleton. *International Journal of Osteoarchaeology* 9: 248–256.

Lubinksy, M. 2012. Hypothesis: Cystic fibrosis carrier geography reflects interactions of tuberculosis and hypertension with vitamin D deficiency, altitude and temperature. Vitamin D deficiency effects and CF carrier advantage. *Journal of Cystic Fibrosis* 11: 68–70.

Luca, F, Perry, G, and Di Rienzo, A. 2010. Evolutionary adaptations to dietary changes. *Annual Review of Nutrition* 30: 291–314.

Lucas, PW, Constantino, PJ, and Wood, BA. 2008. Inferences regarding the diet of extinct hominins: Structural and functional trends in dental and mandibular morphology within the hominin clade. *Journal of Anatomy* 212: 486–500.

Lucas, PW, Omar, R, Al-Fadhalah, K, et al. 2013. Mechanisms and causes of wear in tooth enamel: Implications for hominin evolution. *Journal of the Royal Society Interface* doi:10.1098/rsif.2012.0923.

Luncz, LV, Mundry, R, and Boesch, C. 2012. Evidence for cultural differences between neighboring chimpanzee communities. *Current Biology* 22: 922–926.

Lyn, H, Franks, B, and Savage-Rumbaugh, ES. 2008. Precursors of morality in the use of the symbols "good" and "bad" in two bonobos (*Pan paniscus*) and a chimpanzee (*Pan troglodytes*). *Language and Communication* 28: 213–224.

Maar, M, Erskine, L, McGregor, M, et al. 2009. Innovations on a shoestring: A Study of a Collaborative Community-based Aboriginal Mental Health Service Model in Rural Canada. *International Journal of Mental Health Systems* 3:27.

Maar, M, Manitowabi, D, Gzik, L, et al. 2011. Serious complications for patients, care providers, and policy makers: Tackling the structural violence of First Nations people living with diabetes in Canada. *The International Indigenous Policy Journal* 2(1): Article 6. Retrieved from http://ir.lib.uwo.ca/iipj/vol2/iss1/6, January 25, 2012.

Maar, M, Sutherland, M, and McGregor, L. 2007. A Regional Model for Ethical Engagement: The First Nations Research Ethics Committee on Manitoulin Island. In JP White, S Wingert, D Beavon, and P Maxim, eds., *Aboriginal Policy Research. Moving Forward, Making a Difference. Volume IV.* Thompson Education Publishing: Toronto.

MacArthur, D, and North, K. 2004. A gene for speed? The evolution and function of alpha-actinin-3. *Bioessays* 26: 786–95.

MacArthur, D. 2008. The gene for Jamaican sprinting success? No, not really. *Genetic Future*. www.genetic-future.com. Accessed August 21, 2008.

MacArthur, D, and North, K. 2005. Genes and human elite athletic performance. *Human Genetics* 116: 331–339.

MacCormick, HA, MacNulty, DR, Bosacker, AL, et al. 2012. Male and female aggression: Lessons from sex, rank, age, and injury in olive baboons. *Behavioral Ecology* 23: 684–689.

Mackenzie, H, Messinger, H, and Smith, R. 2008. *Size Matters: Canada's Ecological Footprint, by Income*. Toronto: Centre for Policy Alternatives, Toronto.

MacLeod, CE, Zilles, K, Schleicher, A, et al. 2003. Expansion of the neocerebellum in Hominoidea. *Journal of Human Evolution* 44: 401–429.

Malaivijitnond, S, Lekprayoon, C, Tandavanittj, N, et al. 2007. Stone-tool usage by Thai long-tailed macaques (*Macaca fascicularis*). *American Journal of Primatology* 69: 227–233.

Malhi, RS, Kemp, BM, Eshleman, J, et al. 2007. Mitochondrial haplogroup M discovered in prehistoric North Americans. *Journal of Archaeological Science* 34: 642–648.

Mann, C. 2008. Our Good Earth. *National Geographic* 214: 88–106.

Manzi, G, Magri, D, Milli, S, et al. 2010. The new chronology of the Ceprano calvarium (Italy). *Journal of Human Evolution* 59(5): 580–585.

Marean, CW, Bar-Matthews, M, Bernatchez, J, et al. 2007. Early human use of marine resources and pigment in South Africa during the Middle Pleistocene. *Nature* 449: 905–908.

Margulis, SW, Atsalis, S, Bellem, A, et al. 2007. Assessment of reproductive behaviour and hormonal cycles in geriatric western lowland gorillas. *Zoo Biology* 262: 117–139.

Marks, J. 2007. Long shadow of Linnaeus's human taxonomy. *Nature* 447: 28.

Marks, J. 2008. Race across the physical–cultural divide in American anthropology. In H Kuklick, ed., *A New History of Anthropology*. New York: Blackwell. 242–258.

Marks, J. 2010. Ten facts about human variation. In MH Muehlenbein, ed., *Human Evolutionary Biology*. Cambridge University Press, Cambridge. 265–276.

Marques-Bonet, T, Ryder, OA, and Eichler, EE. 2009. Sequencing primate genomes: What have we learned? *Annual Review of Genomics and Human Genetics* 10: 355–386.

Martín-González, JA, Mateos, A, Goikoetxea, I, et al. 2012. Differences between Neandertal and modern human infant and child growth models. *Journal of Human Evolution* 63: 140–149.

Martinez-Marignac, VL, Valladares, A, Cameron, E, et al. 2007. Admixture in Mexico City: Implications for admixture mapping of Type 2 diabetes genetic risk factors. *Human Genetics* 120: 807–819.

Marvan, R, Stevens, JMG, Roeder, AS, et al. 2006. Male dominance rank, mating, and reproductive success in captive Bonobos (*Pan paniscus*). *Folia Primatologica* 77: 364–376.

Matthews, J. 2011. *Starting from Scratch: The Origin and Development of Expression, Representation and Symbolism in Human and Non-Human Primates*. New York: Psychology Press.

McBrearty, S, and Jablonski, NG. 2005. First fossil chimpanzee. *Nature* 437: 105–108.

McDougall, I, Brown, FH, and Fleagle, JG. 2005. Stratigraphic placement and age of modern humans from Kibish, Ethiopia. *Nature* 433: 733–736.

McGoogan, K, Kivell, T, Hutchison, M, et al. 2007. Phylogenetic diversity and the conservation biogeography of African primates. *Journal of Biogeography* 34(11): 1962–1974.

McGrew, WC. 2010. In search of the last common ancestor: New findings on wild chimpanzees. *Philosophical Transactions of the Royal Society B* 365: 3267–3276.

McGraw, WS, and Daegling, DJ. 2012. Primate feeding and foraging: Integrating studies of behavior and morphology. *Annual Review of Anthropology* 41: 203–219.

McHenry, H. 2012. Origin and diversity of early hominin bipedalism. In SC Reynolds and A Gallagher, eds., *African Genesis: Perspectives on Hominin Evolution*. Cambridge: Cambridge University Press. 205–222.

McLennan, MR, and Huffman, MA. 2012. High frequency of leaf swallowing and its relationship to intestinal parasite expulsion in "village" chimpanzees at Bulindi, Uganda. *American Journal of Primatology* 74: 642–650.

McPherron, SP, Alemseged, Z, Marean, CW, et al. 2010. Evidence for stone-tool-assisted consumption of animal tissues before 3.39 million years ago at Dikika, Ethiopia. *Nature* 466: 857–860.

Mecsas, J, Franklin, G, Kuziel, W, et al. 2005. CCR5 mutation and plague protection. *Nature* 427: 606.

Mekel-Bobrov, N, Gilbert, SL, Evans, PD, et al. 2005. Ongoing adaptive evolution of *ASPM*, a brain size determinant for *Homo sapiens*. *Science* 309: 1720–1722.

Mekel-Bobrov, N, Posthuma, D, Gilbert, SL, et al. 2007. The ongoing adaptive evolution of *ASPM* and *Microcephalin* is not explained by increased intelligence. *Human Molecular Genetics* 16: 600–608.

Melin, AD, Fedigan, LM, Hiramatsu, C, et al. 2007. Effects of colour vision phenotype on insect capture by a free-ranging population of white-faced capuchins, *Cebus capucinus*. *Animal Behaviour* 73(1): 205–214.

Melin, AD, Fedigan, LM, Young, HC, et al. 2010. Can color vision variation explain sex differences in invertebrate foraging by capuchin monkeys? *Current Zoology* 56(3): 300–312.

Mellars, P. 2006. A new radiocarbon revolution and the dispersal of modern humans in Eurasia. *Nature* 439: 931–935.

Mellars, P, French, JC. 2011. Tenfold population increase in western Europe at the Neandertal-to-modern human transition. *Science* 333: 623–627.

Mercader, J, Barton, H, Gillespie, J, et al. 2007. 4,300-year-old chimpanzee sites and the origins of percussive stone technology. *Proceedings of the National Academy of Sciences* 104: 3043–3048.

Merrett, DC, and Pfeiffer, S. 2000. Maxillary sinusitis as an indicator of respiratory health in past populations. *American Journal of Physical Anthropology* 111: 301–318.

Meyer, M, Fu, Q, Aximu-Petri, A, et al. 2013. A mitochondrial genome sequence of a hominin from Sima de los Huesos. *Nature* 505: 403–406.

Mielke, JH, Konigsberg, LW, and Relethford, JH. 2006. *Human Biological Variation*. New York: Oxford University Press.

Miller, G, Tybur, JM, and Jordan, BD. 2007. Ovulatory cycle effects on tip earnings by lap dancers: economic evidence for human estrus? *Evolution and Human Behavior* 28: 375–381.

Milton, K. 2009. Distribution patterns of tropical plant foods as an evolutionary stimulus to primate mental development. *American Anthropologist* 83: 534–548.*Research* 159: 320–327.

Mitchell, KB, Garlie, TN, and Choi, H. 2014. *Anthropometry and Range of Motion (ROM) of the Encumbered Soldier*. Natick, MA: Natick *Soldier* Research, Development, and Engineering Center (NSRDEC). Technical report (under review).

Mithen, S. and Reed, M. (2002). Stepping out: a computer simulation of hominid dispersal from Africa. *Journal of Human Evolution* 43 (4). pp. 433–462.

Mittermeier, RA, Ganzhorn, JU, Konstant, WR, et al. 2008. Lemur diversity in Madagascar. *International Journal of Primatology* 29: 1607–1656.

Mittermeier, RA, Schwitzer, C, Rylands, AB, et al. 2012. Primates in Peril: The World's 25 Most Endangered Primates 2012–14. IUCN/SSC Primate Specialist Group (PSG), International Primatological Society (IPS), Conservation International (CI), and Bristol Conservation and Science Foundation, Bristol, UK.

Mitteroecker, P, and Bookstein, F. 2008. The evolutionary role of modularity and integration in the hominoid cranium. *Evolution* 62: 943–958.

Moffat, T. 2001. A biocultural investigation of the weanling's dilemma in Kathmandu, Nepal: Do universal recommendations for weaning practices make sense? *Journal of Biosocial Science* 33: 321–338.

Moffat, T. 2002. Breastfeeding, wage labor, and insufficient milk in peri-urban Kathmandu, Nepal. *Medical Anthropology* 21: 207–230.

Moffat, T. 2003. Diarrhea, respiratory infections, protozoan gastrointestinal parasites, and child growth in Kathmandu, Nepal. *American Journal of Physical Anthropology* 1221: 85–97.

Moffat, T, and Galloway, T. 2007. Adverse environments: Investigating local variation in child growth. *American Journal of Human Biology* 19: 676–683.

Moffat, T, and Galloway, T. 2008. Food consumption patterns: In elementary school children. *Canadian Journal of Dietetic Practice and Research* 69: 152–154.

Moffat, T, Galloway, T, and Latham, J. 2005. Stature and adiposity among children in contrasting neighborhoods in the city of Hamilton, Ontario, Canada. *American Journal of Human Biology* 17: 355–367.

Moffat, T, and Herring, DA. 1999. The historical roots of high rates of infant death in Aboriginal communities in Canada in the early twentieth century: The case of Fisher River, Manitoba. *Social Science and Medicine* 48: 1821–1832.

Moffat, T, Sellen, D, Amarra, S, et al. 2013. Knowledge and practice: Infant vitamin D supplementation among Canadian-born and immigrant mothers. *Journal of Transcultural Nursing* (published online 5 May 2014).

Molnar, S. 2006. *Human Variation: Races, Types, and Ethnic Groups*, 6th ed. Upper Saddle River: Prentice-Hall.

Moore, DS. 2006. A very little bit of knowledge: Re-evaluating the meaning of the heritability of IQ. *Human Development* 49: 347–353.

Morens, DM, Folkers, GK, and Fauci, AS. 2004. The challenge of emerging and re-emerging infectious diseases. *Nature* 430: 242–249.

Morin, E. 2008. Evidence for declines in human population densities during the early Upper Paleolithic in western Europe. *Proceedings of the National Academy of Sciences* 105(1): 48–53.

Morin, E, and Laroulandie, V. 2012. Presumed symbolic use of diurnal raptors by Neanderthals. *PLOS ONE* 7(3): e32856.

Morris, K. 2008. Shedding light on the role of poverty in brain development. *The Lancet Neurology* 7: 676–677.

Morrow, JE, Fiedel, SJ, Johnson, DL, et al. 2012. Pre-Clovis in Texas? A critical assessment of the "Buttermilk Creek Complex." *Journal of Archaeological Science* 39: 3677–3682.

Morwood, MJ, Soejono, RP, Roberts, RG, et al. 2004. Archaeology and age of a new hominin from Flores in eastern Indonesia. *Nature* 431: 1087–1091.

Morwood, MJ, Sutikna, T, Saptomo, EW, et al. 2009. Preface: Research at Liang Bua, Flores, Indonesia. *Journal of Human Evolution* 57: 437–449.

Mounier, A, Condemi, S, and Manzi, G. 2011. The stem species of our species: A place for the archaic human cranium from Ceprano, Italy. *PLOS ONE* 6(4): e18821.

Moura, ACA, and Lee, PC. 2004. Capuchin stone tool use in Caatinga dry forest. *Science* 306: 1909.

Moya-Sola, S, Kohler, M, Alba, DM, et al. 2004. *Pierolapithecus catalaunicus*, a new Middle Miocene great ape from Spain. *Science* 306(5700): 1339–1344.

Müller, AE, and Soligo, C. 2005. Primate sociality in evolutionary context. *American Journal of Physical Anthropology* 128: 399–414.

Muller, MN, and Wrangham, RW. 2009. *Sexual Coercion in Primates and Humans: An Evolutionary Perspective on Male Violence Against Females.* Cambridge: Harvard University Press.

Mulligan, CJ. 2006. Anthropological applications of ancient DNA: Problems and prospects. *American Antiquity* 71: 365–380.

Mulligan, CJ, Kitchen, A, and Miyamoto, MM. 2008. Updated three-stage model for the peopling of the Americas. *PLOS ONE* 3(9): e3199.

Mustanski, BS, DuPree, MG, Nievergelt, CM, et al. 2005. A genomewide scan of male sexual orientation. *Human Genetics* 116: 272–278.

Nakamichi, M. 2004. Tool-use and tool-making by captive, group-living orangutans (*Pongo pygmaeus abelii*) at an artificial termite mound. *Behavioural Processes* 65: 87–93.

Nakatsukasa, M, Pickford, M, Egi, N, et al. 2007. Femur length, body mass, and stature estimates of *Orrorin tugenensis*, a 6 Ma hominid from Kenya. *Primates* 48: 171–178.

Narr, KL, Woods, RP, Thompson, PM, et al. 2007. Relationships between IQ and regional cortical gray matter thickness in healthy adults. *Cerebral Cortex* 17: 2163–2171.

Navarette, A, van Schaik, CP, and Isler, K. 2011. Energetics and the evolution of human brain size. *Nature* 480: 91–94.

Nesse, RM. 2007. The importance of evolution for medicine. In WR Trevathan, JJ McKenna, and EO Smith, eds., *Evolutionary Medicine,* 2nd ed. New York: Oxford University Press. 416–432.

Ng, P, Murray, S, Levy, S, et al. 2009. An agenda for personalized medicine. *Nature* 461: 724–726.

Ng, PC, Zhao, Q, Levy, S, et al. 2008. Individual genomes instead of race for personalized medicine. *Clinical Pharmacology and Therapeutics* 84: 306–309.

Ngugi, EN, Benoit, C, Hallgrimsdottir, H, et al. 2013. Family kinship patterns and female sex work in the informal urban settlement of Kibera, Nairobi, Kenya. *Human Ecology* 40: 397–403.

Nguyen, N, Van Horn RC, Alberts, SC, et al. 2009. "Friendships" between new mothers and adult males: Adaptive benefits and determinants in wild baboons (*Papio cynocephalus*). *Behavioral Ecology and Sociobiology* 63: 1331–1344.

Ni, X, Gebo, DL, Dagosto, M, et al. 2013. The oldest known primate skeleton and early haplorhine evolution. *Nature* 498: 60–64.

Niewoehner, WA. 2008. Neanderthal hands in their proper perspective. In K Harvati and T Harrison, eds., *Neanderthals Revisited: New Approaches and Perspectives.* Netherlands: Springer. 157–190.

Nikiéma, B, Gauvin, L, Zunzunegui, MV, et al. 2012. Longitudinal patterns of poverty and health in early childhood: Exploring the influence of concurrent, previous, and cumulative poverty on child health outcomes. *BMC Pediatrics* 12: 141. www.biomedcentral.com/1471-2431/12/141.

Nistor Baldea, LA, Martineau, LC, Benhaddou-Andalouossi, A, et al. 2010. Inhibition of intestinal glucose absorption by anti-diabetic medicinal plants derived from the James Bay Cree traditional pharmacopeia. *Journal of Ethnopharmacology* 132: 473–482.

Niven, L, Steele, TE, Rendu, W, et al. 2012. Neandertal mobility and large-game hunting: The exploitation of reindeer during the Quina Mousterian at Chez-Pinaud Jonzac (Charente-Maritime, France). *Journal of Human Evolution* 63(4): 624–635.

Noonan, JP, Coop, G, Kudaravalli, S, et al. 2006. Sequencing and analysis of Neanderthal genomic DNA. *Science* 314: 1113–1118.

Norton, HL, Kittles, RA, Parra, E, et al. 2007. Genetic evidence for the convergent evolution of light skin in Europeans and East Asians. *Molecular Biology and Evolution* 24: 710–722.

O'Connell, JF, and Allen, J. 2004. Dating the colonization of Sahul (Pleistocene Australia–New Guinea): A review of recent research. *Journal of Archaeological Science* 31: 835–853.

O'Connor, CF, Franciscus, RG, and Holton, NE. 2005. Bite force production capability and efficiency in Neandertals and modern humans. *American Journal of Physical Anthropology* 127: 129–151.

Ohl, M. 2007. Principles of taxonomy and classification: Current procedures for naming and classifying organisms. In W Henke and I Tattersall, eds., *Handbook of Paleoanthropology.* Berlin: Springer. 141–166.

Olejniczak, AJ, Smith, TM, Skinner, MM, et al. 2008. Three-dimensional molar enamel distribution and thickness in *Australopithecus* and *Paranthropus*. *Biology Letters* 4: 406–410.

Olejniczak, AJ, Tafforeau, P, Feeney, RNM, et al. 2008. Three-dimensional primate molar enamel thickness. *Journal of Human Evolution* 54: 187–195.

O'Malley, RC, Wallauer, W, Murray, CM, et al. 2012. The appearance and spread of ant fishing among the Kasekala chimpanzees of Gombe. *Current Anthropology* 53: 650–663.

Oppenheimer, S. 2012. A single southern exit of modern humans from Africa: Before or after Toba? *Quaternary International* 258: 88–99.

Ordovas, JM, and Corella, D. 2004. Nutritional genomics. *Annual Review of Genomics and Human Genetics* 5: 71–118.

Orkin, JD, and Pontzer, H. 2011. The narrow niche hypothesis: Gray squirrels shed new light on primate origins. *American Journal of Physical Anthropology* 144(4): 617–624.

Orlando, L, Darlu, P, Toussaint, M, et al. 2006. Revisiting Neanderthal diversity with a 100,000 year old mtDNA sequence. *Current Biology* 16: R400–402.

Orr, CM, Tocheri, MW, Burnett, SE, et al. 2013. New wrist bones of *Homo floresiensis* from Liang Bua (Flores, Indonesia). *Journal of Human Evolution* 64:109–129.

Ostner, J, Nunn, CL, and Schülke, O. 2008. Female reproductive synchrony predicts skewed paternity across primates. *Behavioral Ecology* 19: 1150–1158.

Padiak, J. 2008. The contribution of tuberculosis to the mortality of British soldiers 1830–1913. In *Multiplying and Dividing: Tuberculosis in Canada and Aotearoa New Zealand.* J Littleton, J Park, A Herring, et al., *Research in Anthropology and Linguistics*-e Number 3, 103–112.

Paganotti, GM, Gramolelli, S, Tabacchi, F, et al. 2012. Distribution of human CYP2C8*2 allele in three different African populations. *Malaria Journal* 11: 125.

Palombit, RA. 2009. "Friendship" with males: A female counterstrategy to infanticide in Chacma baboons of the Okavango Delta. In MN Muller and RW Wrangham, eds., *Sexual Coercion in Primates and Humans: An Evolutionary Perspective on Male Aggression Against Females.* Cambridge: Harvard University Press. 377–409.

Palombit, RA, Seyfarth, RM, and Cheney, DL. 1997. The adaptive value of 'friendships' to female baboons: experimental and observational evidence. *Animal Behaviour* 54: 599-614.

Palombit, RA. 2012. Infanticide: Male strategies and female counterstrategies. In JC Mitani, J Call, PM Kappeler et al. *The Evolution of Primate Societies.* Chicago: The University of Chicago Press. 432–468.

Pampush, JD, Duque, AC, Burrows, BR, et al. 2013. Homoplasy and thick enamel in primates. *Journal of Human Evolution* 64: 216–224.

Parga, JA. 2006. Male mate choice in *Lemur catta. International Journal of Primatology* 27: 107–131.

Parga, JA. 2010. Evaluation of male inter-troop transfer as a mating strategy among ring-tailed lemurs on St. Catherines Island, USA. *Folia Primatologica* 81: 146–162.

Parker, M, and Harper, I. 2006. The anthropology of public health. *Journal of Biosocial Science* 38: 1–5.

Patil, CL, and Young, SL. 2012. Biocultural considerations of food cravings and aversions: An introduction. *Ecology of Food and Nutrition* 51(5): 365–373.

Patterson, N, Richter, DJ, Gnerre, S, et al. 2006. Genetic evidence for complex speciation of humans and chimpanzees. *Nature* 441: 1103–1108.

Pavelka, MSM, and Fedigan, LM. 1999. Reproductive termination in female Japanese monkeys: A comparative life history perspective. *American Journal of Physical Anthropology* 109: 455–464.

Pavelka, MSM, Brusselers, OT, Nowak, D, et al. 2003. Population reduction and social organization in *Alouatta pigra* following a hurricane. *International Journal of Primatology* 24: 1037–1055.

Pavelka, MSM, Fedigan, LM, and Zohar, S. 2002. Availability and adaptive value of reproductive and postreproductive Japanese macaque mothers and grandmothers. *Animal Behaviour* 64(3): 407–414.

Pavelka, MSM, McGoogan, KC, and Steffens, TS. 2007. Population size and characteristics of *Alouatta pigra* before and after a major hurricane. *International Journal of Primatology* 28: 919–929.

Pawlowski, B. 2007. Origins of homininae and putative selection pressures acting on the earliest hominins. In W Henke and I Tattersall, eds., *Handbook of Paleoanthropology.* Berlin: Springer. 1409–1440.

Pearson, OM, Cordero, RM, and Busby, AM. 2008. How different were Neanderthals' habitual activities? A comparative analysis with diverse groups of recent humans. In K Harvati and T Harrison, eds., *Neanderthals Revisited: New Approaches and Perspectives.* Netherlands: Springer. 135–156.

Pellan, MJ, and Matzke, NJ. 2006. From *The Origin of Species* to the origin of bacterial flagella. *Nature Reviews Microbiology* 4: 784–790.

Pelto, GH. 2008. Taking care of children: Applying anthropology in maternal and child nutrition and health. *Human Organization* 67: 237–243.

Perego, UA, Achilli, A, Angerhofer, N, et al. 2009. Distinctive Paleo-Indian migration routes from Beringia marked by two rare mtDNA haplogroups. *Current Biology* 19: 1–8.

Perry, GH, Dominy, NJ, Claw, KG, et al. 2007. Diet and the evolution of human amylase gene copy number variation. *Nature Genetics* 39: 1256–1260.

Perry, MJ. 2008. Effects of environmental and occupational pesticide exposure on human sperm: A systematic review. *Human Reproduction Update* 14: 233–242.

Pickering, TR, and Bunn, HT. 2007. The endurance running hypothesis and hunting and scavenging in savanna–woodlands. *Journal of Human Evolution* 53: 434–438.

Pilbeam, D, and Young, N. 2004. Hominoid evolution: Synthesizing disparate data. *Comptes Rendus Paleoevolution* 3: 305–321.

Pilcher, H. 2005. Apeing our language. *News@Nature.com* doi:10.1038/050829–8.

Pitulko, VV, Nikolsky, PA, Girya, EY, et al. 2004. The Yana RHS site: Humans in the Arctic before the last glacial maximum. *Science* 303: 52–56.

Plagnol, V, and Wall, JD. 2006. Possible ancestral structure in human populations. *Public Library of Science Genetics* 2: 972–979.

Plavcan, JM. 2012a. Sexual size dimorphism, canine dimorphism, and male–male competition in primates. Where do humans fit in? *Human Nature* 23: 45–67.

Plavcan, JM. 2012b. Implications of male and female sexual size dimorphism for inferring behaviour in the hominin fossil record. *International Journal of Primatology* 33: 1364–1381.

Plavcan, JM, and Ruff, CB. 2008. Canine size, shape, and bending strength in primates and carnivores. *American Journal of Physical Anthropology* 136: 65–84.

Ponce de León, MS, Golovanova, L, Doronichev, V, et al. 2008. Neanderthal brain size at birth provides insights into the evolution of human life history. *Proceedings of the National Academy of Sciences* 105: 13764–13768.

Pontzer, H, and Wrangham, R. 2006. Ontogeny of ranging in wild chimpanzees. *International Journal of Primatology* 27: 295–309.

Pontzer, H, Rolian, C, Rightmire, GP, et al. 2010. Locomotor anatomy and biomechanics of the Dmanisi hominins. *Journal of Human Evolution* 58: 492–504.

Pontzer, H, Scott, JR, Lordkipanidze, D, et al. 2011. Dental microwear texture analysis and diet in the Dmanisi hominins. *Journal of Human Evolution* 61: 683–687.

Poolman, EM, and Galvani, AP. 2007. Evaluating candidate agents of selective pressure for cystic fibrosis. *Journal of the Royal Society Interface* 4: 91–98.

Potts, R. 2013. Hominin evolution in settings of strong environmental variability. *Quaternary Science Reviews* 73: 1–13.

Prat, S, Brugal, J-P, Tiercelin, J-J, et al. 2005. First occurrence of early *Homo* in the Nachukui Formation (West Turkana, Kenya) at 2.3–2.4 myr. *Journal of Human Evolution* 49: 230–240.

Premo, LS, and Hublin, J-J. 2009. Culture, population structure, and low genetic diversity in Pleistocene hominins. *Proceedings of the National Academy of Sciences* 106(1): 33–37.

Prokosch, MD, Yeo, RA, and Miller, GF. 2005. Intelligence tests with higher g-loadings show higher correlations with body symmetry: Evidence for a general fitness factor mediated by developmental stability. *Intelligence* 33: 203–213.

Prowse, TL, Saunders, SR, Schwarcz, HP, et al. 2008. Isotopic and dental evidence for infant and young child feeding practices in an Imperial Roman skeletal sample. *American Journal of Physical Anthropology* 137: 294–308.

Prowse, TL, Schwarcz, HP, Garnsey, P, et al. 2007. Isotopic evidence for age-related immigration to Imperial Rome. *American Journal of Physical Anthropology* 132: 510–519.

Prowse, TL, Schwarcz, HP, Saunders, SR, et al. 2004. Isotopic paleodiet studies of skeletons from the Imperial Roman-age cemetery of Isola Sacra, Rome, Italy. *Journal of Archaeological Science* 31: 259–272.

Pruetz, JD, and Bertolani, P. 2007. Savanna chimpanzees, *Pan troglodytes verus*, hunt with tools. *Current Biology* 17: 412–417.

Prüfer, K, Munch, K, Hellmann, I, et al. 2012. The bonobo genome compared with the chimpanzee and human genomes. *Nature* (published online June 13, 2012).

Prüfer, K, Racimo, F, Patterson, N, et al. 2014. The complete genome sequence of a Neanderthal from the Altai Mountains. *Nature* 505: 43–49.

Radespiel, U, Ratsimbazafy, JH, Rasoloharijaona, S, et al. 2012. First indications of a highland specialist among mouse lemurs (*Microcebus* spp.) and evidence for a new mouse lemur species from eastern Madagascar. *Primates* 53(2): 157–170.

Rae, TC, Koppe, T, and Stringer, CB. 2011. The Neanderthal face is not cold adapted. *Journal of Human Evolution* 60: 234–239.

Raff, JA, Bolnick, DA, Tackney, J, et al. 2011. Ancient DNA perspectives on American colonization and population history. *American Journal of Physical Anthropology* 146(4): 503–514.

Raff, RA. 2007. Book review: Intelligent design judged and found wanting. *Evolution and Development* 9: 402–404.

Raghavan, M, Skoglund, P, Graf, KE, et al. 2013. Upper Palaeolithic Siberian genome reveals dual ancestry of Native Americans. *Nature* (published online November 20, 2013).

Raichlen, DA, Gordon, AD, Harxcourt-Smith, WEH, et al. 2010. Laetoli footprints preserve earliest direct evidence of human-like bipedal biomechanics. PLOS ONE 5(3): e9769. doi:10.1371/journal.pone.0009769.

Raichlen, DA, Pontzer, H, and Sockol, M. 2008. The Laetoli footprints and early hominin locomotor kinematics. *Journal of Human Evolution* 54: 112–117.

Rakyan, VK, Down, TA, Balding, DJ, et al. 2011. Epigenome-wide association studies for common human diseases. *Nature Reviews: Genetics* 12: 529–541.

Ramankutty, N, Foley, JA, and Olejniczak, NJ. 2008. Land-use change and global food production. In AK Braimoh and PLG Vlek, eds., *Land Use and Soil Resources*. Netherlands: Springer. 23–40.

Ramirez Rozzi, FV, and Bermúdez de Castro, JM. 2004. Surprisingly rapid growth in Neanderthals. *Nature* 428: 936–939.

Rankinen, T, Zuberi, A, Chagnon, YC, et al. 2006. The human obesity gene map: The 2005 update. *Obesity* 14: 529–644.

Rasmussen, DT. 2007. Fossil record of the primates from the Paleocene to the Oligocene. In W Henke and I Tattersall, eds., *Handbook of Palaeoanthropology*, Berlin: Springer. 889–920.

Reed, KE. 2008. Paleoecological patterns at the Hadar hominin site, Afar Regional State, Ethiopia. *Journal of Human Evolution* 54: 743–76.

Reed, KE. 2013. Multiproxy paleoecology. Reconstructing evolutionary context in paleoanthropology. In D Begun, ed., *A Companion to Paleoanthropology*. Wiley-Blackwell, New York. doi:10.1002/9781118332344.ch11.

Reich, D, Green, RE, Kircher, M, et al. 2010. Genetic history of an archaic hominin group from Denisova Cave in Siberia. *Nature* 468: 1053–1060.

Reich, D, Patterson, N, Kircher, M, et al. 2011. Denisova admixture and the first modern human dispersals into Southeast Asia and Oceania. *The American Journal of Human Genetics* 89(4): 516–528.

Reich, D, Patterson, N, Campbell, D, et al. 2012. Reconstructing Native American population history. *Nature* 488: 370–374.

Research Project Steering Committee. 2006. *Northern Saskatchewan HIV/AIDS and HEPATITIS C Awareness Initiative: Research Project*. SPHERU, University of Saskatchewan, Saskatoon.

Richards, CL, Bossdorf, O, and Pigliucci, M. 2010. What role does heritable epigenetic variation play in phenotypic evolution? *BioScience* 60: 232–237.

Richards, MP, Harvati, K, Grimes, V, et al. 2008. Strontium isotope evidence of Neanderthal mobility at the site of Lakonis, Greece, using laser-ablation PIMMS. *Journal of Archaeological Science* 35: 1251–1256.

Richards, MP, Jacobi, R, Cook, J, et al. 2005. Isotope evidence for the intensive use of marine foods by Late Upper Palaeolithic humans. *Journal of Human Evolution* 49: 390–394.

Richards, MP, and Schmitz, RW. 2008. Isotope evidence for the diet of the Neanderthal type specimen. *Antiquity* 82: 553–559.

Richards, MP, and Trinkaus, E. 2009. Isotopic evidence for the diets of European Neanderthals and early modern humans. *Proceedings of the National Academy of Sciences* 106(38): 16034–16039.

Richmond, B, and Jungers, WL. 2008. *Orrorin tugenensis* femoral morphology and the evolution of hominin bipedalism. *Science* 319: 1662–1665.

Richmond, B, and Jungers, WL. 2012. Hominin proximal femur morphology from the Tugen Hills to Flores. In SR Reynolds and A. Gallagher, eds., *African Genesis: Perspectives on Hominin Evolution*. Cambridge: Cambridge University Press. 248–267.

Rightmire, GP. 2007. Later Middle Pleistocene *Homo*. In W Henke and I Tattersall, eds., *Handbook of Paleoanthropology*, Berlin: Springer. 1695–1715.

Rightmire, GP, Lordkipanidze, D, and Vekua, A. 2006. Anatomical descriptions, comparative studies, and evolutionary significance of the hominin skulls from Dmanisi, Republic of Georgia. *Journal of Human Evolution* 502: 115–141.

Robins, AH. 2009. The evolution of light skin color: Role of vitamin D disputed. *American Journal of Physical Anthropology* 139(4): 447–450.

Roebroeks, W, Sier, MJ, Nielsen, TK, et al. 2012. Use of red ochre by early Neandertals. *Proceedings of the National Academy of Sciences* 109(6): 1889–1894.

Roebroeks, W, and Villa, P. 2011. On the earliest evidence for habitual use of fire in Europe. *Proceedings of the National Academy of Sciences* 108(13): 5209–5214.

Roffman, I, Savage-Rumbaugh, S, Rubert-Pugh, E, et al. 2012. Stone tool production and utilization by bonobo-chimpanzees (*Pan paniscus*). *Proceedings of the National Academy of Sciences* 109: 14500–14503.

Rogers AL, Iltis, D, and Wooding, S. 2004. Genetic variation at the MC1R locus and the time since loss of human body hair. *Current Anthropology* 45: 105–108.

Rogers, TL, and Allard, T. 2004. Expert testimony and positive identification of human remains through cranial suture patterns. *Journal of Forensic Sciences* 49: 203–207.

Roksandic, M, Mihailovic, D, Mercier, N, et al. 2011. A human mandible (BH-1) from the Pleistocene deposits of Mala Balanica cave (Sićevo Gorge, Niš, Serbia). *Journal of Human Evolution* 61(2): 186–196.

Rolian, C, Dunsworth, H, McNulty, K, et al. 2013. More than the sum of its parts? Multivariate analysis of locomotor behavior in *Ardipithecus ramidus*. *American Journal of Physical Anthropology* 150(S56): 235.

Rolian, C, Lieberman, DE, and Hallgrímsson, B. 2010. The coevolution of human hands and feet. *Evolution* 64: 1558–1568.

Romita, D, Cheng, Y-L, and Diosady, LL. 2011. Microencapsulation of ferrous fumarate for the production of salt double fortified with iron and iodine. *International Journal of Food Engineering* 7 doi: 10.2202/1556-3758.2122.

Rose, KD, Chester, SGB, Dunn, RH, et al. 2011. New fossils of the oldest North American euprimate *Teilhardina brandti* (Omomyidae) from the Paleocene-Eocene thermal maximum. *American Journal of Physical Anthropology* 146: 281–305.

Rosenberg, NA, Mahajan, S, Ramachandran, S, et al. 2005. Clines, clusters, and the effect of study design on the inference of human population structure. *Public Library of Science Genetics* 1: e70.

Roth, EA, Ngugi, E, and Fujita, M. 2006. Self-deception does not explain high risk sexual behaviour in the face of HIV/AIDS: A test from northern Kenya. *Evolution and Human Behavior* 27: 53–62.

Roth, EA, Ngugi, E, and Fujita, M. 2009. HIV/AIDS risk and worry in Northern Kenya. *Health, Risk and Society* 11(3): 231–239.

Roth, G. 2012. Is the human brain unique? In A Fasalo, ed., *The Theory of Evolution and Its Impact*. Milan: Springer-Verlag 175–187.

Rougier, H, Milota, S, Rodrigo, R, et al. 2007. Peṣtera cu Oase 2 and the cranial morphology of early modern Europeans. *Proceedings of the National Academy of Sciences* 104: 1165–1170.

Ruff, CB. 2008. Relative limb strength and locomotion in *Homo habilis*. *American Journal of Physical Anthropology* 1381: 90–100.

Ruff, CB, Garofalo, E, and Holmes, MA. 2013. Interpreting skeletal growth in the past from a functional and physiological perspective. *American Journal of Physical Anthropology* 150: 29–37.

Ruiz-Torres, A, and Beier, W. 2005. On maximum human lifespan: Interdisciplinary approach about its limits. *Advances in Gerontology* 16: 14–20.

Russon, AE. 2009. Orangutan rehabilitation and reintroduction: successes, failures, and role in conservation. In SA Wich, S Suci, U Atmoko et al., eds., *Orangutans: Geographic Variation in Behavioral Ecology and Conservation*. Cambridge, MA: Oxford University Press. 327–350.

Russon, AE, and Andrews, K. 2011a. Orangutan pantomime: Elaborating the message. *Biology Letters* 7: 627–630.

Russon, AE, and Andrews, K. 2011b. Pantomime in great apes. Evidence and implications. *Communicative and Integrative Biology* 4: 315–317.

Ruxton, GD and Wilkinson, DM. 2011. Thermoregulation and endurance running in extinct hominins: Wheeler's models revisited. *Journal of Human Evolution* 61: 169–175.

Ryan, TM, Silcox, MT, Walker, A, et al. 2012. Evolution of locomotion in Anthropoidea: The semicircular canal evidence. *Proceedings of the Royal Society B. Biologiucal Sciences* 279: 3467–3475.

Sánchez-Quinto, F, Botigué, LR, Civit, S, et al. 2012. North African populations carry the signature of admixture with Neandertals. *PLOS ONE* 7(10): e47765.

Sandgathe, DM, Dibble, HL, Goldberg, P, et al. 2011. The Roc de Marsal Neandertal child: A reassessment of its status as a deliberate burial. *Journal of Human Evolution* 61(3): 243–253.

Sankar, P, and Kahn, JD. 2005 (October 11). BiDil: Race medicine or race marketing? *Health Affairs*.

Sankararaman, S, Mallick, S, Dannermann, M, et al. 2014. The genomic landscape of Neanderthal ancestry in present-day humans. *Nature* doi: 10.1038/nature12961.

Sankhyan, AR, Badam, GL, Dewangan, LN, et al. 2012. New postcranial hominin fossils from the Central Narmada Valley, India. *Advances in Anthropology* 2(3): 125–131.

Sanna, S, Jackson, AU, Nagaraja, R, et al. 2008. Common variants in the GDF5-UQCC region are associated with variation in human height. *Nature Genetics* 40: 198–203.

Sanz, C, Morgan D, and Gulick S. 2004. New insights into chimpanzees, tools, and termites from the Congo Basin. *American Naturalist* 164: 567–581.

Sapolsky, R.M. 2005. The influence of social hierarchy on primate health. *Science* 308: 648–652.

Saunders, SR, DeVito, C, and Katzenberg, MA. 1997. Dental caries in nineteenth century Upper Canada. *American Journal of Physical Anthropology* 104: 71–87.

Saunders, SR, Hoppa, R, and Southern, R. 1993. Diaphyseal growth in a nineteenth century skeletal sample of subadults from St Thomas' church, Belleville, Ontario. *International Journal of Osteoarchaeology* 3: 265–281.

Sawchuk, LA, and Burke, SDA. 1998. Gibraltar's 1804 yellow fever scourge: The search for scapegoats. *Journal of the History of Medicine and Allied Sciences* 53: 3–42.

Sawchuk, LA, and Burke, SDA. 2003. The ecology of a health crisis: Gibraltar and the 1865 cholera epidemic. *Cambridge Studies in Biological and Evolutionary Anthropology* 34: 178–215.

Sayers, K, and Lovejoy, CO. 2008. The chimpanzee has no clothes. *Current Anthropology* 49: 87–114.

Sayers, K, Raghanti, MA, and Lovejoy, CO. 2012. Human evolution and the chimpanzee referential doctrine. *Annual Review of Anthropology* 41: 119–138.

Scally, A, Dutheil, JY, Hillier, JDW, et al. 2012. Insights into hominid evolution from the gorilla genome sequence. *Nature* 483: 169–175.

Schell, L, Ravenscroft, J, Gallo, M, et al. 2007. Advancing biocultural models by working with communities: A partnership approach. *American Journal of Human Biology* 19: 511–524.

Scheonberg, MR, Lange, RT, and Saklofske, DH. 2007. A proposed method to estimate premorbid full scale intelligence quotient (FSIQ) for the Canadian Wechsler Intelligence Scale for Children–Fourth Edition (WISC-IV) using demographic and combined estimation procedures. *Journal of Clinical and Experimental Neuropsychology* 29: 867–878.

Scheper-Hughes, N, and Bourgois, P. 2004. Introduction: Making sense of violence. In N Scheper-Hughes and P Bourgois, eds., *Violence in War and Peace: An Anthology.* Malden: Blackwell. 2–31.

Schillaci, MA, Jones-Engel, L, Engel, GA, et al. 2005. Prevalence of enzootic simian viruses among urban performance monkeys in Indonesia. *Tropical Medicine and International Health* 10: 1305–1314.

Schillaci, MA, Jones-Engel, L, Engel, GA, et al. 2006. Exposure to human respiratory viruses among urban performing monkeys in Indonesia. *American Journal of Tropical Medicine and Hygiene* 75: 716–719.

Schrenk, F, Kullmer, O, and Bromage, T. 2007. The earliest putative *Homo* fossils. In W Henke and I Tattersall, eds., *Handbook of Paleoanthropology.* Berlin: Springer. 1611–1631.

Schroer, K, and Wood, B. 2013. Evolution of hominin postcanine macromorphology: A comparative meta-analysis. In GR Scott and JD Irish, eds., *Anthropological Perspectives on Tooth Morphology: Genetics, Evolution, Variation.* Cambridge: Cambridge University Press. 170–200.

Schuenemann, VJ, Bos, K, DeWitte, S, et al. 2011. Targeted enrichment of ancient pathogens yielding the pPCP1 plasmid of *Yersinia pestis* from victims of the Black Death. *Proceedings of the National Academy of Sciences* 108(38): E746–752.

Schurr, TG. 2004. The peopling of the New World. *Annual Review of Anthropology* 33: 551–583.

Schwartz, GT. 2012. Growth, development, and life history throughout the evolution of *Homo. Current Anthropology* 53: S395–S408.

Sclater, A. 2006. The extent of Darwin's knowledge of Mendel. *Journal of Biosciences* 31: 191–193.

Scott, RS, Godfrey, LR, Jungers, WL, et al. 2009. Dental microwear texture analysis of two families of subfossil lemurs from Madagascar. *Journal of Human Evolution* 56: 405–416.

Scott, RS, Ungar, PS, Bergstrom, TS, et al. 2005. Dental microwear texture analysis shows within-species diet variability in fossil hominins. *Nature* 436: 693–695.

Seevaratnam, R, Coburn, N, Cardoso, R, et al. 2011. A systematic review of the indications for genetic testing and prophylactic gastrectomy among patients with hereditary diffuse gastric cancer. *Gastric Cancer* doi 10.1007/s10120-011-0116-3.

Séguin, L, Nikiéma, B, Gauvin, L, et al. 2007. Duration of poverty and child health in the Quebec Longitudinal Study of Child Development: Longitudinal analysis of a birth cohort. *Pediatrics* 119: e1063–e1070.

Selby, M, Suwa, G, Simpson, S, et al. 2013. *Ardipithecus ramidus* proximal capitate morphology is most consistent with a locomotor ancestry of palmigrade arboreal clambering. *American Journal of Physical Anthropology* 150: 250 (abstract).

Sellen, DW. 2007. Evolution of infant and young child feeding: Implications for contemporary public health. *Annual Review of Nutrition* 27: 123–148.

Sellen, DW. 2010. Infant and young child feeding in human evolution. In T Moffat and T Prowse, eds., *Human Diet and Nutrition in Biocultural Perspective: Past Meets Present.* New York: Berghahn Press. 57–85.

Semaw, A, Simpson, S, Quade, J, et al. 2005. Early Pliocene hominids from Gona, Ethiopia. *Nature* 433: 301–305.

Sepkowski, D, and Ruse, M. 2009. *The Paleobiologic Revolution.* Chicago: University of Chicago Press.

Sepulchre, P, Ramstei, G, Fluteau, F, et al. 2006. Tectonic uplift and eastern African aridification. *Science* 313: 1419–1423.

Serre, D, Langaney, A, Chech, M, et al. 2004. No evidence of Neandertal mtDNA contribution to early modern humans. *Public Library of Science Biology* 2: 313–317.

Shang, H, Tong, H, Zhang, S, et al. 2007. An early modern human from Tianyuan Cave, Zhoukoudian, China. *Proceedings of the National Academy of Sciences* 104(16): 6573–6578.

Shaw, CN, Hofmann, CL, Petraglia, MD, et al. 2012. Neandertal humeri may reflect adaptation to scraping tasks, but not spear thrusting. *PLOS ONE* 7(7): e40349.

Simons, EL. 2008. Eocene and Oligocene Mammals of the Fayum, Egypt. In JC Fleagle and CC Gilbert, eds., *Elwyn Simons: A Search for Origins.* New York: Springer. 87–105.

Simpson, SW, Quade, J, Levin NE, et al. 2008. A female *Homo erectus* pelvis from Gona, Ethiopia. *Science* 322: 1089–1092.

Skinner, MF, and Sterenberg, J. 2005. Turf wars: Authority and responsibility for the investigation of mass graves. *Forensic Science International* 151: 221–232.

Skinner, MM, and Wood, BA. 2006. The evolution of modern human life history. In K Hawkes and RR Paine, eds., *The Evolution of Human Life History*. Albuquerque: School of American Research Press. 331–400.

Skinner, MM, Wood, BA, Boesch, C, et al. 2008. Dental trait expression at the enamel-dentine junction of lower molars in extant and fossil hominoids. *Journal of Human Evolution* 54: 173–186.

Slocombe, KE, and Zuberbühler, K. 2006. Food-associated calls in chimpanzees: Responses to food types or food preferences? *Animal Behaviour* 72: 989–999.

Smaers, JB, and Soligo, C. 2013. Brain reorganization, not relative brain size, primarily characterizes anthropoid brain evolution. *Proceedings of the Royal Society B* 280: 20130269. http://dx.doi.org/10.1098/rspb.2013.0269.

Smith, AC, Surridge, AK, Prescott, MJ, et al. 2012. Effect of colour vision status on insect prey capture efficiency of captive and wild tamarins (*Saguinus* spp.). *Animal Behaviour* 83: 479–486.

Smith, FH, Jankovic, I, and Karavanic, I. 2005. The assimilation model, modern human origins in Europe, and the extinction of Neandertals. *Quaternary International* 137: 7–19.

Smith, JE, Swanson, EM, Reed, D, et al. 2012. Evolution of cooperation among mammalian carnivores and its relevance to hominin evolution. *Current Anthropology* 53 Supplement 6: S436–S452.

Smith, SL. 2004. Skeletal age, dental age, and the maturation of KNM-WT 15000. *American Journal of Physical Anthropology* 125: 105–120.

Smith, T, Rose, KD, and Gingerich, P. 2006. Rapid Asia–Europe–North America geographic dispersal of earliest Eocene primate *Teilhardina* during the Paleocene–Eocene thermal maximum. *Proceedings of the National Academy of Sciences* 103: 11223–11227.

Smith, TM, Olejniczak, A, Reh, S, et al. 2008. Brief communication: Enamel thickness trends in the dental arcade of humans and chimpanzees. *American Journal of Physical Anthropology* 136: 237–241.

Smith, TM, Olejniczak, AJ, Zermeno, JP, et al. 2012. Variation in enamel thickness within the genus *Homo*. *Journal of Human Evolution* 62: 395–411.

Smith, TM, Tafforeau, P, Reid, DJ, et al. 2007. Earliest evidence of modern human life history in North African early *Homo sapiens*. *Proceedings of the National Academy of Sciences* 104(15): 6128–6133.

Smith, TM, Tafforeau, P, Reid, DJ, et al. 2010. Dental evidence for ontogenetic differences between modern humans and Neanderthals. *Proceedings of the National Academy of Sciences* 107(49): 20923–20928.

Smuts, BB. 1985. *Sex and Friendship in Baboons*. New York: Aldine Publishing Co.

Society for Applied Anthropology. 2009. *Mission Statement*. www.sfaa.net/about/governance/mission.

Sockol, MD, Raichlen, DA, and Pontzer, H. 2007. Chimpanzee locomotor energetics and the origin of human bipedalism. *Proceedings of the National Academy of Sciences* 104: 12265–12269.

Soficaru, A, Dobos, A, and Trinkaus, E. 2006. Early modern humans from the Peştera Muierii, Baia de Fier, Romania. *Proceedings of the National Academy of Sciences* 103(46): 17196–17201.

Solyom, S, and Kazazlan, HH Jr. 2012. Mobile elements in the human genome: Implications for disease. *Genome Medicine* 4: 12.

Speakman, JR. 2006. Thrifty genes for obesity and the metabolic syndrome—Time to call off the search? *Diabetes and Vascular Disease Research* 31: 7–11.

Sponheimer, M, Alemseged, Z, Cerling, T, et al. 2013. Isotopic evidence of early hominin diets. *Proceedings of the National Academy of Sciences* www.pnas.org/cgi/doi/10.1073/pnas.1222579110.

Sponheimer, M, Codron, D, Passey, BH, et al. 2009. Using carbon isotopes to track dietary change in modern, historical, and ancient primates. *American Journal of Physical Anthropology* 140: 661–670.

Spoor, F, Leakey, MG, Gathogo, PN, et al. 2007. Implications of new early *Homo* fossils from Ileret, east of Lake Turkana, Kenya. *Nature* 448: 688–691.

Ståhl, PL, and Lundeberg, J. 2012. Toward the single-hour high-quality genome. *Annual Review of Biochemistry* 81: 359–378.

Stanford, C. 2012. Chimpanzees and the behavior of *Ardipithecus ramidus*. *Annual Review of Anthropology* 41: 139–149.

Stanford, D, and Bradley, B. 2004. The North-Atlantic ice-edge corridor: A possible Paleolithic route to the New World. *World Archaeology* 36: 459–478.

Statistics Canada. 2006. *Census*. www.statcan.gc.ca.

Statistics Canada. 2012. *Human Activity and the Environment. Waste Management in Canada*. Minister of Industry Catalogue No. 16-201-XIE.

Steadman, DW, Adams, BJ, and Konigsberg, LW. 2006. Statistical basis for positive identification in forensic anthropology. *American Journal of Physical Anthropology* 131: 27–32.

Steiper, ME, and Seiffert, ER. 2012. Evidence for a convergent slowdown in primate molecular rates and its implications for the timing of early primate evolution. *Proceedings of the National Academy of Sciences* 109: 6006–6011.

Stephens, D, and Dudley, R. 2004. The drunken monkey hypothesis: The study of fruit-eating animals could lead to an evolutionary understanding of human alcohol abuse. *Natural History* 113: 40–44.

Steudel-Numbers, K, and Tilkins, MJ. 2004. The effect of lower limb length on the energetic cost of locomotion: Implications for fossil hominins. *Journal of Human Evolution* 47: 95–109.

Steudel-Numbers, K, Weaver, TD, and Wall-Scheffler, CM. 2007. The evolution of human running: Effects of changes in lower-limb length on locomotor economy. *Journal of Human Evolution* 53: 191–196.

Stock, JT, and Pfeiffer, SK. 2004. Long bone robusticity and subsistence behaviour among Later Stone Age foragers of the forest and fynbos biomes of South Africa. *Journal of Archaeological Science* 31: 999–1013.

Stoneking, M, and Krause, J. 2011. Learning about human population history from ancient and modern genomes. *Nature Reviews: Genetics* 12: 603–614.

Storm, P, Wood, R, Stringer, C, et al. 2013. U-series and radiocarbon analyses of human and faunal remains from Wajak, Indonesia. *Journal of Human Evolution* 64(5): 356–365.

Stringer, CB. 2008. The Neanderthal–*H. sapiens* interface in Eurasia. In K Harvati and T Harrison, eds., *Neanderthals Revisited: New Approaches and Perspectives*. New York: Springer. 315–324.

Stringer, CB. 2012. The status of *Homo heidelbergensis* (Schoetensack 1908). *Evolutionary Anthropology* 21: 101–107.

Stringer, CB, Palike, H, van Andel, TH, et al. 2004. Climatic stress and the extinction of the Neanderthals. In TH van Andel and W Davies, eds., *Neanderthal and Modern Humans in the European Landscape of the Last Glaciation,* Mcdonald Institute Monographs. Toronto: Brown Book Company. 233–240.

Strum, S, and Fedigan, LM, eds. 2000. *Primate Encounters.* Chicago: University of Chicago Press.

Stumpf, RM, Thompson, ME, and Nott, CD. 2008. A comparison of female mating strategies in *Pan troglodytes* and *Pongo* spp. *International Journal of Primatology* 29: 865–884.

Sturm, RA, and Frudakis, TN. 2004. Eye colour: Portals into pigmentation genes and ancestry. *Trends in Genetics* 20: 327–332.

Sun, JX, Helgason, A, Masson, G, et al. 2012. A direct characterization of human mutation based on microsatellites. *Nature Genetics* 44: 1161–1165.

Surbeck, M, Fowler, A, Deimel, C, and Hohmann, G. 2009. Evidence for the consumption of arboreal, diurnal primates by bonobos (*Pan paniscus*). *American Journal of Primatology* 71(2): 171–174.

Surbeck, M, and Hohmann, G. 2008. Primate hunting by bonobos at Lui Kotale, Salonga National Park. *Current Biology* 18: R906–R907.

Surbeck, M, Mundry, R, and Hohmann, G. 2011. Mothers matter! Maternal support, dominance status and mating success in male bonobos (*Pan paniscus*). *Proceedings of the Royal Society B. Biological Sciences* 278: 590–598.

Susman, RL. 2008. Brief communication: Evidence bearing on the status of *Homo habilis* at Olduvai Gorge. *American Journal of Physical Anthropology* 137: 356–361.

Suwa, G, and Kono, R. 2005. A micro-CT-based study of linear enamel thickness in the mesial cusp section of human molars: Re-evaluation of methodology and assessment of within-tooth, serial, and individual variation. *Anthropological Science* 113: 273–289.

Suwa, G, Kono, RT, Katoh, S, et al. 2007. A new species of great ape from the late Miocene epoch in Ethiopia. *Nature* 448, 921–924.

Swedell, L. 2006. *Strategies of Sex and Survival in Hamadryas Baboons: Through a Female Lens.* Upper Saddle River: Pearson.

Swedell, L, and Plummer, T. 2012. A Papionin multilevel society as a model for hominin social evolution. *International Journal of Primatology* 33: 1165–1193.

Tamm, E, Kivisild, T, Reidla, M, et al. 2007. Beringian standstill and spread of Native American founders. *PLOS ONE* 2(9): e829.

Tattersall, I. 2007. *Homo ergaster* and its contemporaries. In W Henke and I Tattersall, eds., *Handbook of Paleoanthropology.* Berlin: Springer. 1633–1653.

Tattersall, I, and Schwartz, JH. 2009. Evolution of the genus *Homo. Annual Review of Earth and Planetary Science* 37: 67–92.

Teaford, MF. 2006. What do we know and not know about diet and enamel structure? In PS Ungar, ed., *Evolution of the Human Diet: The Known, the Unknown, and the Unknowable.* Oxford: Oxford University Press. 56–76.

Teichroeb, JA, and Sicotte, P. 2008. Infanticide in ursine colobus monkeys (*Colobus vellerosus*) in Ghana: New cases and a test of the existing hypothesis. *Behaviour* 145: 727–755.

Temple, R, and Stockbridge, NL. 2007. BiDil for heart failure in black patients: The U.S. Food and Drug Administration perspective. *Annals of Internal Medicine* 146: 57–62.

Thariq, MG, Munasinghe, HP, and Abeysekara, JD. 2010. Designing chairs with mounted desktop for university students: Ergonomics and comfort. *International Journal of Industrial Ergonomics* 40: 8–18.

The ENCODE Project Consortium. 2012. An integrated encyclopedia of DNA elements in the human genome. *Nature* 489: 57–74.

Thompson, CL, Whitten, PL, and Norconk, MA. 2011. Can male white-faced saki monkeys (*Pithecia pithecia*) detect female reproductive state? *Behaviour* 148: 1313–1331.

Thompson, JL, and Nelson, AJ. 2000. The place of Neandertals in the evolution of hominid patterns of growth and development. *Journal of Human Evolution* 38: 475–495.

Thorpe, S, Holder, R, and Crompton, R. 2007. Origin of human bipedalism as an adaptation for locomotion on flexible branches. *Science* 316: 1328–1331.

Timpson, N, Heron, J, Smith, GD, et al. 2007. Comment on papers by Evans et al. and Mekel-Bobrov et al. on evidence for positive selection of *MCPH1* and *ASPM. Science* 317: 1036a.

Tishkoff, SA, Reed, FA, Ranciaro, A, et al. 2007. Convergent adaptation of human lactase persistence in Africa and Europe. *Nature Genetics* 39: 31–40.

Tobias, PV, Wang, Q, and Cormack, J. 2000. Davidson Black and Raymond A. Dart: Asian-African parallels in palaeoanthropology. *Acta Anthropologica Sinica Supplement* 19: 299–306.

Tobias, PV, Wang, Q, and Cormack, J. 2001. The establishment of palaeoanthropology in South Africa and China: With especial reference to the remarkably similar roles of Raymond A. Dart and Davidson Black. *Transactions of the Royal Society of South Africa* 561: 1–9.

Tocheri, MW, Orr, CM, Jacofsky, MC, et al. 2008. The evolutionary history of the hominin hand since the last common ancestor of *Pan* and *Homo. Journal of Anatomy* 212: 544–562.

Tocheri, MW, Orr, CM, Lasen, SJ, et al. 2007. The primitive wrist of *Homo floresiensis* and its implications for hominin evolution. *Science* 317: 1743–5.

Toro, R, and Burnod, Y. 2005. A morphogenetic model for the development of cortical convolutions. *Cerebral Cortex* 15: 1900–1913.

Toro-Moyano, I, Martínez-Navarro, B, Agusti, J, et al. 2013. The oldest human fossil in Europe, from Orce (Spain). *Journal of Human Evolution* 65(1): 1–9.

Toth, N, and Schick, K. 2009. The Oldowan: The tool making of early hominins and chimpanzees compared. *Annual Review of Anthropology* 38: 289–305.

Townsend, SW, Slocombe, KE, Thompson, ME, et al. 2007. Female-led infanticide in wild chimpanzees. *Current Biology* 1710: R355–R356.

Tremblay, MS, Perez, CE, Ardern, CI, et al. 2005. Obesity, overweight, and ethnicity. *Health Reports* 16(4): 23–32.

Trevathan, W. 2007. Evolutionary medicine. *Annual Review of Anthropology* 36: 139–154.

Trinkaus, E. 2005. Early modern humans. *Annual Review of Anthropology* 34: 207–230.

Trinkaus, E. 2007. European early modern humans and the fate of Neandertals. *Proceedings of the National Academy of Sciences* 104: 7367–7372.

Trinkaus, E. 2012. Neandertals, early modern humans, and rodeo riders. *Journal of Archaeological Science* 39: 3691–3693.

Twitchett, RJ. 2006. The palaeoclimatology, palaeoecology, and palaeoenvironmental analysis of mass extinction events. *Palaeogeography, Palaeoclimatology, Palaeoecology* 232: 190–213.

Ulijaszek, SJ, and Lofink, H. 2006. Obesity in biocultural perspective. *Annual Review of Anthropology* 35: 337–360.

Underhill, PA, and Kivisild, T. 2007. Use of Y chromosome and mitochondrial DNA population structure in tracing human migrations. *Annual Review of Genetics* 41: 539–564.

Ungar, P. 2004. Dental topography and diets of *Australopithecus afarensis* and early *Homo*. *Journal of Human Evolution* 46: 605–622.

Ungar, P. 2012. Dental evidence for the reconstruction of diet in African early *Homo*. *Current Anthropology* 53(6): S318–S329.

Ungar, P, Grine, FE, and Teaford, MF. 2006a. Diet in early *Homo*: A review of the evidence and a new model of adaptive versatility. *Annual Review of Anthropology* 35: 209–228.

Ungar, P, Grine, FE, Teaford, MF, et al. 2006b. Dental microwear and diets of African early *Homo*. *Journal of Human Evolution* 50: 78–95.

Ungar, P, Grine, FE, and Teaford, MF. 2008. Dental microwear and diet of the Plio-Pleistocene hominin *Paranthropus boisei*. *Public Library of Science ONE* 3: e2044.

Ungar, P, and Lucas, PW. 2010. Tooth form and function in biological anthropology. In CS Larsen, ed., *A Companion to Biological Anthropology*. Chichester: Wiley-Blackwell. 516–529.

van Arsdale, AP, and Wolpoff, MH. 2012. A single lineage in early Pleistocene *Homo*: Size variation continuity in early Pleistocene *Homo* crania from East Africa and Georgia. *Evolution* (early view, published online December 20, 2012).

van Der Merwe, NJ, Masao, FT, and Bamford, MK. 2008. Isotopic evidence for contrasting diets of early hominins *Homo habilis* and *Australopithecus boisei* of Tanzania. *South African Journal of Science* 104: 153–155.

van Heuverswyn, F, and Peeters, M. 2007. The origins of HIV and implications for the global epidemic. *Current Infectious Disease Reports* 9: 338–346.

van Holst Pellekaan, S. 2013. Genetic evidence for the colonization of Australia. *Quaternary International* 285: 44–56.

van Holst Pellekaan, SM, Ingman, M, Roberts-Thomson, J, et al. 2006. Mitochondrial genomics identifies major haplogroups in Aboriginal Australians. *American Journal of Physical Anthropology* 131: 282–294.

van Oostdam, J, Donaldson, SG, Feeley, M, et al. 2005. Human health implications of environmental contaminants in Arctic Canada: A review. *Science of the Total Environment* 351–352: 165–246.

van Schaik, CP, van Noordwijk, MA, and Vogel, ER. 2009. Ecological sex differences in wild orangutans. In SA Wich, SS Utami Atmoko, T Setia, and CP van Schaik, eds., *Orangutans: Geographic Variation in Behavioral Ecology and Conservation*. New York: Oxford University Press. 49–64.

Varki, A, and Nelson, DL. 2007. Genomic comparisons of humans and chimpanzees. *Annual Review of Anthropology* 36: 191–209.

Varrela, J. 2006. Masticatory function and malocclusion: A clinical perspective. *Seminars in Orthodontics* 12: 102–109.

Vernot, B, and Akey, JM. 2014. Resurrecting surviving Neandertal lineages from modern human genomes. *Science* doi: 10.1126/science.1245938

Vetter, J. 2006. Wallace's *other* line: Human biogeography and field practice in the Eastern colonial tropics. *Journal of the History of Biology* 39: 89–123.

Visalberghi, E, Addessi, E, Truppa, V, et al. 2009. Selection of effective stone tools by wild bearded capuchin monkeys. *Current Biology* 19: 213–217.

Visscher, PM, Macgregor, S, Benyamin, B, et al. 2007. Genome partitioning of genetic variation for height from 11,214 sibling pairs. *American Journal of Human Genetics* 81: 1104–1110.

von Hunnius, TE, Roberts, CA, Boylston, A, et al. 2006. Histological identification of syphilis in pre-Columbian England. *American Journal of Physical Anthropology* 129: 559–566.

Wagner, DP, and McAvoy, JM. 2004. Pedoarchaeology of Cactus Hill, a sandy Paleoindian site in southeastern Virginia, USA. *Geoarchaeology* 19: 297–322.

Wagner, GA, Krbetschek, M, Degering, D, et al. 2010. Radiometric dating of the type-site for *Homo heidelbergensis* at Mauer, Germany. *Proceedings of the National Academy of Sciences* 107(46): 19726–19730.

Waldram, J, Herring, A, and Kue Young, T. 2006. *Aboriginal Health in Canada: Historical, Cultural, and Epidemiological Perspectives*, 2nd ed. Toronto: University of Toronto Press.

Walker, J, Cliff, R, and Latham, A. 2006. U-Pb isotopic age of the StW 573 hominid from Sterkfontein, South Africa. *Science* 314: 1592–1594.

Wall-Scheffler, CM, Geiger, K, and Steudel-Numbers, K. 2007. Infant carrying: The role of increased locomotory costs in early tool development. *American Journal of Physical Anthropology* 133: 841–846.

Wapler, U, Crubezy, E, and Schultz, M. 2004. Is cribra orbitalia synonymous with anemia? Analysis and interpretation of cranial pathology in Sudan. *American Journal of Physical Anthropology* 123: 333–339.

Ward, CV, Kimbel, WH, and Johanson, DC. 2011. Complete fourth metatarsal and arches in the foot of *Australopithecus afarensis*. *Science* 331: 750–753.

Ward, LM, Gaboury, I, Ladhani, M, et al. 2007. Vitamin D-deficiency rickets among children in Canada. *Canadian Medical Association Journal* 1772: 161–166.

Watanabe, T, Watanabe, S, Shinya, K, et al. 2009. Viral RNA polymerase complex promotes optimal growth of 1918 virus in the lower respiratory tract of ferrets. *Proceedings of the National Academy of Sciences* 106: 587–591.

Waters, MR, Forman, SL, Jennings, TA, et al. 2011. The Butter-milk Creek complex and the origins of Clovis at the Debra L. Friedkin site, Texas. *Science* 331: 1599–1603.

Waters, MR, Stafford, TW Jr, McDonald, HG, et al. 2011. Pre-Clovis mastodon hunting 13,800 years ago at the Manis site, Washington. *Science* 334: 351–353.

Waters-Rist, A, Bazaliiskii, VI, Weber, A, et al. 2010. Activity-induced dental modification in Holocene Siberian hunter–fisher–gatherers. *American Journal of Physical Anthropology* 143: 266–278.

Waters-Rist, A, Bazaliiskii, VI, Weber, A, et al. 2011. Infant and child diet in Neolithic hunter–fisher–gatherers from Cis-Baikal, Siberia: Intra-long bone stable nitrogen and carbon isotope ratios. *American Journal of Physical Anthropology* 146: 225–241.

Watson, J, Payne, R, Chamberlain, A, et al. 2009. The kinematics of load carrying in humans and great apes: Implications for the evolution of human bipedalism. *International Journal of Primatology* 80: 309ff.

Watts, DP. 2008. Scavenging by chimpanzees at Ngogo and the relevance of chimpanzee scavenging to early hominin behavioral ecology. *Journal of Human Evolution* 54: 125–133.

Weaver, TD, Roseman, CC, and Stringer, CB. 2007. Were Neandertal and modern human cranial differences produced by natural selection or genetic drift? *Journal of Human Evolution* 53: 135–145.

Webb, E, White, C, and Longstaffe, F. 2013. Dietary shifting in the Nasca Region as inferred from the carbon- and nitrogen-isotope compositions of archaeological hair and bone. *Journal of Archaeological Science* 40: 129–139.

Weiss, K. 2004. The unkindest cup. *The Lancet* 363: 1489–1490.

Weiss, K. 2012. Opinion: What is the human genome? *The Scientist* August 17, 2012.

Weiss, SF. 2006. Human genetics and politics as mutually beneficial resources: The case of the Kaiser Wilhelm Institute for Anthropology, human heredity, and eugenics during the Third Reich. *Journal of the History of Biology* 39: 41–88.

Wells, JCK, DeSilva, JM, and Stock, JC. 2012. The Obstetric Dilemma: An ancient game of Russian Rolette, or a variable dilemma sensitive to ecology? *Yearbook of Physical Anthropology* 55: 40–71.

Weyrich, T, Matusik, W, Pfister, H, et al. 2008. Analysis of human faces using a measurement-based skin reflectance model. Accessed online October 25, 2008 at http://people.csail.mit.edu/addy/research/weyrich06-skin.pdf.

Whitcome, KK, Shapiro, LJ, and Lieberman, DE. 2007. Fetal load and the evolution of lumbar lordosis in bipedal hominins. *Nature* 450: 1075–1078. White, CD, Nelson, AJ, Longstaffe, FJ, et al. 2009. Landscape bioarchaeology at Pacatnamu, Peru: Inferring mobility from δ13C and δ15N values of hair. *Journal of Archaeological Science* 36(7): 1527–1537.

White, R. 2007. Systems of personal ornamentation in the early Upper Palaeolithic: Methodological challenges and new observations. In P Mellars, K Boyle, O Bar-Yosef, and C Stringer, eds., *Rethinking the Human Revolution: New Behavioural and Biological Perspectives on the Origin and Dispersal of Modern Humans*. McDonald Institute Monographs, Cambridge: McDonald Institute for Archaeological Research, 287–302.

White, TD. 2006. Early hominid femora—The inside story. *Comptes Rendus Palevolution* 5: 99–108.

White, TD, Ambrose, SH, Suwa, G, et al. 2010. Response to comment on the paleoenvironment of *Ardipithecus ramidus*. *Science* 328: 1005e doi: 10.1126/science.1185466.

White, TD, Asfaw, B, Beyene, Y, et al. 2009. *Ardipithecus ramidus* and the paleobiology of early hominids. *Science* 326: 75–86.

White, TD, WoldeGabriel, G, Asfaw, B, et al. 2006. Asa Issie, Aramis, and the origin of *Australopithecus*. *Nature* 440: 883–889.

Whitelaw, E. 2006. Sins of the fathers, and their fathers. *European Journal of Human Genetics* 14: 131–132.

Whiten, A. 2007. *Pan* African culture: Memes and genes in wild chimpanzees. *Proceedings of the National Academy of Sciences* 104: 17559–17560.

Wich, SA, Swartz, KB, Hardus, ME, et al. 2009. A case of spontaneous acquisition of a human sound by an orangutan. *Primates* 50: 56–64.

Wiley, A, and Allen, JS. 2008. *Medical Anthropology: A Biocultural Approach*. Oxford: Oxford University Press.

Wilkins, J, and Chazan, M. 2012. Blade production ~500,000 years ago at Kathu Pan 1, South Africa: Support for a multiple origins hypothesis for early Middle Pleistocene blade technologies. *Journal of Archaeological Science* 39: 1883–1900.

Wilkins, J, Schoville, BJ, Brown KS, and Chazan, M. 2012. Evidence for early hafted hunting technology. *Science* 338(6109): 942–946.

Wilkinson, RD, Steiper, ME, Soligo, C, et al. 2011. Dating primate divergences through an integrated analysis of palaeontological and molecular data. *Systematic Biology* 60: 16–31.

Williams, BA, Kay, RF, Kirk, EC, et al. 2010. *Darwinius masillae* is a strepsirrhine—A reply to Franzen et al. (2009). *Journal of Human Evolution* 59: 567–573.

Williams, BA, and Rogers, T. 2006. Evaluating the accuracy and precision of cranial morphological traits for sex determination. *Journal of Forensic Sciences* 51: 729–735.

Williams, J, White, C, and Longstaffe, F. 2005. Trophic level and macronutrient shift effects associated with the weaning process in the Maya Postclassic. *American Journal of Physical Anthropology* 128: 781–790.

Williams, JS, and Katzenberg, MA. 2008. Investigating season of death using carbon isotope data from the hair of 500-year-old Peruvian mummies. *Proceedings of the VI Mummy Congress* (February 2007), Teguise, Lazarote: University of Las Palmas de Gran Canaria.

Williams, JS, and Katzenberg, MA. 2012. Seasonal fluctuations in diet and death during the late horizon: A stable isotopic analysis of hair and nail from the central coast of Peru. *Journal of Archaeological Science* 39: 41–57.

Williams, N. 2008. The population bomb. *Current Biology* 18: R535–R536.

Wilmé, L, Goodman, SM, and Ganzhorn, JU. 2006. Biogeographic evolution of Madagascar's microendemic biota. *Science* 312: 1063–1065.

Wilson, K, Rosenberg, MW, and Abonyi, S. 2011. Aboriginal peoples, health and healing approaches: The effects of age and place on health. *Social Science & Medicine* 72: 355–364.

Wilson, W, Milner, J, Bulkan, J, et al. 2006. Weaning practices of the Makushi of Guyana and their relationship to infant and child mortality: A preliminary assessment of international recommendations. *American Journal of Human Biology* 18: 312–324.

Wilson, WM, Bulkan, J, Piperata BA, et al. 2011. Nutritional status of Makushi Amerinidian children and adolescents of Guyana. *Annals of Human Biology* 38: 615–629.

Winder, IC, King, GCP, Devès, M, et al. 2013. Complex topography and human evolution: The missing link. *Antiquity* 87: 333–349.

Winkler, LA. 2005. Morphology and relationships of the orangutan fatty cheek pads. *American Journal of Primatology* 17: 305–319.

Witherspoon, DJ, Wooding, S, Rogers, AR, et al. 2007. Genetic similarities within and between human populations. *Genetics* 176: 351–359.

Wittiger, L, and Sunderland-Groves, JL. 2007. Tool use during display behavior in wild cross river gorillas. *American Journal of Primatology* 69: 1307–1311.

Wolfe, ND, Heneine, W, Carr, JK, et al. 2005. Emergence of unique primate T–lymphotropic viruses among central African bushmeat hunters. *Proceedings of the National Academy of Sciences* 102(22): 7994–7999.

Wollenweber, B, Porter, JR, and Lübberstedt, T. 2005. Need for multidisciplinary research toward a second green revolution. *Current Opinion in Plant Biology* 8: 337–341.

Wolpoff, MH, Hawks, J, Senut, B, et al. 2006. Is the Toumaï cranium TM 266 a hominid? *PaleoAnthropology* 2006: 36–50.

Wong, MH, Wu, SC, Deng, WJ, et al. 2007. Export of toxic chemicals—A review of the case of uncontrolled electronic-waste recycling. *Environmental Pollution* 149: 131–140.

Wood, BA. 2011. Did early *Homo* migrate "out of" or "in to" Africa? *Proceedings of the National Academy of Sciences* 108(26): 10375–10376.

Wood, BA. 2013. Paleontology: Gritting their teeth. *Nature* 493: 486–487.

Wood, BA, and Harrison, T. 2011. The evolutionary context of the first hominins. *Nature* 470: 347–352.

Wood, BA, and Leakey, M. 2011. The Omo-Turkana Basin fossil hominins and their contribution to our understanding of human evolution in Africa. *Evolutionary Anthropology* 20: 264–292.

Wood, BA, and Lonergan, N. 2008. The hominin fossil record: Taxa, grades, and clades. *Journal of Anatomy* 212: 354–376.

Wooding, S. 2004. Natural selection: Sign, sign, everywhere a sign. *Current Biology* 14: R700–R701.

Wooding, S, Bufe, B, Grassi, C, et al. 2006. Independent evolution of bitter-taste sensitivity in humans and chimpanzees. *Nature* 440: 930–4.

Wooding, S, and Jorde, LB. 2006. Duplication and divergence in humans and chimpanzees. *BioEssays* 28: 35–338.

World Bank Development Indicators 2005. http://data.worldbank.org/products/data-books/WDI-2005.

World Development Bank Indicators 2013. Poverty Rates at National Poverty Lines. http://wdi.worldbank.org/table/2.7.

Worm, B, Barbier, EB, Beaumont, N, et al. 2006. Impacts of biodiversity loss on ocean ecosystem services. *Science* 314: 787–790.

Worm, B, Hilborn, R, Baum, JK, et al. 2009. Rebuilding global fisheries. *Science* 325: 578–585.

Wrangham, RW. 2008. The International Primatological Society as a coalition: Primatologists and the future of primates. *International Journal of Primatology* 29: 3–11.

Wrangham, RW. 2009. *Catching Fire: How Cooking Made Us Human*. New York: Basic Books.

Wrangham, RW, and Carmody, R. 2010. Human adaptation to the control of fire. *Evolutionary Anthropology* 19: 187–199.

Wrangham, RW, Jones, JH, Laden, G, et al. 1999. The raw and the stolen: Cooking and the ecology of human origins. *Current Anthropology* 40: 567–594.

Wu, X. 2004. On the origin of modern humans in China. *Quaternary International* 117: 131–140.

WWF (World Wide Fund for Nature). 2012. *Living Planet Report*. http://awsassets.panda.org/downloads/living_planet_report_2.pdf.

Yaeger, R, Avila-Bront, A, Abdul, K, et al. 2008. Comparing genetic ancestry and self-described race in African Americans born in the United States and in Africa. *Cancer Epidemiology Biomarkers and Prevention* 17: 1329–1338.

Yahya, M. 2007. Polio vaccines—"No thank you!" Barriers to polio eradication in northern Nigeria. *African Affairs* 106: 185–204.

Yang, DY, and Watt, K. 2005. Contamination controls when preparing archaeological remains for ancient DNA analysis. *Journal of Archaeological Science* 32: 331–336.

Yang, N, MacArthur, D, Gulbin, J, et al. 2003. *ACTN3* genotype is associated with human elite athletic performance. *American Journal of Human Genetics* 73: 627–631.

Yotova, V, Lefebvre, J-F, Moreau, C, et al. 2011. An X-linked haplotype of Neandertal origin is present among all non-African populations. *Molecular Biology and Evolution* 28(7): 1957–1962.

Young, A, and Rees, T. 2011. Medical anthropology enters the 21st century. *Journal of Nervous and Mental Disorders* 199: 592–596.

Young, JH, Chang, YP-C, Kim, JD-O, et al. 2005. Differential susceptibility to hypertension is due to selection during the out-of-Africa expansion. *Public Library of Science Genetics* 1: e82.

Yuan, Q, Joiner, WJ, and Sehgal, A. 2006. A sleep-promoting role for the *Drosophila* serotonin receptor 1A. *Current Biology* 16: 1051–1062.

Zalmout, IS, Sanders, WJ, MacLatchy, LM, et al. 2010. New Oligocene primate from Saudi Arabia and the divergence of apes and Old World monkeys. *Nature* 466: 360–364.

Zeller, A. 2007. What's in a picture? A comparison of drawings by apes and children. *Semiotica* 166: 181–214.

Zhu, RX, Potts, R, Xie, F, et al. 2004. New evidence on the earliest human presence at high northern latitudes in northeast Asia. *Nature* 431: 559–562.

Zihlman, AL. 2013. Engendering human evolution. In D. Bolger, ed., *A Companion to Gender History*. New York: John Wiley & Sons. 23–44.

Zilhão, J, Angelucci, DE, and Badal-Garcia, E. 2010. Symbolic use of marine shells and mineral pigments by Iberian Neandertals. *Proceedings of the National Academy of Sciences* 107(3): 1023–1028.

Zollikofer, CPE, and Ponce de León, MS. 2013. Pandora's growing box: inferring the evolution and development of hominin brains from endocasts. *Evolutionary Anthropology* 22: 20–33.

Zollikofer, CPE, Ponce de León, MS, Lieberman, DE, et al. 2005. Virtual cranial reconstruction of *Sahelanthropus tchadensis*. *Nature* 434: 755–759.

Glossary

a priori   arguing from cause to effect; deduced from prior knowledge or presumption (p. 28)

absolute (chronometric) dating a method of dating that assigns a specific age and estimated error to a fossil or site (e.g., 1.6 ± 0.23 million years) (p. 143)

accelerator mass spectrometry (AMS) dating a method of radiocarbon dating used to date very small samples (p. 144)

acclimatization   physiological changes that occur in response to changes in the environment (p. 334)

Acheulian   a Lower Paleolithic stone tool industry usually associated with *Homo erectus* (p. 239)

adapids   lemur-like primates from the Eocene epoch (p. 153)

adaptability   the tendency for an organism to achieve increased functional capacity through a modification of body form and/or physiological pathway when faced with an environmental stressor (p. 14)

adaptation   a state of existence or a process by which an organism is or becomes better suited to its circumstances of life (p. 26)

adaptationist   a perspective that commonly seeks an adaptive explanation or mechanism for the presence or form of a particular phenotypic character (p. 84)

adaptive immune systems   a component of the immune response targets specific pathogens and requires prior exposure to establish an "immunological memory"; a short-term adaptive immune response is transferred to the newborn across the placenta and via breast milk, although it is less effective in resisting infection than that developed by an individual through his or her own exposure to invading organisms (p. 381)

adaptive radiation   the opportunistic and relatively rapid diversification of new forms into new ecological zones through a series of speciation events (p. 83)

additive effect   in quantitative genetics, refers to a genetic contribution to a trait that either increases or decreases (if the effect has a "negative value") the degree of expression (p. 312)

Aegyptopithecus   a propliopithecid from the Oligocene epoch (p. 155)

aerobic metabolism   the conversion of glucose to energy within mitochondria in the presence of oxygen, from sources such as carbohydrates, fatty acids, and amino acids (p. 183)

affiliative   amicable behaviours that promote social cohesion (p. 131)

agonistic behaviours   threatening behaviours that are directed toward an opponent or adversary (p. 130)

albinism   a condition characterized by a complete lack of melanin (p. 332)

aligned sequence   in molecular genetics research, sequences of DNA (or RNA) derived from homologous sites within the genome are literally arranged or aligned to identify similarities and differences between species, the latter resulting from, for example, point mutations, insertions, or deletions (p. 204)

aliphatic acids   a group of fatty acids that, secreted by a sexually receptive female, act as chemical messengers (pheromones) to alert males to her reproductive status (p. 132)

alleles   alternative forms of a gene (p. 59)

allometry   refers to patterns of size and shape change among parts of organisms at different sizes or among related organisms either living or extinct (p. 28)

allopatry   species that "live apart" and do not occupy the same geographic locale; allopatric species are presumed to exist in genetic isolation (p. 77)

alpha   the highest ranking individual in a group (p. 125)

alpha taxonomy   the process of classifying organisms to genus and species, based on extensive data extracted from morphology, behaviour, DNA and so on. In the case of fossil species, detailed analyses of skeletal and dental morphology are essential elements in deriving the alpha taxonomy (p. 196)

altriciality   a state at birth in which the newborn lacks the ability to provide for itself and receives food and care from its mother or other caregiver (p. 176)

altruistic   behaviour that benefits other members of a group but is either of no benefit to the individual engaged in it or is harmful to that individual (p. 131)

alveoli   the bony sockets for teeth present in the upper and lower jaws (p. 204)

amino acids   molecules that make up proteins (p. 55)

amplifying   a step in DNA analysis in which small quantities of DNA collected by investigators are multiplied to provide sufficient material for the subsequent steps of identifying the nucleotide sequence and comparing it with known sequences stored in databases or obtained from putative relatives (p. 365)

anagenesis   a pattern of slow, linear evolutionary change, also known as Darwinian gradualism (p. 81)

analogous   a similarity in structure or function resulting from independent adaptation to comparable circumstances in life, rather than evolutionary descent (p. 26)

ancient DNA (aDNA)   DNA in ancient (i.e., nonmodern) remains recoverable from hard tissues (bones and teeth) and in exceptional cases of preservation, hair and soft tissue. (p. 66)

androcentric   male-centred; the corresponding term for female-centred arguments is gynocentrism (p. 181)

angiosperm radiation hypothesis   the hypothesis that primate features evolved as adaptations to flowering plants (p. 100)

antagonistic pleiotropy theory   the theory that aging is the result of a gene that benefits an organism early in life by enhancing fertility but that is detrimental later on (p. 325)

anthropogenic   literally, "of human origin," as an outcome of human actions or deliberate manufacture (e.g., urban crowding, pollution) (p. 350)

Anthropoidea   the suborder that includes monkeys, apes, and humans (p. 101)

anthropological linguistics   the study of the origin, evolution, and use (social context) of languages (p. 8)

anthropology   the global and comparative study of humankind, past and present (p. 6)

anthropometry   the measurement of body form (p. 13)

apatite   the major inorganic component of bones and teeth (p. 231)

applied anthropology   a subfield emphasizing project-based, problem-oriented, practical applications of anthropological knowledge (p. 8)

arboreal hypothesis   the hypothesis that primate features evolved as adaptations to a life in the trees (p. 100)

archaeology   the systematic study of past human lifeways through an analysis of human interactions with and modifications of the environment, including the origin and development of technology (p. 8)

archaeotourism   a form of tourism in which the attraction consists of archaeological sites, typically megalithic locations (e.g., cities, pyramids) (p. 378)

archaic hominins   hominins that show a mosaic of *Homo erectus* and modern human traits (p. 250)

argon-argon dating   a method of absolute dating that measures the isotopic ratio of ^{40}A to ^{39}A (p. 144)

aridification   a drying trend resulting from lower seasonal or annual precipitation levels (p. 201)

assemblages   the collection of all remains of plants or animals from paleontological contexts (p. 204)

assumption   a condition or feature unverified or uncontrolled but taken to be as stated for the purpose of argument (p. 29)

atlatl a device fashioned from bone, antler, or wood that increases mechanical advantage in spear-throwing, increasing distance and force (p. 284)

autosomal chromosomes   chromosomes other than the sex chromosomes (p. 57)

avidity   having a physiological craving for a particular thing (p. 303)

balanced polymorphism   polymorphism means "many types" and in genetic terms denotes phenotypes established at proportions that do not require mutation to maintain their existence; balanced polymorphism occurs when a heterozygote has a selective advantage over alternative homozygotes, thereby maintaining allele diversity within the population (p. 86)

basal anthropoids   the earliest anthropoids (p. 154)

basal hominins   a qualitative term distinguishing the earliest widely accepted hominins from those forms later assigned to the genus *Homo* (p. 198)

basal metabolic rate   the amount of energy needed to sustain organ function while at rest and without needing to produce or lose body heat (p. 178)

base   a chemical unit making up part of a DNA and RNA molecule. There are four bases in DNA: adenine, thymine, guanine, and cytosine. In RNA, thymine is replaced with uracil (p. 53)

basicranial flexion   the degree of angling of the base of the skull from which the position of the larynx and size of the pharynx can be inferred (p. 267)

behavioural ecology   the study of the ways in which primates adapt behaviourally to their environments (p. 120)

behavioural modernity   having the attributes of modern human behaviour (e.g., cognition, language, symbolism, social relationships) (p. 283)

beriberi   a disease caused by a deficiency of vitamin B_1 resulting in a number of neurological, cardiovascular, and physiological ailments (p. 326)

Beringia   an exposed land bridge that connected Siberia and Alaska during the last glacial period when sea levels were lower (p. 290)

bifacial tool   a stone tool that has had flakes removed from opposite sides to produce a cutting edge (p. 239)

bilophodont   molar teeth characterized by four cusps connected by two ridges of enamel (p. 157)

binomial nomenclature   a "two-name" system developed by Linnaeus to identify all plants and animals according to genus and species (p. 37)

bioarchaeology   the study of human remains from archaeological contexts (p. 337)

biocultural   a research perspective that recognizes the interrelationship of biology and the many facets of culture, including technology and social behaviour (p. 8)

biodiversity   variation in life forms within a given ecosystem (p. 147)

biogeography   the study of the geographic distribution of organisms, habitats, and evolutionary history as it relates to landscape and ecology (p. 77)

biological anthropology   the study of the biological origins, evolution, and contemporary diversity of humans and their primate relatives (p. 4)

biological profile   in forensic anthropology, the fundamental biological characteristics of a person, including age, sex, body size, and ancestry (p. 363)

biological reductionism   a method of analysis which argues that biological complexity can be explained in terms of physical laws applied to individual parts (p. 84)

biological species concept   species defined on the basis of reproductive inclusion within its membership and reproductive isolation from other species (p. 39)

biological systematics   the formal science of classification and taxonomy, specifying a set of rules and guidelines for categorizing biological diversity and deriving phylogenies (p. 196)

biomedical anthropology   the study of health from a biocultural and epidemiological perspective (p. 318)

biostratigraphic dating   a method of relative dating that involves dating a fossil based on associated faunal remains that have been securely dated using other methods (p. 143)

bipedalism   moving on two legs (p. 103)

birth spacing   the amount of time that passes between life births, e.g., birthdate to birthdate. In primate life history, birth spacing is correlated with a number of variables, including female rank, and access to food resources is a primary determinant of birth spacing (p. 181)

blade tools   tools made of long, parallel-sided flakes struck from a prepared core (p. 283)

body mass index   a measure of body fatness, calculated as body weight $(kg)/height(m)^2$ (p. 327)

brachiation   a form of locomotion characterized by arm-over-arm movement (p. 103)

breccia   a rock formation composed of stone fragments embedded within a fine-grained cement-like matrix (p. 216)

burins   stone tools used to shape bone, wood, antler, and ivory into other tools (p. 284)

calvarium   the skull, excluding the facial bones and mandible (p. 251)

canine honing   sharpening, in this instance of one tooth, the upper canine, through repeated contact with another tooth, the lower third premolar (p. 184)

captive   housed in environments such as zoos and colonies where movement is restricted (p. 120)

carbon-14 (radiocarbon) dating   a method of absolute dating based on the radioactive decay of ^{14}C into ^{14}N (p. 144)

carriers   individuals who are heterozygous for a recessive trait and who do not physically manifest the trait (p. 62)

carrying capacity the population size of a given organism that a habitat could comfortably sustain given available resources, denoted by the symbol K; K fluctuates with variation in resources, and for human populations these include not only space, food, and water but also variables such as sanitation, health care, and social capital (p. 377)

Catarrhines Old World monkeys, apes, and humans (p. 109)

catastrophism Cuvier's notion that fossil forms are produced through series of cataclysmic events and that changes from one kind to the next in succession result from new forms arriving from areas not affected by the event (p. 36)

Cenozoic era the geological era in which mammals, including primates, evolved (p. 145)

Châtelperronian an Upper Paleolithic tool industry associated with late Neandertals (p. 263)

chromosome a structure composed of DNA and found in the nucleus of cells (p. 53)

chronospecies designation of species identity by virtue of the passage of time; two fossils may be deemed species if separated by sufficient time (p. 81)

cingulum a raised ridge of enamel found on the upper molar teeth (p. 159)

clades groups of species sharing a closer ancestry among themselves than any of them do with species of other clades (p. 81)

cladistic a taxonomic method emphasizing phylogenetic relatedness and based on the existence of *clades* composed of members of evolving lineages (p. 89)

cladogenesis a pattern of evolution characterized by branching, in which a single species may give rise to one (or more) "daughter" species that subsequently diverge; also known as horizontal speciation (p. 81)

cladogram a branching depiction of relationships among taxa based on proximity of evolutionary descent (p. 90)

classic Neandertals Neandertals of western Europe that exhibited the most pronounced morphological characteristics of this group of hominins (p. 256)

classification the act of arranging or sorting objects according to features held in common; assigning such objects to a proper class (p. 37)

cline a continuous gradient observed in geographical space over which the frequency of expression of a character changes across contiguous populations (p. 302)

coca-colonialism refers to the ability of multinational companies to usurp local traditions and lifeways, effectively replacing local customs with Western surrogates (p. 380)

co-dominant a trait in which both alleles are expressed (p. 61)

codons each codon is a unit of three bases/nucleotides that code for a particular amino acid (p. 56)

collagen a type of protein that forms the main organic component of bone (p. 231)

commingled in burial contexts, the situation in which more than one individual is present in the same grave, making it difficult to distinguish which skeletal elements belong to which individual (p. 362)

community-based research an approach in which investigators work directly with a community to develop, organize, and implement a research program (p. 10)

comparative method understanding relationships among organisms by examining the similarities and differences present in various aspects of their biology (p. 36)

competitive exclusion a phenomenon in which two species closely related in phenotype and ecology come into direct competition for resources. In these cases one species will either become extinct or adopt a new phenotype (morphology and/or behaviour), allowing it to exploit other resources. (p. 219)

composite tools tools consisting of two or more components (e.g., stone tools hafted onto wooden spear shafts) (p. 283)

concealed ovulation ovulation occurs during that stage in a placental female mammal's reproductive cycle (estrus) during which she is receptive to sexual intercourse (either physiologically or induced through copulation); it may be signalled with swelling and reddening of the genital area, or through chemical means such as pheromones. Thus, concealed ovulation refers to the absence of signalling, such that the male is unable to detect when a female may be likely to conceive. Some recent evidence suggests that chemical signalling still occurs between human females and males (p. 181)

conditio sine qua non a Latin term meaning "without which there is nothing." In this context, large brains were once thought to be the preeminent hominin feature from which all else followed. We know now that this is not the case (p. 170)

consortships among primates, temporary affiliations of males and females for the purposes of mating and reproduction; in some species (e.g., chimpanzees), males may forcibly coerce females into a consortship (p. 132)

conspecific belonging to the same species (p. 80)

constraint genetic or functional limitation on the activity or expression of a characteristic (p. 84)

continental drift the movement of the plates that make up the earth's continents (p. 146)

contingency being dependent on the occurrence or existence of a prior event or thing (p. 27)

convective cooling reduction of body temperature by air movement facilitating heat loss through evaporation of sweat (p. 175)

convergence a path toward development of homoplasy: evolution acts on different ancestral structures to converge upon a similar outcome in response to similar adaptive pressures (p. 91)

coprolite preserved feces (p. 342)

copy number variation inter-individual variations in the number of copies of a gene present in the genome; classic Mendelian genetics suggests that we should possess two copies for each gene, one inherited from each parent. Recent studies suggest, however, that individuals can have more than two copies, through processes such as duplication and recombination (p. 385)

core area the portion of a primate's home range that contains the greatest concentration of resources and that is most heavily used by a group (p. 102)

correlated response changes that occur in one feature are consistently associated with changes occurring in another (p. 185)

cosmogenic nuclide dating a method of absolute dating that looks at the ratio of aluminum-26 (^{26}Al) to beryllium-10 (^{10}Be) in quartz sand crystals (p. 145)

cranial morphology the relative size and shape configuration of the various bones of the skull (p. 9)

craniodental a descriptive term referring to the hard tissues, bone, and teeth comprising the skull (p. 208)

craniometry the metrical assessment of the size and shape of the human skull (p. 20)

cross-fertilized plants (or animals) that are fertilized by fusing the reproductive cells of two different organisms belonging to the same species (p. 59)

cross-sectional geometry the mass and distribution (shape) of cortical bone viewed in a plane perpendicular to the long axis of a tubular bone, such as the femur or metacarpal (p. 259)

crown group   the last common ancestor of a clade plus all of its descendants, including living members of the clade (p. 148)

cultural anthropology   the study of the structure and function of human societies, usually from a cross-cultural perspective (p. 8)

cultural intelligence   the capacity of humans to acquire early in life complex skills for negotiating social situations (p. 312)

cursorial   pertaining to animals adapted for efficient running (p. 183)

cytokines   proteins produced by white blood cells in response to the presence of pathogens; they interact with cells of the immune system and stimulate them to respond to the infection (p. 330)

cytoplasm   the substance found within the cell membrane and surrounding the nucleus (p. 56)

Darwinism   evolution resulting from natural selection acting on random variation in populations, through which more fit individuals are favoured in "the struggle for existence"; as conceived by Charles Darwin (p. 27)

data   observations, measurements, facts (known or assumed) that form the basis for a conclusion; singular *datum* (p. 28)

dating error   the degree to which a date derived from an absolute or relative technique differs from the actual date (p. 143)

day ranges   the geographic space through which primates move in one day (p. 102)

deletions   mutations characterized by the loss of DNA (p. 53)

demes   local breeding populations; a deme is a subset of a species within which most members find a mate (p. 77)

demographers   researchers who study population dynamics, including measures such as fertility, mortality, migration, survivorship, and life expectancy (p. 371)

demographic transition   the change in a population's age and sex structure with changing birth and death rates. Declines in mortality are typically followed by declines in fertility, shifting a population from an expansion phase to one of stability or contraction (p. 371)

dental formula   the number of each type of tooth in one quadrant of the mouth (p. 100)

dental microwear   microscopic wear on the enamel surfaces of the teeth, primarily due to diet (p. 150)

dental topographic analysis   a method of analysis that involves using a laser scanner to generate 3D models of teeth and GIS to measure features on the surfaces of those teeth (p. 231)

developmental adaptation hypothesis   the hypothesis that the physiological characteristics exhibited by high-altitude populations arise during growth and development (p. 334)

diaphyses   the shafts of the long bones (p. 235)

diastema   a space between adjacent teeth in the dental row into which the protruding canine from the opposite jaw fits in a closed mouth, found   in nonhuman primates and some early hominins (p. 184)

dichromatic   a condition in which an animal possesses two light-sensitive pigments in the cones in the retina of the eye, making it possible to see blue and green (p. 98)

diphyodont   having two sets of teeth: permanent (adult) and deciduous (baby) teeth (p. 99)

diploid   having a full set of paired chromosomes; in humans, each somatic cell contains 23 pairs of chromosomes (p. 56)

directional selection   a form of positive or negative selection resulting in a shift in phenotypes toward one end of the distribution, typically occurring in dynamic and changing environments (p. 82)

discrete (Mendelian) traits   traits that are controlled by genes at a single locus; also referred to as monogenic traits (p. 59)

disposable soma theory   the theory that   organisms balance their energy needs by directing more of their energy to reproduction and less to maintaining the body (p. 325)

distal   in skeletal anatomy, a position farther from the midline of the body (e.g., the elbow is distal to the shoulder joint); in teeth, the term refers to the tooth surface facing the back of the mouth (p. 207)

distolingual   the conjunction of the rearward (distal, away from the midline of the mouth) and inner (lingual, or tongue-facing) surfaces of a tooth (p. 184)

diurnal   active during the day (p. 98)

diversifying selection   a form of positive selection favouring the extremes of the distribution of phenotypes and/or negative

selection against the most common expression; may result in sympatric speciation (p. 83)

DNA   deoxyribonucleic acid, the fundamental genetic material of life (p. 53)

DNA methylation   a chemical modification of DNA that adds methyl group compounds to certain base pairs (adenine and cytosine) during cell division and differentiation and which may be inherited (p. 366)

dominance hierarchies   social structures in which males or females hold positions of rank determined either through competition or inheritance (p. 125)

dominant   the allele or trait that is expressed (p. 59)

Dryopithecus   a genus of large-bodied hominoids that lived in Europe during the Miocene epoch (p. 160)

ecological footprint   a measure of the ecological impact of human behaviour and activity, measured in the amount of land and seascape required, per person, to produce resources consumed and to absorb waste produced (p. 377)

ectoparasites   parasites on the outside of the body (e.g., in the fur) (p. 131)

effective population size   a measure of reproductive potential based on the likelihood that individuals in a population of a given size contribute genes equally to succeeding generations (p. 283)

electron spin resonance (ESR) a method of absolute dating that involves measuring electrons trapped in materials such as teeth (p. 144)

empty-calorie foods   in nutritional science, empty-calorie foods offer no nutrition other than energy (calories); the vast majority of "junk foods" fall into this category (p. 380)

encephalized   "encephalization" refers to the ratio of brain size to body size; the higher this ratio for a given species, the more encephalized it is said to be (p. 169)

endemism   the state of being found exclusively in a particular place (p. 147)

endocasts   impressions of the inner surface of the cranium and outer surface of the brain, which may occur naturally as "fossils" or from moulds created in the laboratory (p. 187)

endurance running the idea that our ancestors evolved the capability for long distance, metabolically efficient running as a unique aspect of human bipedal locomotion (p. 183)

energetic efficiency the assessment of the relative metabolic cost of performing a given task (p. 175)

energetics of gestation and growth the hypothesis that the evolution of larger brain size required babies to be born at an earlier stage of fetal development due to the increasing cost of gestation for the mother; in effect, it requires less energy to feed a newborn infant than to prolong gestation (p. 177)

energy budget a compendium of the sources and expenditures of energy, typically measured in calories or kilojoules (p. 181)

entheseal relating to entheses, sites of attachment of muscles, ligaments, and tendons to bone (p. 342)

entoptic images that arise from within the eye during altered states of consciousness (p. 286)

enzymes proteins that catalyze chemical reactions in the body (p. 53)

Eocene the second epoch of the Cenozoic era, dating from about 56 to 34 Ma (p. 153)

epicanthic fold a fold of skin of the upper eyelid adjacent to the bridge of the nose covering the medial canthus (corner) of the eye, commonly present in peoples of Central and East Asian ancestry (p. 301)

epidemics outbreaks of disease exceeding the normal level of occurrence (p. 319)

epidemiologic transition model developed by epidemiologist Abdel Omran to explain changing patterns of health and disease over time (p. 319)

epidemiology the study of the distribution and determinants of disease (p. 318)

epigenetic mechanisms acting during mitosis (development) to modify gene expression without modifying the actual DNA sequence; may result in heritable variation (p. 74)

epiphyses the caps at the ends of the long bones; bone growth ceases when the epiphyses fuse to the diaphysis (p. 235)

epistemology the study or theory of knowledge, including its production, validation, and application (p. 26)

epoch a measure of geologic time that partitions geologic eras (e.g., Cenozoic) into smaller units, defined with regard to major climatological/environmental events (p. 145)

ergonomics the application of anthropological methods and analysis in the design of functional and efficient clothing and work environments, with the intent of maximizing comfort and safety (p. 358)

essentialism Plato's idea that what exists in the world and is experienced by the human senses is an imperfect representation of an underlying, perfect, and immutable ideal, or essence, knowable only by the mind (p. 32)

estrus period of sexual receptivity in females, correlated with ovulation (p. 98)

ethnography an account of field research exploring various practices and phenomena within a given society; in contrast, ethnology is the comparative study of different cultural systems (p. 8)

eugenics literally "true breeding," a social philosophy proposing that humankind might be improved through direct intervention in reproduction, including the restriction or elimination of particular groups deemed unworthy (p. 21)

eukaryotes organisms that have within their cells a nucleus containing DNA (p. 53)

eurytopic organisms that are able to live in diverse habitats and geographic ranges; the prefix "eury" means "broad, wide" and the affix "topic" refers to "place" (p. 209)

evidentiary anything that constitutes evidence or that has the quality of evidence, as a substantiation of fact, related to a court proceeding (p. 365)

evo-devo evolutionary developmental biology; a branch of evolutionary theory that invokes a prominent role for embryonic development and epigenetic mechanisms in the ontogeny and phylogeny of phenotypes (p. 74)

evolutionary medicine the application of Darwinian evolutionary theory to medicine (p. 355)

exemplar a sample of DNA obtained from a known individual to be used in comparison with an unknown sample for purposes of matching and identification (p. 365)

expensive tissue hypothesis (ETH) a hypothesis accounting for the added metabolic cost of increasing brain size

through the reduction of other "fixed cost" tissues; the hypothesis suggests that human ancestors reduced the cost of digestion to transfer energy resources to the expanding brain (p. 190)

experimental archaeology a field of archaeology that uses a number of different methods to test hypotheses about how artifacts and structures may have been made and used (p. 230)

extant still existing; commonly used to refer to living species (p. 149)

extinction the complete disappearance of a particular species from a local habitat owing to factors that may be internal (related to the organism's biology) or external (related to environmental change over which the organism has no influence) (p. 36)

facultative bipedalism adopting a two-legged posture only under particular circumstances as an exception to a habitual non-bipedal form of locomotion (p. 170)

fallback foods resources on which a species relies when its preferred, more easily acquired and processed foods are unavailable (p. 219)

Fayum a fossil-rich region of Egypt once home to many Oligocene anthropoids (p. 155)

feeble-mindedness an artificial construct that suggested that defects of personality, intellect, ethnicity, or behaviour were inborn, and so could be selected against by policies restricting reproduction; sterilization was often the method of choice (p. 308)

fission–fusion a type of multi-male/multi-female social group whose membership changes frequently as sub-units split apart (fission) and later rejoin (fusion) (p. 124)

fission-track dating a method of absolute dating that involves counting the number of tracks produced by the decay (fission) of the uranium isotope ^{238}U contained in certain kinds of rocks (p. 144)

floating island model the hypothesis that the ancestors of New World monkeys rafted across the Atlantic from Africa to South America on floating islands of vegetation (p. 157)

fluorine dating a method of relative dating that involves comparing the amount of fluorine that has accumulated in fossils found at the same site (p. 143)

folivorous leaf-eating (p. 103)

folk taxonomies informal albeit consensual classifications of the world used by ordinary people in everyday life (p. 298)

food insecurity the real or anticipated lack of safe, nutritious foods that would normally be available at all times and in socially acceptable ways (p. 381)

foramen magnum "large passage," the foramen magnum is the largest hole in the cranium, through which the brain stem passes to become the spinal cord (p. 206)

forensic anthropology the application of anthropological knowledge to solving offences committed against people, including homicide and war crimes (p. 6)

forest hypothesis the suggestion that the hominin clade diverged from panins while still occupying a woodland/forest habitat, as suggested by paleoecological reconstruction of fossil localities (p. 202)

founder effect the potentially biased sampling of the genetic variation in a species due to the isolation of a small number of its members (p. 72)

free radicals unstable molecules that react with other molecules, causing damage to the body's cells (p. 325)

free-ranging animals whose movements are not hindered by humans (p. 120)

frugivorous fruit-eating (p. 103)

functional genomics the study of the dynamic actions and interactions of genes and proteins (p. 14)

gallery forest dense, canopied forest found along water courses such as rivers and lakeshores (p. 202)

gamete sex cell; ovum or sperm (p. 57)

gene flow the movement of genes with or without the movement of individuals over geographic space (p. 82)

genes sequences of DNA that code for proteins (p. 52)

genetic bottleneck a sudden constriction on the genetic diversity appearing in a generation, commonly associated with a reduction in population size (p. 88)

genetic code the sequence of nucleotides in DNA or RNA that determines the specific amino acid sequence in protein synthesis (p. 56)

genetic divergence an estimate of the time since two genomes diverged, based on the number of differences observed and assuming a constant rate of mutation (p. 204)

genetic drift random changes in allele frequencies in small populations independent of selection (p. 82)

genetic load formally, the average deviation of an individual from the best possible phenotype determined by the relative proportion of deleterious alleles he or she carries; because genetic load varies from 0 (maximum fitness) to 1.0 (minimum fitness), it can also be taken as a measure of the probability that an individual will die before reproducing (p. 385)

genetic screening a practice in medical genetics involving identification of potentially harmful genotypes (p. 87)

genetics the study of genes and how traits are transmitted from one generation to the next (p. 52)

genomics the comparative and evolutionary study of the genomes of different species (p. 14)

genotype the genetic makeup of an organism (p. 61)

geocentrism the concept that the earth is the centre of the known universe, around which all other heavenly bodies revolve, attributed to the Greek astronomer Ptolemy but known before his time (p. 32)

geologic time scale the division of the earth's geologic events into time periods such as eras and epochs (p. 145)

geophagy the intentional consumption of soil (p. 130)

Gondwanaland the landmass consisting of South America, Africa, Antarctica, Australia, Madagascar, and India as a supercontinent from 510 to 180 Ma (p. 146)

gracile small or slightly built; among australopithecines, refers to those species lacking the skeletal and dental features associated with the megadont adaptation (p. 209)

gradistic a taxonomic method that groups forms into named categories (the major units of which are termed *grades*) based on similarity of form, behaviour, and/or ecology; also known as phenetics (p. 89)

graminivorous grass-eating (p. 103)

Great Chain of Being Aristotle's ordered, hierarchical, and static view of the world (p. 33)

grooming claw a claw found on the second toe, used in grooming (p. 106)

gummivorous gum-eating; may also consume sap or resin (p. 103)

habituated accustomed to the presence of humans (p. 121)

half-life the amount of time it takes for half of an existing quantity of radioactive material to decay (p. 144)

hand axe a teardrop-shaped stone tool characteristic of the Acheulian industry (p. 240)

haplogroups groups of similar haplotypes that share a common ancestor; haplotypes are groups of genes that are inherited together (p. 291)

haploid having a single set of unpaired chromosomes; in humans, each of our sex cells contains 23 single-stranded chromosomes (p. 57)

Haplorhini the suborder that comprises the tarsiers, monkeys, apes and humans (p. 101)

Hardy-Weinberg Equilibrium a model specifying the conditions under which the frequency of alleles or phenotypes in a natural population remain in equilibrium unless acted on by one or more evolutionary forces (p. 73)

healthy immigrant effect a pattern in which the initially positive health status of new immigrants declines following immigration as they adopt less healthy lifestyles in their new country of residence (p. 327)

height-for-age a measure of achieved growth in height, standardized for age; a person suffering significant growth deficits for their age compared to normal standards is considered stunted (p. 380)

heliocentrism the now well-established view that the planets in our solar system revolve about the sun; the Copernican model also incorporates the essential ideas of the daily rotation of the earth on a tilted axis (p. 33)

heritability the proportion of phenotypic variation that can be ascribed to genotypic variation in a specific population (p. 64)

heterodont having different kinds of teeth e.g., molars, premolars, incisors, canines (p. 99)

heterosis also known as heterozygote advantage; the tendency for offspring of genetically distinct individuals to have increased vigour as they are less likely to express deleterious recessive alleles, which increase in frequency when males and females with similar genetic background mate (p. 74)

heterozygous having two different alleles at a single genetic locus (p. 61)

holism the integrated study of all aspects of human life (biological, cultural, historical, psychological, etc.) in order to develop a comprehensive view of the whole of the human condition (p. 6)

holotype the specimen that serves as the "name-bearer" of a fossil species and from which a description of the salient features of the taxon are obtained. It need not be the sole source of information for identifying a member of the taxon, nor does the holotype need to be a typical example (p. 197)

home base an area likely associated with shelter and water to which hominins would repeatedly return from foraging (p. 181)

home range the entire area exploited by an animal or group of animals (p. 102)

homeostasis the maintenance within the body of a stable environment (p. 335)

hominin a term inclusive of modern humans and their bipedal ancestors (p. 12)

Homininae the taxonomic subfamily that includes modern humans and our earlier ancestors, as well as chimpanzees and bonobos (p. 101)

hominoids members of the superfamily Hominoidea; they include apes and humans (p. 110)

homoiology similarities that occur among organisms by virtue of a bone's ability to respond to existing mechanical forces; similar behaviours will reproduce such forces and thus the associated morphology, which may be confused with genetic relationships (p. 220)

homologous chromosomes chromosomes that go together in a pair (p. 58)

homologous traits referring to homology, which is similarity among characters as a result of inheritance from a common ancestor (p. 90)

homoplasies analogous characters in different taxa that appear as a result of independent evolution; such a character, (the singular form is "homoplasy") is not present in the last common ancestor of the taxa in question (p. 90)

homozygous having two identical alleles at a single genetic locus (p. 61)

human biology a branch of biological anthropology that examines modern population diversity (p. 13)

human factors engineers specialists who study the relationship between humans and the products they interact with on a daily basis (p. 358)

human leukocyte antigens HLAs are the chief component of the major histocompatibility complex and regulate the human immune response (p. 305)

hybrid zones ecological regions in which closely related species overlap in occurrence, allowing for interbreeding to occur, producing hybrid offspring (p. 77)

hyoid bone a bone in the neck that supports the tongue and provides attachment for muscles that connect to the larynx (p. 268)

hypoxia low oxygen availability, characteristically associated with high altitude (p. 14)

immutable unchanging over time, or unchangeable; an idea traceable to the Greek philosopher Aristotle, stating that forms exist today as they were when created, have not changed in the past, and cannot change in the future (p. 32)

inbreeding depression reduced vigour in an organism by virtue of increased homozygosity resulting from mating between related individuals having similar DNA (p. 85)

incipient species related populations that, although capable of successful reproduction, are prevented from doing so by some barrier and that as a result may increasingly diverge to the point of becoming separate species (p. 41)

industrial melanism increased pigmentation resulting from human modification of the environment, such as occurred during the Industrial Revolution (p. 54)

infanticide the killing of infants, in this context as a strategy to solicit reproductive opportunity by the adult male (p. 135)

insectivorous insect-eating (p. 103)

insertions mutations characterized by the addition of DNA into a length of chromosome (p. 53)

insular dwarfism a process by which a founding population becomes isolated in a small environment such as an island and consequently undergoes a reduction in size (p. 245)

insulin resistance the failure of body cells to respond to insulin in order to regulate plasma glucose, resulting in elevated levels of both insulin (hyperinsulemia) and glucose (hyperglycemia) (p. 329)

interbirth interval the length of time between successive births (p. 125)

interdisciplinary an investigative approach that brings diverse fields together to create a new arena of study (p. 6)

intermembral index a measure of the relative lengths of the upper and lower limbs, calculated as (humerus length + radius length) × 100/(femur length + tibia length) (p. 102)

intrasexual "intra" means within; thus intrasexual variation refers to differences that exist within males or females separately (p. 185)

inversions mutations in which a section of DNA is reversed (p. 53)

ischial callosities patches of hardened skin on the rear end that facilitate sitting (p. 109)

isotopes an isotope is a measurable form of a chemical element varying in the number of neutrons within its nucleus (e.g., ^{12}C and ^{14}C are different isotopes of carbon; an atom of the former has 6 protons and 6 neutrons and the latter has two extra neutrons) (p. 11)

isotopic signatures refers to the ratio of stable isotopes of a particular element, for example, $^{13}C/^{12}C$; this is expressed as $\delta^{13}C$ in per mil (‰) (p. 231)

karyotype arrangement of the full set of chromosomes by numbered pairs (p. 57)

keystone species a species whose ecological role produces a significant impact on its environment, including the status of other species; the loss of a keystone species often has deleterious consequences for the local ecosystem (p. 16)

kin selection the tendency of individuals to direct beneficial behaviour toward relatives living within the same social group (p. 132)

klinorhynchy downward tilting of the face relative to the cranial base (p. 161)

knuckle-walkers primates that display a form of locomotion characterized by walking on all four limbs with the body weight partially supported by the middle phalanges of the hands (p. 102)

K-selection strategy a reproductive strategy in which females have few offspring and invest greater parental care in those offspring (p. 100)

lactase persistence in humans, the continued production of the enzyme lactase necessary for digesting the milk sugar lactose, past childhood (p. 82)

laryngeal sac an expanded larynx or voice box used to produce vocalizations (p. 111)

larynx an organ in the neck responsible for the production of sound; also known as the voice box (p. 267)

last common ancestor   a term designating that species from which diverging clades evolved (p. 178)

Later Stone Age   the period of time spanning 40,000 to 10,000 years ago in Africa (p. 284)

Laurasia   the landmass consisting of North America, Europe, and Asia (p. 146)

Law of Inheritance of Acquired Characteristics   Lamarck's second law stipulates that those changes resulting from use and disuse will, if occurring in both parents, be transmitted to offspring (p. 39)

Law of Superposition   layers ("strata", sing. "stratum") within a sedimentary geological deposit are laid down from oldest to most recent, permitting assignment of relative dates to items contained in the deposit (p. 30)

Law of Use and Disuse   Lamarck's first law, which suggests that the use or disuse of parts, reflecting an organism's needs and circumstances, will cause that part to develop or reduce accordingly (p. 39)

Levallois   a tool-manufacturing technique of the Middle Paleolithic that involved making tools from a prepared core (p. 262)

Lewis hunting phenomenon   a physiological reaction characterized by alternating cycles of vasoconstriction and vasodilation (p. 337)

Liem's Paradox   a model in biology that describes the apparent paradox between a specialized phenotype and a generalized behaviour; the paradox is resolved if the specialized phenotype does not restrict an organism from nonspecialized behaviours (p. 219)

life history   the occurrence (timing, duration, etc.) of specific events and traits characteristic of a species. Common life history variables include gestation length, interbirth interval, age at sexual maturity, and maximum life span (p. 112)

linear enamel hypoplasia   horizontal defects in tooth enamel that represent episodes of physiological stress that occurred while the teeth were forming (p. 262)

local breeding populations   members of a geographically dispersed species who find mates in a local region rather than from farther afield (p. 301)

locus   the location of a gene on a chromosome (p. 53)

Lower Paleolithic   the period associated with the Oldowan and Acheulian stone tool industries (p. 229)

lunate sulcus (LS)   a fissure found in the anterior portion of the occipital lobe that demarcates the primary visual cortex; readily visible in nonhuman primate brains, the LS is often not seen in humans (p. 187)

macroevolution   large-scale evolutionary events, typically viewed over geological time, leading to speciation and the formation of higher taxonomic categories (p. 39)

Mammalia   the class to which all mammals belong; this includes placental, egg-laying, and marsupial mammals (p. 96)

mandibular symphysis   the midline of the lower jaw, where the left and right sides of the dental arcade meet (p. 214)

masticatory   related to mastication (chewing) (p. 258)

mate guarding   actions by dominant male primates aimed at restricting sexual access to receptive females (p. 133)

matrilineal   groups in which descent is traced through the female line (p. 124)

medical anthropology   a branch of applied anthropology examining the interplay of culture, biology, health/wellness, disease/illness, and the art of medicine, both traditional and Western (p. 18)

megadont   literally, large teeth; megadont hominins are characterized by expansion of the posterior teeth (i.e., premolars and molars) (p. 198)

meiosis   cell division resulting in the formation of the sex cells (p. 57)

melanocytes   cells that produce melanin (p. 332)

mesiobuccal   the conjunction of the forward (mesial, toward the midline) and buccal (outer, cheek-facing) surfaces of a tooth (p. 184)

messenger RNA (mRNA)   a form of RNA that carries the genetic instructions of a DNA molecule to the site of protein synthesis. (p. 56)

methodology   the study of the methods applied to research generally or within a particular discipline (p. 27)

microcephaly   a congenital condition characterized by an abnormally small head (p. 245)

microevolution   small-scale evolutionary events occurring within a population over the span of a few generations, affecting the frequency of specific characters and not involving species formation (p. 39)

microliths   small, flaked tools made from blades or parts of blades (p. 283)

microstructure   the arrangement of cells and their associated structures that contribute to the material properties of a tissue; usually, microstructure is only viewable with the use of instruments such as microscopes and microCT scanners (p. 185)

Middle Palaeolithic   the period dating from about 250,000 to 40,000 years ago and associated with Mousterian tools (p. 262)

Middle Stone Age   the period spanning 250,000 to 40,000 years ago in Africa; it is associated with archaic and anatomically modern humans (p. 283)

midfacial prognathism   forward projection of the nasal region of the face (p. 257)

Miocene   the fourth epoch of the Cenozoic era, dating from 23 to 5.3 Ma (p. 158)

missing links   variation of a popular term referring to transitional fossils, which typically bear a combination of primitive and derived traits linking them with earlier and later forms within a clade (p. 196)

mitochondria   structures within a cell that generate energy for that cell (p. 53)

mitochondrial DNA   DNA found within the mitochondria in a cell (p. 14)

mitosis   division of the somatic cells resulting in the production of two identical daughter cells (p. 56)

model organism   an extensively studied and well-understood species from which new insights into human biology and disease might be obtained; examples range from bacteria such as *E. coli* to mammals such as mice (p. 84)

molecular anthropology   the study of population diversity at the level of the gene and its products (both structural and regulatory proteins) (p. 14)

molecular clock   a concept involving the use of molecular data to estimate the sequence and timing of divergence of various evolutionary lineages (p. 163)

molecular systematics   the use of molecular data to reconstruct the evolutionary history of early primates and determine the time of divergence of different species (p. 163)

monogamous characterized by one adult male, one adult female, and their offspring (p. 124)

monogenic traits traits that are controlled by genes at a single locus (p. 61)

monogenists 18th- and 19th-century scholars who believed that all human populations ("races") could be traced to a single origin (mono + genesis), specifically related to the Judeo-Christian account of human origins; the diversity of human races was ascribed to exposure to different climates following humanity's Fall from Grace as related in the Old Testament (p. 300)

monosomy a condition characterized the absence of one copy of a chromosome pair (p. 59)

monozygotic twins derived from a single zygote; commonly called "identical twins," they result from splitting of the fertilized egg very early in pregnancy (at the blastocyst stage), and so possess the same genome (p. 311)

morbidity a measure of the state of disease or disability from any cause in a population (p. 324)

morphology study of the size, shape, and configuration of an organism and its various parts (p. 26)

morphospecies designation of species in the fossil record according to similarity in form irrespective of time (p. 80)

mosaic evolution the concept that functional complexes in organisms have independent evolutionary histories and have changed at different times and rates in the fossil record (p. 19)

mosaic habitats areas characterized by a range of habitat types, from forest to grassland (p. 201)

Mousterian a Middle Paleolithic stone tool industry generally associated with Neandertals (p. 262)

multidisciplinary an investigative approach that brings the expertise of a number of disciplines to bear on a particular question within an existing field of study (p. 6)

multilocus analysis a method for characterizing genetic diversity at multiple sites, or loci, within the genome (p. 307)

multi-male/multi-female consisting of a number of adult males and females and their offspring (p. 124)

muscle markings impressions on a bone surface that define the point of origin or insertion of a muscle; activities that build up muscles can also create more prominent muscle markings (p. 207)

mutations alterations to genes or chromosomes (p. 53)

narrow niche hypothesis the hypothesis that the suite of characteristics seen in primates evolved not only from selection pressure for fine branch feeding, but also from the relaxation of previous selection pressures (p. 101)

natal groups the groups in which individuals are born (p. 112)

natural capital the organic and inorganic resources contained in the Earth's lands and waters providing for the goods we produce and consume (p. 376)

natural selection the nonrandom preservation or elimination of variants through competition within and between species promoting differential reproductive success (p. 41)

Natural Theology a philosophy of theology founded on principles of observation of the world in a context of Creation, rather than on arguments from divine revelation (p. 37)

Neandertals a group of Late Pleistocene hominins who lived in Europe and western Asia between approximately 130,000 and 30,000 years ago (p. 250)

negative eugenics programs or policies designed to prevent successful reproduction in targeted groups (via conception or sterilization) (p. 308)

neocortex the outer part of the brain that is involved in higher functions such as reasoning, abstract thought, and language (p. 98)

Neogene period a geological time period comprising the Miocene and Pliocene epochs, associated with global climate change and diversification of a number of avian and mammal species, particularly open woodland and grassland forms (p. 200)

niches the conditions of environments in which organisms live, including climate, space, predator–prey relationships, and mate availability (p. 26)

nocturnal active during the night (p. 98)

noncoding DNA multiple copies of a base sequence which may be repeated on the same chromosome or dispersed throughout the genome (p. 65)

nondisjunction the failure of chromosome pairs to separate properly during meiosis (p. 58)

Notharctus an Eocene primate of the family Adapidae (p. 154)

nuclear DNA (nDNA) DNA found within the nucleus of a cell (p. 53)

nucleotide the basic structural unit of a DNA or RNA molecule, consisting of a phosphate, sugar, and base (p. 53)

nucleus a structure in eukaryotic cells that contains the genetic material (p. 52)

null hypothesis in statistics, a proposition that there is no difference among samples, conditions, outcomes, etc., that can be disproved through experiment or observation (p. 28)

obligate by virtue of necessity; our recent ancestors of the past 2–3 million years had developed a number of adaptations that effectively obliged them to adopt a terrestrial, bipedal form of locomotion (p. 112)

obligate bipeds in biology, "obligate" denotes a condition of necessity; being a "biped" refers to the condition of walking on two legs; therefore, obligate bipeds walk on only two legs (p. 169)

obstetric dilemma the hypothesis that evolution of larger brains competed with narrowing of pelvic structure associated with adopting a bipedal gait, resulting in babies being born in a more helpless stage of development (p. 176)

occipital bun a bulge on the occipital bone of the skull that projects posteriorly, typical of Neandertals (p. 257)

occipital torus a horizontal ridge of bone running across the occipital bone (p. 233)

occlusal the chewing surface of a tooth (p. 151)

occlusal plane The occlusal plane refers to the orientation of the chewing (i.e., occlusal) surfaces of the upper and lower dentitions (p. 184)

occlusal relief the ratio of the three-dimensional surface area of a tooth to the two-dimensional occlusal surface area (p. 230)

Oldowan industry the earliest stone tool industry, characterized by pebble and chopping tools made and used by early hominins (p. 229)

olfactory relating to the sense of smell (p. 98)

Oligocene the third epoch of the Cenozoic era, dating from about 34 to 23 Ma (p. 155)

oligopithecids early anthropoids from the Oligocene epoch (p. 155)

omnivorous eating a variety of different foods, including both plants and animals (p. 99)

omomyids tarsier-like primates from the Eocene epoch (p. 153)

ontogeny the development of an organism from embryo to adult (p. 261)

oogonia ovarian cells (p. 57)

opposable the thumb or big toe can make contact with the tip of each of the other digits on the same hand/foot (p. 97)

optically stimulated luminescence (OSL) a method of absolute dating that involves determining the last time mineral grains such as quartz or feldspar were exposed to daylight by using light to measure the amount of energy trapped in the minerals' crystals (p. 145)

orthognathic "ortho" refers to vertical or flat, and "gnathic" to the jaws; thus, orthognathic means "flat face" (p. 214)

orthograde indicating upright or erect posture, notably with regard to the trunk (p. 170)

orthograde clamber a form of arboreal hand-assisted bipedal locomotion applied specifically to orangutans, involving extension at the knee, hip, and shoulder (p. 180)

ossuary a repository for collections of human skeletal remains. In pre-contact Canada, these typically were large secondary burial pits containing the commingled remains of dozens of individuals who had earlier been interred in separate primary graves (p. 21)

osteology the descriptive and comparative study of bones and teeth (p. 10)

osteomyelitis an infection of the marrow cavity of bone (p. 340)

oxygen isotope analysis the use of stable oxygen isotopes to reconstruct ancient climates; it can also be used to examine the geographic origins of organisms such as humans (p. 147)

paleoanthropology the study of human evolution through fossils and the circumstances in which they are found (p. 12)

paleobiology the study of the behaviour and ecology of fossil organisms (p. 150)

paleobotanists specialists who study ancient plant remains (p. 147)

Paleocene the first epoch of the Cenozoic era, dating from 66 to 56 Ma (p. 151)

paleoecology the study of ancient environments (p. 147)

paleohistology the microscopic study of ancient tissues (p. 340)

Paleo-Indians the name given to the first occupants of North and South America (p. 288)

paleomagnetism a method of relative dating that involves comparing reversals in the earth's magnetic field (p. 143)

paleoneurology the study of the evolution of the brain and its functions (p. 187)

paleontologists specialists who study the fossilized remains of extinct life forms (p. 147)

paleontology the study of fossilized life forms (p. 32)

paleonutrition the study of diet in past populations (p. 341)

paleopathology the study of ancient disease and trauma in skeletal remains (p. 12)

palynologists specialists who study pollen (p. 147)

pandemic a disease affecting populations across a large area, typically used in reference to a global occurrence (p. 8)

Pangaea the original landmass made up of the seven continents we recognize today (p. 146)

pangenesis a discredited theory of heredity arguing that particles in body cells and organs can be influenced by their environment, and once transferred to the sex cells pass on these influences to the next generation (p. 38)

pantomime gesture that expresses meaning (p. 136)

paradigm a conceptual framework within which bodies of theory are developed, directing the course of future investigation (p. 30)

parallelism a path toward development of homoplasy; evolution modifies an ancestral character to achieve similar outcomes in response to similar adaptive pressures (p. 91)

paranasal sinuses a group of four pairs of air-filled spaces located on both sides of the nasal cavity, above and between the eyes, and within the sphenoid bone (p. 257)

parapatry refers to species whose ranges are contiguous but not overlapping; gene flow is possible (p. 77)

parapithecids a group of early anthropoids from the Oligocene epoch (p. 155)

parental investment a model describing the apportionment of resources (time, food, protection, caregiving, etc.) by males and females into the successful rearing of offspring (p. 133)

pathogens microorganisms or other agents that cause disease (p. 320)

pathophysiology a disturbance of normal body function as a result of disease, genetic disorder, or impaired development (p. 313)

pedigree a diagram that illustrates the transmission of a genetic trait from one generation to subsequent generations of a family (p. 62)

percussive stone tools implements fashioned by purposefully striking one stone against another to produce a cutting edge (p. 209)

perimortem occurring at or around the time of death (p. 360)

periosteal relating to the periosteum, the connective tissue membrane that covers the outer (periosteal) surface of a bone (p. 340)

petrosal bulla a bony outgrowth on the base of the skull that houses the three bones of the middle ear (p. 99)

phalanx one of a series of short bones that make up the fingers in the hand, or toes in the foot (p. 207)

pharynx part of the neck and throat located superior to the larynx that modifies sounds made by the larynx (p. 207)

phenotype the observable characteristic of an organism (p. 59)

phenotypic plasticity a potential for individuals to modify their phenotype in response to variation in external conditions in order to maintain homeostasis and function (p. 75)

phenylketonuria (PKU) a genetic disorder characterized by a deficiency in the enzyme phenylalanine hydroxylase, resulting in the accumulation of excessive amounts of phenylalanine (p. 63)

pheromone a chemical signal capable of causing a specific response in members of the same or closely related species (p. 26)

philopatric remaining in one's birth group (p. 124)

phyletic evolution an alternative term for anagenesis, with "phyletic" denoting a line of direct ancestor–descendant relationship (p. 81)

phyletic sequence an unbroken lineage of ancestor–descendant species (p. 209)

phylogenetic relating to evolutionary histories of ancestry and descent; also *phylogeny* (p. 28)

phylogenetic diversity a measure of the taxonomic distinctness of a species (p. 115)

phytoliths   silica particles found in plants; variation in their size and shape allows scientists to identify the particular species from which they derive (p. 342)

placebo   a medical intervention (drug or procedure) that has no demonstrable therapeutic effect, often used in clinical trials (p. 314)

Platyrrhines   New World monkeys (p. 107)

pleiotropies   genes that influence more than one trait (p. 63)

plesiadapiforms   a group of primate-like mammals that lived during the Paleocene epoch (p. 152)

pluripotent   having the ability to differentiate into different tissue types (p. 52)

point mutations   changes in base pairs of gene sequences (p. 53)

polar bodies   small cells that are the by-product of meiosis in females (p. 58)

polyandry   a type of mating pattern in which one female mates with more than one male (p. 124)

polydactyly   a congenital condition in which an individual has more than five fingers or toes on hands or feet; one side or both may be affected (p. 87)

polygenesis   in contrast to monogenesis, polygenesis maintains that different human races were created as separate species. Note that both monogenesis and polygenesis assign primacy to European peoples (p. 300)

polygenic traits   traits phenotypic characteristics influenced by multiple genes; also known as continuous traits (p. 64)

polygynous   a type of mating pattern in which one male mates with more than one female (p. 124)

polymerase chain reaction (PCR)   a technique used to amplify or make copies of DNA (p. 67)

polymorphic   refers to the existence of alternative forms of a trait (e.g., eye colour in humans is polymorphic) (p. 301)

polypeptide   a chain of amino acids (p. 55)

polytypic   "many types"; refers to the existence of geographic variation within species (p. 301)

population bottleneck   an evolutionary event in which a population is reduced in number, resulting in the loss of genetic variation (p. 282)

population genetics   a science concerned with variation in gene frequencies within populations and the forces that modify them over time (p. 73)

population momentum   the reproductive potential of those yet to reproduce; typically measured as the proportion of a population under 18 years of age. Expanding populations with broad-based demographic pyramids have considerable population momentum (p. 377)

positive eugenics   programs or policies advocating reproduction among the favoured sectors of society, typically those of the dominant social and economic classes (p. 309)

postmortem   occurring after death (p. 360)

postorbital bar   the bony ring that separates the eye orbit from the back of the skull; within Primates, this feature is found among the prosimians (p. 98)

potassium-argon dating   a method of absolute dating based on the radioactive decay of potassium (^{40}K) into argon gas (^{40}Ar) (p. 144)

prehensile   grasping (p. 97)

prevalence   the proportion of a population exhibiting a particular feature at any one point in time (p. 8)

primary oocytes   immature ova (p. 57)

primatology   the study of the morphology, behaviour, and evolution of nonhuman primates (p. 15)

principle of correlation of parts   the idea that organisms are integrated wholes and that change in one part cannot occur without altering the whole (usually by rendering it dysfunctional) (p. 36)

principle of independent assortment   the distribution of one pair of alleles into the sex cells does not influence the distribution of another pair of alleles (p. 62)

principle of segregation   the separation of alleles during the production of sex cells such that each sex cell contains only one allele from each parent (p. 62)

proceptive behaviours   actions, typically on the part of females, to initiate a sexual interaction; may include facial gestures, limb and body postures or movements, and sounds (p. 132)

processual   a view of organismic diversity and evolution emphasizing the current and historical dynamic interactions of organisms with their environment and ecology (p. 19)

Proconsul   the best-known genus of early Miocene hominoids (p. 159)

proconsulids   early Miocene hominoids from Africa (p. 159)

procumbent   forward-projecting (p. 152)

prognathic   refers to the degree to which the lower face projects forward (p. 218)

prognathism   projection of the lower face; the gnathic portion of the face is that which contains the upper and lower jaws (p. 185)

prokaryotes   organisms that lack a cell nucleus (p. 52)

pronograde   a posture in which the trunk is held more or less horizontal and approximately parallel with the surface on which the animal moves (p. 178)

propliopithecids   the largest group of the Oligocene anthropoids (p. 155)

Prosimii   the suborder that includes lemurs, lorises, and tarsiers (p. 101)

protein synthesis   the process by which amino acids are assembled to form proteins (p. 55)

provenance   the original location of a fossil or artifact (p. 142)

provisioned   supplied with food (p. 120)

proximal   in anatomy, a position closer to the midline of the body (p. 207)

pubic ramus   the portion of the pubic bone of the pelvis that extends medially (p. 260)

public anthropology   an emerging field within anthropology emphasizing community engagement with an aim to bring awareness to issues of inequity in the human domain, be they social, political, economic or other (p. 115)

punctuated anagenesis   speciation has two tempos, slow and gradual (anagensis) or rapid followed by stasis (punctuated equilibrium); punctuated anagenesis combines these into a pattern of rapid change within a continually evolving lineage; the possibility of punctuated anagenesis is not universally held among evolutionary biologists (p. 211)

punctuated equilibrium   a pattern of evolution characterized by periods of stasis interrupted by rapid evolutionary change; more commonly found in small, peripheral populations on the edge of a species range (p. 81)

Punnett square   a way of graphically representing the genotypic outcomes when crossing organisms with the same or different genotypes (p. 61)

quadrupedal   walking on all four limbs (p. 97)

quarrying sites   sites from which hominins obtained raw materials to make stone tools (p. 229)

race   in general biology, a category often considered synonymous with "subspecies," into which individuals can be placed based on distinctive physiological, morphological, and/or ecological features; it is now generally held that the complexity of human biobehavioural variation cannot be usefully understood in terms of race (p. 298)

radioactive isotopes   unstable isotopes that decay, emitting radioactivity (p. 143)

radiometric dating   an absolute method of dating based on the radioactive decay of isotopes (p. 144)

rank   the social position or status of an individual within a group (p. 125)

recessive   the unexpressed allele or trait that is genetically hidden by its dominant counterpart (p. 59)

recognition species concept (RSC)   a concept of the species as a group whose members, according to particular cues, identify potential mates with whom they might successfully interbreed (in contrast, the BSC emphasizes an absence of breeding potential) (p. 80)

recombination (crossing over)   the exchange of genes between homologous chromosomes during meiosis (p. 58)

reconciliation   the process of making peace after an altercation (p. 132)

recurrent mutation   a mutation that tends to occur repeatedly at the same locus; a number of genetic disorders are maintained at high frequencies through recurrent mutation (e.g., Marfan syndrome in humans, leading to impaired collagen formation) (p. 204)

relative brain size   the absolute size of the brain adjusted to reflect the absolute size of the body of which it is a part, since we expect a larger body to have a proportionately larger brain. Primates tend to have larger brains for a given body size than other mammals (p. 186)

relative dating   a method of dating that identifies objects as being younger or older than other objects (p. 143)

replacement rate fertility   the rate of fertility required to replace a parental generation and to account for differences in local mortality rates (p. 372)

replication   the process whereby a duplicate copy of a molecule (i.e., DNA) is made (p. 53)

reproductive fitness   a measure of the success of an individual in the production of offspring across generations; your children, and their children, and so on all constitute your reproductive fitness (p. 44)

retromolar space   a gap between the third molar and the ascending ramus of the mandible (p. 257)

rhinarium   the bare, wet surface at the end of the nose, seen in most mammals (p. 106)

ribosomes   structures found in cells that are involved in the assembly of proteins (p. 56)

RNA   ribonucleic acid (p. 56)

robust   rugged or strongly built; several australopithecine species possess skeletal and dental features associated with large chewing muscles and crushing and grinding of hard foods (p. 209)

r-selection strategy   a reproductive strategy in which females have many offspring and invest little parental care in those offspring (p. 100)

sacculated   divided into chambers (p. 104)

sagittal crests   a large ridge of bone runs along the sagittal suture of the skull; it serves to anchor the muscles involved in chewing (p. 111)

sagittal keel   a raised area of bone running along the sagittal suture (p. 233)

sample   a subset of a whole that represents its qualities with regard to the characteristics under study; for example, if three-quarters of a population of university students have a piercing, approximately the same proportion in a sample selected from that population should have a piercing (p. 28)

savannah hypothesis   the now discredited idea that the development of open savannah grassland created conditions leading to the evolution of hominins (p. 202)

scaling   in biology, refers to the pattern of change of a part in relation to a whole; may be *isometric* (a unit of change in body size is matched by a unit of change in the part) or *allometric* (the change in a part is greater or less than the change in the whole) (p. 186)

scent markings   a form of communication characterized by the deposition of chemicals such as urine or pheromones to mark territories (p. 108)

sectorial P3   in Old World primates, a lower third premolar in which the mesiobuccal surface appears as a long, sloping surface due to contact with the upper canine (p. 184)

secular   separate and apart from religious tradition or edict; worldly (p. 26)

secular trend   a directional change in phenotypic expression over time independent of change in the underlying genotype (p. 324)

selective differential   a measure of the probability that a given phenotype will reproduce compared to an alternative phenotype (p. 175)

semibrachiators   animals that combine arm-over-arm movement with other forms of locomotion (p. 103)

seminal   relating to "seed"; in this context, a seminal work is one that becomes a foundation for generations of subsequent ideas and developments (p. 30)

senescence   the biological process by which an individual reaches an advanced age (p. 3)

sex-linked   traits that are controlled by genes located on one of the sex chromosomes (p. 62)

sexual dimorphism   differences in physical characteristics between males and females of the same species (p. 109)

sexual selection   a theory proposed by Charles Darwin to explain why males of some species adopt behaviours or morphologies that may not appear adaptive in terms of natural selection, but that in fact enhance reproductive opportunities as a result of successful competition with other males and their subsequent selection by females as potential mates (p. 125)

shearing quotient   a measure of the relative shear potential of molar teeth (p. 151)

shovel-shaped incisors   front teeth with marginal ridges of enamel on the lingual (tongue) surface (p. 233)

signification   a sign (a character, a word, an image) that identifies an entity or assigns meaning to a situation; for example, a red light at an intersection or a dollar sign (p. 276)

silverbacks   mature adult male gorillas characterized by a saddle of white hair across the back (p. 111)

single nucleotide polymorphisms (SNPs)   genetic variations that are produced by the substitution of a single nucleotide in a sequence; SNPs are point mutations that occur in at least 1% of the population (p. 54)

single-male/multi-female   consisting of a single adult male and several adult females and their offspring (p. 124)

sister taxon   in systematics, sister taxa are those forms that are related by virtue of a divergence event and that share a last common ancestor; panins and hominins are sister taxa, as are *Australopithecus* and *Ardipithecus* (p. 197)

Sivapithecus   a genus of large-bodied hominoids that lived in Asia during the Miocene epoch (p. 161)

social brain hypothesis the hypothesis that the cognitive demands of living in complex social groups explains why primates have unusually large brains for their body size (p. 124)

social capital the resources available to a person or group deriving from their connection to social networks (p. 373)

social determinants of health economic and social factors that influence health, recognizing that health is determined by more than genetic make-up and individual-level lifestyle decisions (p. 354)

somatic cells all cells in the body with the exception of the sex cells (p. 56)

speciation the formation of new species from pre-existing forms (p. 74)

species divergence an estimate of time since speciation; because genetic differences are constantly accumulating within lineages, estimates of genetic divergence time will always be older than species divergence time (p. 204)

specific dynamic action (SDA) a measure of energy consumed in digesting, absorbing, and assimilating nutrients from a meal (p. 191)

speciose literally, "full of species," denoting a taxonomy consisting of many rather than fewer named species (p. 196)

sperm competition when a female mates with multiple partners over a short period of time, males who are able to deposit a larger volume of higher quality sperm further into the female reproductive tract should succeed in impregnating more females; sperm competition is facilitated in multi-male social systems by large testes, large penises, longer tailed sperm, and the formation of copulatory plugs (p. 135)

spermatogonia testicular cells (p. 57)

stabilizing selection a form of selection favouring the most common phenotype at the expense of extreme expressions of a character (p. 83)

stable isotope analysis a type of chemical analysis that looks at stable isotopes of certain elements in bones and other tissues of the body; it can tell us something about the diet and residential history of an individual (p. 231)

stable isotopes different forms of an element that have different atomic mass and that are not radioactive (p. 148)

stasis a state of equilibrium characterized by the absence of change (p. 32)

stem cells unspecialized cells that have the ability to differentiate into specialized cells in the body (p. 52)

stem group a group of extinct organisms that are not part of the crown group (p. 148)

stem hominin the progenitor of all later hominin species within a clade, arising from the last common ancestor (p. 206)

stereoscopic vision characterized by overlapping fields of view, allowing humans and other primates to see in three dimensions (p. 98)

stratigraphy the study of the different layers (strata) that have been deposited over time (p. 143)

Strepsirhini the suborder that comprises the lemurs, lorises, and galagos (p. 101)

subordinate a lower ranking individual (p. 125)

supraorbital torus a ridge of bone running across the top of the eyes; also referred to as the browridge (p. 233)

sympatry refers to species that coexist in the same geographic region (p. 77)

synchronic at the same time; thus synchronic species coexist in time (p. 198)

taphonomy the study of what happens to the remains of an organism after death (p. 142)

tariff the determination of each size of an item needed to fit a specific user population (p. 358)

taurodontism enlargement of the pulp cavity in molar teeth, a characteristic of Neandertals (p. 257)

taxon a formal designation of biological classification; pl. taxa (e.g., we are all members of the taxon *Homo sapiens*) (p. 13)

taxonomy the method by which organisms are classified and assigned to a group (a taxon; pl. taxa) based on shared biological, ecological, and behavioural relationships (p. 34)

Tay-Sachs a genetic disease affecting neurological development caused by a mutation on chromosome 15; the most common form occurs in infancy and early childhood and is fatal within the first five years of life (p. 87)

teleology a perspective proposing that there are end points, or "final causes," toward which natural phenomena are oriented and suggestive of a design, goal, or purpose in the world (p. 33)

tempo and mode of evolution refers to the pace and manner of evolutionary change (p. 81)

temporomandibular joint the location on the skull base where the mandible articulates with the temporal bone (p. 257)

territory an area that is defended against conspecific members of neighbouring groups (p. 102)

theory explanatory statements or arguments related to particular sets of phenomena supported by observation or experiment (p. 28)

thermoluminescence (TL) a method of absolute dating that involves measuring the amount of light produced by the release of electrons trapped in objects such as stones and ceramics when they are heated (p. 145)

thermoregulation the adjustment of body temperature within a normal physiological range under varying environmental conditions (p. 8)

time allocation in the study of life history, time allocation studies document how much time is spent during a given time period (day, season, age stage, etc.) performing particular tasks (p. 181)

tool marks with regard to the skeleton, these are marks left on the surface of bone that may be linked through a process of replication in the lab to a suspect instrument (e.g., knife, axe, saw) (p. 364)

tooth comb a feature formed by horizontally projecting front teeth on the lower jaw (p. 106)

total fertility rate the average number of children born per woman if all women in the country concerned lived to the end of their childbearing years and bore children according to the age-specific pattern for the region or group (p. 373)

transcription transfer of genetic information carried by DNA to RNA (p. 56)

transfer RNA (tRNA) RNA molecules that carry amino acids to ribosomes, where they are used in protein synthesis (p. 56)

transgenerational epigenetic inheritance the transmission of novel phenotypic features from parent to offspring acquired without recourse to modification in DNA base sequences (p. 75)

translation synthesis of a chain of amino acids based on a message carried in RNA (p. 56)

trichromatic a condition in which an animal possesses three light-sensitive pigments in the cones in the retina of the eye, making it possible to see blue, green, and red (p. 98)

trier of fact in law, the person or persons who decide which facts are to be accepted as evidence; in a jury trial, the trier of fact is the jury; in a "bench trial" in which no jury is present, the trier of fact is the judge (p. 364)

tripedalism a theoretical model proposing that early Miocene hominins may have adopted a three-limbed gait prior to bipedalism, in order to carry objects such as stones (p. 175)

trisomy a condition characterized by an extra chromosome (p. 58)

typology a static perspective of the world ascribed to the 4th-century BCE Greek philosopher Plato, in which "ideals" or "types" were perceived to be real, and variation as observed in the world was considered a deviation from ideal reality (p. 18)

tyrosinase the enzyme that controls the production of melanin (p. 332)

uniformitarianism a philosophy in geology which argues that the natural processes affecting the earth and observable today have remained constant (uniform) through geologic time (p. 34)

uranium-lead dating a method of absolute dating that looks at the radioactive decay of ^{238}U to ^{206}Pb and ^{235}U to ^{207}Pb in minerals (p. 144)

uranium-series dating a method of absolute dating that looks at the decay of uranium-234 (^{234}Ur) to thorium-230 (^{230}Th) in calcium carbonate materials (p. 144)

variability the tendency for members of a population to exhibit different versions of a particular trait (p. 73)

variability selection hypothesis a model that suggests that the operating factor in hominin evolution was environmental disparity, rather than stability, which promoted adaptive flexibility in hominin traits, including locomotion, dental adaptations, and technology (p. 202)

variants individuals within populations having different expressions of a trait (p. 73)

variation observable differences within a class of objects, the source of which may be genetic or environmental or both in interaction (p. 5)

vasoconstriction the narrowing of the peripheral blood vessels to reduce blood flow to the skin and thereby reduce heat loss at the skin's surface (p. 337)

vasodilation expansion of the peripheral blood vessels, resulting in increased blood flow to the skin surface, with subsequent transfer of body heat to the environment (p. 335)

vertical clinging and leaping a form of locomotion characterized by leaping using the hindlimbs and clinging to branches and tree trunks using the forelimbs (p. 102)

Victoriapithecidae the family to which the earliest Old World monkeys belong (p. 157)

visual predation hypothesis the hypothesis ascribed to Matt Cartmill that primate features evolved as adaptations to insect predation (p. 100)

vowel space the space within the oral cavity in which vowel sounds are created by altering the relative position of tongue and pharynx (p. 268)

weaning the process by which infants gradually shift from a diet of breast milk to one consisting of other foods (p. 323)

weight-for-height a measure of body mass standardized for a given height; high weight-for-height values indicate overweight/obesity (p. 380)

whole-genome variation the presence of many common genetic variants throughout the genome, the study of which permits a more detailed reconstruction of evolutionary events and population history (p. 14)

X-linked traits that are controlled by genes located on the X chromosome (p. 62)

Y-5 pattern cusp pattern formed by five cusps on the lower (mandibular) molar teeth in hominoids (p. 155)

zero population growth (ZPG) arises when the balance of birth and death, and the sum of net migration (immigration and emigration), is zero; ZPG denotes a stationary population that neither increases nor declines (p. 377)

zooarchaeological nonhuman, typically used to refer to animal bones (p. 264)

zoogeography the study of the geographic distribution of animals and the ecological communities to which they belong (p. 38)

zoonotic diseases diseases that can be transmitted from wild or domesticated animals to humans (p. 320)

zoopharmacognosy the self-medication by animals with plants, soils, and other natural substances (p. 130)

zygote fertilized egg (p. 57)

Index

Note: Page numbers followed by "b" indicate boxes; "f" indicate figures; "n" indicate footnotes; "t" indicate tables.

Anti-aging genes, 325
Antibiotic-resistant bacteria, 322, 375
Antón, S.C., 242
Apatite, 231
Apes. *See* Greater apes, classifications of
Apidium, 155
Applied anthropology, 8
Applied biological anthropology, 16–18
    anthropometry and ergonomics, 13–14, 358
    evolutionary medicine, 14, 18, 355–357
    forensic anthropology, 6, 16–17f, 360–367
    medical anthropology, 18, 350–355
    military, 359b
    nutritional anthropology, 8, 325–331
    overview, 6–8, 349, 367
    primate conservation, 113–116
Arashiyama West group, 120
Arboreal hypothesis, 100
Archaeology, 8
Archaeotourism, 378–379
Archaic hominins, 250–255f
    African, 196–199, 250
    Asian, 253–254
    behavioural adaptations, 255–256
    classification, 250–254
    climate change, 115
    defined, 250
    European, 251–253
    sites in Africa, Europe, and Asia, 254f
    species classification issues, 253–254
Ardipithecus, 208–209
    taxon, 208–209
Ardipithecus kaddaba, 202–203, 208n
Ardipithecus ramidus, 181–182, 198t, 199f, 208, 209, 211, 220
Argon-argon dating, 144
Arguments from design, 31b
Aridification, 201
Aristotle, 32–33
Armstrong, Robert, 14
Asfaw, B., 197b, 213
ASPM, and cultural developments, 387
Assemblages, 204
Assimilation model, 277
Assumptions, 29
Atlatl, 284
Atwood, Margaret, *Oryx and Crake*, 310b
Auger, Frank, 21
Australia, *Homo sapiens* in, 287–288
Australopithecines, 209–219
    Africa, 201–210f, 209, 211, 214–215
    evolution, 216–218
    Homo in relation to, 243b
    megadont adaptation, 218–219
    origins, 203b, 209, 211–215
    overview, 209
    robust, 209, 218–219

-sediba, 216–218
    sites for, 210f
    skeletal analysis, 214–215, 217b
Australopithecus afarensis, 198t, 199f, 209–215
Australopithecus africanus, 20, 187f, 188, 198t, 199f, 205b, 210f, 215–221
Australopithecus anamensis, 198f, 199f, 209, 210f, 211–212
Australopithecus bahrelghazali, 198t, 210f, 214
Australopithecus garhi, 198t, 210f, 211, 214–215, 220f
Australopithecus robustus, 218–219
Australopithecus sp, indet., 215
Autosomal chromosomes, 57
Autosome, 203b
Avidity, 303–304

B

Bacteria, antibiotic-resistant, 322, 375
The Bad Seed (film), 64
Bala, Arun, 27
Balanced polymorphism, 86
Baldea, Lidia Nistor, 18
Balter, Michael, 384
Bamshad, M., 307
Barker, David, 76b
Barrett, Louise, 122
Barrett, R., 320
Basal, 198
Basal anthropoids, 154
Basal metabolic rate, 178
Bases, 53
Basicranial flexion, 267
Bateson, William, 74
Beattie, Owen, 337, 345
Begun, David, 160, 180, 185
Behavioural ecology, 119–139
    affiliative behaviours, 131–132
    agonistic behaviours, 130–131
    culture, 127–130
    defined, 120
    language and communication, 136–137
    nonhuman primates as models for, 138
    overview, 119
    sexual behaviour, 132–136
    sexual strategies, 133–136
    social living, 123–124
Behavioural genetics, 64
Behavioural modernity, 283
Behrensmeyer, A., 199, 209, 211
Benedict, Ruth, 349
Berger, T.D., 217b, 218, 261
Bergmann's Rule, 335, 336b
Beriberi, 326–327
Beringia, 290
Bermúdez de Castro, J.M., 261
Bertulli, M., 338

Exotropia, 384f
Expensive tissue hypothesis (ETH), 190–191
Experimental archaeology, 230
Expert witnesses, 365, 366
Extant, 149–150, 160–161, 162f
Extinction, 36, 115
Eyelids, 299f, 300–301

F

Faccia, K.J., 12
Facultative bipedalism, 170
Fallback foods, 219
Falsification, 29n, 31b
Faunal correlation, 143
Faunal remains, 143, 147, 215f, 231, 240, 256
Fayum, 155, 156–157
Fedigan, Linda, 21, 122b
Feeble-mindedness, 308
Feeding
    hominins, 181–183
    primates, 103–105
    See also Diet; Subsistence
Females
    dominance hierarchies, 125
    mate choice, 134
    reproductive strategies, 133–134
    reproductive timing, 134
Fertility rates, 125, 372, 373, 373–374t, 378
Fetal programming, 76b
Fink, B., 133
Fire, 192, 202, 241, 263, 272
First Nations, 7b, 330f
Fish resources, 372f
Fission–fusion, 124
Fission–track dating, 144
Fleagle, J.G., 147b
Floating island model, 157
Fluorine dating, 143
Fluted projectile points, 288
Folivorous, 103
Folk taxonomy, 37, 298
Food insecurity, 381–382
Foraging, 103–105
Foramen magnum, 206
Forensic anthropology, 6, 16–17f, 360–367
    as bone fide discipline, 367
    career in, 361b
    field investigation, 360–364
    lab work, 360–364
    modern advances, 365–367
Forest hypothesis, 202
Fossey, Dian, 16, 120
Fossils
    classification, 13, 148–150
    dating, 142–144

fossil record, 12–13
hominin evolution, 12–13
Homo erectus, 235f
Homo sapiens, 12–13, 278–281
Miocene sites, 158f
primates, 142–146
process of becoming, 142
Scientific Revolution, 34
species, 80–81
Founder effect, 72, 86–88
FOXP2 gene, 269
Franklin, John, 338
Franklin, Rosalind, 53
Free radicals, 325
Free-ranging, 120
Fricke, H.C., 338
Frisancho, Roberto, 334
Frost, Peter, 387
Frugivorous, 103, 104f
Frumkin, D., 366
Full Scale Intelligence Quotient (FSIQ), 311, 312
Functional genomics, 14

G

g (general intelligence factor), 311
Gait analysis, 171f
Galago moholi, 77, 78f
Galagos, 80, 105–107
Galago senegalensis, 77, 78f
Galdikas, Biruté, 16, 116, 119, 120f, 127, 132
Galileo Galilei, 34
Gallery forest, 202
Galloway, Tracey, 18, 328, 355
Galton, Francis, 308, 311
Gamete, 57, 59f
Gangstad, S.W., 133
Ganzhorn, J.U., 147b
Gardner, Allen, 136
Gardner, Beatrice, 136
Garget, Rob, 265
Garlie, Todd, 324, 359b
Garn, Stanley, 300n
Garvie-Lok Sandra, 11b
Gautieri, Guiseppe, 40
Gay gene, 64
Geiger, K., 179b
Gene conversion, 64–65
Gene flow, 82, 84–86,
Genes, 52
Gene therapy, 64–65
Genetic bottleneck, 88
Genetic divergence, 203b, 204
Genetic drift, 82, 86–88
Genetic load, 384–385
Genetic manipulation, 64–65

Principle of independent assortment, 62

Principle of segregation, 62

Principles of Geology, 35–36, 43

Proceptive behaviour, 132

Proconsul, 159, 162f

Proconsulids, 159

Procumbent, 152

Profet, Margie, 356

Prognathic, 218

Prognathism, 185

Prokaryotes, 52–53

Pronograde, 178

Propliopithecids, 155–156

Prosimians, 99b, 105–106
    home range of, 100
    infanticide, 135
    locomotion, 102
    Madagascar, 16
    postorbital bar, 98

Prosimii, 101

Protein, 55–56, 326t

Protein synthesis, 55

Protohominins, 202–209
    defined, 169n
    origin, 203b
    Orrorin tugenensis, 206–207
    overview, 202–204
    Sahelanthropus tchadensis, 204–206

Provenience, 142

Provisioned, 120

Prowse, Tracy, 11, 343

Proximal, 207

Ptolemy, 33

Pubic ramus, 260

Public anthropology, 115

Punctuated anagenesis, 211–212

Punctuated equilibrium, 81

Punnett square, 61

Purgatorius, 151–153

Q

Quadrupedal, 97

Quantitative trait loci, 200t

Quarrying sites, 229

Quebec Longitudinal Study of Child Development, 381–382

Quintus Ennius, 95

R

Race, 298–307
    abuse of classifications, 307–310
    as advantage, 310–312
    ancestry, 300–301, 314
    between-group genetic diversity, 307
    biomedicine, 313–314, 315
    classification systems, 299t
    continuously varying traits, 305
    defined, 298
    genotypic expression, through space, 303
    geographic distance and 306–307
    homogeneity, 304
    linked traits, 305
    measurement of traits, 304–305, 306–307
    number theory of, 306–307
    overview, 298–300, 314–315
    quantification of, 301–304
    six fallacies, 304–307
    skin colour, geographic distribution, 332f

Radioactive isotopes, 143–144

Radiometric dating, 144

Ramapithecus, 203b

Ramirez Rozzi, 261

Randomized clinical trials, 314

Rank, 125

Raposo, Joe, 318

Ray, John, 37

Reader, S.M., 312

Reagan, Ronald, 96

Recent out-of-Africa model, 277

Receptors, 54, 113, 387

Recessive traits, 59

Recognition species concept (RSC), 80

Recombinant DNA technology, 65

Recombination (crossing over), 58, 59f, 60f–61

Reconciliation, 132

Recurrent mutation, 203b, 204

Red-green colour blindness, 62f

Red List, IUCN, 115

Reich, David, 270b

Reichs, Kathy, 360

Relative dating, 143

Relethford, J.H., 282

Relief index (RFI), 151

Renaissance, and science, 33–34

Rendall, Drew, 122b

Replacement rate fertility, 372

Replication, 53, 54

Reproductive fitness, 44, 83f

Reproductive health, 356–357

Reproductive isolating mechanisms, 79t

Reproductive rate, 100

Reproductive strategies, 100
    female, 133–134
    male, 134–135
    sexual behaviour, 132–133

Reprogenetics, 310b

Resources, use and distribution of, 44, 103, 123, 125, 380, 381
    as natural capital, 376–377
    as social capital, 373

Retromolar space, 257

Revolutions, 33–34

Rhinarium, 106

Ribosomes, 56

So, Joseph, 21
Solecki, R., 262
Somatic-cell gene therapy, 64
Somatic cells, 56
South Africa. *See* Taung, South Africa specimen
South America, *Homo sapiens* in, 288, 289–290, 293
Spearman, Charles, 311
Speciation, 74
Species, 77–82
    classification, 71
    concepts, 77–80
    evolution of new, 81–82
    fossil record, 12–13, 80–81
    new discoveries of, 96
    overview, 92
Species divergence, 77–78, 91, 203b, 204
Specific dynamic action (SDA), 191
Specific Mate Recognition System (SMRS), 80
Speciose, 196
Speck, George, 354
Speed, adaptation, 182–183
Spermatogonia, 57
Sperm competition, 135
Spider monkeys, 105, 108
Stabilizing selection, 83
Stable carbon, 231–232
Stable isotope analysis, 11b
Stable isotopes, 11b, 148, 231, 343
Stable oxygen isotope analysis, 148, 343f
Stanford, Dennis, 126, 290
Starch consumption, 385
Stasis, 32
Stem Cell Network, 52b
Stem cell research, 52b
Stem cells, 52
Stem group, 148
Stem hominin, 206
Stereoscopic vision, 98
Sterilization, 308–309, 315
Steudel-Numbers, Karen, 175–176, 179b
Stimberg, Bonifatius, 357f
Stini, William, 379b
Stock, Jay, 336b
Strabismus, 384–385
Stratigraphy, 143
Strepsirhini, 101, 105–106, 153–155
Streptococcus, 322
Stumptail macaque, 79
Subordinate individuals, 125
Subsistence
    Homo, 226, 236, 283–284
    Homo sapiens, 283–284
    Neandertals, 264–266
    See also Diet; Feeding
Supraorbital torus, 233
Sussman, Randall, 100

Suwa, G., 197b
Symbolic behaviour, 265–266, 283, 285–286
Sympatric, 77
Sympatry, 78f
Synchronic, 198
Szathmáry, Emöke, 21

T

Taphonomy, 142
Tariffs, 358
Tarsiers, 101, 107
Tarsiiformes, 107
Taung, South Africa specimen, 205b
Taurodontism, 257
Taxon, 13
Taxonomy, 34, 89, 197b
    living primates, 101f
Taylor, 354
Tay-Sachs, 87
Teaford, M.F., 151, 219
Technology
    chimpanzees, 127–129
    Homo erectus, 239–241
    Homo sapiens, 370, 384–385
    human evolution, 384–385
    innovations, 370
    Neandertals, 262–264
    See also Tool use
Teeth
    Australopithecus and megadont adaptation, 197b, 218–219
    canine honing, 184–185
    compositon, 185f
    decay, 341
    enamel thickness, 185–186
    food habits, 184, 185
    Neandertals, 257–259, 261, 262
    nutrition, 262, 341
    overview, 192
Teichroeb, J.A., 135
Teilhardina asiatica, 153, 163
Teleology, 33
Tempo and mode, 81
Temporomandibular joint, 257
Terrace, Herbert, 137
Territory, 102, 131, 132
Thalidomide, birth defects, 357n
Theory, 28
Thermoluminescence (TL), 144, 145
Thermoregulation, 8
Thomas, Lewis, 51
Thompson, J.L., 261
Thorne, 278
Thorpe, S., 178
"Thrifty" genotype, 329–330
Thumbs, opposable, 97–98

Wilford, John Noble, 275
Wilkins, Maurice, 53
Wilkinson, D.M., 183
Williams, George, 355
Williams, Jocelyn, 11b, 12
Wilmé, L., 147b
Wilson, A.C., 327
Wilson, Warren, 323–324, 327, 351b, 379b
Wolpoff, Milford, 206, 278
Woman the Gather models, 230
Wood, B., 132, 185, 196, 199f, 220
Wood-Jones, Frederic, 100
World Health Organization (WHO), 350
    breastfeeding, 323–324
    globesity, 7b
    health defined by, 382
    healthy children, 379b
    infant mortality rates, 374f
    international growth standards, for healthy children, 379b
    Smallpox Eradication Programme, 352
World Trade Center bombing, 361, 365, 366f
Worm, B., 371, 372f
Worm, Ole, cabinet of curiosity, 35f
Wrangham, Richard, 5
Wray, Fay, 1515

X

X-chromosome, 59, 62, 203b
X-linked, 62

Y

Yaeger, R., 314
Yap, 282
Y chromosome, 14, 63, 282, 291
Yerkes, Robert, 120
Young, 304
Young, Kue, 328, 355

Z

Zeller, Anne, 21, 122b, 137–138
Zero population growth, 377
Zhi, 278
Zhoukoudian, 237, 238b
Zihlman, Adrienne, 138
Zollikofer, C.P.E., 206
Zooarchaeological, 264
Zoogeography, 38
Zoonotic diseases, 320
Zoopharmacognosy, 130
Zygote, 57